ELECTRICAL
ENGINEERING

McGRAW-HILL ELECTRICAL AND ELECTRONIC ENGINEERING SERIES

Frederick Emmons Terman, *Consulting Editor*
W. W. Harman, Hubert Heffner, and J. G. Truxal,
Associate Consulting Editors

Ahrendt and Savant · Servomechanism Practice
Angelo · Electronic Circuits
Aseltine · Transform Method in Linear System Analysis
Atwater · Introduction to Microwave Theory
Bailey and Gault · Alternating-current Machinery
Beranek · Acoustics
Brenner and Javid · Analysis of Electric Circuits
Brown · Analysis of Linear Time-invariant Systems
Bruns and Saunders · Analysis of Feedback Control Systems
Cage · Theory and Application of Industrial Electronics
Cauer · Synthesis of Linear Communication Networks
Chen · Linear Network Design and Synthesis
Chen · The Analysis of Linear Systems
Chirlian and Zemanian · Electronics
Clement and Johnson · Electrical Engineering Science
Cote and Oakes · Linear Vacuum-tube and Transistor Circuits
Cuccia · Harmonics, Sidebands, and Transients in Communication Engineering
Cunningham · Introduction to Nonlinear Analysis
Eastman · Fundamentals of Vacuum Tubes
Evans · Control-system Dynamics
Feinstein · Foundations of Information Theory
Fitzgerald and Higginbotham · Basic Electrical Engineering
Fitzgerald and Kingsley · Electric Machinery
Frank · Electrical Measurement Analysis
Friedland, Wing, and Ash · Principles of Linear Networks
Geppert · Basic Electron Tubes
Ghose · Microwave Circuit Theory and Analysis
Greiner · Semiconductor Devices and Applications
Hammond · Electrical Engineering
Hancock · An Introduction to the Principles of Communication Theory
Happell and Hesselberth · Engineering Electronics
Harman · Fundamentals of Electronic Motion
Harman · Principles of the Statistical Theory of Communication
Harman and Lytle · Electrical and Mechanical Networks
Harrington · Introduction to Electromagnetic Engineering
Harrington · Time-harmonic Electromagnetic Fields
Hayt · Engineering Electromagnetics
Hill · Electronics in Engineering
Huelsman · Circuits, Matrices, and Linear Vector Spaces
Javid and Brenner · Analysis, Transmission and Filtering of Signals
Javid and Brown · Field Analysis and Electromagnetics
Johnson · Transmission Lines and Networks
Koenig and Blackwell · Electromechanical System Theory
Kraus · Antennas

Kraus · Electromagnetics
Kuh and Pederson · Principles of Circuit Synthesis
Ledley · Digital Computer and Control Engineering
LePage · Analysis of Alternating-current Circuits
LePage and Seely · General Network Analysis
Ley, Lutz, and Rehberg · Linear Circuit Analysis
Linvill and Gibbons · Transistors and Active Circuits
Lynch and Truxal · Introductory System Analysis
Lynch and Truxal · Principles of Electronic Instrumentation
Lynch and Truxal · Signals and Systems in Electrical Engineering
Millman · Vacuum-tube and Semiconductor Electronics
Millman and Seely · Electronics
Millman and Taub · Pulse and Digital Circuits
Mishkin and Braun · Adaptive Control Systems
Moore · Traveling-wave Engineering
Nanavati · An Introduction to Semiconductor Electronics
Pettit · Electronic Switching, Timing, and Pulse Circuits
Pettit and McWhorter · Electronic Amplifier Circuits
Pfeiffer · Linear Systems Analysis
Reza · An Introduction to Information Theory
Reza and Seely · Modern Network Analysis
Rogers · Introduction to Electric Fields
Ryder · Engineering Electronics
Schwartz · Information Transmission, Modulation, and Noise
Seely · Electromechanical Energy Conversion
Seely · Electron-tube Circuits
Seely · Electronic Engineering
Seely · Introduction to Electromagnetic Fields
Seely · Radio Electronics
Seifert and Steeg · Control Systems Engineering
Siegman · Microwave Solid State Masers
Siskind · Direct-current Machinery
Skilling · Electric Transmission Lines
Skilling · Transient Electric Currents
Spangenberg · Fundamentals of Electron Devices
Spangenberg · Vacuum Tubes
Stevenson · Elements of Power System Analysis
Stewart · Fundamentals of Signal Theory
Storer · Passive Network Synthesis
Strauss · Wave Generation and Shaping
Terman · Electronic and Radio Engineering
Terman and Pettit · Electronic Measurements
Thaler · Elements of Servomechanism Theory
Thaler and Brown · Analysis and Design of Feedback Control Systems
Thaler and Pastel · Analysis and Design of Nonlinear Feedback Control Systems
Thompson · Alternating-current and Transient Circuit Analysis
Tou · Digital and Sampled-data Control Systems
Truxal · Automatic Feedback Control System Synthesis
Valdes · The Physical Theory of Transistors
Van Bladel · Electromagnetic Fields
Weinberg · Network Analysis and Synthesis
Williams and Young · Electrical Engineering Problems

S. B. HAMMOND

Associate Professor of Electrical Engineering, University of Utah

ELECTRICAL
ENGINEERING

New York   Toronto   London   1961
McGRAW-HILL BOOK COMPANY, INC.

ELECTRICAL ENGINEERING

Copyright © 1961 by the McGraw-Hill Book Company, Inc.
Printed in the United States of America.
All rights reserved. This book, or parts thereof,
may not be reproduced in any form
without permission of the publishers.

v

Library of Congress Catalog Card Number: 61-7578

25902

This book has been set in Monotype Scotch,
a version of an early modern type face
thought to have originated in Edinburgh near the beginning
of the nineteenth century. Heads and illustration lettering are
in Bodoni Bold and Twentieth Century.
Felix Cooper made the illustrations.

This book is intended for use with electrical engineering courses for students whose special interests are in other areas of engineering. No single volume can pretend to encompass the subject of electrical engineering. Certainly this one does not. Yet in the age of the push button it seems necessary for all technical men to know some of the basic principles of electricity, its use, and its control; such is the justification for this text.

It has, of course, been necessary to limit severely the subject matter of the book and to include only topics considered to be important and fundamental. In a sense the choice has been arbitrary, but the philosophy and contents have as their aims to (a) reinforce the background of the engineering student as an engineer, (b) develop understanding in electrical science, and (c) familiarize the student with the fundamentals of electric machines, electronics, computers, and automatic controls in order to support the first two aims.

There is a trend in engineering education toward the teaching of broad principles and their applications rather than the teaching of specific applications only. Thus the emphasis in this book is on the science underlying electrical engineering rather than on the practice of electrical engineering. Fortunately, many ideas in electrical engineering can be expressed quantitatively by algebra, trigonometry, or differential equations. Ability in the use of mathematics makes the study of engineering easier and more meaningful. Yet a qualitative physical understanding of the problem and its solution is also a necessity for the engineer. It is certainly desirable that the quantitative mathematical solution be found while the qualitative physical picture of the problem and its solution is maintained. Each aspect is essential to the understanding of the problem and one should not be stressed at the expense of the other. Where mathematics is useful, it has been employed, that is, where avoiding mathematics might result in hazy or incomplete understanding of the problem and its solution. It is assumed that the student has had some preparation in calculus, and preferably also in ordinary differential equations. However, all analysis involving the use of differential equations is so developed in the text that the student with no previous study in the subject can follow it.

Many excellent volumes are available on the subject matter of the single chapters in this book. Some of them are referred to in the annotated bibliographies at the ends of the chapters. It is to be hoped that important concepts developed in this text will naturally lead the student to the more detailed discussion in the reference material.

The author extends grateful appreciation to the many persons who have assisted in the preparation of the manuscript. In particular, the long-suffering students on whom the early versions of the manuscript were tried are to be congratulated for their fortitude.

S. B. Hammond

CONTENTS

Preface vii

1 FIRST PRINCIPLES 1

2 CHARACTERISTICS OF VOLTAGES
AND CURRENTS 40

3 NATURAL RESPONSE 68

4 SERIES ELECTRIC CIRCUITS
IN THE STEADY STATE 96

5 COMPLETE SOLUTIONS OF SERIES CIRCUITS 123

6 PARALLEL AND SERIES-PARALLEL CIRCUITS 141

7 ELECTRIC NETWORKS 168

8 NONLINEAR RESISTIVE CIRCUITS 190

9 ELECTRON PHYSICS 212

ix

10 ELECTRONIC DEVICES 241

11 LINEAR OPERATION 282

12 NONLINEAR OPERATION 306

13 FEEDBACK CIRCUITS 333

14 ELECTRONIC ANALOG COMPUTERS 357

15 DIGITAL COMPUTERS 382

16 MAGNETIC FIELDS AND CIRCUITS 404

17 GENERATION OF VOLTAGES 429

18 ELECTROMAGNETIC FORCES AND TORQUE 462

19 LINEAR APPROXIMATIONS
TO MACHINE ANALYSIS 503

20 AUTOMATIC CONTROL SYSTEMS 522

APPENDIX **1** CHARACTERISTICS OF VACUUM TUBES
AND TRANSISTORS 549

APPENDIX **2** ELECTRIC INDICATING INSTRUMENTS 552

APPENDIX **3** LETTER SYMBOLS USED IN THE TEXT 558

APPENDIX **4** ANSWERS TO SOME PROBLEMS 561

Index 563

FIRST PRINCIPLES 1

1.1 INTRODUCTION

Electrical engineering is concerned with the uses of electric energy. This book is about electric circuits and devices and their reactions when excited by sources of electric energy. Electric circuits guide electric energy to its destination, where devices called "transducers" convert electric energy to mechanical energy, heat, chemical energy, or other useful forms of energy.

The first part of this book is devoted to electric-circuit analysis. The study of electric circuits and the effect of electric-circuit elements on energy transmission is fundamental to electrical engineering. Electric current and voltage are electric-circuit variables closely associated with the rate of energy flow. Often in electric-circuit-analysis problems the unknown voltages and currents are sought rather than energy flow.

Electronics is the subject of the middle portion of the book. The study of electronics is the study of electric circuits in which are included electronic devices such as vacuum tubes and transistors. Electronic devices are often low-power devices used in communications or in the handling of information; amplifiers and computers are examples of circuits and systems using electronic devices.

The latter part of the book is largely concerned with the conversion of energy from one form to another. Energy converters, or transducers, are devices such as generators, motors, and loud-speakers. Often the energy converter is part of a complex system consisting of several interconnected electric and electromechanical devices. These systems often contain feedback, and they must be analyzed as a system and not merely as a collection of unrelated individual devices.

Electric phenomena can be studied by laboratory observation, just as other physical phenomena are subject to laboratory experiments. A number of ingenious experiments have revealed several basic laws and concepts which describe the behavior of electric circuits. Although these laws are few in number, their applications are far-reaching. By means of these laws it is possible to predict how an electric circuit behaves under a given set of conditions without resorting to direct laboratory measurements. Engineers use analysis extensively to predict the behavior of physical systems before building them. A structural-design engineer designs his structures by analyzing them, successively modifying and analyzing, until he finds a design that supports the required loads and is economical to build and maintain. In general, engineering design consists of successive analysis and modification until the desired results are achieved.

Electric circuits are particularly susceptible to engineering analysis. The application of analytical methods to electric circuits is a highly organized science. An understanding of electric circuits and circuit analysis is fundamental to the study of electric machines, electronics, and systems. Electric-circuit analysis proceeds through a logical thought process, commencing with known and verified physical laws, many of which are reviewed in this chapter. With the help of these laws, a system of equations can be formulated, relating the variables and parameters of the electric circuit. Finally, the equations are solved for the unknown variables, and the engineer uses this solution to decide whether the circuit is doing what he wants it to do or whether to modify it and then analyze it again.

The electrical characteristics of electric-circuit elements and devices are an important part of electrical engineering. The engineer must know the electrical characteristics of such devices as vacuum tubes, transistors, electric motors, and generators before he can incorporate them intelligently into circuits. But these devices tend to become obsolete, while the laws of electric circuits only become better understood with the passage of time. For this reason, physical principles and circuit analysis will be stressed in this textbook, as will the general characteristics of electric-circuit devices and machines. But no effort is made to discuss completely and extensively the electrical nature of these devices.

1.2 MKS UNITS

A unit is a standard quantity by which other physical quantities are measured. Units by which physical quantities are measured are somewhat arbitrary. For example, the dimension length, or distance, can be measured in units of inches, miles, light-years, spans, cubits, millimeters, microns, or any of several other more or less standard distances. Custom and convenience dictate which unit is used for a particular measurement. Electrical engineers almost universally now use a system of units based on the *meter*, *kilogram*, and *second* for units of *length*, *mass*, and *time*. Length, mass, and time are dimensions by which all purely mechanical quantities can be expressed. Linear velocity, for example, has dimensions of length divided by time and is defined as the rate of change of distance with respect to time. In the mks system of units, the length dimension is expressed in units of meters, and the time dimension is expressed in units of seconds. Linear acceleration, defined as the second derivative of length or distance with respect to time, has dimensions of length divided by time squared, and the mks units are meters per second squared.

An electrical dimension is required along with length, time, and mass in order to express electric quantities. In addition, a physical relationship between mechanical quantities and electric quantities must be known. The mks system of units has adopted electric *charge* as the electrical dimension and the *coulomb* as the unit of electric charge. Electric charges are subject to electric forces, and moving charges subject to electric forces represent changes in potential energy. This is the relationship between mechanical and electric quantities that is used in the mks system of units. All electric quantities can now be expressed in units of meters, kilograms, seconds, and coulombs. Many electric quantities have names of their own but they can also be expressed in terms of these four units, known as the four *fundamental* units, from which the mks system of units receives its name, and from which other *derived* units (such as energy, power, volts, amperes, etc.) are obtained.

The mks system of units is used throughout this book for two reasons. First, it is the system of units used in virtually all elec-

TABLE 1.1 *MKS and English Units and Their Conversion Factors*

Quantity	English unit	MKS unit
Length	Foot (0.3048 m)	Meter (3.280 ft)
Time	Second	Second
Mass	Slug (14.6 kg)	Kilogram (0.0685 slug)
Force	Pound (4.45 newtons)	Newton (0.225 lb)
Weight	Pound (4.45 newtons)	Newton (0.225 lb)
Energy	Foot-pound (1.35 joules)	Joule (0.742 ft-lb) (newton-m)
Power	Ft-lb/sec (1.35 watts)	**Watt (0.742 ft-lb/sec)**

trical-engineering literature published since about 1946 and in much of the literature published before that date. Second, the common electrical units volt, ampere, and watt are mks units, and they are used with the mks mechanical units without conversion factors. The comparison between the mks system and the English system of units is not always precise because of the ambiguity in the English system of units. The comparison is made in Table 1.1, where the English system uses the pound as the unit of force or weight.

1.3 ELECTRIC CHARGE

We postulate that all atoms in nature are inherently electrically neutral, that is, that they have the same number of electrons (negative charges) as protons (positive charges). When an atom loses an electron, it is left with a surplus of positive charge equal in magnitude to the charge of the electron it has lost. All positive charges within the atom are tightly bound within the nucleus. The electrons in the orbits around the nucleus exist in various energy levels such that a certain discrete amount of energy is necessary to remove each electron completely from the influence of the field of attraction of the positive nucleus. The electrons in the orbits nearest the nucleus are tightly bound to the nucleus and require a comparatively large amount of energy properly applied to be removed from the influence of the nucleus. The electrons in the outermost orbits are those farthest from the nucleus and are comparatively loosely bound to the nucleus. These are the electrons shared with other atoms in chemical compounds. When one of these outermost electrons has been removed from the atom, the atom is left with a positive charge and is said to be a "positive" ion.

If a number of electrons are removed from their parent atoms and concentrated in one place, they constitute a negative electric charge equivalent to the combined charge of the electrons removed. The positive ions likewise possess a combined positive charge of the same magnitude. The charge on the electron is the smallest increment of charge. All quantities of charge found in nature or established in the laboratory are made up of one or more electronic charges but may be either positive or negative. The charge on the electron represents an extremely small amount of charge compared with the quantities of charge usually encountered in electrical problems, and a larger unit of charge is desirable. The unit of electric charge adopted in the mks system of units is the *coulomb*, chosen such that common electrical units of volts, amperes, and watts can be used as mks units.

$$1 \text{ coulomb} = 6.249 \times 10^{18} \text{ electronic charges}$$
$$1 \text{ electronic charge} = 1.602 \times 10^{-19} \text{ coulomb}$$

The relationships above are in magnitude only. A coulomb of charge carries either a positive or a negative sign, depending on whether it represents a surplus of positive charges or a surplus of electrons.

1.4 CONDUCTORS AND INSULATORS

As stated previously, the outer electrons in an atom are the only ones that can be tampered with conveniently by electrical means. In most metals that are good conductors, there is only one electron in the outer, or valence, orbit. The atoms themselves are electrically neutral but tend to form themselves in regularly spaced patterns, or crystals, in which the nuclei are equally spaced from each other.

Figure 1.1 shows a two-dimensional representation of the crystalline structure of a conductor. The positive charges shown represent the nuclei, each with its full complement of electrons, but without its valence electron. Thus each positive charge shown carries a net charge equal to an electronic charge. The negative charges shown are the valence electrons of the conductor atoms. They are not tightly bound to the atoms and are shown nearly equidistant between two or more positive charges. Since unlike charges attract each other, the electron is attracted in several directions at once. The net force on the electron is nearly zero, and the electron is free to move about in the space between the positive charges, forming what is sometimes called a "sea" of free electrons.

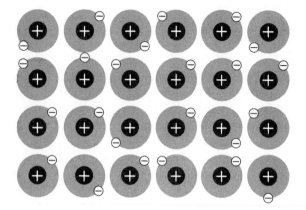

FIG. 1.1 *Two-dimensional representation of the crystalline structure of a conductor.*

The heat energy which the conductor possesses is partly represented by the average velocity of the free electrons. The forces of attraction of the nuclei and collisions with the nuclei vibrating or oscillating around their mean positions cause the free electrons to move in paths which are irregular and random. The free electrons change direction, change velocity, and, on the average over a long period of time, go nowhere.

An electric field is characterized by the force it produces on an electric charge. The direction of the force depends on the sign of the charge, and the magnitude of the force is proportional to the amount of charge. The electric-field strength, defined as the force on a unit of positive charge, has both magnitude and direction. If an electric field is superimposed over the crystal, the free electrons experience a force in the direction opposite to the direction of the electric field. The electric field makes the free electrons drift in the direction of the force with average velocity proportional to the strength of the electric field. The drift of electrons gives rise to electric current. Yet at any instant any sample volume of the conductor is electrically neutral, since the average number of electrons that leaves the volume in a unit of time is equal to the average number of electrons that enters during that unit of time.

The electrons in some materials are all tightly bound to the nuclei of the atoms. In these materials, the valence electrons are shared with neighboring atoms, although they remain tightly bound to their own nuclei. Materials with tightly bound valence electrons are known as "insulators," which do not permit the relatively easy flow of electrons among the atoms as the conductors do. Insulators are nonmetallic materials and are used to confine the flow of electrons to certain desired paths of conducting material by surrounding the conducting material with insulating material. Some common insulating materials are paper, glass, plastic, rubber, varnish, and mica. Under normal conditions, air is also a good insulator.

1.5 ELECTRIC CURRENT

A net flow of electric charge gives rise to electric current. In some cases, both positive and negative charges are in motion. Electric current is a measure of the net motion of both kinds of charge. Direction is also a characteristic of electric current. The direction of electric-current flow is arbitrarily defined as the direction of motion of positive charges. Positive charges moving in one direction are electrically equivalent to negative charges moving in the opposite direction. In a conductor, electrons are the charge carriers, and there is no motion of positive charges. By convention, the positive direction of the current flow is defined opposite to the direction of motion of the electrons, or in the direction of positive-charge flow. Although the positive direction of current is arbitrarily defined as the direction of motion of positive charges, it is sometimes convenient to speak of the direction of electron flow as the direction of electron current. Electron current, made up only of the flow of negative charges, is in the opposite direction to conventional current.

A quantitative definition of electric current can be formed by considering a cross-sectional area of a hypothetical conductor which conducts either positive or negative charge. Assume that the electric charge moving along the conductor passes through the cross-sectional area in a direction at right angles to the area surface. If positive charges only are in motion, the current through the cross-sectional area at any instant is defined as

$$i = \frac{dq}{dt} \quad \text{amp} \tag{1.1}$$

where q is charge and the direction of the current is the same as the direction of motion of the positive charges. Equation (1.1) is a definition of electric current. Current i signifies an instantaneous value of electric current, which is equal to the rate of flow of charge with respect to time at that particular instant. Obviously, the rate of flow of charge through the area need not be constant, and therefore i is a function of time.

Equation (1.1) also defines current if the charge in motion consists of electrons or negative charges. In this case it must be remembered that direction of current is opposite to the direction of motion of the electrons. If both positive- and negative-charge carriers are in motion, they flow in opposite directions, owing to the opposite effect of the electric-field forces on them. Current caused by the motion of positive charges and current caused by the opposite motion of negative charges are additive. The resultant current can be expressed

$$i = \frac{dq(+)}{dt} + \frac{dq(-)}{dt} \qquad \text{amp} \tag{1.2}$$

where $dq(+)/dt$ is the rate of flow of $+$ charges in one direction and $dq(-)/dt$ is the rate of flow of $-$ charges in the opposite direction. This situation is represented in Fig. 1.2, where the direction

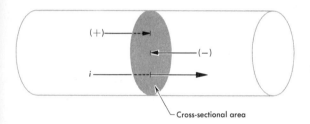

Cross-sectional area

FIG. 1.2 *Electric charges in motion produce current i.*

of flow of both positive and negative charges is shown and the current i is shown in the direction of flow of positive charge.

The unit of electric current in the mks system of units is the *ampere*. One ampere is defined as the unit of current when the rate of flow of charge with respect to time is one coulomb per second.

1 amp = 1 coulomb/sec

1.6 ELECTRIC CIRCUITS

Electric circuits can be defined as closed, or continuous, paths in which electric currents are confined and around which electric currents can be caused to flow. In electric circuits the current is confined to a particular path or to paths which are conductors.

This is in contrast to electric fields, which give rise to electric phenomena distributed throughout space, including circuits and the media surrounding them.

The electric circuit can be separated into parts, or elements, which are separate entities and which have two terminals and one conducting path. Circuit elements can be classified in a number of ways. It is sometimes useful to classify them according to whether they convert or induce electric energy into the circuit or whether they do not. An active element is one which supplies electric energy to the circuit. A passive element does not supply electric energy to the circuit. An active element is a transducer. It converts mechanical energy, light energy, heat energy, etc., into electric energy. At least one active element is required in every electric circuit if current is to flow indefinitely in that circuit.

If active circuit elements are sources of electric energy, passive circuit elements either store that electric energy or convert it to other forms of energy. Passive circuit elements, then, are either energy-storing devices or transducers of energy. The conservation-of-energy principle must be satisfied by the electric circuit. All energy that is converted to electric energy is either stored as electric energy or converted to another form of energy.

Several electric circuits are represented in Fig. 1.3. A battery is shown as the active element, being the source of electric energy

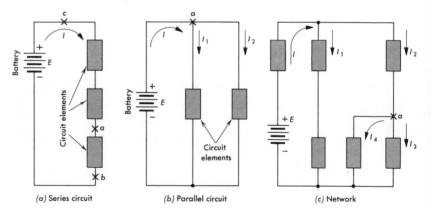

FIG. 1.3 *Examples of circuit configuration.*

(a) Series circuit   (b) Parallel circuit   (c) Network

in the circuit. Each of the rectangles represents one circuit element through which a current flows. Figure 1.3a shows a circuit referred to as a series circuit, since the current flows through each of the elements in sequence as it completes its path around the closed loop. Figure 1.3b shows a parallel circuit; the current I in this circuit divides to form I_1 and I_2, which flow through the two parallel branches of the circuit. Circuits may be formed by series and parallel combinations of circuit elements. Such a circuit is often referred to as a "network." Figure 1.3c is an example of a network with one electric-energy source and several series and parallel branches. The junction between two or more branches is called a "node"; junctions marked a in Fig. 1.3a, b, and c are examples of nodes.

1.7 POTENTIAL ENERGY AND POTENTIAL DIFFERENCE

The *potential energy* which a mass possesses is that energy which is a consequence of the position of the mass in a gravitational field in space. Likewise, the potential energy which an electric charge possesses is a consequence of its position in an electrostatic field or in a circuit. In either case the change in potential energy between two points a and b in the field is given by

$$W = \int_a^b f \, ds \qquad \text{joules} \qquad (1.3)$$

where f is the component of force in the direction of ds and ds is an increment of a line joining points a and b. If the force is constant and always in the direction of ds, then the integral of Eq. (1.3) reduces to

$$W = Fs \qquad \text{joules} \qquad (1.4)$$

where F is the constant force and s is the length of the line along which the force operates. Equation (1.4) is the well-known force-times-distance equation, which is valid only when the force is constant and uniform in the direction of motion.

As an example of the potential energy of a mass, consider a reference plane above which the mass M can be raised. The mass is assumed to have a weight of 5 newtons and is raised a distance of 4 m above the reference plane, as shown in Fig. 1.4. The force of gravity is assumed to be constant, so that 20 newton-m, or 20 joules, of potential energy is added to the mass to raise the mass to its new position. This much work is done to raise the mass to its position above the plane, and this much energy can be extracted from the mass by allowing it to fall back to the reference plane. If the mass is lowered below the reference plane, energy is extracted from the mass and it is said to possess "negative" potential

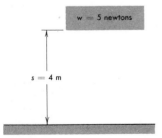

FIG. 1.4 *Potential energy of a weight above a reference plane.*

energy with respect to the reference plane. The position of the reference plane is arbitrary; but once a reference plane is established, the potential energy of the mass can be defined with respect to the reference position.

Now define *potential* at b with respect to the reference plane at a as the *work per unit mass* needed to raise the mass from a to b. Then the potential at b with respect to a, symbolized by V_{ba}, can be written

$$V_{ba} = \frac{1}{M} \int_a^b f \, ds \qquad \text{joules/kg} \tag{1.5}$$

If f is constant in the direction of s and s is the distance from a to b, then

$$V_{ba} = \frac{Fs}{M} \qquad \text{joules/kg} \tag{1.6}$$

where F is the constant force. By Newton's second law, the force opposing gravity can be written $f = -Ma$, where a is the acceleration; this is substituted into Eq. (1.6) and a replaced by g, the acceleration due to gravity. The result is

$$V_{ba} = -sg \qquad \text{joules/kg} \tag{1.7}$$

Potential V_{ba} is positive in sign if the potential energy of the mass increases as the mass moves from a to b.

Newton's second law is useful in defining the strength of a gravitational field as the force (weight) per unit mass, or

$$g = \frac{f}{M} \qquad \text{newtons/kg}$$

In an electric field the field strength can be defined as the force per unit of positive charge, or

$$\mathcal{E} = \frac{f}{q} \qquad \text{newtons/coulomb} \tag{1.8}$$

where $\mathcal{E}$ is the electric-field strength, f is force, and q is charge. Then the force on a charge q in an electric field of strength $\mathcal{E}$ is

$$f = \mathcal{E}q \qquad \text{newtons} \tag{1.9}$$

If we define *electric potential* as *work per unit charge*, the electric potential at a point b with respect to a point a is

$$V_{ba} = \frac{1}{q} \int_a^b -\mathcal{E}q \, ds \qquad \text{joules/coulomb} \tag{1.10}$$

where the force $\mathcal{E}q$ is assumed to be in the direction of the path s. By dividing out q, Eq. (1.10) can be written

$$V_{ba} = -\int_a^b \mathcal{E}\,ds \qquad \text{joules/coulomb} \tag{1.11}$$

just as Eq. (1.5) can be written

$$V_{ba} = -\int_a^b a\,ds \qquad \text{joules/kg} \tag{1.12}$$

with the aid of Newton's second law.

If the electric-field strength $\mathcal{E}$ is constant and uniform in the direction of s, Eq. (1.11) can be written

$$V_{ba} = -\mathcal{E}s \qquad \text{joules/coulomb} \tag{1.13}$$

where s is the distance from a to b.

It is apparent from Eq. (1.8) that the appropriate mks unit for electric-field strength $\mathcal{E}$ is newtons per coulomb. From Eq. (1.11) it is apparent that potential V_{ba} has units of newton-meters per coulomb, or joules per coulomb. For convenience, one joule per coulomb is defined as one *volt*, the common unit of potential difference.

An electric field established parallel to an electric circuit produces forces on the electric charges in the circuit resulting in charge motion and hence current. These moving charges experience changes in potential energy as they progress around the circuit; the potential difference between two nodes in the circuit is the change in potential energy per unit positive charge as it proceeds along the circuit from one node to another. Potential difference, or voltage, has a sign as well as a magnitude associated with it. If energy must be added to a positive charge to move it along a circuit between two nodes a and b, the potential difference between a and b is said to be positive; if the positive charge gives up energy, the potential difference is said to be negative.

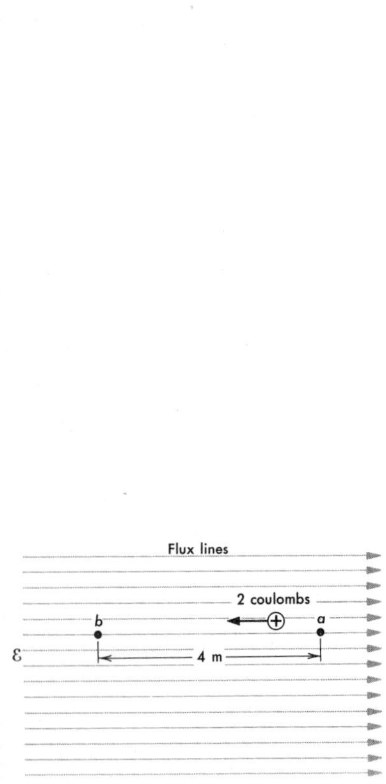

Example 1.1

An electric field of strength $\mathcal{E}$ is known to be uniform and constant everywhere and directed to the right. This is represented by lines of force equally spaced, as shown in Fig. 1.5. A 2-coulomb positive charge moves from a to b, a distance of 4 m, along a line of force. The potential difference from a to b is 50 volts.

FIG. 1.5 *Uniform electric field directed to the right (Example 1.1).*

To find the electric-field strength,

$$V_{ba} = \varepsilon s$$

or

$$\varepsilon = \frac{V_{ba}}{s} = \frac{50 \text{ volts}}{4 \text{ m}} = 12.5 \text{ volts/m}$$

To find the potential energy of the charge at b with respect to its energy at a, energy = work per unit charge × charge.

$$W = V_{ba} \times q$$
$$= 50 \text{ joules/coulomb} \times 2 \text{ coulombs} = 100 \text{ joules}$$

An electric-energy source, such as a battery or generator, is capable of moving electric charges against the electric field, thus adding potential energy to the charge. For example, a positive charge in passing clockwise from b to c in Fig. 1.3a is raised in potential energy by the battery. As this unit of charge continues around the circuit path through the circuit elements, it experiences a loss of potential energy, or drop in potential. The increase in voltage by such means as a battery or a generator provides the electromotive force (emf), sometimes thought of as a pressure or force which causes charge to flow through the circuit. Electromotive force is a synonym for potential difference.

Voltage sources produce emfs measured in volts, which are functions of time. A voltage that is constant with time is called "direct" voltage; battery voltage is an example. Some rotating generators produce direct voltages. Time-varying voltages may follow any pattern. In practical use they are often periodic and occasionally sinusoidal. A periodic function is one that repeats itself over equal intervals of time. Figure 1.6 shows several useful shapes of voltage sources, all plotted as functions of time. The first two, namely, the sine wave and the rectangular wave, are periodic.

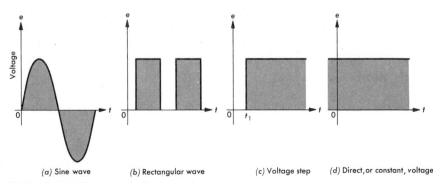

(a) Sine wave   (b) Rectangular wave   (c) Voltage step   (d) Direct, or constant, voltage

FIG. 1.6 *Examples of voltage waveforms.*

The voltage step is obtained when a direct voltage is applied to a circuit by closing a switch at t_1.

A potential "rise" does not necessarily occur only in a battery or generator but may occur in a passive element as well. Whether the potential rises or drops in any element depends upon which direction the positive charge takes in passing through the element. Thus, in Fig. 1.3a, there is a potential rise from b to c clockwise, but, in going from c to b counterclockwise, a positive charge undergoes a drop in potential. Likewise, from a to b clockwise there is a drop in potential, but from b to a counterclockwise there is a rise in potential.

The battery as an electric-energy source converts chemical energy into electric energy. A rotating generator converts mechanical energy to electric energy. In an electric circuit it is necessary for the law of the conservation of energy to hold. If electric-energy sources are present, electric-energy "sinks" must also exist. Resistance in a circuit acts as an electric-energy sink by converting electric energy to heat.

Potential rise, potential drop, and potential difference all represent a change in potential energy which a unit positive charge experiences as it moves along the circuit. But the term "potential" by itself has an arbitrary meaning. Potential must be measured with respect to some position or point on the circuit. Once the reference position is established, potential difference between that point and any other point on the circuit can be determined. As long as the reference point is understood, the term "potential" or "voltage" has meaning. In Fig. 1.3a, position b can be chosen as a reference position, and, with that arbitrary choice made, we can say that the potential at a is, say, 10 volts positive. This means that the potential difference from b to a is $+10$ volts. In other words, "potential" implies potential difference between a reference position and another position in the circuit, no matter what circuit path is taken between the two points. Often "ground" is the term used for the reference position, especially if the reference position is at the same potential as the earth.

1.8 ELECTRIC ENERGY AND POWER

We have seen that the electric potential difference between two points in a circuit is the work per unit of positive charge in moving from one point in the circuit to another. If v is the potential difference, w is the work or change in energy of the charge, and q is the quantity of charge, then

$$v = \frac{w}{q} \quad \text{volts} \tag{1.14}$$

where w has units of joules, q is in coulombs, and v is joules per coulomb, or volts. From Eq. (1.14), if a differential increase in energy dw is experienced by a differential quantity of charge dq, the increase in the potential of the charge is

$$v = \frac{dw}{dq} \quad \text{volts} \tag{1.15}$$

To find the relationship between potential v and power, multiply both sides of Eq. (1.15) by $i = dq/dt$.

$$vi = \frac{dw}{dq}\frac{dq}{dt} = \frac{dw}{dt} \tag{1.16}$$

Since power is defined as the rate of change or transfer of energy with respect to time, in an electric circuit power is expressed by

$$p = \frac{dw}{dt} = vi \quad \text{watts} \tag{1.17}$$

Equation (1.17) for power p applies at any instant in time. Thus, instantaneous power p is the product of the instantaneous voltage v and the instantaneous current i. Since nominal values of constant or direct voltages and currents are identical with their instantaneous values, Eq. (1.17) applies for instantaneous as well as average or nominal values for this special case of direct current. If v and i are time-varying, the instantaneous power can be calculated from Eq. (1.17). Average power delivered by time-varying voltages and currents are discussed in Chap. 2.

Equation (1.17) shows that the unit of power p is newton-meters per second; this unit is called a *watt*. Power can also be expressed as volts times amperes, but since a volt is a newton-meter per coulomb and an ampere has units of coulombs per second, there is no ambiguity in the units.

1.9 DIMENSIONS OF ELECTRIC QUANTITIES

Sometimes it is desirable to check the dimensions of a particular unit as it appears in an equation to verify the equation. The dimensions that can be used independently of the system of units are

TABLE 1.2   *Common Electric Quantities*

Quantity	Common mks unit	Dimensions
Potential	Volt	$ML^2Q^{-1}T^{-2}$
Current	Ampere	QT^{-1}
Energy	Joule	ML^2T^{-2}
Power	Watt	ML^2T^{-3}
Resistance	Ohm	$ML^2T^{-1}Q^{-2}$
Inductance	Henry	L^2MQ^{-2}
Capacitance	Farad	$L^{-2}M^{-1}T^2Q^2$

length L, time T, mass M, and charge Q. All mechanical and electric quantities can be shown to have one or more of these dimensions, and the system of units has no effect on the dimensions. Velocity, for example, has dimensions of LT^{-1}, which is distance per unit time in mks units, cgs units, or any other system of units. Force is related to mass by Newton's second law, written as $f = -Ma$. Since a has dimensions of LT^{-2}, force has the dimensions of MLT^{-2}.

Electric quantities can be analyzed in terms of these fundamental dimensions also. From Eq. (1.1), current is seen to have dimensions of QT^{-1}, and, from Eq. (1.10), potential has the dimensions of FLQ^{-1}, or $ML^2Q^{-1}T^{-2}$. Table 1.2 summarizes some of the common electric quantities in terms of mks units and the basic dimensions.

1.10 SYMBOLS

In order to simplify our discussions and mathematics regarding electric quantities, a consistent system of symbols must be adopted. Already we have used e or v for voltage, i for current, etc., but it is also necessary to be able to indicate whether the voltage or current is constant or changing with time. We shall use capital letters to denote constant values and lower-case letters to denote time-varying values. Thus I indicates the constant, or direct, current or an average value of a periodic current. The symbol i means instantaneous current, which need not be constant but may vary with time.

The instantaneous value of a sinusoidal voltage can be expressed by use of the symbols mentioned. Thus

$$e = E_m \sin \omega t \qquad \text{volts} \tag{1.18}$$

where e is the instantaneous value of voltage, E_m is the maximum value of the sine wave of voltage, ω is the radian frequency in radians per second, and t is time in seconds. The capital E is used for the maximum value because the maximum value of a sine wave is constant and does not change even though the sine wave has this value only once each cycle.

1.11 RESISTANCE

In an electric circuit, resistance is often thought of as a characteristic of the circuit which "resists" the flow of current. More specifically, resistance is that property of an electric circuit which converts electric energy to heat energy. A resistive circuit element is an energy sink. Electric energy is poured into it, and heat energy flows from it.

Resistance is a property of all conductors and can be defined for resistive circuit elements as the ratio of a small voltage increment across the element to the increment of current through the element. In the limit, resistance is expressed in the well-known Ohm's law as

$$dv = R\,di \qquad \text{or} \qquad R = \frac{dv}{di} \tag{1.19}$$

where R is the resistance expressed in ohms, dv is the increment of voltage, and di is the increment of current. The resistance of a given circuit element is often independent of the voltage applied and is therefore constant for all values of voltage or current; when this is true, Eq. (1.19) can be written

$$v = Ri \qquad \text{volts} \tag{1.20}$$

Equation (1.20) is a linear algebraic equation. It has two variables, v and i, each with an exponent of unity. Thus R is the proportionality constant between v and i. But it must be kept in mind that a constant R is a special case, and that Eq. (1.19) is more generally descriptive of the physical world. An analogy can be drawn here comparing resistance, voltage, and current with velocity, distance, and time, respectively. Velocity is defined as $v = dx/dt$, where x is distance and t is time. If the velocity is constant (a very special case), then velocity $V = x/t$.

It is arbitrary which of the variables in Eq. (1.20) is the independent variable and which is the dependent one. Equation (1.20) is plotted in Fig. 1.7, where i has been chosen as the independent variable and v as the dependent variable. Since the curve is a straight line, only two points are necessary to plot it and one point can be taken at the origin. The value of the resistance R is the slope of the curve, as given by Eq. (1.19). The curve in Fig. 1.7 is known as the *characteristic curve* of resistance R and shows the voltage-current relationship for R.

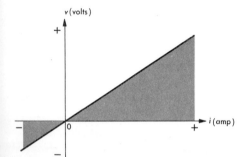

FIG. 1.7 *Voltage-versus-current curve for an ideal resistor.*

Ideal resistive elements do not have the ability to store energy as do inductive and capacitive elements. Ohm's law applies for instantaneous voltages and currents that vary with time, as well as for constant values of voltage and current that do not change with time.

Joule's law describes the rate at which resistance causes electric energy to be converted to heat energy. This law states that the electric power delivered to the resistive element and thus converted to heat is equal to the product of the square of the instantaneous current and the resistance. It is derived by substituting Eq. (1.17) into the linear form of Ohm's law [Eq. (1.20)]. Joule's law states that

$$p = i^2 R \qquad \text{watts} \tag{1.21}$$

where p is instantaneous power, i is instantaneous current, and R is resistance. Energy is the integral of power with respect to time, or

$$w = \int_{t_1}^{t_2} p \, dt \qquad \text{joules} \tag{1.22}$$

where the integral is taken over the interval of time from t_1 to t_2. For a constant resistance and a time-varying current, the total energy converted to heat during the time interval from t_1 to t_2 is

$$w = \int_{t_1}^{t_2} R i^2 \, dt \tag{1.23}$$

For direct current, i is constant, and the total energy converted to heat during the interval of time $t = t_2 - t_1$ is

$$W = I^2Rt \quad \text{joules} \tag{1.24}$$

Example 1.2

A sinusoidal current is expressed by the equation $i = 10 \sin 2\pi t$. The linear resistance through which this current flows is 5 ohms. It is desired to find the energy converted to heat during the first second of the sine wave. Using Eq. (1.23),

$$w = 5 \int_0^1 (10 \sin 2\pi t)^2 \, dt$$

$$= 5 \int_0^1 (100 \sin^2 2\pi t) \, dt$$

$$= 500 \int_0^1 \left(\frac{1}{2} - \frac{1}{2} \cos 4\pi t \right) dt$$

$$= 500 \left[\frac{t}{2} - \frac{1}{8\pi} \sin 4\pi t \right]_0^1$$

$$= 250 \text{ joules}$$

Example 1.3

It is necessary to provide 125,000 joules/hr to an electric water heater. The voltage source is constant at 110 volts. Find the value of the resistance necessary to transform the required amount of energy to heat in the time given.

From Eq. (1.24), $W = RI^2t$, where t is 60 sec/min $\times$ 60 min/hr $\times$ 1 hr, or 3,600 sec. Then

$$R = \frac{125{,}000}{3{,}600I^2}$$

But $I = E/R = 110/R$. Then

$$R = \frac{125{,}000}{3{,}600 \left(\dfrac{110}{R} \right)^2}$$

Solving for R,

$$R = 348 \text{ ohms}$$

The resistance of a conductor of uniform cross section can be shown experimentally to be proportional to its length and inversely proportional to its cross-sectional area. If the resistance is linear, this relationship can be expressed by the equation

$$R = \rho \frac{L}{A} \quad \text{ohms} \tag{1.25}$$

where L is the length of the conductor, A is the uniform cross-sectional area, and ρ, a constant, is a function of the material and temperature of the conductor. R is measured in ohms, but L, A, and ρ can be measured in any units as long as Eq. (1.25) is satisfied for units. In units, resistivity must be expressed in terms of resistance times area per length.

In the mks system, the unit of resistivity is ohm-meters squared per meter, or ohm-meters, according to Eq. (1.25). Some engineers still use as a unit of area the circular mil, which is the area of a circle with a diameter of one-thousandth of an inch, and the foot as the unit for length; resistivity in this case has units of ohm-circular mils per foot. The cross-sectional area of a round conductor, expressed in circular mils, is equal to the square of its diameter expressed in mils. The resistivities of some common conducting materials are shown in Table 1.3.

If the cross-sectional area varies as a function of the distance along the conductor, Eq. (1.25) must be modified to relate increments of resistance to increments of length. Thus

$$dR = \rho \frac{dL}{A} \quad \text{ohms} \tag{1.26}$$

where A is now a function of the distance along the conductor and dR is the differential resistance of a short length dL of the resistance. An example of the use of this equation is given in Example 1.4.

TABLE 1.3 *Resistivity of Some Common Conductors*

Material	Resistivity, ohm-m at 20°C	Resistivity, ohm-cir mils/ft at 20°C	Temperature coefficient at 20°C, ohms/(ohm)(°C)
Aluminum	2.83×10^{-8}	17.10	0.00400
Bismuth	119×10^{-8}	717.00	0.00400
Copper (hard-drawn)	1.77×10^{-8}	10.68	0.00382
Nichrome	99.5×10^{-8}	601.00	0.00044
Nickel	7.77×10^{-8}	47.00	0.00600
Silver	1.63×10^{-8}	9.65	0.00380

Example 1.4

Determine the resistance of the aluminum conductor of dimensions shown in Fig. 1.8. Assume ρ is constant and uniform.

$$dR = \rho \frac{dL}{A}$$

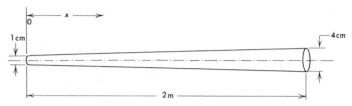

FIG. 1.8 *Conductor of aluminum (Example 1.4).*

Radius $r = (0.005 + 0.0075x)$ m

$$A = \pi r^2$$

$$dR = \rho \frac{dx}{A}$$

$$= \rho \frac{dx}{\pi(0.005 + 0.0075x)^2}$$

$$R = \int_0^2 \frac{\rho}{\pi} \frac{dx}{(0.005 + 0.0075x)^2}$$

$$= \frac{\rho}{\pi} \left[\frac{-1}{0.0075(0.005 + 0.0075x)} \right]_0^2$$

$$= \frac{\rho}{\pi} \left[\frac{1}{0.0075(0.005)} - \frac{1}{0.0075(0.020)} \right]$$

$$= \frac{2.83 \times 10^{-8}}{\pi} (2.00 \times 10^4) = 1.80 \times 10^{-4} \text{ ohm}$$

The resistivity of conducting material is a function of the temperature of the material. Table 1.3 gives the resistivities of some common conducting materials at 20°C; resistivities at other temperatures can be calculated or measured. By measuring the resistivities of a large number of conducting materials over common temperature ranges, it has been found experimentally that over these ranges resistivity varies with temperature in a fairly linear manner. If the resistance (or resistivity) of a conductor is known at a particular temperature, the resistance (or resistivity) of the conductor can be found for another temperature, assuming the linear relationship mentioned above. Recall that a straight line can be represented by an equation of the form

$$y = mx + b \tag{1.27}$$

where m is the slope of the line and b is the value of the intercept on the y axis. The resistance-versus-temperature curve is shown in Fig. 1.9 where $T_2 - T_1$ corresponds to x in Eq. (1.27). If α is

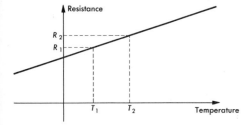

FIG. 1.9 *Resistance-versus-temperature curve for common conductors.*

the temperature coefficient of resistance in ohms per ohm per degree centigrade, then αR_1 corresponds to the slope m of Eq. (1.27). Resistance R_2 corresponds to y, and we have

$$R_2 = R_1 + \alpha R_1(T_2 - T_1)$$
$$= R_1[1 + \alpha(T_2 - T_1)] \qquad \text{ohms} \qquad (1.28)$$

Note that the units of α are ohms per ohm per degree centigrade and that αR_1 has units of ohms per degree centigrade. Table 1.3 also contains values of α for several conducting materials at 20°C.

The linear relationship of resistivity-versus-temperature applies to the range of operating temperatures often found in practice. If Eq. (1.28) is assumed to be valid for all temperatures, a value of temperature T_2 can be found at which R_2 is zero. Below this value of T_2, R_2 would be negative. It must be pointed out, however, that Eq. (1.28) is not valid near zero resistance and absolute zero in temperature.

1.12 INDUCTANCE

In Sec. 1.11 resistance was defined as the ratio of an increment of applied voltage to the resulting increment of current in a circuit element. A constant voltage applied to a constant resistance produces a proportional constant current. Now consider a circuit element characterized by having a terminal voltage proportional only to a time rate of change of current. This can be expressed as

$$v = K\frac{di}{dt} \qquad \text{volts} \qquad (1.29)$$

where K is a constant, independent of the magnitude of voltage or current. Under some conditions (the presence of iron in the vicinity of the circuit element), K is a function of i (or v) and is not constant.

As an example of a circuit element represented by Eq. (1.29), consider an inductor consisting of a coil of wire with an air core and zero resistance. The coil of wire has two terminals, and the voltage across these two terminals is expressed by the above equation with K independent of i, the current through the coil. If the current expressed in Eq. (1.29) flows through the terminals across which potential difference v is observed, the constant is known as the "coefficient of self-inductance" and the symbol L is used for K. The voltage-current relationship then becomes

$$v = L \frac{di}{dt} \quad \text{volts} \tag{1.30}$$

where v and i are as shown in Fig. 1.10a. Equation (1.30) describes the magnitude of the voltage between the terminals of the inductor,

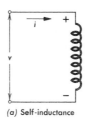

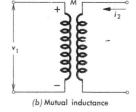

FIG. 1.10 *Inductance as defined by Eqs. (1.30) and (1.31).*

(a) Self-inductance

(b) Mutual inductance

but more information is required to describe the direction of the voltage. To Eq. (1.30) we must add Lenz's law, which states that the direction of the induced voltage between the terminals of the inductor is such as to tend to oppose the changing current. Thus in Fig. 1.10a, if the current i is increasing, the voltage v will have the polarity as shown by the $+$ and $-$ signs in order to tend to oppose the increasing current through the inductance.

The voltage and current expressed in Eq. (1.29) need not be common to a single pair of terminals as shown in Fig. 1.10a. If mutual inductance exists between two circuits, the potential v of Eq. (1.29) results from the changing current in another branch of the circuit. This is shown in Fig. 1.10b, where the voltage v_1 between the terminals on the left results from current i_2 flowing through the terminals on the right. This effect, known as "mutual inductance," is expressed in Eq. (1.31).

$$v_1 = M \frac{di_2}{dt} \quad \text{volts} \tag{1.31}$$

Equations (1.30) and (1.31) define self- and mutual inductance in terms of the circuit variables of voltage and current. A magnetic field exists here, and should be mentioned. Recall that a moving electric charge has associated with it a magnetic field. Now, if the current should change, the magnetic field changes and the changing magnetic flux linking the turns of the coil induces an emf in the coil. This is the voltage v expressed as a function of a current in Eqs. (1.30) and (1.31). A precise quantitative statement of this relationship between induced voltage and changing magnetic field, known as "Faraday's law," is given in Chap. 17.

The coefficient of self-inductance L is a function of the physical characteristics and dimensions of the coil. If no magnetic material such as iron, cobalt, or nickel is nearby, one empirical equation for inductance is

$$ L = \frac{\mu N^2 A}{l + 0.45d} \qquad \text{henrys} \qquad (1.32) $$

where N is the number of turns, A is the cross-sectional area in square meters, l is the length of the coil in meters, d is diameter of the coil in meters, and μ is the constant $4\pi \times 10^{-7}$, known as the permeability of free space (see Chap. 16). This equation is fairly accurate for long coils, but the accuracy decreases rapidly when the length becomes less than one-half the diameter. Figure 1.11 shows the definition of l, d, and A of Eq. (1.32).

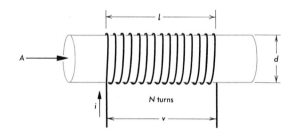

FIG. 1.11 *Inductor dimensions used in Eq. (1.32).*

Example 1.5

How many turns are needed on a cylindrical coil of 0.001 m² cross section if the length of the coil is to be 10 cm and the inductance 0.002 henry?

$$ \pi r^2 = 0.001 \qquad r = \sqrt{\frac{0.001}{\pi}} $$

$$ d = 2r = 2\sqrt{\frac{0.001}{\pi}} = 0.0356 \text{ m} $$

From Eq. (1.32)

$$N^2 = \frac{L(l + 0.45d)}{\mu A} = \frac{0.002(0.1 + 0.45 \times 0.0356)}{4\pi \times 10^{-7} \times 0.001}$$

$$= \frac{0.0320}{1.257 \times 10^{-7}} = 2.552 \times 10^5$$

$$N = 5.05 \times 10^2 \text{ turns}$$

Now let us investigate the energy considerations in the inductor. A perfect inductor has no resistance, and any energy that flows into it is stored in the magnetic field around it. Since energy is the integral of power with respect to time, during the interval from $t = 0$ to time t the energy change is

$$w = \int_0^t vi \, dt \qquad (1.33)$$

Substituting Eq. (1.30) into Eq. (1.33) gives, for $i = 0$ at $t = 0$,

$$w = \int_0^i Li \, di$$

$$= \frac{Li^2}{2} \qquad (1.34)$$

Thus, the energy stored in the inductor is proportional to the product of the self-inductance L and the square of the current i in the inductor.

1.13 CAPACITANCE

If the voltage between the terminals of a circuit element is proportional to di/dt, the element is an ideal inductor. In contrast, if the voltage between the terminals is proportional to the integral of the current with respect to time, the circuit element is an ideal capacitor. More specifically, the terminal voltage of a capacitor at time t is given by

$$v = \frac{1}{C} \int_0^t i \, dt + V_0 \qquad \text{volts} \qquad (1.35)$$

where V_0 is the voltage at $t = 0$. The constant C is known as "capacitance."

If we differentiate both sides of Eq. (1.35) with respect to time and solve for i,

$$i = C\frac{dv}{dt} \qquad \text{amp} \tag{1.36}$$

As expressions for the voltage-current relationship in a capacitance, Eqs. (1.35) and (1.36) are equivalent.

Recalling from Eq. (1.1) that

$$i = \frac{dq}{dt} \qquad \text{amps}$$

we can solve for q by multiplying both sides of Eq. (1.1) by dt and integrating; the resulting equation is

$$q = \int_0^t i\,dt + Q_0 \qquad \text{coulombs} \tag{1.37}$$

where Q_0, the constant of integration, is the charge on the capacitor at time $t = 0$. Substituting Eq. (1.37) into Eq. (1.35) results in

$$v = \frac{q}{C} \qquad \text{volts} \tag{1.38}$$

where q is the total instantaneous charge and v is the instantaneous voltage on the capacitor. The voltage at time $t = 0$ is

$$V_0 = \frac{Q_0}{C} \qquad \text{volts} \tag{1.39}$$

In the mks system of units, with v in volts and q in coulombs, the unit of capacitance is the farad. Smaller, more practical units are the microfarad (10^{-6} farad), abbreviated μf, and the micromicro-farad (10^{-12} farad), abbreviated $\mu\mu$f.

A capacitor consisting of two parallel-plane conducting plates separated a small distance d by an insulator has capacitance of

$$C = \frac{\epsilon A}{d} \qquad \text{farads} \tag{1.40}$$

where A is the area of the plates in square meters, d is the distance between them in meters, which is also the thickness of the insulator, and ϵ is a constant depending on the kind of insulator used. Some common insulators, or dielectrics, are listed in Table 1.4, together with the values of their dielectric constant ϵ.

TABLE 1.4 *Common Insulators*

Material	Dielectric constant ϵ
Air or vacuum	$\dfrac{10^{-9}}{36\pi} \times 1.00 = 8.854 \times 10^{-12}$
Glass	$\dfrac{10^{-9}}{36\pi} \times 4.50 = 3.985 \times 10^{-11}$
Mica	$\dfrac{10^{-9}}{36\pi} \times 5.45 = 4.825 \times 10^{-11}$
Paper	$\dfrac{10^{-9}}{36\pi} \times 3.50 = 3.100 \times 10^{-11}$
Distilled water	$\dfrac{10^{-9}}{36\pi} \times 78.0 = 6.910 \times 10^{-10}$

Example 1.6

Find the capacitance of the parallel-plane capacitor shown in Fig. 1.12 where the dielectric is mica.

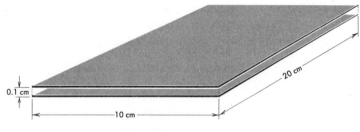

FIG. 1.12 *Parallel-plate capacitor of Example 1.6.*

$$A = 10 \text{ cm} \times 20 \text{ cm} \times \frac{10^{-4}\text{m}^2}{\text{cm}^2}$$

$$= 0.02 \text{ m}^2$$

$$C = \epsilon \frac{A}{d} = 4.825 \times 10^{-11} \times \frac{0.020}{0.001}$$

$$= 9.650 \times 10^{-10} \text{ farad}$$

$$= 9.650 \times 10^{-4} \text{ } \mu\text{f}$$

$$= 9.650 \times 10^{2} \text{ } \mu\mu\text{f}$$

Energy stored in a capacitor can be found by integrating power with respect to time. Assuming that the charge is zero at $t = 0$,

$$W = \int_{0}^{t} vi \, dt \qquad \text{joules or watt-sec}$$

1.13 *Capacitance* **27**

Substituting in Eq. (1.36),

$$W = \int_0^t v \left(C \frac{dv}{dt} \right) dt \quad \text{joules}$$

Changing the variable of integration to voltage,

$$W = \int_0^v Cv \, dv \quad \text{joules}$$

Then

$$W = C \frac{v^2}{2} \quad \text{joules} \tag{1.41}$$

Thus the energy stored in a capacitor is proportional to the product of the square of the voltage and the capacitance C.

1.14 KIRCHHOFF'S LAWS

Two circuit laws, stated by Kirchhoff in 1847, are extremely useful in the solution of electric-circuit problems. These laws may be stated as follows:

At any instant, the algebraic sum of all currents flowing into a node or junction in a circuit is zero. Or at any instant the sum of the currents flowing toward a node in a circuit is equal to the sum of the currents flowing away from the node.

At any instant, the algebraic sum of the voltages around any closed path in an electric circuit is zero. In other words, the sum of the voltage rises around any closed loop must equal the sum of the voltage drops.

Kirchhoff's laws as stated above apply for instantaneous values of voltage and current and are true regardless of whether the voltages and currents in the circuit are constant or whether they vary with time. Kirchhoff's laws are sometimes stated as

$$\Sigma i = 0$$

$$\Sigma v = 0 \tag{1.42}$$

which carries the same meaning as the word statement of the laws.

In the application of Kirchhoff's laws, an algebraic sign must be attached to each current and each voltage to indicate its direction. At any instant, current has both magnitude and direction. In order to write Kirchhoff's current-law equations, it is necessary to define a direction to be known as the "positive direction" of current flow. By establishing a positive direction we have not established the actual direction of current flow. Indeed, in some circuits the current is periodic and reverses direction periodically. But we do establish that, if the current flows in the defined positive direction, its algebraic sign is positive and, if it flows in the opposite direction, it carries a negative sign.

There are several ways in which the positive direction of current can be specified. One is to use an arrow, as shown in Fig. 1.13a. The current through R in Fig. 1.13a is designated I_1 in magnitude and is positive when in the direction of the arrow. Another possible designation for the positive direction of current through R is to designate it I_{ab}; this is interpreted that the positive direction is through R from a to b. An obvious identity is $I_{ab} = -I_{ba}$.

The potential difference between two points also has magnitude and direction associated with it. In writing Kirchhoff's voltage-law equations, actual voltage signs do not have to correspond to the arbitrarily defined direction of positive voltage. The defined positive direction of a voltage can be expressed by $+$ and $-$ signs, by an arrow in the direction of decreasing potential, or by double subscripts such as V_{ab}. These are all shown in Fig. 1.13b, and they all mean that the positive direction of voltage is defined as when terminal a is positive with respect to b. This brings about the identity $V_{ab} = -V_{ba}$.

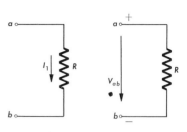

(a) Positive current   (b) Positive voltage

FIG. 1.13 *Conventions for defining positive direction of current and voltage.*

Example 1.7

In the circuit shown in Fig. 1.14, the generator produces an arbitrary voltage $e(t)$. Using ground as reference, write Kirchhoff's current-law equations for the nodes or junctions marked a and b.

First, positive direction of currents i_1, i_2, and i_3 are defined as shown in Fig. 1.14. Since the sum of the currents entering node a must be zero,

$$i_1 - i_2 - i_3 = 0$$

But, by Ohm's law,

$$i_1 = \frac{e(t) - v_a}{R_1}$$

where v_a is the voltage at node a. Then

$$i_2 = \frac{v_a - v_b}{R_2}$$

and

$$i_3 = \frac{v_a - 0}{R_3}$$

where v_b is the potential at node b and the potential at ground is zero.

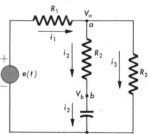

FIG. 1.14 *Electric circuit of Example 1.7.*

Then

$$\frac{e(t) - v_a}{R_1} + \frac{v_b - v_a}{R_2} - \frac{v_a}{R_3} = 0$$

or

$$-\left(\frac{1}{R_1} + \frac{1}{R_2} + \frac{1}{R_3}\right)v_a + \frac{1}{R_2}v_b = -\frac{1}{R_1}e(t)$$

At node b,

$$i_2 - i_2 = 0$$

$$\frac{v_a - v_b}{R_2} - C\frac{dv_b}{dt} = 0$$

Example 1.8

Write a Kirchhoff's voltage-law equation around the closed loop in the circuit shown in Fig. 1.15 after the switch is closed.

Since the positive direction of the generator voltage and the positive current direction are shown, then

$$-e(t) + iR + L\frac{di}{dt} + \frac{1}{C}\left(\int_0^t i\,dt + Q_0\right) = 0$$

[Since going downhill in potential is used here as a positive voltage, in proceeding through the generator in a clockwise direction, an increase in potential of $-e(t)$ is experienced. In proceeding around the loop, there is a decrease in potential of iR, $L\,di/dt$, and

$$\frac{1}{C}\left(\int_0^t i\,dt + Q_0\right),$$

where Q_0 is the charge on C at $t = 0$.]

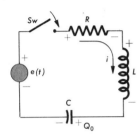

FIG. 1.15 *Series circuit of Example 1.8.*

1.15 D'ALEMBERT'S PRINCIPLE

A basic law of mechanics based on Newton's second law is attributed to D'Alembert and is known as "D'Alembert's principle." This law can be stated as follows:

When a mass m is acted on by external forces, the resultant of the external forces and the inertia force of the mass is zero at any instant, or f − ma = 0, where a is acceleration and f is the sum of all forces except the inertia force.

This principle is often modified to say that the sum of all translational forces acting on a particle at any instant is zero, or

$$\Sigma f = 0 \qquad (1.43)$$

D'Alembert's principle for rotational torques can be stated as follows:

When a mass with moment of inertia J is acted on by external torques, the resultant of the external torques and the inertia torque of the mass is zero at any instant, or $T = J\alpha$, where T is the sum of all torques except inertia and α is the angular acceleration.

This principle is often expressed as: The sum of all torques acting on a mass is zero at any instant, or

$$\Sigma T = 0 \tag{1.44}$$

It may seem strange to include these principles of mechanics as fundamental electrical concepts. They are fundamental, however, in the study of electromechanical devices such as motors and generators, which are discussed at length in later chapters. Furthermore, D'Alembert's principle in mechanics is an interesting analogy to Kirchhoff's laws as stated by Eq. (1.42). D'Alembert's principle is to dynamic mechanical systems what Kirchhoff's laws are to electric-circuit analysis.

1.16 APPROXIMATIONS AND MODELS

Electric-circuit analysis, in common with other areas in science, makes use of models which are approximations of real situations. The model, which is a symbolic representation or drawing of the circuit, takes into account only the most significant electrical properties of the circuit and overlooks the insignificant ones. From the electric model, mathematical equations are written which become the mathematical model of the electric system under study. The solution of the mathematical equations describes the behavior of the model and approximates the behavior of the actual circuit.

Practical circuit elements must be treated by models. For example, a *resistor*, a device placed in a circuit for the purpose of adding *resistance* to the circuit, may also exhibit the properties of inductance and capacitance to a slight degree. Usually the inductive and capacitive characteristics can be neglected, and an ideal resistor (one with no inductance or capacitance) becomes the model for the practical resistor. An *inductor*, which is a device placed in a circuit for the purpose of adding *inductance* to the circuit, is likely to possess some resistance and capacitance. Yet it is convenient to approximate the actual inductor with a model which possesses only inductance. Often the resistance of an inductor is appreciable, and the model of the inductor must include inductance and resistance. A *capacitor*, a device placed in a circuit to add *capacitance* to the circuit, can usually be approximated very closely by an ideal capacitor which possesses no inductance or resistance.

As a representation of an electric circuit, the model must not be confused with the actual circuit. In this book, models are used throughout. When a resistor is mentioned, it is assumed that the inductance and capacitance of the resistor are negligible; under some conditions these assumptions may not be justified. When an inductor is mentioned, it is assumed that the resistance and capacitance of the inductor can be neglected. But engineering approximations must be applied to all engineering problems, and the approximation of establishing the model is a good place to start. The solution of the model may be only a first approximation to the solution of the circuit, but the models can be refined as more exact analysis is required. In this sense, actual problems are often solved by making successively more precise approximations until sufficient conformity of model behavior to the actual circuit behavior has been obtained.

When two circuits have the same voltage-current relationships at their terminals, they are said to be "equivalent." Equivalent circuits are exact models of each other with regard to their voltage-current relationships at their terminals. Kirchhoff's laws are useful for finding equivalent circuits. For example, suppose that two resistors R_1 and R_2 are connected in parallel and an equivalent circuit consisting of a single resistor is sought. If the parallel combination of R_1 and R_2 is equivalent to the single resistor R_{eq} as shown in Fig. 1.16, the ratio of v/i in (a) must be the same as the ratio of v/i in (b). By Kirchhoff's current law,

$$i = i_1 + i_2$$

$$\frac{v}{i} = R_{eq} = \frac{v}{i_1 + i_2}$$

Then

$$\frac{1}{R_{eq}} = \frac{i_1}{v} + \frac{i_2}{v}$$

$$= \frac{1}{R_1} + \frac{1}{R_2}$$

and

$$R_{eq} = \frac{R_1 R_2}{R_1 + R_2} \tag{1.45}$$

From the two terminals, then, R_{eq} in Fig. 1.16b is equivalent to the parallel combination of R_1 and R_2 in (a).

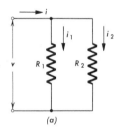

(a)

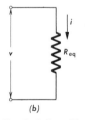

(b)

FIG. 1.16 *Circuit (b) is equivalent to (a) if Eq. (1.45) is satisfied.*

1.17 ANALOGIES

When two physical systems can be described by equations of the same form, they are said to be "analogs" of each other and the relationship is an "analogy." Individual physical elements can also be analogous if they can be described by equations of the same form. The existence of analogies makes it easier for an engineer trained in one field to project his thinking into another field.

Analogies exist in many forms, and some of them are mentioned from time to time throughout this textbook. An example of analogous physical parameters is shown in Table 1.5, where the analogies exist between electric and mechanical parameters. From the relationships shown in Table 1.5, it is seen that voltage is analogous to force, current analogous to velocity, inductance to mass, $1/C$ analogous to the spring constant K, and resistance analogous to the friction constant B.

1.18 SUMMARY

Electric current is defined as the rate of flow of electric charge with respect to time, or as in Eq. (1.1):

$$i = \frac{dq}{dt} \quad \text{amp}$$

TABLE 1.5

Electric		Mechanical	
Parameter	Voltage-current relationship *	Parameter	Force-velocity relationship †
Inductance	$v = L\dfrac{di}{dt}$	Mass	$f = m\dfrac{dv}{dt}$
Resistance	$v = Ri$	Viscous friction	$f = Bv$
Capacitance	$v = \dfrac{1}{C}\displaystyle\int_0^t i\,dt + V_0$	Spring	$f = K\displaystyle\int_0^t v\,dt + F_0$

* v = voltage, i = current.
† f = force, v = velocity.

The direction of conventional current flow is the direction of flow of positive charge.

Electric potential difference between two points is the change of energy per unit charge in moving between those points, or as in Eq. (1.15)

$$v = \frac{dw}{dq} \qquad \text{volts}$$

Power, the rate of change of energy with respect to time [see Eq. (1.17)]

$$p = \frac{dw}{dt} \qquad \text{watts}$$

in electric units can be expressed as the product of instantaneous voltage and current [Eq. (1.17)],

$$p = vi \qquad \text{watts}$$

As in Eqs. (1.20), (1.30), and (1.35), respectively, voltage-current relationships for linear resistance, inductance, and capacitance can be expressed as

$$v = Ri \qquad \text{volts}$$

$$v = L\frac{di}{dt} \qquad \text{volts}$$

$$v = \frac{1}{C}\int_0^t i\, dt + V_0 \qquad \text{volts}$$

Conductors of uniform cross section of area A and with length dL have resistance dR of

$$dR = \rho\,\frac{dL}{A} \qquad \text{ohms}$$

[see Eq. (1.26)], where ρ is the resistivity. Instantaneous power loss in a resistance [Eq. (1.21)] according to Joule's law is

$$p = i^2 R \qquad \text{watts}$$

Kirchhoff's laws state that: (a) At any instant the algebraic sum of all currents flowing into a node in an electric circuit is zero. (b) At any instant the algebraic sum of the voltages around any closed path in a circuit is zero.

The kinetic energy of a mass M with linear velocity v is

$$w = \tfrac{1}{2}Mv^2 \quad \text{joules}$$

The energy stored in an inductor of L henrys carrying current i amp [Eq. (1.34)] is

$$w = \tfrac{1}{2}Li^2 \quad \text{joules}$$

The energy stored in a capacitor of C farads charged to v volts [see Eq. (1.41)] is

$$w = \tfrac{1}{2}Cv^2 \quad \text{joules}$$

PROBLEMS

1.1 A glass tube contains an ionized gas at low pressure. The tube has a cross-sectional area of 0.001 m² and is very long. Positive-ion density in the tube is 9.52×10^8 (+) ions per cubic meter. The positive ions are moving at an average velocity of 1.77×10^4 m/sec in the direction of an electric field along the tube, and the negative ions have an average velocity of 1.821×10^4 m/sec in the opposite direction. Find the electric current at a cross section of the tube. Assume that negative-ion density is equal to positive-ion density.

1.2 A linear resistor of 10 ohms has a sinusoidal voltage of $v = 40 \sin 200t$ impressed across it. Find the energy delivered to the resistor during the first second that the voltage is connected to the resistor.

1.3 A voltage generator provides a triangular voltage wave as a function of time (see the illustration). This voltage is impressed across a 10-ohm resistor. How much energy is delivered to the resistor in 1 sec?

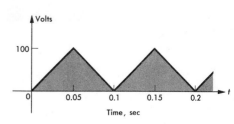

PROB. 1.3

PROB. 1.4

1.4 A disk-shaped conductor of resistivity ρ ohm-m is shown in the figure. Find the resistance as measured from the edge of the center hole to the rim of the conductor. Assume that the inside "hub" is an equipotential surface and the outside "rim" is an equipotential surface. $r_1 = 0.0100$ m; $r_2 = 0.6000$ m.

1.5 Determine the number of electrons that flow through a 60-watt 115-volt light bulb in a 24-hr period.

1.6 In the circuit shown in the illustration, the voltage source is a sine wave with a frequency of 60 cycles/sec. Find the voltage across R_2 at a time 0.001 sec after the beginning of the sine wave.

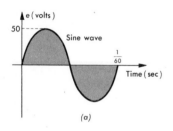

(a)

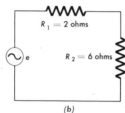

(b)

PROB. 1.6

1.7 In the figure a single square pulse of voltage with peak value of 750 volts and duration of 15 μsec (15 $\times$ 10^{-6} sec) is applied to the circuit of Prob. 1.6 instead of the sine wave. How much heat energy is produced by R_1 and R_2?

1.8 A square conductor 46.5 ft long and 0.175 by 0.175 in. at the cross section is made of aluminum. Using the resistivity in ohm-meters given in Table 1.3, find the resistance of the conductor.

1.9 A tapered silver conductor has the dimensions shown in the illustration. Find the resistance between ends A and B.

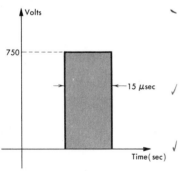

PROB. 1.7

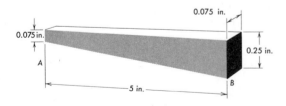

PROB. 1.9

1.10 In the figure a single rectangular pulse of voltage is applied to a load consisting of an electronic circuit which draws a current that increases linearly with time. (The electronic circuit does not follow Ohm's law.)

Find the total energy delivered to the electronic circuit during the time
of the voltage pulse.

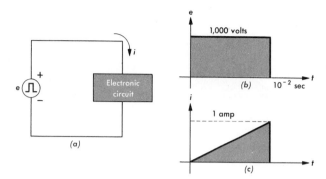

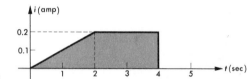

PROB. 1.10

1.11 The current through an inductor varies with time as shown in the
curve in the illustration. The value of inductance is 5 henrys. Find the
voltage across the inductor as a function of time, for all values of time.

PROB. 1.11

1.12 The current through a capacitor of 10^{-4} farad has the same wave
shape as in the preceding problem. Find the voltage across the capacitor
as a function of time for all values of time. Assume that at $t = 0$ the voltage on the capacitor is 500 volts and that the direction of current into the
capacitor is such as to add to the original charge on the capacitor.

1.13 An inductor and a resistor are connected in series and are connected
to a constant-voltage source (a battery) (see the illustration). When the
switch is closed, the current increases in the circuit and eventually reaches
a constant value of 10 amp. (*a*) Find the value of R. (*b*) What is the
rate at which the battery is delivering energy to the circuit? (*c*) How
much power is being delivered to the inductor? To the resistor?

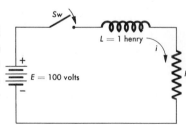

PROB. 1.13

1.14 An RL circuit is excited by the current source represented in the
figure on the next page. The current is zero at $t = 0$ and increases
linearly with time. Find the rate at which the generator is delivering
energy 20 sec after the switch is closed.

1.15 Find the fundamental dimensions of dielectric constant ϵ; of
permeability μ.

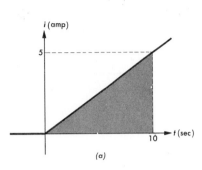

(a)

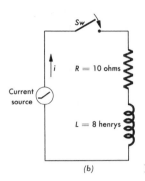

(b)

PROB. 1.14

1.16 A two-wire transmission line is composed of hard-drawn copper wire 0.225 cm in diameter and 2,735 m long. Find the total resistance of this transmission line (a) at 70°C and (b) at −20°C.

1.17 The voltage across a pure inductor of 0.100 henry is periodic as shown in the illustration. It is known that, at $t = 0$, the current through the inductor is 1 amp. Sketch the current wave, and show maximum and minimum currents, slopes, etc., for one period.

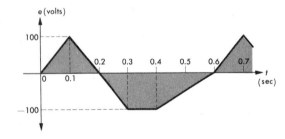

PROB. 1.17

1.18 The voltage across a capacitor is that shown in Prob. 1.17. At $t = 0$ the capacitor voltage is zero. Sketch capacitor current in amperes and capacitor charge in coulombs as functions of time. Show slopes of curves and maxima and minima.

1.19 A capacitor has no charge on it initially. Then a constant current of 0.500 amp furnishes charge for 1 sec. If $C = 10$ μf, find (a) voltage on the capacitor and (b) energy stored after the current has existed for 1 sec.

1.20 A capacitor consists of concentric cylindrical conductors of radius $r_1 = 1.000$ cm and $r_2 = 1.020$ cm (see the figure). The dielectric separating them is air. Find the capacitance per meter of this capacitor by approximating it to an equivalent plane capacitor.

1.21 Three resistors R_1, R_2, and R_3 are in parallel. Prove that the equivalent resistance to this parallel combination is

$$R_{eq} = \frac{R_1 R_2 R_3}{R_1 R_2 + R_1 R_3 + R_2 R_3}.$$

PROB. 1.20

38 FIRST PRINCIPLES

1.22 Two inductors L_1 and L_2 with no mutual inductance are in series. Prove that the equivalent inductance of this series combination is $L_{eq} = L_1 + L_2$.

1.23 Two capacitors C_1 and C_2 are in series. Prove that the equivalent capacitance of this series combination is $C_{eq} = \dfrac{C_1 C_2}{C_1 + C_2}$.

2
CHARACTERISTICS
OF VOLTAGES AND CURRENTS

2.1 INTRODUCTION

Kirchhoff's laws were introduced in Chap. 1 as the basis for writing systems of equations for the solution of electric circuits. Kirchhoff's laws are stated in terms of instantaneous values of voltage and current, just as D'Alembert's principle applies to instantaneous forces.

Voltage, current, and power which vary with time can be partially described in several ways besides expressing instantaneous values for all values of time. In particular, periodic functions, or functions which repeat themselves at regular intervals, can be partially described by their average values or maximum values or by defining an effective value. In this chapter, some of these partial descriptions, as well as their significance and application in electrical analysis, are investigated.

2.2 AVERAGE VALUES OF PERIODIC FUNCTIONS

The concept of average, or mean, value is a well-established one, and a function of time such as voltage, current, or power can be described by its average value. The average, or mean, value of $f(t)$ is defined as the value of the integral over a given interval of time divided by the duration of the time interval, or

$$F_a = \frac{1}{t_2 - t_1} \int_{t_1}^{t_2} f(t) \, dt \qquad (2.1)$$

where F_a is the average value of $f(t)$ and $t_2 - t_1 = T$ is the time interval. Note that the interval of the integration is an important part of the definition of the average value of a function of time.

As an example of an average value of a function of time, consider an electric circuit in which electric power is changing as a function of time as shown in Fig. 2.1. The time interval for finding the average value is defined as $t_2 - t_1 = T$. The energy delivered during this interval is

$$W = \int_{t_1}^{t_2} p \, dt \qquad \text{watt-sec} \qquad (2.2)$$

since energy is the integral of power with respect to time for the interval from t_1 to t_2. Energy is shown as the shaded area in Fig. 2.1. The average power during this interval is the integral of power (represented by the area), divided by the duration over which the integral is effected, or the energy W divided by the interval $t_2 - t_1 = T$. Then

$$P_a = \frac{W}{T} = \frac{1}{t_2 - t_1} \int_{t_1}^{t_2} p \, dt \qquad \text{watts} \qquad (2.3)$$

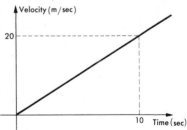

From Eq. (2.3) and Fig. 2.1, the average depends not only on the length of the interval $t_2 - t_1 = T$ but also on the particular positions of t_2 and t_1 on the time scale.

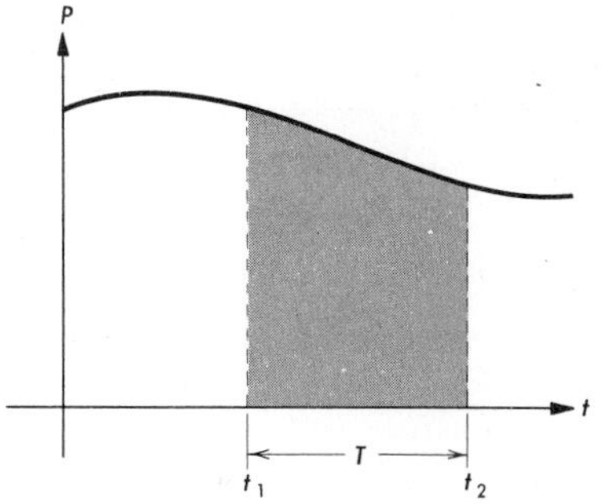

FIG. 2.1 *An arbitrary power-versus-time curve.*

Example 2.1

The velocity of a vehicle increases from zero in a linear fashion as shown in Fig. 2.2. At the end of 10 sec the velocity reaches 20 m/sec. The equation for velocity as a function of time is

$$v = 2t$$

where v is in meters per second and t is in seconds. The average velocity *during the interval from 0 to 10 sec* is

$$V_a = \frac{1}{10} \int_0^{10} 2t \, dt$$

$$= \frac{1}{10} [t^2]_0^{10} = \frac{1}{10} (100 - 0)$$

$$= 10 \text{ m/sec}$$

FIG. 2.2 *Velocity-versus-time curve (Example 2.1).*

2.2   Average Values of Periodic Functions   41

Of course, it is obvious that the area under the curve is the area of a right triangle of height of 20 m/sec and with base of 10 sec. The area under the curve can be found by inspection without performing the integration. From the geometry, average velocity during the interval from 0 to 10 sec is seen to be

$$V_a = \frac{1}{10 \text{ sec}} \left(\frac{1}{2} (20 \text{ m/sec} \times 10 \text{ sec}) \right) = 10 \text{ m/sec}$$

The average value of a periodic function can be found by the same procedure merely by averaging over one period of the function or by defining the interval of time over which the average is taken. Consider the periodic functions shown in Fig. 2.3. The

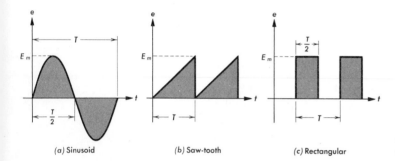

(a) Sinusoid   (b) Saw-tooth   (c) Rectangular

FIG. 2.3 *Some periodic voltage-wave shapes.*

period (the time required for one complete cycle before repeating) of each function is the same, being T sec. The sinusoid of Fig. 2.3a has an average value for one complete period of zero, since the positive area is equal to the negative area under the curve. But the average value of the positive half cycle can be defined and found by integrating over the positive part of the sine wave and dividing by one-half the period, or $T/2$. Thus

$$E_a = \frac{2}{T} \int_0^{T/2} E_m \sin \frac{2\pi}{T} t \, dt \tag{2.4}$$

where $\omega = 2\pi f = 2\pi/T$. Integrating,

$$E_a = \frac{2}{T} \frac{E_m T}{2\pi} \left[-\cos \frac{2\pi t}{T} \right]_0^{T/2}$$

$$= \frac{E_m}{\pi} (1 + 1)$$

or

$$E_a = \frac{2}{\pi} E_m = 0.636 E_m \tag{2.5}$$

Equation (2.5) shows the relationship between the half-cycle average value and the peak value E_m of a sine wave.

Often the integration process can be accomplished by inspection. Since the periodic voltage of Fig. 2.3b is triangular in shape, the area under the curve is $E_m T/2$ for one period. Dividing by T yields an average height of $E_m/2$ for the voltage wave. In Fig. 2.3c, the average voltage is also $E_m/2$. Since the value of the integral is equal to the area under the curve, the process of integration can be accomplished effectively in any way that the area can be found.

The value of a periodic voltage or current, when averaged over one or more periods, is known as the "direct," or "d-c," value. A d-c voltmeter or ammeter reads the average value of voltage or current, respectively. Thus the d-c value of a sinusoidal voltage (Fig. 2.3a) is zero, and the d-c value of the saw-tooth wave of Fig. 2.3b is $E_m/2$.

2.3 EFFECTIVE, OR ROOT-MEAN-SQUARE, VALUES OF PERIODIC FUNCTIONS

An effective value of a periodic current can be defined by comparison with a direct current. Suppose that the periodic current i is flowing through the resistance R. In one period T the energy W_1 delivered to R is, according to Joule's law,

$$W_1 = \int_{t_1}^{t_2} i^2 R \, dt \qquad \text{joules} \tag{2.6}$$

where $t_2 - t_1 = T$. Now assume that an identical resistance R has a direct current I flowing through it and that I is of such a magnitude that in the same time interval T the amount of electric energy delivered to R is also W_1. Then

$$W_1 = \int_{t_1}^{t_2} I^2 R \, dt \tag{2.7}$$

Then Eqs. (2.6) and (2.7) can be equated, and

$$\int_{t_1}^{t_2} I^2 \, dt = \int_{t_1}^{t_2} i^2 \, dt$$

Integrating and solving for I,

$$I = \sqrt{\frac{1}{T} \int_{t_1}^{t_2} i^2 \, dt} = I_{rms} \tag{2.8}$$

where $T = t_2 - t_1$. The current I in Eq. (2.8) is known as the effective, or root-mean-square (rms), value of the current; henceforth it is designated by I_{rms}. Notice that I_{rms} is the square root of the average or mean of the square of the current; hence the term "root-mean-square" value.

By substituting V/R for i in Eqs. (2.6) and (2.7), the effective, or rms, voltage is found as

$$V_{rms} = \sqrt{\frac{1}{T} \int_{t_1}^{t_2} v^2 \, dt} \tag{2.9}$$

where $t_2 - t_1 = T$. The rms value of any function F is the square root of the mean-square value, or

$$F_{rms} = \sqrt{\frac{1}{t_2 - t_1} \int_{t_1}^{t_2} [f(t)]^2 \, dt} \tag{2.10}$$

where $t_2 - t_1$ is the interval over which the rms value is found. For periodic functions it is convenient to let $t_2 - t_1$ be a period T of the function.

The rms value of a sinusoid of current is found by letting

$$i = I_m \sin \frac{2\pi t}{T} \tag{2.11}$$

and equating the energy dissipated in the resistance R during one period of the wave to the energy dissipated in the same length of time by a direct current I in an equal resistance R. Thus,

$$\int_0^T \left(I_m \sin \frac{2\pi t}{T}\right)^2 R \, dt = \int_0^T i^2 R \, dt \tag{2.12}$$

Now dividing out R and using the identity

$$\sin^2 \frac{2\pi t}{T} = \frac{1}{2}\left(1 - \cos \frac{4\pi t}{T}\right)$$

in order to integrate the left side of Eq. (2.12) results in

$$I_m^2 \left[\frac{t}{2} - \frac{T}{8\pi} \sin \frac{4\pi t}{T}\right]_0^T = I^2 t \Big]_0^T \tag{2.13}$$

Substituting in the limits and solving for I in Eq. (2.13), which is the rms current gives

$$I^2_{rms} = \frac{I_m^2}{2} \tag{2.14}$$

or

$$I_{rms} = \frac{I_m}{\sqrt{2}}$$

$$= 0.707 I_m \qquad (2.15)$$

The effective value of the sine wave of current is shown by Eq. (2.15) to be 0.707 times the maximum value of the sinusoid. By substituting Eq. (2.11) directly into Eq. (2.8), I_{rms} can be found. Thus

$$I_{rms} = \sqrt{\frac{1}{T}\int_0^T \left(I_m \sin \frac{2\pi t}{T}\right)^2 dt}$$

$$(2.16)$$

$$= \sqrt{\frac{1}{T}\frac{I_m{}^2}{2}T}$$

or

$$I_{rms} = \frac{I_m}{\sqrt{2}} = 0.707 I_m \qquad (2.17)$$

which is, of course, the same rms value as in Eq. (2.15).

Alternating-current-indicating instruments measure rms values. An a-c ammeter indicates the rms value of the current it measures, and an a-c voltmeter reads the rms voltage seen at its terminals.

Example 2.2

A periodic sequence of rectangular voltage pulses is shown (Fig. 2.4) with a peak value of 100 volts, a period of 0.100 sec, and a duration of 0.050 sec. To find the effective value of this voltage,

$$V_{rms} = \sqrt{\frac{1}{T}\int_{t_1}^{t_2} v^2 \, dt}$$

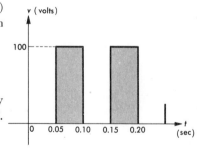

FIG. 2.4 *Rectangular voltage pulses (Example 2.2).*

Notice in this example that the limits of integration need only be for one half the period, since the voltage is zero for the other half.

$$V_{rms} = \sqrt{\frac{1}{0.1}\int_{0.05}^{0.1} 100^2 \, dt}$$

$$= \sqrt{\frac{1}{0.1}\left[10^4 t\right]_{0.05}^{0.1}}$$

$$= \sqrt{\frac{1}{0.1}(1{,}000 - 500)}$$

$$= \sqrt{5{,}000} = 70.7 \text{ volts}$$

For this voltage wave, $V_a = 50$ volts.

2.3 Effective, or Root-mean-square, Values of Periodic Functions **45**

2.4 THE SINUSOID

Any sinusoidal function of time can be expressed in the form

$$f_1(t) = F_1 \sin (\omega t + \alpha) \qquad (2.18)$$

as shown in Fig. 2.5. The term ω in Eq. (2.18) is known as the "radian frequency" of f_1 and has units of radians per second. It

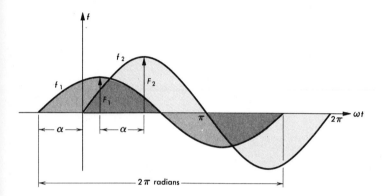

FIG. 2.5 *Two sinusoids, f_1 and f_2, where f_1 leads f_2 by the angle $\omega t = \alpha$.*

is related to the frequency f in cycles per second by the expression

$$\omega = 2\pi f \qquad \text{radians/sec} \qquad (2.19)$$

where 2π is the number of radians per cycle. The frequency f in cycles per second defines the period T of one cycle by

$$T = \frac{1}{f} \qquad \text{sec/cycle} \qquad (2.20)$$

F_1 is the maximum value, or peak value, of the sine wave. The parameter α in Eq. (2.18) is known as the "phase difference" of f_1 in comparing f_1 to f_2, where

$$f_2(t) = F_2 \sin \omega t \qquad (2.21)$$

Thus, f_1 leads f_2 by an angle α, since f_1 arrives at its maximum at an angle α before f_2 does, as shown in Fig. 2.5. Notice that, when $\alpha = \pi/2$, f_1 is a cosine wave, for then

$$f_1 = F_1 \sin \left(\omega t + \frac{\pi}{2} \right)$$

$$= F_1 \cos \omega t$$

All sinusoids, including sine and cosine waves, can be expressed by Eq. (2.18).

A sinusoidal voltage applied to the terminals of any linear circuit element yields a current that is a sinusoid, and vice versa. This can be seen from the voltage-current relationships for linear circuit elements.

$$v = Ri \tag{2.22a}$$

$$v = L\frac{di}{dt} \tag{2.22b}$$

$$v = \frac{1}{C}\int_0^t i\,dt + V_0 \tag{2.22c}$$

Though these relationships appear to be quite different in form, there is a very striking similarity in them. Assuming that R, L, and C are constant and independent of voltage and current, if the current through any of these elements is sinusoidal, the resulting voltage is a sinusoid also. This conclusion is obvious in Eq. (2.22a), where the voltage v is proportional to the current i in the resistance. Thus, voltage and current are in phase, which means that the phase difference between them is zero. For the resistance R,

$$i = I_m \sin \omega t \qquad v = RI_m \sin \omega t \tag{2.23}$$

In Eq. (2.22b), if the current i is a sine wave, then differentiation of the voltage v results in a cosine wave. By expressing the cosine as a sine wave advanced in time by $\pi/2$ radians, for the inductance L,

$$i = I_m \sin \omega t \qquad v = LI_m\omega \cos \omega t$$

$$= \omega L I_m \sin\left(\omega t + \frac{\pi}{2}\right) \tag{2.24}$$

Similarly, if a sinusoidal current exists in a capacitor, the voltage across the capacitor is a sinusoid retarded $\pi/2$ radians. From Eq. (2.22c),

$$i = I_m \sin \omega t \qquad v = \frac{-I_m}{\omega C} \cos \omega t$$

$$= \frac{I_m}{\omega C} \sin\left(\omega t - \frac{\pi}{2}\right) \tag{2.25}$$

The sinusoids expressed in Eqs. (2.23) to (2.25) are plotted in Fig. 2.6.

It has been demonstrated that, if a sinusoidal current passes through a resistor, an inductor, or a capacitor, the voltage across the element is a sinusoid also. Similarly, it can be shown that, if the applied voltage is sinusoidal, the current in each element is a sinusoid also. Furthermore, the sum of two sinusoids of the same frequency, but not necessarily of the same phase, is a sinusoid. Thus, if two or more circuit elements are connected in series and are excited by a sinusoidal current, the voltage across each element is a sinusoid and the total applied voltage is

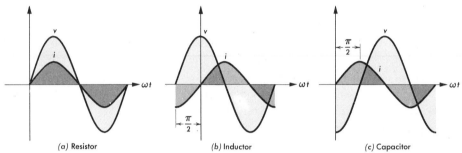

(a) Resistor   (b) Inductor   (c) Capacitor

FIG. 2.6 *Sinusoidal voltage-current relationships for ideal circuit elements.*

also a sinusoid. This idea can be extended further to show that, if the voltage applied to any linear circuit containing resistance, inductance, and capacitance is sinusoidal, then the voltage across each element and the current through each element are sinusoids. Of all possible periodic functions, only sinusoids reproduce their own form when integrated or differentiated.

2.5 THE EXPONENTIAL FUNCTION

Integration and differentiation of a sinusoid change the magnitude and phase difference of the sinusoid, but the result is still a sinusoid. Although the sinusoid is the only *periodic* function which reproduces its own form upon integration and differentiation, the non-periodic exponential function also reproduces its own form upon integration or differentiation. Consider the exponential function

$$f = F\epsilon^{-\alpha t} \tag{2.26}$$

where α is positive and real. Differentiation of the exponential function of Eq. (2.26) gives

$$\frac{df}{dt} = -\alpha F \epsilon^{-\alpha t} \qquad (2.27)$$

where the coefficient of the exponential term is now $-\alpha F$. Integration of Eq. (2.26) results in

$$\int_0^t f \, dt = -\frac{F}{\alpha} \epsilon^{-\alpha t} + F_0 \qquad (2.28)$$

where the coefficient of the exponential term is now $-F/\alpha$ and where F_0 is the constant of integration.

When a current of the form

$$i = I\epsilon^{-\alpha t} \qquad 0 \le t < \infty$$

$$= 0 \qquad t < 0 \qquad (2.29)$$

passes through a resistor of R ohms, the voltage between the terminals of the resistor is

$$v_R = Ri = RI\epsilon^{-\alpha t} \qquad 0 \le t < \infty$$

$$= 0 \qquad t < 0 \qquad (2.30)$$

Resistor voltage and current are shown in Fig. 2.7a.

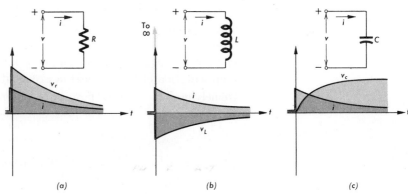

(a)   (b)   (c)

FIG. 2.7 *Exponential voltage-current relationships for a resistor, an inductor, and a capacitor excited by an exponential current.*

If the same current passes through an inductor, the voltage between the terminals of the inductor is

$$v_L = L\frac{di}{dt} = -LI\alpha\epsilon^{-\alpha t} + \delta(t) \qquad 0 \le t < \infty$$

$$= 0 \qquad t < 0 \qquad (2.31)$$

where $\delta(t)$ is an impulse of voltage caused by the discontinuous current rising from zero to I at $t = 0$. The inductor current and voltage are shown in Fig. 2.7b, where the impulse $\delta(t)$ is shown going to infinity at $t = 0$.

If the current of the form of Eq. (2.29) passes through a capacitor, the terminal voltage of the capacitor is given by

$$v_C = \frac{1}{C} \int_0^t i \, dt + V_0 = \left[\frac{-I}{C\alpha} \, \epsilon^{-\alpha t} \right]_0^t + V_0$$

$$= \frac{I}{C\alpha} (1 - \epsilon^{-\alpha t}) + V_0 \qquad 0 \le t < \infty$$

$$= V_0 \qquad\qquad\qquad t < \infty \qquad\qquad (2.32)$$

Capacitor voltage is shown in Fig. 2.7c for $V_0 = 0$.

Conversely, by the same reasoning, it can be shown that, if the voltage across the various circuit elements is of exponential form, the current is also of exponential form.

2.6 EXPONENTIAL REPRESENTATION OF SINUSOIDS

The sinusoidal function of time is perhaps most readily visualized as a plot on rectangular coordinates of the $\sin \omega t$ on the vertical axis and time or ωt on the horizontal axis, as in Fig. 2.5. For purposes of visualization, these plots on rectangular coordinates are of considerable use. For the purposes of circuit analysis, however, representation of the sinusoid in exponential, or polar, form is extremely useful. Consider now the polar form, which is derived from the identity

$$\epsilon^{j\theta} = \cos \theta + j \sin \theta \qquad\qquad (2.33)$$

where $j = \sqrt{-1}$ and θ is real. The meaning of the imaginary exponent in Eq. (2.33) is not readily apparent, except as it relates to the cosine and sine terms.

To verify Eq. (2.33), the Maclaurin-series expansions can be written for each term.

$$\cos \theta = 1 - \frac{\theta^2}{2!} + \frac{\theta^4}{4!} - \frac{\theta^6}{6!} + \cdots \qquad\qquad (2.34)$$

$$\sin \theta = \theta - \frac{\theta^3}{3!} + \frac{\theta^5}{5!} - \frac{\theta^7}{7!} + \cdots \qquad\qquad (2.35)$$

Then

$$j \sin \theta = j\theta - j\frac{\theta^3}{3!} + j\frac{\theta^5}{5!} - j\frac{\theta^7}{7!} + \cdots \qquad (2.36)$$

Adding the expansions for $\cos \theta$ and $j \sin \theta$ [Eqs. (2.34) and (2.36)] results in

$$\cos \theta + j \sin \theta = 1 + j\theta - \frac{\theta^2}{2!} - j\frac{\theta^3}{3!} + \frac{\theta^4}{4!} + j\frac{\theta^5}{5!} - \cdots \qquad (2.37)$$

Notice that Eq. (2.37) resembles the series expansion for ϵ^θ, whose Maclaurin-series expansion is

$$\epsilon^\theta = 1 + \theta + \frac{\theta^2}{2!} + \frac{\theta^3}{3!} + \frac{\theta^4}{4!} + \cdots \qquad (2.38)$$

Now substituting $j\theta$ for θ in Eq. (2.38) results in

$$\epsilon^{j\theta} = 1 + j\theta + \frac{j^2\theta^2}{2!} + \frac{j^3\theta^3}{3!} + \frac{j^4\theta^4}{4!} + \frac{j^5\theta^5}{5!} + \cdots \qquad (2.39)$$

Since $j = \sqrt{-1}$, it follows that

$$j^2 = -1$$
$$j^3 = -j$$
$$j^4 = (j^2)^2 = 1$$
$$j^5 = j(j^4) = j$$
$$j^6 = j^2(j^4) = -1, \text{ etc.} \qquad (2.40)$$

These expressions for the powers of j, when substituted into Eq. (2.39), yield

$$\epsilon^{j\theta} = 1 + j\theta - \frac{\theta^2}{2!} - j\frac{\theta^3}{3!} + \frac{\theta^4}{4!} + j\frac{\theta^5}{5!} - \cdots \qquad (2.41)$$

The right-hand side of Eq. (2.41) is identical with that of Eq. (2.37), and hence Eq. (2.33) is verified.

Notice that Eq. (2.33) has a real part ($\cos \theta$) and an imaginary part ($j \sin \theta$). In any complex equation, which is an equation containing real parts and imaginary parts, the real part on one side of the equation must equal the real part on the other side, and the imaginary part on one side must equal the imaginary part on the other. This allows us to refer to $\cos \theta$ as the real part of $\epsilon^{j\theta}$ (abbreviated Re $\epsilon^{j\theta}$) and to refer to $\sin\theta$ as the imaginary part of $\epsilon^{j\theta}$ (abbreviated Im $\epsilon^{j\theta}$). Representation of complex numbers is often plotted in rectangular coordinates, where the real part is plotted along the x axis and the imaginary part along the y axis. Thus

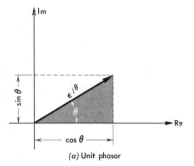

(a) Unit phasor

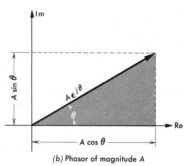

(b) Phasor of magnitude A

FIG. 2.8 *Representing phasors on real-imaginary, or xy, plane.*

$\epsilon^{j\theta}$ is represented in Fig. 2.8a as the vector sum of $\cos\theta$ and $j\sin\theta$. From the identity

$$\sin^2\theta + \cos^2\theta = 1$$

it is seen that the magnitude of $e^{j\theta}$ is always unity and that the line from the origin representing $\epsilon^{j\theta}$ makes an angle of θ with the x axis.

2.7 PHASORS

Now if we let $\theta = \omega t$, so that θ is proportional to time, then $\epsilon^{j\omega t}$ is represented by a line of unit length rotating about the origin with an angular velocity of ω. This line is called a "phasor." One end of the line is always at the origin, and the locus of the other end is a circle of radius 1 centered at the origin. Yet at any particular instant in time $\epsilon^{j\omega t}$ can be represented as a line in a particular position or angle $\theta = \omega t$ from the x axis.

A phasor $A\epsilon^{j\omega t}$ can be represented by the same geometry as $\epsilon^{j\omega t}$ merely by multiplying all radial scales by the constant A, as shown in Fig. 2.8b. Then

$$A\epsilon^{j\omega t} = A\cos\omega t + jA\sin\omega t \qquad (2.42)$$

where $\theta = \omega t$. The term $A\cos\omega t$ is the projection of the phasor of magnitude A on the horizontal, or x, axis, and $A\sin\omega t$ is the projection of the phasor on the vertical, or y, axis. Keep in mind that all phasors represented in Fig. 2.8 with $\theta = \omega t$ are rotating counterclockwise at a constant angular velocity ω radians/sec and are represented on the diagram at only one instant in time. The term $A \cos \omega t$ can be expressed as Re $A \epsilon^{j\omega t}$, and $A \sin \omega t$ can be expressed as Im $A \epsilon^{j\omega t}$, the real and imaginary components of $A \epsilon^{j\omega t}$.

Equation (2.42) shows two ways to represent a phasor. The left-hand side shows the phasor represented in exponential form with a magnitude of A and an angle θ from the horizontal axis. The right-hand side shows the phasor as the sum of a real part and an imaginary part. These are the exponential, or polar, and rectangular forms, respectively, for representing complex numbers. A complex number is a number which has both real and imaginary parts.

Example 2.3

Express $10\epsilon^{j(\pi/4)}$ in rectangular form.

$$\cos \frac{\pi}{4} = \cos 45° = 0.707$$

$$\sin \frac{\pi}{4} = \sin 45° = 0.707$$

$$10 \cos \theta + j10 \sin \theta = 7.07 + j7.07$$

$$10\epsilon^{j(\pi/4)} = 7.07 + j7.07$$

This is shown in Fig. 2.9.

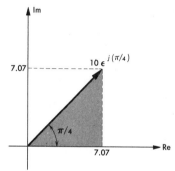

FIG. 2.9 $10\epsilon^{j(\pi/4)} = 7.07 + j7.07$.

Example 2.4

Express $20 + j50$ in exponential form.

$$A = \sqrt{20^2 + 50^2} = 53.7$$

$$\theta = \tan^{-1} \frac{50}{20} = 68.2°$$

Then

$$20 + j50 = 53.7\epsilon^{j68.2°}$$

as shown in Fig. 2.10.

In Fig. 2.11a is shown the phasor $A \epsilon^{j\omega t}$ and the locus of points at radius A from the origin. For various values of ωt are shown the projections of the phasor on the real and imaginary axes. The projection of the phasor on the real axis is plotted in (c) as $A \cos \omega t$ versus ωt on rectangular coordinates. Likewise, the projection of the phasor on the imaginary axis is shown in (b) as $A \sin \omega t$ versus ωt in rectangular coordinates.

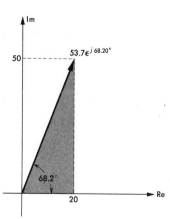

FIG. 2.10 $20 + j50 = 53.7\epsilon^{j68.2°}$

2.7 *Phasors* **53**

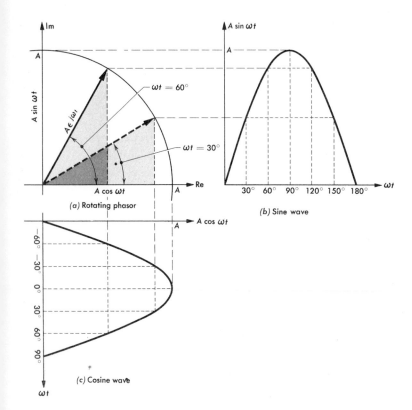

(a) Rotating phasor

(b) Sine wave

(c) Cosine wave

FIG. 2.11 *Generation of sine and cosine waves from a rotating phasor.*

2.8 ADDITION AND SUBTRACTION OF SINUSOIDS AS PHASOR QUANTITIES

A sinusoid is completely specified by its maximum value, its frequency, and its phase. Since the sum of two sinusoids of the same frequency is itself a sinusoid of that frequency, only the maximum value and the phase of the sum need be found in the process of addition.

The addition of complex quantities requires the addition of the real parts and the addition of the imaginary parts. An equation of complex numbers requires the sum of the real parts on one side of the equation to equal the sum of the real parts on the other side and the sum of the imaginary parts on one side to equal the sum of the imaginary parts on the other. Consider two phasors **A** and **B**, where

$$\mathbf{A} = A \cos \theta_a + jA \sin \theta_a$$

$$\mathbf{B} = B \cos \theta_b + jB \sin \theta_b$$

(2.43)

Define C such that $\mathbf{A} + \mathbf{B} = \mathbf{C}$; the real part of $\mathbf{C}$ is the sum of the real parts of $\mathbf{A}$ and $\mathbf{B}$, and the imaginary part of $\mathbf{C}$ is the sum of the imaginary parts of $\mathbf{A}$ and $\mathbf{B}$. Thus,

$$\mathbf{C} = (A \cos \theta_a + B \cos \theta_b) + j(A \sin \theta_a + B \sin \theta_b) \qquad (2.44)$$

or

$$\mathbf{C} = C \cos \theta_c + jC \sin \theta_c$$

where, from the geometry of Fig. 2.12a,

$$C = \sqrt{(A \cos \theta_a + B \cos \theta_b)^2 + (A \sin \theta_a + B \sin \theta_b)^2} \qquad (2.45)$$

and

$$\theta_c = \tan^{-1} \frac{A \sin \theta_a + B \sin \theta_b}{A \cos \theta_a + B \cos \theta_b} \qquad (2.46)$$

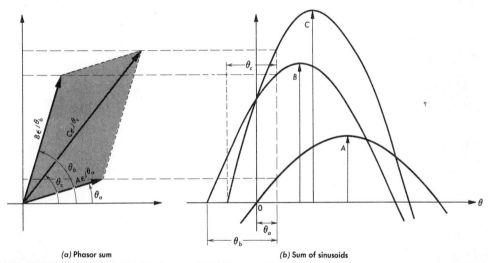

(a) Phasor sum   (b) Sum of sinusoids

FIG. 2.12 *Adding sinusoids in exponential form as phasors (a) and in rectangular form (b).*

Notice that the phase angles between $\mathbf{C}$ and $\mathbf{A}$ or $\mathbf{C}$ and $\mathbf{B}$ can be specified as $\theta_c - \theta_a$ and $\theta_c - \theta_b$. Notice also that if we allow the angles to increase at a constant rate, keeping the phase angles between $\mathbf{A}$, $\mathbf{B}$, and $\mathbf{C}$ constant, the imaginary parts of the phasors trace out sinusoids, as shown in Fig. 2.12b.

Now let

$$\theta_a = \omega t$$
$$\theta_b = \omega t + \phi_b \qquad (2.47)$$
$$\theta_c = \omega t + \phi_c$$

2.8 Addition and Subtraction of Sinusoids as Phasor Quantities   55

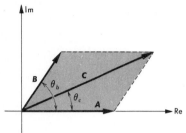

FIG. 2.13 *Phasor addition of A and B.*

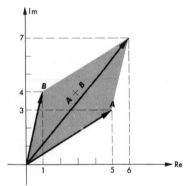

FIG. 2.14 *Adding $5 + j3$ and $1 + j4$ (Example 2.5).*

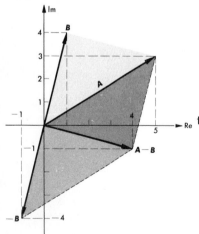

FIG. 2.15 *Subtracting $1 + j4$ from $5 + j3$ (Example 2.6).*

Then

$$\text{Im } \mathbf{A} = A \sin \omega t$$

$$\text{Im } \mathbf{B} = B \sin (\omega t + \phi_b) \tag{2.48}$$

$$\text{Im } \mathbf{C} = C \sin (\omega t + \phi_c)$$

Since the phase difference between the three phasors does not change with time, the three phasors can be represented with **A** as a reference phasor by letting ωt be zero. This makes **A** entirely real on the phasor diagram of Fig. 2.13, and the equations corresponding to Eqs. (2.45) and (2.46) can be written

$$C = \sqrt{(A + B \cos \phi_b)^2 + (B \sin \phi_b)^2} \tag{2.49}$$

$$\phi_c = \tan^{-1} \frac{B \sin \phi_b}{A + B \cos \phi_b} \tag{2.50}$$

Thus the sum of two sinusoids $A \sin \omega t + B \sin (\omega t + \phi_b)$ has been found. The maximum value of the sum is C in Eq. (2.49), the frequency of the sum is the frequency of the other two sinusoids, and the phase difference of the sum with respect to $A \sin \omega t$ is ϕ_c.

Example 2.5

Two phasors are expressed in complex form as $\mathbf{A} = 5 + j3$ and $\mathbf{B} = 1 + j4$. The sum of **A** and **B** is

$$\begin{aligned}
\mathbf{A} &= 5 + j3 \\
\mathbf{B} &= 1 + j4 \\
\hline
\mathbf{A} + \mathbf{B} &= 6 + j7
\end{aligned}$$

The sum is found by adding the real parts together and the imaginary parts together, as shown in Fig. 2.14.

The process of subtraction is accomplished merely by changing the sign of the subtrahend and adding.

Example 2.6

If $\mathbf{A} = 5 + j3$ and $\mathbf{B} = 1 + j4$, find $\mathbf{A} - \mathbf{B}$.

$$\begin{aligned}
\mathbf{A} &= 5 + j3 \\
-\mathbf{B} &= -1 - j4 \\
\hline
\mathbf{A} - \mathbf{B} &= 4 - j1
\end{aligned}$$

$\mathbf{A} - \mathbf{B}$ is shown in Fig. 2.15.

Example 2.7

Given two voltages $v_1 = 50 \sin \omega t$ and $v_2 = 100 \sin (\omega t + 60°)$. To find $v_1 + v_2$, first express their phasors in complex form.

$$\begin{array}{rcl} \mathbf{V}_1 &=& 50 + j0 \\ \mathbf{V}_2 &=& 50 + j86.6 \\ \hline \mathbf{V}_1 + \mathbf{V}_2 &=& 100 + j86.6 = \mathbf{V}_3 \end{array}$$

$$|V_3| = \sqrt{100^2 + 86.6^2} = 132.0 \text{ volts}$$

The phase of $\mathbf{V}_3$ with respect to $\mathbf{V}_1$ is

$$\theta_1 = \tan^{-1} \frac{86.6}{100} = 40.95°$$

and $v_1 + v_2 = v_3$ can be expressed as

$$v_3 = 132.0 \sin (\omega t + 40.95°)$$

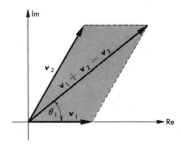

FIG. 2.16 *Phasor sum of two sinusoidal voltages (Example 2.7).*

2.9 PHASOR MULTIPLICATION AND DIVISION

The process of multiplication and division of complex numbers can be accomplished either in the exponential form or in the rectangular form. According to the rules for multiplying exponential terms together, if $\mathbf{A} = A\epsilon^{j\theta_1}$ and $\mathbf{B} = B\epsilon^{j\theta_2}$, then

$$\mathbf{A} \times \mathbf{B} = AB\epsilon^{j(\theta_1+\theta_2)} \tag{2.51}$$

To multiply complex numbers, then, the magnitudes are multiplied, and the angles are added.

In Eq. (2.51), if $\theta_1 = \omega t + \alpha_1$ and $\theta_2 = \omega t + \alpha_2$, then

$$\mathbf{A} \times \mathbf{B} = AB\epsilon^{j(2\omega t+\alpha_1+\alpha_2)} \tag{2.52}$$

Notice in Eq. (2.52) that the product of $\mathbf{A}$ and $\mathbf{B}$ has twice the frequency of $\mathbf{A}$ or $\mathbf{B}$.

In rectangular form the multiplication process requires multiplication term by term. If $\mathbf{A} = a_1 + ja_2$ and $\mathbf{B} = b_1 + jb_2$, then

$$\mathbf{A} \times \mathbf{B} = (a_1 + ja_2)(b_1 + jb_2)$$

$$= a_1b_1 + ja_1b_2 + ja_2b_1 + j^2a_2b_2$$

or, since $j^2 = -1$,

$$\mathbf{A} \times \mathbf{B} = (a_1b_1 - a_2b_2) + j(a_1b_2 + a_2b_1) \tag{2.53}$$

2.9 *Phasor Multiplication and Division* 57

Division of **A** by **B** is also accomplished in the exponential form in a manner similar to multiplication.

$$\frac{A \epsilon^{j\theta_1}}{B \epsilon^{j\theta_2}} = \frac{A}{B} \epsilon^{j(\theta_1 - \theta_2)} \tag{2.54}$$

If $\theta_1 = \omega t + \alpha_1$ and $\theta_2 = \omega t + \alpha_2$, the exponent on the right side of Eq. (2.54) loses all frequency terms and the quotient has a constant angle $\alpha_1 - \alpha_2$ associated with it.

In rectangular form, division is accomplished by rationalizing the denominator.

$$\frac{A}{B} = \frac{a_1 + ja_2}{b_1 + jb_2} \frac{b_1 - jb_2}{b_1 - jb_2}$$

or

$$\frac{A}{B} = \frac{(a_1 b_1 + a_2 b_2) + j(a_2 b_1 - a_1 b_2)}{b_1^2 + b_2^2} \tag{2.55}$$

Notice that, by rationalizing the denominator and multiplying, the quotient in the form of Eq. (2.55) is recognized as consisting of a real part and an imaginary part which must be equivalent to the polar, or exponential, form of the quotient [Eq. (2.54)].

2.10 DIRECT VOLTAGES AND CURRENTS

Some interesting relationships between constant voltages and constant currents result when the passive circuit elements are considered. Suppose that a constant current flows through resistance R. Equation (2.22a) shows that the voltage across R must also be constant. If we designate the current as I_{dc} and the voltage as V_{dc}, we have

$$V_{dc} = I_{dc} R \tag{2.56}$$

Now suppose that a constant current flows through a pure inductor. The derivative term in Eq. (2.22b) is zero, and the voltage across the inductor must be zero.

Next assume that the current through a capacitor is constant. From Eq. (2.22c) it is seen that, if there is no initial charge on the capacitor at $t = 0$, the voltage is proportional to the integral of the current,

$$v = \frac{1}{C} \int_0^t i \, dt$$

Thus, for constant $i = I_{dc}$, we can write

$$v = \frac{1}{C} \int_0^t I_{dc} \, dt$$

or

$$v = \frac{I_{dc}}{C} t \qquad (2.57)$$

Thus, for a capacitor subjected to constant current, the potential across it increases linearly with time.

Next, let the voltage across each of the circuit elements be constant and designated $v = V_{dc}$. Then the resistor has a constant current through it, and Eq. (2.56) applies. A constant voltage across the inductor [Eq. (2.22b)] requires that the derivative term be constant, and thus i in the inductor must increase linearly with time. Multiplying Eq. (2.22b) by dt and integrating, we have

$$i = \frac{1}{L} \int_0^t V_{dc} \, dt + I_0$$

so that, if the current $I_0 = 0$ at $t = 0$,

$$i = \frac{V_{dc}}{L} t \qquad (2.58)$$

For the capacitor, we can use Eq. (1.36) with constant voltage $v = V_{dc}$.

$$i = C \frac{dV_{dc}}{dt} \qquad (2.59)$$

But the derivative term in Eq. (2.59) is zero; so i must be zero. The capacitor looks like an open circuit for a constant voltage, since no current flows.

The average value of a constant voltage or current is the same as the instantaneous value. The effective, or rms, value of a constant voltage or current is also equal to the instantaneous value.

2.11 FOURIER-SERIES REPRESENTATION OF PERIODIC FUNCTIONS

Nonsinusoidal periodic exciting voltages and currents are common in electric communications and control systems. For example, if a microphone is used to convert a continuous middle-C note from a musical instrument such as an organ into analogous voltage, a fundamental frequency of 256 cycles/sec would be present, simultaneously with multiples or harmonics of this fundamental frequency. The instantaneous voltage, the summation of the fundamental and harmonic components, is periodic of the same fundamental frequency of 256 cycles/sec, but it is not sinusoidal. An example of a nonsinusoidal periodic function is shown in Fig. 2.17,

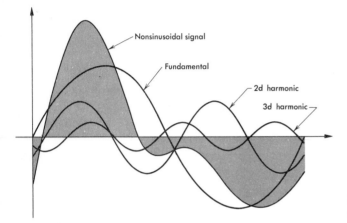

Nonsinusoidal signal

Fundamental

2d harmonic

3d harmonic

FIG. 2.17 *This nonsinusoidal voltage is the sum of the fundamental, second, and third harmonics.*

where a first harmonic or fundamental-frequency voltage, a second harmonic with frequency of twice the fundamental frequency, and a third harmonic with frequency of three times the fundamental frequency are added at each instant of time to produce the nonsinusoidal voltage shown. This particular nonsinusoidal waveform can be analyzed into the three separate sinusoids whose frequencies are the first, second, and third multiple of the fundamental frequency.

Time-varying nonsinusoidal periodic voltages and currents, or any other periodic physical quantities for that matter, can be represented by the Fourier series, which can be written

$$f(t) = \frac{a_0}{2} + a_1 \cos \omega t + a_2 \cos 2\omega t + a_3 \cos 3\omega t + \cdots$$

$$+ b_1 \sin \omega t + b_2 \sin 2\omega t + b_3 \sin 3\omega t + \cdots \qquad (2.60)$$

The constant term $a_0/2$ is the direct, or **average**, value of the voltage or current represented by Eq. (2.60). A d-c-indicating instrument measuring direct voltage or current would indicate $a_0/2$ when excited by the function [Eq. (2.60)]. The fundamental radian frequency is ω, with 2ω the frequency of the second harmonic, 3ω the frequency of the third harmonic, etc. The coefficients a_0, a_1, a_2, a_3,

..., b_1, b_2, b_3, ..., are obtained from the equations

$$a_n = \frac{1}{\pi} \int_{-\pi}^{+\pi} f(\omega t) \cos n\omega t \, d(\omega t) \qquad (2.61)$$

$$b_n = \frac{1}{\pi} \int_{-\pi}^{+\pi} f(\omega t) \sin n\omega t \, d(\omega t) \qquad (2.62)$$

where n is the subscript integer of the coefficients of the sinusoids in Eq. (2.60) and $f(t)$ is the periodic function of time as represented by Eq. (2.60). The limits of integration need not necessarily be $-\pi$ to $+\pi$ but must be over one complete period of the fundamental frequency; limits of 0 to 2π can also be used.

Example 2.8

The square wave of voltage shown in Fig. 2.18a is to be resolved into its Fourier series. The constant, or direct-voltage, component is found from Eq. (2.61) for $n = 0$.

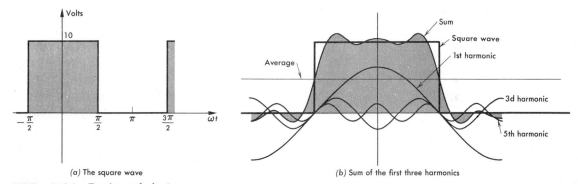

(a) The square wave   (b) Sum of the first three harmonics

FIG. 2.18 *Fourier analysis of a square wave.*

$$\frac{a_0}{2} = \frac{1}{2\pi} \int_{-\pi/2}^{+\pi/2} f(t) \cos 0 \, d(\omega t) = \frac{1}{2\pi} \int_{-\pi/2}^{+\pi/2} 10 \, d(\omega t) = 5 \text{ volts}$$

The period of integration is from $-\pi/2$ to $\pi/2$, since $v = 0$ from $-\pi$ to $-\pi/2$ and from $\pi/2$ to π. $a_0/2$ can also be found from inspection, since it is the average value of v over one period.

The fundamental-frequency coefficients are

$$a_1 = \frac{1}{\pi} \int_{-\pi/2}^{+\pi/2} 10 \cos \omega t \, d(\omega t) = \frac{10}{\pi} \sin \omega t \Big]_{-\pi/2}^{\pi/2} = \frac{20}{\pi}$$

$$b_1 = \frac{1}{\pi} \int_{-\pi/2}^{+\pi/2} 10 \sin \omega t \, d(\omega t) = \frac{-10}{\pi} \cos \omega t \Big]_{-\pi/2}^{\pi/2} = 0$$

2.11 Fourier-series Representation of Periodic Functions   61

Second-harmonic coefficients are

$$a_2 = \frac{1}{\pi} \int_{-\pi/2}^{\pi/2} 10 \cos 2\omega t \, d(\omega t) = \frac{10}{2\pi} \sin 2\omega t \Big]_{-\pi/2}^{\pi/2} = 0$$

$$b_2 = \frac{1}{\pi} \int_{-\pi/2}^{\pi/2} 10 \sin 2\omega t \, d(\omega t) = \frac{-10}{2\pi} \cos 2\omega t \Big]_{-\pi/2}^{\pi/2} = 0$$

Thus there are no second-harmonic terms present in the Fourier series. Third- and higher-harmonic coefficients are now evaluated as functions of n.

$$a_n = \frac{1}{\pi} \int_{-\pi/2}^{\pi/2} 10 \cos n\omega t \, d(\omega t) = \frac{10}{n\omega} \sin n\omega t \Big]_{-\pi/2}^{\pi/2}$$

$$= \frac{10}{n\pi} \left(\sin \frac{n\pi}{2} + \sin \frac{n\pi}{2} \right) = \frac{20}{n\pi} \sin \frac{n\pi}{2}$$

$$b_n = \frac{1}{\pi} \int_{-\pi/2}^{\pi/2} 10 \sin n\omega t \, d(\omega t) = \frac{-10}{n\omega} \cos n\omega t \Big]_{-\pi/2}^{\pi/2}$$

$$= \frac{-10}{n\pi} \left(\cos \frac{n\pi}{2} - \cos \frac{n\pi}{2} \right) = 0$$

Thus, when n is even, $a_n = 0$, and when n is odd,

$$a_n = \frac{2}{n\pi} (-1)^{\frac{n-1}{2}}$$

The coefficients $b_n = 0$ for all values of n.

The Fourier series representing the square wave can then be written

$$v(t) = 5 + \frac{20}{\pi} \cos \omega t - \frac{20}{3\pi} \cos 3\omega t + \frac{20}{5\pi} \cos 5\omega t$$

$$- \frac{20}{7\pi} \cos 7\omega t + \cdots \tag{2.63}$$

The first four terms of Eq. (2.63) are shown in Fig. 2.18b, and their sum is seen to approach a square wave. In the limit, the sum of the infinite Fourier series reproduces the square wave exactly.

The Fourier series is significant because it shows that any periodic function can be represented by a series of sinusoids. By means of the Fourier integral (not discussed here), nonperiodic functions can be represented by a continuous spectrum of sinusoids. Although sinusoidal analysis is emphasized to some extent in Chaps. 4, 6, and 7, nonsinusoidal analysis follows from the application of the Fourier series or the Fourier integral.

SUMMARY

Average values of periodic functions can be found by integrating to find the value of the area under the curve over a period $t_2 - t_1$ and dividing by the period, or [Eq. (2.1)]

$$F_a = \frac{1}{t_2 - t_1} \int_{t_1}^{t_2} f(t) \, dt$$

The rms value of a periodic function is the square root of the average of the square of the function, or [Eq. (2.10)]

$$F_{rms} = \sqrt{\frac{1}{t_2 - t_1} \int_{t_1}^{t_2} [f(t)]^2 \, dt}$$

A sinusoid has an average value of zero, but for the positive half cycle the average value is 0.636 times the maximum value. The rms value of a sinusoid is 0.707 times the maximum value. The average value of a constant and the rms value of a constant are both equal to the constant.

From Eq. (2.33) the identity

$$\epsilon^{j\theta} = \cos \theta + j \sin \theta$$

is justification for referring to $\cos \theta$ as the real part of $\epsilon^{j\theta}$ and $\sin \theta$ as the imaginary part of $\epsilon^{j\theta}$. Complex numbers (numbers with real and imaginary parts) can be expressed in exponential form or in rectangular form, as

$$\mathbf{A} = a_1 + j a_2 \quad \text{or} \quad \mathbf{A} = A \epsilon^{j\theta_1}$$

where $A = \sqrt{a_1^2 + a_2^2}$, $\theta_1 = \tan^{-1}(a_2/a_1)$.

$$\mathbf{B} = b_1 + j b_2 \quad \text{or} \quad \mathbf{B} = B \epsilon^{j\theta_2}$$

where $B = \sqrt{b_1^2 + b_2^2}$, $\theta_2 = \tan^{-1}(b_2/b_1)$.

To add or subtract $\mathbf{A}$ and $\mathbf{B}$, add or subtract their real parts and their imaginary parts separately.

$$\mathbf{A} \pm \mathbf{B} = (a_1 \pm b_1) + j(a_2 \pm b_2)$$

Multiplication and division in exponential form follow the rules for multiplying exponentials [see Eqs. (2.51) and (2.54)].

$$\mathbf{A} \times \mathbf{B} = A\epsilon^{j\theta_1} \times B\epsilon^{j\theta_2} = AB\epsilon^{j(\theta_1+\theta_2)}$$

$$\frac{\mathbf{A}}{\mathbf{B}} = \frac{A\epsilon^{j\theta_1}}{B\epsilon^{j\theta_2}} = \frac{A}{B}\,\epsilon^{j(\theta_1-\theta_2)}$$

As in Eq. (2.53) multiplication in rectangular coordinates yields

$$\mathbf{A} \times \mathbf{B} = (a_1 + ja_2)(b_1 + jb_2)$$

$$= (a_1b_1 - a_2b_2) + j(a_1b_2 + a_2b_1)$$

Division in rectangular form requires that the denominator be rationalized [Eq. 2.55].

$$\frac{\mathbf{A}}{\mathbf{B}} = \frac{a_1 + ja_2}{b_1 + jb_2}\frac{b_1 - jb_2}{b_1 - jb_2} = \frac{a_1b_1 + a_2b_2}{b_1{}^2 + b_2{}^2} + j\frac{a_2b_1 - a_1b_2}{b_1{}^2 + b_2{}^2}$$

The exponential function reproduces itself upon integration and differentiation; the sinusoid also reproduces itself upon integration and differentiation. A series of sinusoids, the Fourier series [Eq. (2.60)],

$$f(t) = \frac{a_1}{2} + a_1 \cos \omega t + a_2 \cos 2\omega t + a_3 \cos 3\omega t + \cdots$$

$$+ b_1 \sin \omega t + b_2 \sin 2\omega t + b_3 \sin 3\omega t + \cdots$$

can be used to represent any periodic function of time encountered in engineering problems.

FURTHER READING

Any basic text on electric circuits discusses average and rms values of periodic functions. H. H. Skilling, *Electrical Engineering Circuits* (John Wiley & Sons, Inc., New York, 1957), chap. 3, and Egon Brenner and Mansour Javid, *Analysis of Electric Circuits* (McGraw-Hill Book Company, Inc., New York, 1959), chap. 8, are two excellent references on complex numbers applied to sinusoids. The Fourier series is extensively discussed by Skilling, chap. 14, and by Brenner and Javid, chap. 19.

PROBLEMS

2.1 Three different combinations of voltages and current are shown in (a), (b), and (c) in the illustration. Find the average power from $p = vi$ for the period T of each.

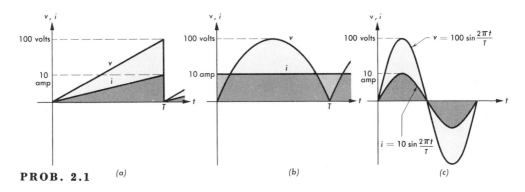

PROB. 2.1   (a)   (b)   (c)

2.2 Refer to Prob. 2.1 and its illustration. Find the average voltage and the average current for (a), (b), and (c). Show that average power is not necessarily equal to the product of average voltage times average current. Explain why.

2.3 Find the effective, or rms, value of the voltage and current waves of Prob. 2.1. Does $P_a = E_{eff}I_{eff}$? Explain.

2.4 Find the rms values of the voltages shown in (a), (b), (c), and (d) in the figure, where T is the period of each.

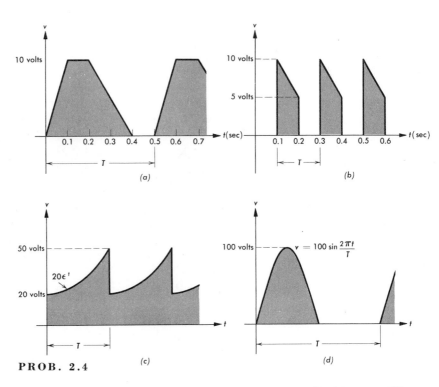

PROB. 2.4   (c)

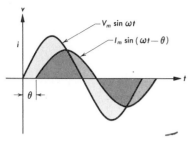

PROB. 2.5

2.5 The voltage and current associated with a particular unknown circuit element is shown in the figure. Find the average power delivered to the element as a function of angle θ.

2.6 Find the rms, or effective, value of the voltage wave shown in the illustration. Take advantage of the geometry in order to perform your integration by inspection.

2.7 Suppose that $v_1 = 100 \sin (500t + 25°)$, $v_2 = 50 \cos (500t - 45°)$, $i_1 = 10 \sin (500t - 10°)$, $i_2 = 15 \sin (500t + 90°)$. Find the phase difference of: (a) v_1 with respect to i_1, (b) v_1 with respect to v_2, (c) i_1 with respect to v_1, (d) v_2 with respect to i_2.

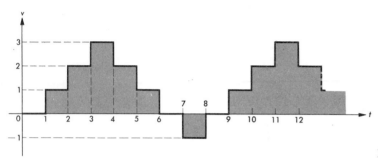

PROB. 2.6

2.8 Prove that the rms value of a constant, or direct, current is equal to the instantaneous value, and prove that the average value of a direct current is equal to the instantaneous value.

2.9 Perform the operations on the complex numbers as indicated below. The results should be expressed in rectangular form as the sum of a real part and an imaginary part. (a) $(1 + j5) + (7 - j3)$. (b) $(-1 - j5) + (-7 - j3)$. (c) $(1 + j5) - (7 - j3)$. (d) $(1 + j5)(7 - j3)$. (e) $(-1 - j5)(-7 - j3)$. (f) $\dfrac{1 + j5}{7 - j3}$. (g) $\dfrac{-1 - j5}{7 - j3}$. (h) $\dfrac{1 + j0}{0 + j1}$.

2.10 Perform the following operations on phasors $\mathbf{A} = 10\epsilon^{j30°}$ and $\mathbf{B} = 2\epsilon^{j60°}$: (a) Convert $\mathbf{A}$ to rectangular form. (b) Multiply $\mathbf{A}$ and $\mathbf{B}$, and give the product in the exponential form. (c) Add $\mathbf{A}$ and $\mathbf{B}$. (d) Divide $\mathbf{A}$ by $\mathbf{B}$, and leave the quotient in exponential form.

2.11 If $\mathbf{A} = 10\epsilon^{j0°}$, $\mathbf{B} = 2\epsilon^{j60°}$, $\mathbf{C} = 5\epsilon^{j0°}$, and $\mathbf{D} = 20\epsilon^{j90°}$: (a) Find $\mathbf{A} \times \mathbf{B} \times \mathbf{C} \times \mathbf{D}$. (b) Find $\dfrac{\mathbf{A} \times \mathbf{B}}{\mathbf{C} \times \mathbf{D}}$, and express it in rectangular form.

2.12 Using Eqs. (2.33) to (2.35), prove that $\epsilon^{j(\pi/2)} = j$.

2.13 Find the real and imaginary parts of: (a) $(10 + j5)(-2 + j2)$, (b) $(15\epsilon^{j(\pi/6)})(10\epsilon^{j(\pi/10)})$, (c) $2\epsilon^{j(\pi/12)}$.

2.14 Using the series expansion for $\sin \theta$, find $\sin \theta$ for: (a) $\theta = 0.1$ radian, (b) $\theta = 0.2$ radian, (c) $\theta = 0.5$ radian, (d) $\theta = 1$ radian, (e) $\theta = \pi/2$ radians, (f) $\theta = \pi$ radians.

2.15 If $A = 3\epsilon^{j(\omega t + 30°)}$ and $B = 4\epsilon^{j(\omega t + 120°)}$, plot Im **A**, Im **B**, and Im (**A** × **B**) as a function of ωt.

2.16 Two currents i_1 and i_2 combine at a node to form $i = i_1 + i_2$. If $i_1 = 10 \sin (377t + 30°)$ and $i_2 = 20 \sin (377t - 15°)$, find: (a) the instantaneous value of i, (b) the rms value of i.

2.17 Verify that, if $v = V_m \sin \omega t$ and $i = I_m \cos \omega t$, the average power is zero. Repeat for $v = V_m \sin \omega t$ and $i = -I_m \cos \omega t$.

2.18 A periodic rectangular voltage wave of the form shown in the figure causes a d-c (average-reading) voltmeter to read 200 volts and an a-c (rms) voltmeter to read 300 volts. The period of the wave is $t_1 + t_2 = 0.01$ sec. Find E_m, t_1, and t_2.

2.19 The square wave in Fig. 2.18 is shifted ahead in time by the angle $\omega t = \pi/2$ and appears as shown in the illustration to this problem. Verify that the Fourier series representing this square wave is $v(t) = 5 + \dfrac{20}{\pi} \sin \omega t + \dfrac{20}{3\pi} \sin 3 \omega t + \dfrac{20}{5\pi} \sin 5 \omega t + \cdots$.

2.20 Verify that the saw-tooth wave shown can be represented by the Fourier series $v(t) = 10 + \dfrac{20}{\pi} \sin \omega t - \dfrac{10}{\pi} \sin 2 \omega t + \dfrac{20}{3\pi} \sin 3 \omega t - \dfrac{5}{\pi} \sin 4 \omega t + \cdots$.

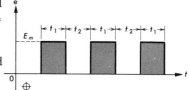

PROB. 2.18

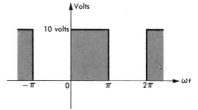

PROB. 2.19

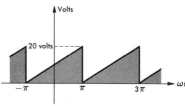

PROB. 2.20

3

NATURAL RESPONSE

3.1 INTRODUCTION

A source of energy is necessary in order to excite and produce a response in any physical system. A source of energy can be external, such as an electric generator supplying energy to an electric circuit or an external force acting on a mechanical system in motion. Or the source of energy can be internal, consisting of energy-storage elements such as inductors and capacitors in electric circuits or masses and springs in mechanical systems. Whenever stored energy in a circuit is suddenly released, the circuit responds to the released energy in a manner depending upon the circuit configuration and upon the circuit parameters. The magnitude of the response to the stored energy is a function of the amount of energy released, but the form of the response depends only upon the circuit itself. Because the circuit response to internally stored energy is a characteristic of the circuit itself, it is known as the "natural response" of the circuit.

The opening or closing of a switch is usually necessary to release energy stored in the energy-storage elements in the circuit. The switching action may, in addition to releasing stored energy, connect external-energy sources to the circuit as well. The external-energy source also produces a response in the circuit. A long time after the switching action has occurred, the original stored energy has been dissipated by the resistance in the circuit, and the circuit response depends entirely upon the external energy being supplied. The response caused by the exciting function is known as the "steady-state response."

Immediately after the switching action, both natural response and steady-state response are present. By superposition, the net response is the sum of the natural response and the steady-state response. "Transient response" is the term used for the net response immediately after the switching action when both steady-state response and natural response are present; transient response occurs between two steady-state conditions, that before the switching action and that a long time afterward.

In this chapter we are primarily concerned with the natural response of electric circuits. Several electric circuits and mechanical systems will be investigated, and general conclusions concerning the natural response of linear systems will be made. Natural response is a characteristic of the physical system itself; the form of the natural response is independent of the exciting function of the system.

3.2 FORMULATION OF EQUATIONS

Kirchhoff's laws provide the information necessary to formulate the differential equations of any electric circuit; D'Alembert's principle is useful in formulating differential equations of mechanical systems. The natural response of the physical system is found from the differential equations of that system. In this section, the formulation of differential equations for physical systems is considered, and from these differential equations the natural response of the system is obtained.

The RL circuit of Fig. 3.1 is an example of a series circuit connected to an arbitrary voltage source e. When the switch Sw is open, the circuit is in a steady state with $i = 0$. At time $t = 0$, the switch is closed, completing the circuit and permitting the current i to flow in the circuit. The problem is to find the current i for any time t after the switch has been closed.

The first step is to define the positive direction of current, as shown in Fig. 3.1, and positive directions of the voltages across each element. Then, assuming that the switch is closed, the voltages are added by proceeding in the same consistent direction around the loop until all the voltages have been encountered and

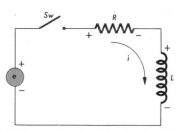

FIG. 3.1 *An RL circuit with arbitrary exciting voltage e, described by Eq. (3.2).*

recorded; thus we can write

$$Ri + L\frac{di}{dt} - e = 0 \tag{3.1}$$

which can be rearranged to

$$L\frac{di}{dt} + Ri = e \tag{3.2}$$

Equation (3.2) is known as a "first-order differential equation," since the first derivative is the highest-order derivative present. Any system describable by a first-order equation is known as a "first-order system." Notice that only one energy-storage element, the inductor, is present in the first-order circuit of Fig. 3.1.

Equation (3.1) was written by proceeding clockwise around the circuit of Fig. 3.1, commencing with the resistor. Each voltage encountered in going from positive to negative through a circuit element is shown in Eq. (3.1) as a positive voltage. Each of these voltages could have been recorded with a negative sign, and then the equation could have been multiplied by -1 to change the sign of each term to that of Eq. (3.1).

The sign of the voltage across L in Fig. 3.1 assumes that the current is positive, that is, in the direction indicated by the arrow, and increasing with time. By Lenz's law, the emf induced in the inductor by the changing current is in a direction that opposes the changing current. Thus, the emf induced in L is in the direction shown, tending to produce a counterclockwise current around the loop to oppose the increasing clockwise current i.

In Fig. 3.2 is shown an RC circuit connected to an arbitrary voltage source. Kirchhoff's voltage law allows us to write

$$Ri + \frac{1}{C}\int_0^t i\,dt + V_0 = e \tag{3.3}$$

where V_0 is the voltage attributed to the charge on the capacitor at $t = 0$. Notice that the positive current i tends to accumulate positive charge on the top plate of the capacitor, making the potential of the top plate positive with respect to the bottom plate and thus justifying the capacitor voltage signs shown in Fig. 3.2.

Equation (3.3) is an integral equation and can be transformed into a differential equation by differentiating each term with respect to time. After differentiation, Eq. (3.3) becomes

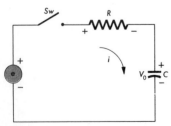

FIG. 3.2 *An RC circuit with arbitrary exciting voltage e, described by Eq. (3.3).*

$$R\frac{di}{dt} + \frac{1}{C}i = \frac{de}{dt} \tag{3.4}$$

which is a first-order differential equation where de/dt can be
thought of as the exciting function.

A series circuit with all three kinds of circuit elements is shown
in Fig. 3.3. Kirchhoff's voltage law around the circuit loop yields

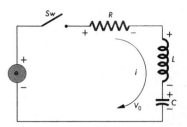

$$L\frac{di}{dt} + Ri + \frac{1}{C}\int_0^t i\,dt + V_0 = e \qquad (3.5)$$

where V_0 again is the capacitor voltage at $t = 0$ when the switch is
closed. Equation (3.5) is an integrodifferential equation which can
be changed to a second-order differential equation by differentiating throughout with respect to time, yielding

FIG. 3.3 *RLC circuit with arbitrary exciting voltage e, described by Eq.
(3.5).*

$$L\frac{d^2i}{dt^2} + R\frac{di}{dt} + \frac{1}{C}i = \frac{de}{dt} \qquad (3.6)$$

Or, instead of differentiating Eq. (3.5), recall that

$$i = \frac{dq}{dt} \qquad (3.7)$$

and substitute Eq. (3.7) into Eq. (3.5), resulting in

$$L\frac{d^2q}{dt^2} + R\frac{dq}{dt} + \frac{1}{C}q + V_0 = e \qquad (3.8)$$

Both Eqs. (3.6) and (3.8) are second-order linear differential equations with constant coefficients. Notice that there are two kinds
of energy-storage elements in Fig. 3.3, the circuit which Eqs. (3.6)
and (3.8) describe.

A mechanical system consisting of a mass M, a spring, and
viscous friction is shown in Fig. 3.4, where the viscous friction is
represented by the dashpot. The mass is displaced downward a
distance X from the neutral position X_0, and then the mass is released. Potential energy stored in the extended spring excites the
system, and D'Alembert's principle allows us to add the inertia
force to the spring force and the friction force and equate the sum
of the three forces to zero. Then

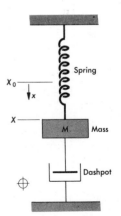

$$M\frac{d^2x}{dt^2} + B\frac{dx}{dt} + Kx = 0 \qquad (3.9)$$

where M is the mass, B is the friction constant, and K is the spring
constant. The first term in Eq. (3.9) is the inertia force (proportional to acceleration), the second term is the viscous-friction force
(proportional to velocity), and the third term is the spring force
(proportional to displacement). Gravity force has been neglected,

FIG. 3.4 *Schematic of
a spring-mass-dashpot me-
chanical system displaced a
distance X from the neutral,
or reference, position X_0 and
described by Eq. (3.9).*

since it is constant and tends to establish the neutral position X_0 about which the mass moves.

The algebraic signs of each term in Eq. (3.9) can be determined by considering the forces at the time $t = 0+$ immediately after the mass has been released. Since positive x has been defined as downward and the spring force is upward at this instant, we write the spring force Kx with a positive sign and thus define forces upward as positive. The friction force is opposite to the direction of the velocity, but since dx/dt is negative at $t = 0+$, a positive algebraic sign must also precede the friction force term in Eq. (3.9). Acceleration is upward in the $-x$ direction, and d^2x/dt^2 is negative, since velocity increases in the $-x$ direction. The inertia force is downward at this instant, and a positive algebraic sign must precede the inertia term. All the algebraic signs in each term of Eqs. (3.8) and (3.9) are the same; that is, all are positive.

The conservation-of-energy principle can also be used to establish system differential equations. For instance, the power being dissipated by viscous friction in the spring-mass-dashpot system of Fig. 3.4 must be equal to the time rate at which the stored energy is changing in the spring and the mass. This can be expressed by

$$B\frac{dx}{dt}v + \frac{d}{dt}\left(M\frac{v^2}{2} + \int_0^x Kx\,dx\right) = 0 \tag{3.10}$$

where $B\dfrac{dx}{dt}v$ is the power lost by friction, $M(v^2/2)$ is kinetic energy stored in the mass, and $\displaystyle\int_0^x Kx\,dx$ is the energy stored in the spring. Equation (3.10) reduces to

$$B\frac{dx}{dt}v + Mv\frac{dv}{dt} + \frac{d}{dt}\left(\frac{Kx^2}{2}\right) = 0$$

or

$$B\frac{dx}{dt}v + Mv\frac{dv}{dt} + Kx\frac{dx}{dt} = 0 \tag{3.11}$$

Substituting $v = dx/dt$ into Eq. (3.11) and dividing through by dx/dt results in [see Eq. (3.9)],

$$M\frac{d^2x}{dt^2} + B\frac{dx}{dt} + Kx = 0$$

which is identical to the equation derived from D'Alembert's principle.

3.3 NATURAL RESPONSE
AND THE HOMOGENEOUS EQUATION

The natural response of a dynamic system is obtained when the exciting function is zero. An example is the mechanical spring-mass-dashpot system of Fig. 3.4 and the differential equation which describes it [Eq. (3.9)]. There are no external forces applied to the system after the mass has been released from its displaced position, and therefore the forcing function is zero.

The electric circuit of Fig. 3.3 is an example of a system with an external forcing function e applied after closing the switch. Notice that the forcing function appears on the right-hand side of Eqs. (3.5) and (3.8). The electric circuit has a natural response which can be found by equating the forcing function to zero. When a second-order system differential equation can be written in the descending order of derivatives in the form

$$a_2 \frac{d^2x}{dt^2} + a_1 \frac{dx}{dt} + a_0x = 0 \qquad (3.12)$$

after replacing the forcing function with zero, the equation is known as the "homogeneous" equation of the system. The solution of the homogeneous equation of the system is the natural response of the system. In the next section the natural response of some first-order systems is obtained.

3.4 NATURAL RESPONSE OF FIRST-ORDER
SYSTEMS

As an example of a first-order system with a forcing function of zero, let us now modify the circuit of Fig. 3.1 to that of Fig. 3.5. The switch Sw is initially in position A. At $t = 0$, the switch is instantaneously thrown from position A to position B without interrupting the current in the circuit. The problem is to find the current i as a function of time after $t = 0$, when the switching action occurs. By Kirchhoff's voltage law,

$$L \frac{di}{dt} + Ri = 0 \qquad (3.13)$$

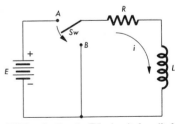

FIG. 3.5 *An RL circuit described by Eq. (3.13).*

Notice that the battery, which is the original source of electric energy to the circuit, has been switched out of the circuit. Recall, however, that the inductor L has the ability to store energy in its magnetic field, and this stored energy is the source of energy in the circuit after the switch has been thrown to position B.

Examining Eq. (3.13) for a solution of i as a function of time, we observe that i and its derivative with respect to time must both be of the same form to satisfy the equation. We recall that the exponential function is the only function which is identical in form to its derivative, and we assume that the solution of Eq. (3.13) is of the form

$$i = A\epsilon^{pt} \tag{3.14}$$

where A and p are constants. If Eq. (3.14) is a solution of Eq. (3.13), it must satisfy Eq. (3.13). Substituting Eq. (3.14) into Eq. (3.13) yields

$$LAp\epsilon^{pt} + RA\epsilon^{pt} = 0 \tag{3.15}$$

or

$$(Lp + R)A\epsilon^{pt} = 0 \tag{3.16}$$

The factor $Lp + R$ in Eq. (3.16) must equal zero for Eq. (3.16) to be valid, and therefore

$$p = -\frac{R}{L} \tag{3.17}$$

When Eq. (3.17) is substituted into the assumed solution [Eq. (3.14)], we have

$$i = A\epsilon^{-(R/L)t} \tag{3.18}$$

which is a solution of Eq. (3.13) for all values of A. In order to restrict A to a unique value, we must know the initial value of the current immediately after the switch was thrown. Since the circuit was in a steady state prior to the switching action, by Ohm's law, the current before switching was E/R. Since for finite voltage the current through the inductor cannot change instantaneously, the current in the circuit before switching action must equal the current immediately after switching. Thus, at $t = 0+$, i must be equal to E/R, and

$$i = \frac{E}{R}\epsilon^{-(R/L)t} \qquad \text{amp} \tag{3.19}$$

is the natural response of the circuit.

Example 3.1

A mass M, sliding along a flat surface, has external forces removed at $t = 0$. Assume that the friction force is proportional to the velocity and that the friction constant is B. Summing the forces on the mass to zero, we have

$$M \frac{dv}{dt} + Bv = 0$$

where v is the instantaneous velocity. Assuming a solution of the form

$$v = V_0 \epsilon^{pt} \qquad \text{m/sec}$$

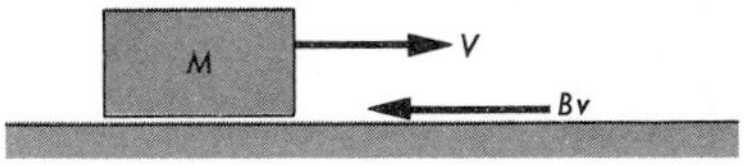

we substitute this solution into the differential equation and solve for p. Thus,

$$p = -\frac{B}{M}$$

and

$$v = V_0 \epsilon^{-(B/M)t} \qquad \text{m/sec}$$

where V_0 is the velocity of the mass M at $t = 0+$.

FIG. 3.6 *Mass-friction first-order system (Example 3.1).*

A first-order homogeneous equation of the form

$$a_1 \frac{di}{dt} + a_0 i = 0 \tag{3.20}$$

can also be solved by separating the variables and integrating. Notice that i is the dependent variable and t is the independent variable in Eq. (3.20). Multiplying Eq. (3.20) through by dt and dividing by i, we have

$$a_1 \frac{di}{i} + a_0 \, dt = 0 \tag{3.21}$$

Integrating both terms of Eq. (3.21) yields

$$a_1 \log_\epsilon i + a_0 t + K = 0 \tag{3.22}$$

where K is the constant of integration. Solving Eq. (3.22) for i gives

$$i = \epsilon^{-(a_0/a_1)t + K/a_1} \tag{3.23}$$

or

$$i = \epsilon^{-(a_0/a_1)t} \epsilon^{K/a_1} \tag{3.24}$$

The exponential term with a constant exponent is also a constant, which can be expressed as I_0, the initial current at $t = 0+$. Thus

$$i = I_0 \epsilon^{-(a_0/a_1)t} \tag{3.25}$$

where I_0 is the initial current at $t = 0+$. Notice that Eq. (3.25) is identical in form to Eq. (3.18).

A first-order system with nonzero exciting function is shown in Fig. 3.1, where the switch is closed at $t = 0$. The nonhomogeneous circuit equation is shown in Eq. (3.2), where e is the exciting function. The homogeneous form of Eq. (3.2), found by letting the exciting function be zero, is identical to Eq. (3.13). The natural response of the circuit of Fig. 3.1 is of the same form as for Fig. 3.5, namely, Eq. (3.18), where A is a constant to be evaluated from the initial conditions of the problem. The complete solution of the nonhomogeneous equation is the sum of the steady-state response and the natural response and is discussed in Chap. 5.

3.5 TIME CONSTANT

The natural response of a first-order circuit is exponential in form and decays with time for positive values of R, L, and C. The natural response of the RL series circuit is given by Eq. (3.19) and decays with time, eventually approaching zero as t becomes large. Equation (3.19) is plotted in Fig. 3.7 for values of t after the switch-

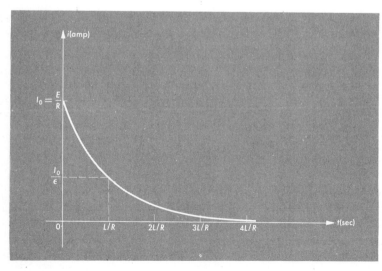

FIG. 3.7 *Natural response of an RL series circuit with time constant of L/R.*

ing action at $t = 0$. Upon rewriting Eq. (3.19) here,

$$i = \frac{E}{R} \epsilon^{-(R/L)t}$$

it can be seen that, when $t = L/R$, the current has decayed to $1/\epsilon$ of its original value E/R at $t = 0+$. This provides a convenient means for expressing the rate at which the current decays. The "time constant" of the circuit is the time it takes the natural-response current to decay to $1/\epsilon$ of its original value; time constant τ is the time t at which the exponent of ϵ in the natural-response equation is -1. In Eq. (3.19), if $t = L/R$, the exponential term is ϵ^{-1}, which has a value of 0.368. Thus, if $i = I_0$ at $t = 0+$, $i = 0.368I_0$ at $t = L/R$. In five time constants the natural response current has decayed to less than 1 per cent of its original value.

To illustrate further the natural-response concept and the time-constant concept, consider the RC circuit shown in Fig. 3.8. The capacitor is charged to voltage V_0 and is then allowed to discharge through the resistor R. If the switch is closed at $t = 0$, the voltage equation for the time after the switch is closed is

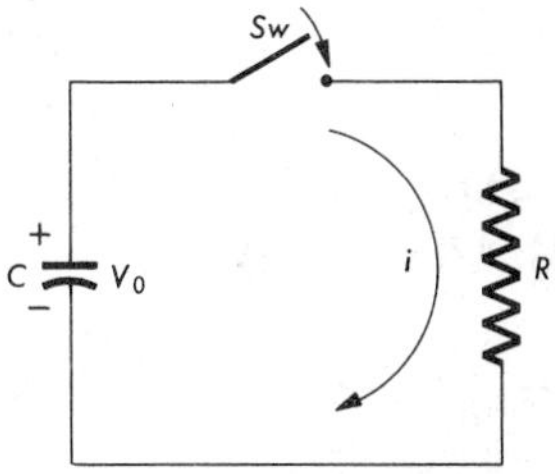

FIG. 3.8 *RC circuit with initial voltage V_0 caused by an initial charge C.*

$$iR + \frac{1}{C}\int_0^t i\,dt - V_0 = 0 \tag{3.26}$$

Differentiating Eq. (3.26) with respect to time to remove the integral term results in the first-order differential equation

$$R\frac{di}{dt} + \frac{1}{C}i = 0$$

the solution of which, by Eq. (3.25), is

$$i = I_0\epsilon^{-t/RC} \tag{3.27}$$

where $I_0 = V_0/R$. The time constant of the circuit is that value of t which makes the exponent in Eq. (3.27) equal to -1, or $t/RC = 1$. Thus $RC = \tau$, the time constant. To verify that the time constant RC has units of seconds, we write

$$RC = \frac{\text{volts coulombs}}{\text{amp volts}} = \frac{\text{coulombs}}{\text{coulombs/sec}} = \text{sec}$$

Thus RC is the time in seconds for the current to decay to 0.368 of its original value.

Example 3.2

The mass sliding along the flat surface in Example 3.1 is allowed to coast to rest. We saw that its velocity can be expressed as

$$v = V_0 \epsilon^{-(B/M)t}$$

where V_0 is the velocity at $t = 0$. After one time constant $\tau = M/B$ sec, the velocity has dropped to

$$v_1 = V_0\epsilon^{-1} = \frac{V_0}{\epsilon} = 0.368V_0$$

When t is two time constants,

$$v_2 = V_0\epsilon^{-2} = 0.135V_0$$

For $t = 3\tau$,

$$v_3 = V_0\epsilon^{-3} = 0.0498V_0$$

For $t = 4\tau$,

$$v_4 = V_0\epsilon^{-4} = 0.0183V_0$$

At $t = 5\tau$,

$$v_5 = V_0\epsilon^{-5} = 0.00674V_0$$

At $t = 10\tau$,

$$v_{10} = V_0\epsilon^{-10} = 0.000045V_0$$

Notice that after five time constants the mass velocity is less than 1 per cent of its original value, and to a good approximation we can use this as the time it takes for the mass to come to rest.

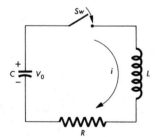

FIG. 3.9 *An RLC series circuit with no external exciting voltage. Initial charge on C excites the circuit, which is described by Eq. (3.29).*

3.6 NATURAL RESPONSE OF SECOND-ORDER SYSTEMS

The RLC series circuit of Fig. 3.3 and the mass-spring-dashpot system of Fig. 3.4 are examples of physical systems which can be described by linear differential equations of the second order. If the exciting functions of these systems are zero, the differential equations describing the systems reduce to homogeneous equations, the solution of which is the natural response of the system.

Consider the RLC series circuit of Fig. 3.9, where V_0 is the voltage to which the capacitor has been charged before the switch is closed. After the switch is closed, the differential equation of the circuit can be written

$$L\frac{di}{dt} + Ri + \frac{1}{C}\int_0^t i\,dt - V_0 = 0$$

Upon differentiation this becomes

$$L\frac{d^2i}{dt^2} + R\frac{di}{dt} + \frac{1}{C}i = 0 \tag{3.28}$$

by substituting $de/dt = 0$ into Eq. (3.6). The solution of Eq. (3.28) can be found by the procedure illustrated previously for the first-order system, namely, by assuming an exponential form of the solution and then evaluating the constants of the assumed solution to make sure that it satisfies the differential equation. The exponential form of the assumed solution is justified, since i, its first derivative, and its second derivative with respect to time must be of the same form so that, when they are substituted into Eq. (3.28), they satisfy the equation. Thus we assume that

$$i = A\epsilon^{pt} \tag{3.29}$$

where A and p are constants. Substituting Eq. (3.29) into Eq. (3.28) yields

$$ALp^2\epsilon^{pt} + ARp\epsilon^{pt} + \frac{1}{C}A\epsilon^{pt} = 0$$

which can be divided and factored in the form

$$A\epsilon^{pt}\left(Lp^2 + Rp + \frac{1}{C}\right) = 0 \tag{3.30}$$

If Eq. (3.30) is to be satisfied, the term in the parentheses must be zero, or

$$Lp^2 + Rp + \frac{1}{C} = 0 \tag{3.31}$$

Notice that Eq. (3.31) can be obtained directly from Eq. (3.28) by replacing the first-derivative term in Eq. (3.28) with p and the second derivative with p^2. Equation (3.31) is known as the "characteristic equation" of Eq. (3.28). Solving Eq. (3.31) for p by the quadratic equation results in

$$p = -\frac{R}{2L} \pm \sqrt{\frac{R^2}{4L^2} - \frac{1}{LC}} \tag{3.32}$$

Equation (3.32) is ambiguous; there are two values of p, either of which used in Eq. (3.29) satisfies Eq. (3.28). Define p_1 and p_2 as the two values of p in Eq. (3.32). Then we can define i_1 in terms of p_1 by

$$i_1 = A_1 \epsilon^{p_1 t} \tag{3.33}$$

where

$$p_1 = -\frac{R}{2L} + \sqrt{\frac{R^2}{4L^2} - \frac{1}{LC}} \tag{3.34}$$

Likewise i_2 is defined by

$$i_2 = A_2 \epsilon^{p_2 t} \tag{3.35}$$

where

$$p_2 = -\frac{R}{2L} - \sqrt{\frac{R^2}{4L^2} - \frac{1}{LC}} \tag{3.36}$$

If i_1 and i_2 each satisfies Eq. (3.28), their sum also satisfies Eq. (3.28). Let $i = i_1 + i_2$. Then as a consequence of the superposition principle

$$i = A_1 \epsilon^{p_1 t} + A_2 \epsilon^{p_2 t} \tag{3.37}$$

is also a solution.

Consider now the characteristics of p_1 and p_2. Notice that if

$$\frac{R^2}{4L^2} - \frac{1}{LC} > 0 \tag{3.38}$$

p_1 and p_2 are real and unequal. If

$$\frac{R^2}{4L^2} - \frac{1}{LC} = 0 \tag{3.39}$$

then p_1 and p_2 are real and equal. Furthermore, if

$$\frac{R^2}{4L^2} - \frac{1}{LC} < 0 \tag{3.40}$$

then p_1 and p_2 are complex conjugates.

p_1 **and** p_2 **real.** If p_1 and p_2 are real, Eq. (3.37) can be written as the sum of two exponential terms with real exponents, which are both plotted in Fig. 3.10. Notice that p_1 and p_2 must be negative, since R, L, and C are positive values in Eqs. (3.34) and (3.36).

To evaluate the constants A_1 and A_2, we must know the initial conditions of the circuit at the instant after the switch is closed. If we know the initial current at that instant and the initial rate of change of current with respect to time at that instant, the con-

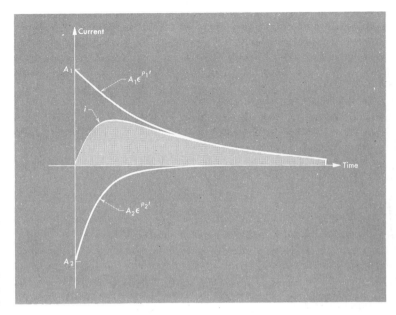

FIG. 3.10 *Response of RLC circuit of Fig. 3.9 when p_1 and p_2 of Eqs. (3.34) and (3.36) are real and unequal.*

stants can be evaluated by substituting these initial conditions into Eq. (3.37). At $t = 0+$ then,

$$i \big|_{t=0+} = A_1 + A_2 \tag{3.41}$$

and

$$\frac{di}{dt}\bigg|_{t=0+} = A_1 p_1 + A_2 p_2 \tag{3.42}$$

Since i and $\dfrac{di}{dt}$ are known at $t = 0+$, Eqs. (3.41) and (3.42) can be solved simultaneously for A_1 and A_2.

Example 3.3

The capacitance in an RLC series circuit is charged to 100 volts. At $t = 0$, switch Sw is closed. Find the current i as a function of time after the switch is closed. First we solve for p_1 and p_2.

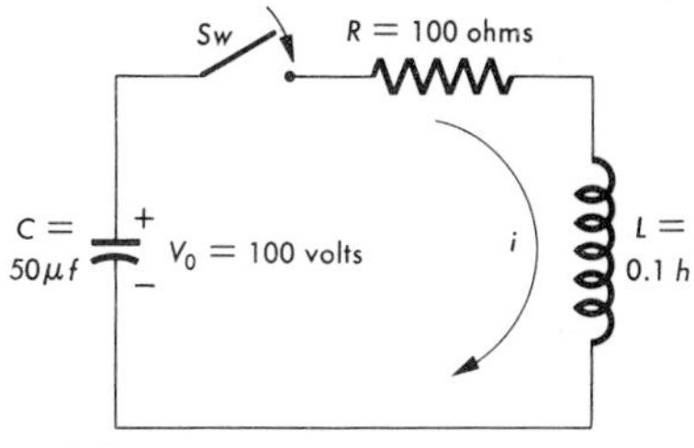

$$p_1 = -\frac{R}{2L} + \sqrt{\frac{R^2}{4L^2} - \frac{1}{LC}}$$

$$= -\frac{100}{0.2} + \sqrt{\frac{10^4}{4 \times 0.01} - \frac{1}{0.1 \times 50 \times 10^{-6}}}$$

$$= -277$$

$$p_2 = -500 - 223 = \cancel{-277}$$

$$: -723$$

FIG. 3.11 *RLC series circuit of Example 3.3.*

Then

$$i = A_1\epsilon^{-277t} + A_2\epsilon^{-723t} \qquad \text{amp}$$

At $t = 0+$, $i = 0$, since the current has not had time to build up in the inductor. Then

$$A_1 + A_2 = 0$$

Also at $t = 0+$, if $i = 0$, $L\,di/dt = V_0$, or $di/dt = V_0/L$. Numerically,

$$\left.\frac{di}{dt}\right|_{t=0+} = \frac{100}{0.1} = 1{,}000 \text{ amp/sec}$$

and

$$\left.\frac{di}{dt}\right|_{t=0+} = -277A_1 - 723A_2 = 1{,}000 \text{ amp/sec}$$

Solving simultaneously,

$$A_1 + A_2 = 0$$

$$-277A_1 - 723A_2 = 1{,}000$$

$$A_1 = +2.23$$

$$A_2 = -2.23$$

and

$$i = 2.23\epsilon^{-277t} - 2.23\epsilon^{-723t} \qquad \text{amp}$$

Notice that the time constant of the first term is $\frac{1}{277} = 0.036$ sec and the time constant of the second term is $\frac{1}{723} = 0.00138$ sec.

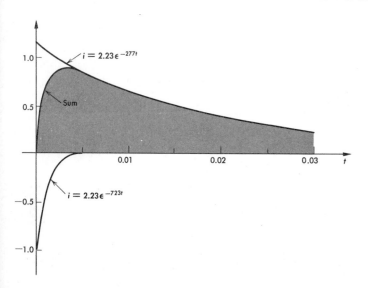

FIG. 3.12 *Solution of i as a function of time for circuit of Fig. 3.11.*

p_1 and p_2 equal. Since Eq. (3.37) is a solution of the second-order differential equation [Eq. (3.28)] for all values of the constants A_1 and A_2, suppose that A_1 and A_2 are chosen such that

$$A_1 = -A_2 = \frac{1}{p_1 - p_2} \tag{3.43}$$

Substituting Eq. (3.43) into Eq. (3.37) yields

$$i = \frac{1}{p_1 - p_2}(\epsilon^{p_1 t} - \epsilon^{p_2 t}) \tag{3.44}$$

Now, if we let $p_2 \to p_1$, Eq. (3.44) becomes an indeterminant of the form 0/0. Differentiating the numerator and the denominator separately with respect to p_2 according to L'Hospital's rule, we have

$$i = \lim_{p_2 \to p_1} \frac{-t\epsilon^{p_2 t}}{-1} \tag{3.45}$$

or

$$i = t\epsilon^{p_1 t} \tag{3.46}$$

Equation (3.46) is justification for assuming that the complete solution of Eq. (3.27) when $p_1 = p_2$ is of the form

$$i = A_1 \epsilon^{p_1 t} + A_2 t \epsilon^{p_1 t} \tag{3.47}$$

where A_1 and A_2 are again the two required arbitrary constants for the second-order equation. As in the preceding case, A_1 and A_2 can be evaluated from a knowledge of the initial conditions.

p_1 and p_2 complex conjugates. If p_1 and p_2 are complex conjugates of the form

$$p_1 = -\alpha + j\omega \tag{3.48}$$

$$p_2 = -\alpha - j\omega \tag{3.49}$$

where $\alpha = R/2L$ and $\omega = \sqrt{1/LC - R^2/4L^2}$, then according to Eq. (3.37) the solution becomes

$$i = A_1 \epsilon^{(-\alpha + j\omega)t} + A_2 \epsilon^{(-\alpha - j\omega)t} \tag{3.50}$$

By Euler's equation

$$\epsilon^{j\omega t} = \cos \omega t + j \sin \omega t \tag{3.51}$$

and, when Eq. (3.51) is substituted into Eq. (3.50), the result can be written

$$i = \epsilon^{-\alpha t}[(A_1 + A_2) \cos \omega t + j(A_1 - A_2) \sin \omega t] \tag{3.52}$$

Now let

$$B_1 = A_1 + A_2$$

and

$$B_2 = j(A_1 - A_2)$$

Then

$$i = \epsilon^{-at}(B_1 \cos \omega t + B_2 \sin \omega t) \qquad (3.53)$$

which can be written

$$i = \epsilon^{-at} \sqrt{B_1{}^2 + B_2{}^2} \sin(\omega t + \theta) = Be^{-at} \sin(\omega_d t + \theta) \qquad (3.54)$$

where

$$\theta = \tan^{-1} \frac{B_1}{B_2} \qquad (3.55)$$

The nature of the response represented by Eq. (3.54) is shown in Fig. 3.13. In (a), the exponential term is plotted, in (b) the

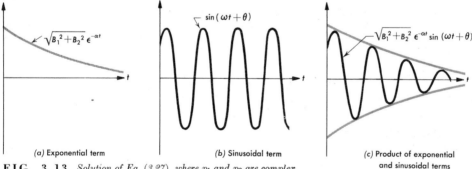

(a) Exponential term

(b) Sinusoidal term

(c) Product of exponential and sinusoidal terms

FIG. 3.13 *Solution of Eq. (3.27), where p_1 and p_2 are complex.*

sinusoidal term is plotted, and in (c) is seen the product of the two. The damped sine wave of Fig. 3.13c eventually decays to zero. Notice that, if R is zero, α is also zero and the sinusoid does not decay. Likewise, if R is relatively large, the sinusoid decays very rapidly.

Let us next investigate Eq. (3.28) for the purpose of determining the nature of the solution as a function of the magnitude of R in the equation. We have just seen how the solution is a damped sinusoid for the special case where p_1 and p_2 are complex conjugates. A circuit is said to be "underdamped" if this form of the solution exists. When R is increased to such a value that p_1 is equal to p_2, the circuit is said to be "critically damped." For large values of R, when the solution is the sum of two decaying exponential terms, the circuit is said to be "overdamped."

A second-order linear differential equation with constant coefficients such as Eq. (3.28) is often written in the general form

$$\frac{d^2x}{dt^2} + 2\omega_n\zeta\frac{dx}{dt} + \omega_n{}^2x = 0 \tag{3.56}$$

where ω_n and ζ are constants. The solution of Eq. (3.56) takes the general form of Eq. (3.54) and can be written

$$i = A\epsilon^{-\omega_n\zeta t}\sin(\omega_n\sqrt{1-\zeta^2}\,t + \theta) \tag{3.57}$$

where A and θ are arbitrary constants. Notice that the "natural frequency" of the sine term in Eq. (3.57) is

$$\omega = \omega_n\sqrt{1-\zeta^2} \qquad \text{radians/sec} \tag{3.58}$$

and the exponent of ϵ in the solution of Eq. (3.57) is one half the coefficient of the first derivative (the damping term). If the co-efficient of the first-order term in Eq. (3.56) is zero, then ζ must be zero and $\omega = \omega_n$. We call ω_n the "undamped natural frequency" of the system represented by Eq. (3.56). If ζ is greater than zero, the natural frequency as represented by Eq. (3.58) is less than ω_n. Notice that the time constant of the exponential term can be expressed as

$$\tau = \frac{1}{\omega_n\zeta} \qquad \text{sec} \tag{3.59}$$

and ζ is often referred to as the "damping ratio." Equation (3.59) shows that the time constant of the response is inversely proportional to ζ.

3.7 GEOMETRICAL INTERPRETATION OF ROOTS OF CHARACTERISTIC EQUATION

The characteristic equation of the second-order system represented by Eq. (3.28) is Eq. (3.31),

$$p^2 + \frac{R}{L}p + \frac{1}{LC} = 0$$

which has roots [Eq. (3.32)]

$$p = -\frac{R}{2L} \pm \sqrt{\frac{R^2}{4L^2} - \frac{1}{LC}}$$

Suppose that L and C have constant values but that R is adjustable. At $R = 0$, $p = \pm j/\sqrt{LC}$ and can be represented in the complex plane on the imaginary axis as shown in Fig. 3.14a. Next, let

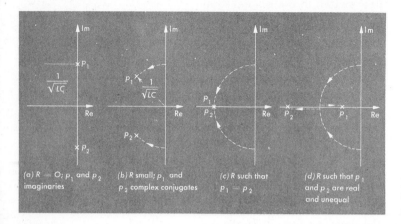

(a) $R = 0$; p_1 and p_2 imaginaries

(b) R small; p_1 and p_2 complex conjugates

(c) R such that $p_1 = p_2$

(d) R such that p_1 and p_2 are real and unequal

FIG. 3.14 *Roots of the characteristic equation of an RLC series circuit as a function of R.*

R increase, making the exponential term in the solution [Eq. (3.54)] decay with time. The real part of p_1 and p_2, which we have called $-\alpha$ in Eqs. (3.48) and (3.49), increases in the negative direction as R increases. The imaginary part ω decreases as R increases. Notice that p_1 and p_2 follow a circular path of radius r as R increases, where

$$r = \sqrt{\left(-\frac{R}{2L}\right)^2 + \left(\frac{1}{LC} - \frac{R^2}{4L^2}\right)}$$

or

$$r = \frac{1}{\sqrt{LC}} \tag{3.60}$$

as shown in Fig. 3.14b. Then letting R increase until

$$\frac{1}{LC} - \frac{R^2}{4L^2} = 0$$

$p_1 = p_2$, and both roots occur on the real axis at $-1/\sqrt{LC}$. As R increases further [see Eq. (3.34)],

$$p_1 = -\frac{R}{2L} + \sqrt{\frac{R^2}{4L^2} - \frac{1}{LC}}$$

and [see Eq. (3.36)]

$$p_2 = -\frac{R}{2L} - \sqrt{\frac{R^2}{4L^2} - \frac{1}{LC}}$$

Both p_1 and p_2 are now real and can be shown on the real axis, p_1 approaching zero and p_2 becoming more negative as R increases without bound.

One can tell at a glance from a plot of the roots of the characteristic equation the nature of the natural response of the system. In Fig. 3.14a, the roots are on the imaginary axis, response is sinusoidal, and there is no damping since the roots lie on the imaginary axis. In Fig. 3.14b, the roots are complex, and the response is a damped sinusoid. In Fig. 3.14c, $p_1 = p_2$, and we have critical damping; in Fig. 3.14d, the circuit is overdamped, as the roots are real and unequal.

3.8 IMPEDANCE

The response of a circuit to an exciting function of exponential form has great significance in electric-circuit analysis. Assume now that the current in an electric circuit is of the form

$$i = I\epsilon^{pt} \tag{3.61}$$

The voltage between the terminals of the electric circuit can be found from the differential equation. For instance, if the RL circuit of Fig. 3.1 is excited by a current of Eq. (3.61), substituting Eq. (3.61) into the circuit differential equation [Eq. (3.2)]

$$L\frac{di}{dt} + Ri = e$$

gives

$$(Lp + R)I\epsilon^{pt} = e \tag{3.62}$$

where

$$\frac{e}{i} = Lp + R \qquad \text{ohms} \tag{3.63}$$

The ratio of voltage to current given by Eq. (3.63) is known as the "impedance" of the circuit, written $Z(p)$. Electric impedance has somewhat the characteristics of resistance in that it is a measure of the extent to which the circuit impedes the flow of current. Impedance has the same units as resistance, namely, ohms or volts per ampere.

In the RC circuit of Fig. 3.2, if i is of the exponential form of Eq. (3.61), substituting Eq. (3.61) into the circuit integral equation

$$Ri + \frac{1}{C}\int i\, dt = e \tag{3.64}$$

gives

$$\left(R + \frac{1}{Cp}\right) I\epsilon^{pt} = e \tag{3.65}$$

The impedance of the RC series circuit is given by

$$Z(p) = \frac{e}{i} = R + \frac{1}{Cp} \qquad \text{ohms} \tag{3.66}$$

A series RLC circuit has a circuit differential equation of

$$L\frac{di}{dt} + Ri + \frac{1}{C}\int i\, dt = e \tag{3.67}$$

If the current is constrained to be of exponential form, substituting Eq. (3.61) into Eq. (3.67) gives

$$\left(Lp + R + \frac{1}{Cp}\right) I\epsilon^{pt} = e \tag{3.68}$$

where the circuit impedance is

$$Z(p) = Lp + R + \frac{1}{Cp} \tag{3.69}$$

From the impedance equations given by Eqs. (3.63), (3.66), and (3.68) it is apparent that the circuit impedance can be written directly from the characteristic equation of the circuit. Indeed, the characteristic equation is obtained in the same way by substituting the exponential current into the integrodifferential equation. Admittance, given the symbol Y, is the reciprocal of impedance and is often a convenient concept in parallel circuits. Some circuits and their impedances and admittances are shown in Fig. 3.15. Admittance of a parallel combination of circuit elements is found by assuming that the voltage across the parallel elements is of

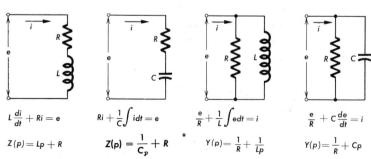

$$L\frac{di}{dt} + Ri = e$$
$$Z(p) = Lp + R$$

$$Ri + \frac{1}{C}\int i\, dt = e$$
$$Z(p) = \frac{1}{C_p} + R$$

$$\frac{e}{R} + \frac{1}{L}\int e\, dt = i$$
$$Y(p) = \frac{1}{R} + \frac{1}{Lp}$$

$$\frac{e}{R} + C\frac{de}{dt} = i$$
$$Y(p) = \frac{1}{R} + Cp$$

FIG. 3.15 *Impedance and admittance of some RC and RL circuits.*

exponential form, or

$$e = E\epsilon^{pt} \tag{3.70}$$

The natural response of a circuit is found from the energy stored in the circuit at some initial time. The natural response of a series circuit was found when the exciting voltage was zero but the current was of exponential form. Since current flows when no external voltage is applied, the impedance must be zero. This is a convenient way to find the natural response: Set the impedance to zero, and solve for p. In the RL series circuit with no external excitation, the impedance is given by

$$Z(p) = Lp + R = 0 \tag{3.71}$$

from which

$$p = -\frac{R}{L} \tag{3.72}$$

In an RLC series circuit, with no external excitation, setting the impedance equal to zero gives

$$Lp + R + \frac{1}{Cp} = 0 \tag{3.73}$$

from which

$$p = -\frac{R}{2L} \pm \sqrt{\frac{R^2}{4L^2} - \frac{1}{LC}} \tag{3.74}$$

But notice that the values of p found in Eqs. (3.72) and (3.74) are identical to the values of p shown in Eqs. (3.17) and (3.32).

Example 3.4

An automobile suspension system can be represented approximately for one wheel by the mass-spring-dashpot system shown in Fig. 3.16, where the dashpot is the shock absorber, the mass is one-fourth the mass of the car, and the spring is one of the rear leaf springs of the car. The mechanical impedance is found from the system differential equation

$$M\frac{dv}{dt} + Bv + K\int v\,dt = 0$$

where M is the mass, B is the friction constant, and K is the spring constant. Assume that the velocity is of the exponential form

$$v = V\epsilon^{pt}$$

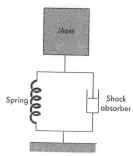

FIG. 3.16 *The suspension system of one wheel of a car.*

and substitute it into the differential equation. Then

$$\left(Mp + B + \frac{K}{p} \right) V \epsilon^{pt} = 0$$

and the mechanical impedance

$$Z(p) = Mp + B + \frac{K}{p} = 0$$

Solving for p gives

$$p = -\frac{B}{2M} \pm \sqrt{\frac{B^2}{4M^2} - \frac{K}{M}}$$

The concept of impedance is extensively used in the study of steady-state solutions discussed in the next chapter. The use of the impedance concept in the study of natural response is a convenient way to find the exponents of the natural-response terms.

SUMMARY

Finding the natural response of a physical system involves three steps: (1) the formulation of the differential equation or equations by using Kirchhoff's laws for electric circuits or by adding the forces or torques to zero in a mechanical system; (2) solving the homogeneous differential equation, the solution containing arbitrary constants; (3) the evaluation of the arbitrary constants from a knowledge of the initial conditions of the system.

1. By Kirchhoff's voltage law, the sum of the voltages around any closed loop in the circuit at any instant is zero. The homogeneous form of the circuit equation for an RL series circuit is [Eq. (3.13)]

$$L\frac{di}{dt} + Ri = 0$$

and for an RC circuit is [Eq. (3.26)]

$$Ri + \frac{1}{C}\int_0^t i\, dt - V_0 = 0$$

where V_0 is the initial charge on the capacitor. When Eq. (3.26) is differentiated with respect to t, it becomes the differential equation

$$R\frac{di}{dt} + \frac{1}{C}i = 0$$

The second-order homogeneous equation for an RLC series circuit is obtained by differentiating the integrodifferential equation of the circuit, which results in [Eq. (3.28)]

$$L\frac{d^2i}{dt^2} + R\frac{di}{dt} + \frac{1}{C}i = 0$$

A second-order differential equation is often written in the general form [Eq. (3.56)]

$$\frac{d^2x}{dt^2} + 2\omega_n\varsigma\frac{dx}{dt} + \omega_n{}^2x = 0$$

where x is now the dependent variable.

2. The natural response of the series circuit is obtained by assuming a solution of the form [Eq. (3.14)]

$$i = A\epsilon^{pt}$$

where p is the root of the characteristic equation. Substituting Eq. (3.14) into the differential equation [Eq. (3.28)] results in Eq. (3.30),

$$\left(Lp^2 + Rp + \frac{1}{C}\right)A\epsilon^{pt} = 0$$

from which the characteristic equation (3.31)

$$Lp^2 + Rp + \frac{1}{C} = 0$$

is obtained. The roots of the characteristic equation are found, and the final form of the natural response can then be obtained from Table 3.1.

TABLE 3.1

$p^2 + 2\omega_n\varsigma p + \omega_n{}^2$	Solution of the form	Roots of the characteristic equation
p_1, p_2 real and unequal	$x = A_1\epsilon^{p_1t} + A_2\epsilon^{p_2t}$	$\varsigma > 1$: $p_1 = -\omega_n\varsigma + \omega_n\sqrt{\varsigma^2 - 1}$ $p_2 = -\omega_n\varsigma - \omega_n\sqrt{\varsigma^2 - 1}$
$p_1 = p_2$	$x = A_1\epsilon^{p_1t} + A_2t\epsilon^{p_1t}$	$\varsigma = 1$: $p_1 = -\omega_n\varsigma$ $p_2 = -\omega_n\varsigma$
$p_1 = -\alpha + j\omega_d$ $p_2 = -\alpha - j\omega_d$	$x = \epsilon^{-\alpha t}(B_1 \cos \omega t + B_2 \sin \omega t)$ $x = A\epsilon^{-\alpha t} \sin(\omega t + \theta)$ $\theta = \tan^{-1}\frac{B_1}{B_2}$ $A = \sqrt{B_1{}^2 + B_2{}^2}$	$\varsigma < 1$: $p = -\alpha \pm j\omega_d$ $p = -\omega_n\varsigma \pm j\omega_n\sqrt{1 - \varsigma^2}$

3. The arbitrary constants (one for a first-order system, two for a second-order system) are evaluated from a knowledge of the initial conditions of the problem. A first-order equation with one arbitrary constant requires the initial value of the dependent variable to be substituted, together with $t = 0$, into the solution to solve for the arbitrary constant. For a second-order equation, substitute the initial value of the dependent variable and $t = 0$ into the solution from Table 3.1; this results in one equation in two arbitrary constants. Then differentiate the solution with respect to time, set $t = 0$, and substitute the initial value of di/dt into the differentiated solution. This gives the second independent equation in the two arbitrary constants; the two equations can now be solved simultaneously for the constants.

Electric impedance is defined as the ratio of applied voltage to current when the current is an exponential function as in Eq. (3.61),

$$i = I\epsilon^{pt}$$

Thus the impedance of an inductor is Lp, a resistor is R, and a capacitor is $1/Cp$. The natural response of a circuit can be found by letting $Z(p) = 0$ and solving for the values of p which satisfy $Z(p) = 0$.

FURTHER READING

For further study of mechanical vibrations and electric oscillations see R. L. Sutherland, *Engineering Systems Analysis* (Addison-Wesley Publishing Company, Reading, Mass., 1958), chaps. 2 and 3. M. E. Van Valkenburg, *Network Analysis* (Prentice-Hall, Inc., Englewood Cliffs, N.J., 1955), has an excellent chapter on initial conditions in networks (chap. 5) as well as chapters on first- and second-order differential equations (chaps. 4 and 6) and network equations (chap. 3). The natural response of simple circuits is discussed in H. H. Skilling, *Electrical Engineering Circuits* (John Wiley & Sons, Inc., New York, 1957), pp. 34ff. and chap. 16, and in chaps. 7 and 9 of Egon Brenner and Mansour Javid, *Analysis of Electric Circuits* (McGraw-Hill Book Company, Inc., New York, 1959).

PROBLEMS

✓ **3.1** In the figure a capacitor is charged to V_0; at time $t = 0$, switch Sw is thrown from position A to position B. Derive an expression for charge q on the capacitor as a function of time after the switch is thrown.

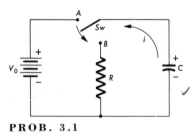

PROB. 3.1

3.2 In the figure capacitor C_1 is charged to a potential V_0. At $t = 0$, switch Sw is closed. Derive an expression for current i as a function of time. The initial charge on C_2 is zero.

3.3 An electric motor has an armature with a moment of inertia J. It is running at no load at an angular velocity ω_0. At $t = 0$ it is disconnected from the line and allowed to coast to rest. Assume that only the inertia force $J\,d\omega/dt$ and viscous friction force $B\omega$ proportional to angular velocity ω are present. Derive the expression for angular velocity as a function of time. Then integrate to find the number of radians the machine turns as a function of time after $t = 0$.

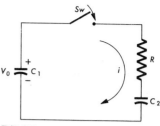

PROB. 3.2

3.4 In the figure an RC series circuit is connected to a constant voltage E at $t = 0$. Prior to this time there is no charge on the capacitor. Write an integral equation for the circuit using Kirchhoff's voltage law. Differentiate to find the natural response i as a function of t after the switch is closed.

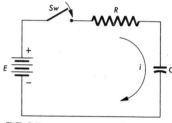

PROB. 3.4

3.5 In the figure an RLC series circuit is connected to a battery of voltage $E = 100$ volts at $t = 0$. The initial charge on C is zero. At $t = 0+$, the instant after the switch is closed, find i, di/dt, and d^2i/dt^2, if $R = 100$, $L = 0.01$, and $C = 10^{-8}f$.

3.6 Radioactive decay takes place in such a way that the number of disintegrations occurring per unit time is proportional to the total number of radioactive atoms present. The number dN of atoms disintegrating in a time interval dt is proportional to N, the number of radioactive atoms present, or $\dfrac{dN}{dt} = -\lambda N$, which can be written $\dfrac{dN}{dt} + \lambda N = 0$, where λ is the constant of proportionality, known as the "decay constant."

Assume that at $t = 0$, $N_0 = 5 \times 10^{18}$ radioactive atoms, and that $\lambda = 1.55 \times 10^{-5}$. Find the "half-life," or the time it takes for one-half of the radioactive atoms to disintegrate. Compare the half-life to the time constant of the equation.

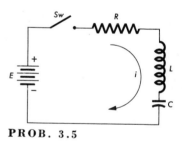

PROB. 3.5

3.7 An electric motor, running without load at an angular velocity $\omega_0 = 5.40 \times 10^3$ radians/sec, is suddenly disconnected from the line. Its moment of inertia is J, and its viscous friction constant is B. As it slows down, the sum of the torques is $J\dfrac{d\omega}{dt} + B\omega = 0$, where ω is the angular velocity. (a) Solve for ω as a function of time by separation of variables. (b) Solve for ω as a function of time by assuming an exponential solution. Evaluate the arbitrary constant.

3.8 A torsional system consisting of a flywheel of moment of inertia J, a torsional shaft of spring constant K, and a viscous-friction damper of friction constant B is shown in the figure. At $t = 0$, the flywheel is

Problems **93**

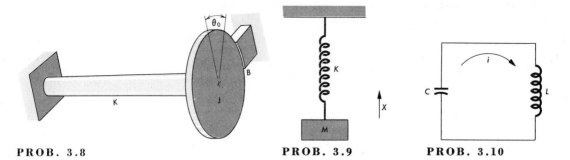

PROB. 3.8   PROB. 3.9   PROB. 3.10

twisted through an angle θ_0 radians and released. Find the natural response of θ as a function of time for the differential equation

$$J \frac{d^2\theta}{dt^2} + B \frac{d\theta}{dt} + K\theta = 0$$

which sums the torques to zero.

3.9 In the figure a mass bobs up and down on the end of a spring. There is no friction to dissipate energy. Write the differential equation of the system by making the sum of the kinetic and potential energy constant and the time derivative of their sum zero.

3.10 An LC circuit is in oscillation as shown in the illustration. There is no resistance to dissipate energy. Write the circuit differential equation by making the sum of the energy stored in L and C a constant and making their time derivative zero.

3.11 The exponential current pulse shown in the figure charges a 100-μf capacitor. (a) What is the final charge on the capacitor in volts? (b) After 1 sec, to what voltage has the capacitor been charged?

3.12 In the illustration a voltage pulse generator consists of an RC circuit. The capacitor is charged to 100 volts and then discharged through the resistor. The output voltage is a decaying exponential pulse which has fallen to 10 volts after 0.0001 sec. Available capacitors are 0.01 μf,

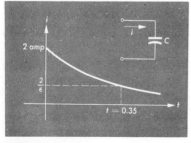

PROB. 3.11

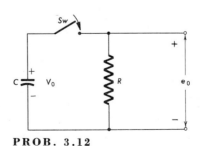

PROB. 3.12

1 μf, and 100 μf. Find three values of R that satisfy time-constant requirements when used with each of the three values of C.

3.13 An LC circuit, shown in the illustration, is excited by an initial charge on the capacitor. At $t = 0$ the switch is closed. Find: (a) the natural frequency of oscillation; (b) the maximum current; (c) the maximum voltage across the inductor.

3.14 In the figure a charged capacitor C is discharged through a parallel combination of R and L. Using Kirchhoff's current law, write a differential equation for voltage v as the dependent variable. Then show an inequality that must be satisfied if the solution of the differential equation (voltage v as a function of time) is a damped sinusoid.

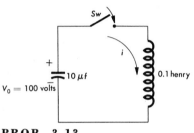

PROB. 3.13

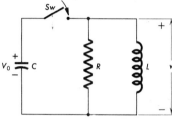

PROB. 3.14

3.15 Find the mechanical impedance for the torsional system of Prob. 3.8.

3.16 Find the electric impedance $Z(p)$ of the series circuits of: (a) Prob. 3.12; (b) Prob. 3.13.

3.17 Find the parallel admittance $Y(p)$ for a parallel RLC circuit.

3.18 The natural response of a second-order system is of the form given in Table 3.1, where $p_1 = -1$ and $p_2 = -10$, $A_1 = 5$ and $A_2 = -5$. Plot x as a function of time. What is the maximum value of x?

3.19 The natural response of a second-order system is given in Table 3.1, where $p_1 = -1 + j10$ and $p_2 = -1 - j10$, $A = 5$, and $\theta = 25°$. Plot x as a function of time. What is the maximum value of x?

3.20 The natural response of a second-order system is given in Table 3.1, where $p_1 = p_2 = -2$, $A_1 = 10$, and $A_2 = -10$. Plot x as a function of time. What is the maximum value of x? At what time t does it occur?

4

SERIES ELECTRIC CIRCUITS
IN THE STEADY STATE

4.1 INTRODUCTION

A series circuit is one in which several circuit elements, including electric-energy sources, are connected in such a way that the same current flows through each element. Each circuit requires at least one electric-energy source and one or more combinations of resistance, inductance, and capacitance. The energy source can be an energy-storage element such as an inductor or a capacitor, or it can be a separate voltage or current generator which supplies electric energy to the passive circuit elements.

The natural response of the circuit to energy stored within the circuit was explained in Chap. 3, and it was shown that the natural response decays with time, if there is resistance in the circuit, and eventually approaches zero. If an energy source supplies an exciting voltage or current at a periodic rate or at a constant rate after the natural response has vanished, the response of the circuit to the exciting function is known as the "steady-state" or "forced" response.

A series circuit is shown in Fig. 4.1, with i common to all the circuit elements. When an electric circuit is established, there is one final action which completes the circuit so that current can flow; often this is the act of closing a switch, such as Sw in Fig. 4.1. When the switch is open, it represents an infinite resistance and no

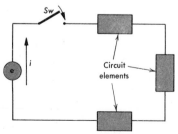

FIG. 4.1 *A series circuit characterized by the current i being common to all circuit elements.*

current can flow. After the switch is closed, the circuit is completed and the transient current consisting of the natural response and the steady-state or forced response occurs. The steady-state response remains after the natural response has vanished. In this chapter we study the steady-state response separate from the natural response by assuming that the switch has been closed a long time so that the switching transient has vanished. In the next chapter we shall consider the simultaneous occurrence of the steady-state response and the natural response. In a series circuit the response of the circuit excited by a voltage generator is the circuit current.

4.2 INDUCTIVE AND CAPACITIVE REACTANCE

Impedance was defined in Chap. 3 as the ratio of the voltage to the current at the circuit terminals when the current is constrained to the exponential function

$$i = I\epsilon^{pt} \tag{4.1}$$

When the exponential current of Eq. (4.1) is substituted into any voltage-current relationship for linear-circuit elements, the terminal voltage is also an exponential function, or

$$e = E\epsilon^{pt} \tag{4.2}$$

For example, an RLC series circuit whose integrodifferential equation is

$$L\frac{di}{dt} + Ri + \frac{1}{C}\int i\, dt = E\epsilon^{pt} \tag{4.3}$$

has an exponential exciting current, as can be seen by substituting Eq. (4.1) into Eq. (4.3). Thus

$$\left(Lp + R + \frac{1}{Cp}\right)I\epsilon^{pt} = E\epsilon^{pt} \tag{4.4}$$

where as in Eqs. (4.1) and (4.2)

$$e = E\epsilon^{pt} \quad \text{and} \quad i = I\epsilon^{pt}$$

and

$$E = \left(Lp + R + \frac{1}{Cp}\right)I \tag{4.5}$$

The circuit impedance is given by

$$Z(p) = \frac{E\epsilon^{pt}}{I\epsilon^{pt}} = Lp + R + \frac{1}{Cp} \qquad (4.6)$$

Often the current through a circuit is alternating, or sinusoidal, in form. It was shown in Chap. 2 that, whenever the current through a circuit element is sinusoidal, the voltage across the element is also sinusoidal. Furthermore, the sinusoid is closely related to the exponential function, and the relationship is shown by

$$\epsilon^{j\omega t} = \cos \omega t + j \sin \omega t \qquad (4.7)$$

a variation of Eq. (2.33) for $\omega t = \theta$. According to Eq. (4.7), $\cos \omega t$ is the real part of $\epsilon^{j\omega t}$, and $\sin \omega t$ is the imaginary part of $\epsilon^{j\omega t}$. Since a sinusoid can be defined in terms of $\epsilon^{j\omega t}$, impedance to a sinusoidal current can be expressed by letting $p = j\omega$. The impedance of the RLC series circuit described by Eq. (4.3) whose current is constrained to be a sinusoid can be expressed from Eq. (4.6) by

$$Z(j\omega) = j\omega L + R + \frac{1}{j\omega C} = R + j\left(\omega L - \frac{1}{\omega C}\right) \qquad (4.8)$$

Thus the impedance concept can be extended to sinusoidal voltages and currents, where it has a multitude of applications.

The impedance concept can also be developed directly for phasor voltages and currents. Define impedance for alternating current as the ratio of the phasor voltage to the phasor current when the voltage and current are expressed in exponential form. Since the voltage across any element of resistance, inductance, or capacitance carrying a sinusoidal current is also a sinusoid, the a-c impedance, designated $Z(j\omega)$, is the ratio of a voltage phasor to a current phasor.

Consider now an inductor of L henrys whose current is of the form

$$i = I_m \sin \omega t \qquad \text{amp} \qquad (4.9)$$

The voltage between the inductor terminals is

$$e = L\frac{di}{dt} = \omega L I_m \cos \omega t = \omega L I_m \sin\left(\omega t + \frac{\pi}{2}\right) \qquad (4.10)$$

where the inductor voltage is $\pi/2$ radians, or 90°, ahead of the current. The ratio of voltage to current can be written

$$\mathbf{Z} = \frac{\mathbf{E}}{\mathbf{I}} = \frac{\omega L I_m \epsilon^{j90°}}{I_m \epsilon^{j0°}} \qquad (4.11)$$

where $E_m = \omega L I_m$. The coefficient ωL in Eq. (4.11) is known as "inductive reactance" and given the symbol X_L. Inductive reactance can also be expressed by the ratio of the maximum values of voltage and current, or

$$X_L = \frac{E_m}{I_m} = \omega L \qquad (4.12)$$

The phasors $\mathbf{E}$ and $\mathbf{I}$ in Eq. (4.11) are shown in Fig. 4.2a. First,

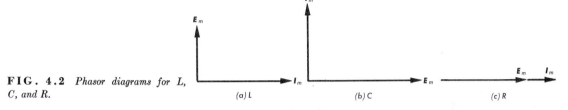

FIG. 4.2 *Phasor diagrams for L, C, and R.*

        (a) L   (b) C   (c) R

the phasor voltage can be expressed as a function of phasor current by

$$\mathbf{E}_m = j\omega L \mathbf{I}_m \qquad (4.13)$$

and the complex impedance is given by

$$\mathbf{Z} = \frac{\mathbf{E}}{\mathbf{I}} = j\omega L \qquad \text{ohms} \qquad (4.14)$$

Thus the impedance of the inductor is imaginary.

Now consider a capacitor of C farads excited by a terminal voltage

$$e = E_m \sin \omega t \qquad (4.15)$$

The capacitor current leads the terminal voltage by 90°, as seen by the voltage-current relationship for the capacitor,

$$i = C \frac{de}{dt} = \omega C E_m \cos \omega t = \omega C E_m \sin (\omega t + \pi/2) \qquad (4.16)$$

Then the capacitor impedance is given by

$$\mathbf{Z} = \frac{\mathbf{E}}{\mathbf{I}} = \frac{E_m \epsilon^{j0°}}{\omega C E_m \epsilon^{j90°}} \qquad (4.17)$$

where the impedance magnitude is $1/\omega C$. "Capacitive reactance," whose symbol is X_C, is the name given to the impedance magnitude when the current leads the voltage by 90°. Then

$$X_C = \frac{E_m}{I_m} = \frac{1}{\omega C} \qquad \text{ohms} \qquad (4.18)$$

4.2 *Inductive and Capacitive Reactance*   99

The capacitor voltage and current are represented by phasors in Fig. 4.2b, and the current is shown leading the voltage phasor by 90°. From the phasor diagram, the current phasor is seen to be

$$\mathbf{I}_m = j\omega C \mathbf{E}_m \tag{4.19}$$

and the complex impedance is given by

$$\mathbf{Z} = \frac{\mathbf{E}}{\mathbf{I}} = \frac{-j}{\omega C} \tag{4.20}$$

Notice that the complex-impedance equations for the inductor and for the capacitor, as given by Eqs. (4.14) and (4.20), show that the inductor voltage leads the inductor current by 90° and the capacitor voltage lags the capacitor current by 90°. The phase angle between voltage and current is relative, and it is also correct to say that the inductor current lags the inductor voltage and the capacitor current leads the capacitor voltage.

The impedance of a resistor to an alternating current is the resistance R. Since voltage is proportional to current in a resistor and impedance is the ratio of voltage to current, for a resistor excited by $i = I_m \sin \omega t$,

$$\mathbf{Z} = R \tag{4.21}$$

Thus voltage and current are exactly in phase in a resistor excited by an alternating current, as shown in Fig. 4.2c.

Another common steady-state exciting function is direct voltage or direct current, expressible by Eqs. (4.1) and (4.2) when $p = 0$. The impedance of the circuit elements to direct current can be found from the impedance of each element by letting $p = 0$. Thus from Eq. (4.1) the exciting current $i = I$, from which the voltage and then the impedance can be found. In Table 4.1 the impedances of the circuit elements are summarized. Notice that, when $p = 0$, the resistor still has impedance R ohms but the inductor has zero impedance and the capacitor has infinite impedance.

TABLE 4.1 *Summary of the Impedances of the Circuit Elements* *

	$Z(p)$	$Z(j\omega)$	$Z(0)$
Resistor	R	R	R
Inductor	Lp	$j\omega L$	0
Capacitor	$\dfrac{1}{Cp}$	$\dfrac{-j}{\omega C}$	∞

* $Z(j\omega)$ is a-c impedance, and $Z(0)$ is d-c impedance.

4.3 COMPLEX IMPEDANCE
OF ELEMENTS IN SERIES

A series combination of resistance and inductance is connected to a generator of the arbitrary voltage e, as shown in Fig. 4.3a. The circuit differential equation is written following Kirchhoff's laws as

$$L\frac{di}{dt} + Ri = e \qquad (4.22)$$

where i and e are instantaneous values of current and voltage, respectively. We consider now the steady-state, or forced, response of the circuit when the exciting voltage is a sinusoid and when the exciting voltage is a constant.

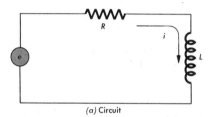

FIG. 4.3 *RL series circuit described by Eq. (4.22).*

(a) Circuit

(b) Phasor diagram

First, the impedance of the circuit is written

$$Z(p) = R + Lp \qquad (4.23)$$

It is already apparent from Eq. (4.6) that the individual impedances of elements in series can be added to find the total impedance of the circuit. The sinusoidal steady-state impedance is found by replacing p with $j\omega$, or

$$Z(j\omega) = R + j\omega L = \mathbf{Z} \qquad (4.24)$$

Now, if the circuit current can be represented by the sinusoid

$$i = I_m \sin \omega t$$

[see Eq. (4.9)], the current phasor can be represented in Fig. 4.3b along the real axis as the reference phasor. Then $\mathbf{I} = I$, and

$$\mathbf{E} = \mathbf{IZ} = RI + j\omega LI \qquad (4.25)$$

as shown in the phasor diagram. The magnitude of the complex impedance of Eq. (4.24) is

$$Z = \sqrt{R^2 + (\omega L)^2} \qquad (4.26)$$

The angle of Z is $\tan^{-1}\dfrac{\omega L}{R}$

and therefore the magnitude of the voltage in Eq. (4.25) can be written

$$E = I\sqrt{R^2 + (\omega L)^2} \tag{4.27}$$

The phase angle θ of the current with respect to the terminal voltage is

$$\theta = -\tan^{-1}\frac{\omega L}{R} \tag{4.28}$$

The voltage across the resistor is RI, in phase with the current, and the voltage across the inductor is $j\omega LI$, leading the current by 90°. Notice that the magnitude of the terminal voltage E is proportional to the impedance magnitude and can be found directly from Eqs. (4.27) and (4.26). But the most important lesson of this example is shown in Eq. (4.25), where the phasor sum (not the algebraic sum) of the voltage across R and the voltage across L is the terminal voltage supplied by the generator.

If the voltage generator of Fig. 4.3a is a direct-voltage source, the current in the steady state is constant, too. Substituting $p = 0$ into Eq. (4.23), we see that the circuit impedance to direct current is $Z(0) = R$ and $\mathbf{E} = \mathbf{I}R$, where E is the constant-voltage source and I is the constant current. Again, the impedance of the inductor to direct current is zero.

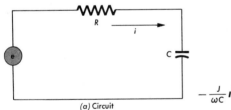

(a) Circuit

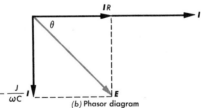

(b) Phasor diagram

FIG. 4.4 *RC series circuit described by Eq. (4.29).*

An RC series circuit can be studied in much the same way that the RL circuit has been studied. An RC series circuit is shown in Fig. 4.4a, and the circuit equation is

$$Ri + \frac{1}{C}\int i\, dt = e \tag{4.29}$$

where the initial charge on the capacitor V_0/C has vanished, producing the natural response. The impedance of the circuit is

$$Z(p) = R + \frac{1}{Cp} \tag{4.30}$$

and the impedance in the sinusoidal steady state is

$$Z(j\omega) = R + \frac{1}{j\omega C} = R - \frac{j}{\omega C} = \mathbf{Z} \qquad (4.31)$$

If the circuit current can again be constrained to the sinusoid

$$i = I_m \sin \omega t$$

[see Eq. (4.9)], the circuit current can be represented by the phasor along the real axis in Fig. 4.4b. The phasor current $\mathbf{I} = I$, and

$$\mathbf{E} = \mathbf{I}\mathbf{Z} = RI - \frac{j}{\omega C} I \qquad (4.32)$$

as shown in the phasor diagram. The magnitude of the complex impedance is

$$Z = \sqrt{R^2 + \left(\frac{1}{\omega C}\right)^2} \qquad (4.33)$$

and the magnitude of the voltage can therefore be written

$$E = I \sqrt{R^2 + \left(\frac{1}{\omega C}\right)^2}$$

The phase angle θ is

$$\theta = \tan^{-1} \frac{1/\omega C}{R} \qquad (4.34)$$

measured with respect to the voltage phasor. Notice that the voltage supplied from the generator is the phasor sum of the resistor voltage and the capacitor voltage, and the current leads the terminal voltage by the phase angle θ.

The d-c steady-state impedance of the series RC circuit of Fig. 4.4a is

$$Z(0) = R - \frac{j}{0} = \infty$$

Thus no steady-state current flows when a constant voltage is applied. The capacitor charges to the constant exciting voltage during its natural response, after which current no longer flows. Again, the impedance of the capacitor to direct current is infinite.

The RLC series-circuit impedance was expressed by Eq. (4.6) as

$$Z(p) = Lp + R + \frac{1}{Cp}$$

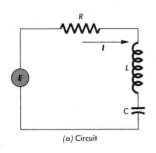

(a) Circuit

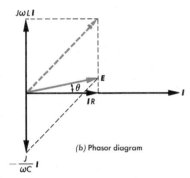

(b) Phasor diagram

FIG. 4.5 *Voltage-current relationships in the RLC series circuit.*

In the sinusoidal steady state, the complex impedance can be written as in Eq. (4.8),

$$Z(j\omega) = R + j\left(\omega L - \frac{1}{\omega C}\right)$$

The phasor diagram is shown in Fig. 4.5b, where

$$\mathbf{E} = R\mathbf{I} + j\omega L\mathbf{I} - \frac{j}{\omega C}\mathbf{I} \tag{4.35}$$

Once again the current $\mathbf{I}$ is shown as the reference phasor, and the terminal voltage $\mathbf{E}$ is the phasor sum of the voltages across the resistor, the inductor, and the capacitor. The phase angle θ is the angle between the terminal voltage $\mathbf{E}$ and the current $\mathbf{I}$, measured with respect to $\mathbf{E}$. Then

$$\theta = -\tan^{-1}\frac{\omega L - 1/\omega C}{R} \tag{4.36}$$

The impedance magnitude is

$$Z = \sqrt{R^2 + \left(\omega L - \frac{1}{\omega C}\right)^2} \tag{4.37}$$

Notice that the terminal voltage in the RLC series circuit can either lead or lag the current, depending upon whether or not ωL is greater than $1/\omega C$.

The d-c impedance of the RLC series circuit is infinite, since the impedance of the capacitor is infinite.

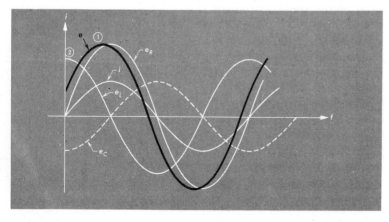

FIG. 4.6 *Current and voltages of an RLC series circuit of Fig. 4.5a plotted as functions of time.*

Example 4.1

A 50-ohm resistor and a 0.1-henry inductor are connected in series to a 110-volt 60-cycles/sec voltage source. Find the current and the phase angle between current and the applied voltage.

$$Z = R + j\omega L = 50 + j(2\pi \times 60)0.1 = 50 + j37.7 \text{ ohms}$$

$$Z = \sqrt{50^2 + 37.7^2} = 62.5 \text{ ohms}$$

$$I = \frac{E}{Z} = \frac{110}{62.5} = 1.76 \text{ amp rms}$$

$$\theta = -\tan^{-1}\frac{X_L}{R} = -\tan^{-1}\frac{37.7}{50}$$

$$= -37°, \text{ current lagging terminal voltage}$$

By convention it is customary to measure the phase angle as the angle of the current phasor with respect to the voltage phasor. Thus in Example 4.1 the phase angle can be expressed as 37° lagging. Also, whenever impedance, current, or voltage is expressed as Z, I, E (or V), it is understood to be the magnitude. Often both voltage and current are carried through as rms values, instead of maximum values.

Example 4.2

An RC series circuit is excited by an alternating voltage of 10 volts rms at a radian frequency of $\omega = 5,000$ radians/sec. Find the magnitude of the voltage across the resistor if $R = 10^4$ ohms and $C = 0.01$ μf.

$$Z = \sqrt{R^2 + \left(\frac{1}{\omega C}\right)^2} = \sqrt{(10^4)^2 + \left(\frac{1}{5,000 + 10^{-8}}\right)^2}$$

$$= \sqrt{10^8 + 4 \times 10^8}$$

$$= \sqrt{5} \times 10^4 \text{ ohms}$$

$$I = \frac{E}{Z} \quad \text{and} \quad V_r = IR = \frac{ER}{Z} = \frac{10 \times 10^4}{\sqrt{5} \times 10^4}$$

$$= 4.48 \text{ volts rms}$$

4.4 SERIES RESONANCE

Some interesting characteristics of a series RLC circuit of Fig. 4.5a can be predicted from Eqs. (4.37) and (4.36) reproduced below:

$$Z = \sqrt{R^2 + \left(\omega L - \frac{1}{\omega C}\right)^2}$$

$$\theta = -\tan^{-1}\frac{\omega L - 1/\omega C}{R}$$

Keeping in mind that the voltage applied to the impedance is sinusoidal, we examine the above equations to see what happens when ω, R, L, or C is allowed to vary and the other parameters are held constant.

Suppose that R, L, and C are constant and that frequency ω is variable. As ω approaches zero, the inductive-reactance term in Eq. (4.37) also approaches zero but the capacitive-reactance term becomes very large. The magnitude of the impedance increases as the frequency becomes small. At zero frequency, when the applied voltage is constant, the impedance is infinite because of the infinite reactance of the capacitor. For a constant driving voltage, the current is zero in the steady state. Now let the frequency increase from zero. The inductive-reactance term in Eq. (4.37) increases, and the capacitive-reactance term decreases. Their difference decreases, causing the impedance to decrease. A frequency exists such that

$$\omega L = \frac{1}{\omega C} \tag{4.38}$$

at which frequency $Z = R$. When this condition exists, the circuit is said to be in "series resonance," a condition of zero phase difference between the current and applied voltage and of minimum impedance. The resonant frequency can be found from Eq. (4.38) by solving for ω.

$$\omega_0 = \frac{1}{\sqrt{LC}} \qquad \text{radians/sec} \tag{4.39}$$

and

$$f_0 = \frac{1}{2\pi\sqrt{LC}} \qquad \text{cycles/sec} \tag{4.40}$$

where ω_0 is the resonant radian frequency and f_0 is the resonant frequency.

As the frequency increases further past the resonant frequency, the impedance again becomes larger than R. As the frequency becomes very large, the inductive-reactance term in Eq. (4.37) becomes very large and the impedance increases accordingly. This variation of impedance with frequency is shown in Fig. 4.7, along with R, X_L, and X_C as functions of frequency.

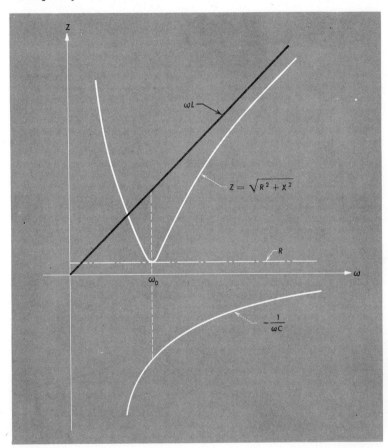

FIG. 4.7 *Impedance, resistance, and reactance versus frequency for the RLC series circuit of Fig. 4.5a.*

The resonant frequency ω_0 is identical to the undamped natural frequency of the RLC series circuit found in Chap. 3. Resonance occurs when the circuit is excited by a sinusoid of the same frequency as the undamped natural frequency of the circuit.

As another example of the resonant, or minimum-impedance, condition, suppose that the frequency of the driving voltage is constant and that R and L are also constant. Let C be adjustable so that the impedance Z varies as a function of the variable C. Notice that, by adjusting C to C_0 in Fig. 4.8, resonance occurs, since $1/\omega C_0 = \omega L$. Notice also the similarity of the impedance curve to that of Fig. 4.7.

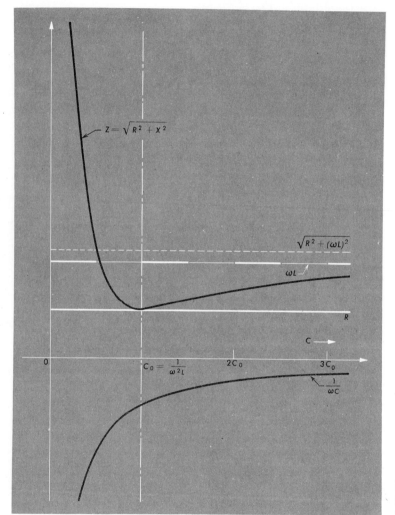

FIG. 4.8 *Impedance-versus-capacitance curve for an RLC series circuit with constant R and L.*

The parameter R presents some interesting variations of the current resonance curve. If L and C are constant, a constant voltage is applied and I is plotted against frequency for various values of R. The resonance curve is the reciprocal of the impedance-versus-frequency curve, and the resonance curve becomes narrower and sharper as the parameter R decreases, as illustrated in Fig. 4.9. Suppose that we examine the curves to find the frequencies at which the current has dropped to $1/\sqrt{2}$ of its value at resonance. These frequencies are called "band limits," "cutoff frequencies," or "half-power frequencies." We know that the impedance is equal to the value of the resistance at resonance.

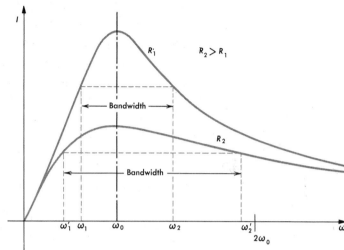

FIG. 4.9 *Current-versus-frequency curve for an RLC series circuit with R as a parameter. Bandwidth is proportional to R.*

For the current to drop to $1/\sqrt{2}$ of its resonance value, the impedance must increase to $\sqrt{2}$ times its resonance value R. Equation (4.37) provides a means of calculating the frequencies at which this occurs. Substituting $\sqrt{2} R$ for Z in Eq. (4.37) gives

$$\sqrt{2} R = \sqrt{R^2 + \left(\omega L - \frac{1}{\omega C}\right)^2} \tag{4.41}$$

In order to solve Eq. (4.41) for ω, first square both sides.

$$2R^2 = R^2 + \left(\omega L - \frac{1}{\omega C}\right)^2$$

which can be written

$$\left(\omega L - \frac{1}{\omega C}\right)^2 = R^2 \tag{4.42}$$

Taking the square root of both sides of Eq. (4.42) gives

$$\omega L - \frac{1}{\omega C} = \pm R \tag{4.43}$$

Multiplying Eq. (4.43) through by ω/L and solving for ω,

$$\omega^2 \pm \frac{R}{L}\omega - \frac{1}{LC} = 0$$

$$\omega = \pm\frac{R}{2L} \pm \frac{1}{2}\sqrt{\left(\frac{R}{L}\right)^2 + \frac{4}{LC}} \qquad \text{radians/sec} \qquad (4.44)$$

Four frequencies are defined by Eq. (4.44), two being positive and two being negative. Since only the positive frequencies have significance in the physical world, the negative ones can be discarded. Then the highest positive frequency which satisfies Eq. (4.44) is

$$\omega_2 = \frac{R}{2L} + \frac{1}{2}\sqrt{\left(\frac{R}{L}\right)^2 + \frac{4}{LC}} \qquad \text{radians/sec} \qquad (4.45)$$

and the lowest positive frequency is

$$\omega_1 = \frac{-R}{2L} + \frac{1}{2}\sqrt{\left(\frac{R}{L}\right)^2 + \frac{4}{LC}} \qquad (4.46)$$

½ power

Notice from Eq. (4.45) that, as R approaches zero, ω_2 approaches resonant frequency $\omega_0 = 1/\sqrt{LC}$ and in Eq. (4.46), as R approaches zero, ω_1 approaches ω_0. Thus the bandwidth $\omega_2 - \omega_1$ shrinks toward zero as R becomes small and approaches zero. This is illustrated in Fig. 4.9 for two values of R, where $R_2 > R_1$.

The applications of RLC circuits in communications are many. A series resonant circuit is a filter. Notice that the current is maximum at the resonant frequency ω_0 in Fig. 4.9 and the current decreases as the frequency varies from ω_0. If several sinusoidal voltages at various frequencies are applied simultaneously to excite a series RLC circuit, the voltage of the frequency closest to or at the resonant frequency of the circuit produces proportionately the largest current, while voltages of frequencies furthest from the resonant frequency of the circuit produce the least proportionate current. The principle of resonance is used to select radio stations by a radio receiver. The resonant frequency of an RLC circuit is tuned, by adjusting the capacitance, to the frequency of the desired radio stations. Radio stations not at the resonant frequency of the RLC circuit are discriminated against. The sharpness of the tuning, known as "selectivity," depends on the relative amount of resistance in the circuit. If R is relatively small, the selectivity is high, as demonstrated by Fig. 4.9.

If an *RLC* series circuit is excited by a sinusoidal voltage whose frequency is the same as the resonant frequency of the circuit, the following characteristics are apparent: (*a*) the terminal voltage and current are in phase; (*b*) the inductive reactance is equal to the capacitive reactance; (*c*) the impedance magnitude is equal to the resistance in the circuit; (*d*) the rms current is equal to V_{rms}/R; (*e*) if the resistance inherent in the inductor and the capacitor is negligible compared with their reactances, the magnitude of the voltage is the same across both the inductor and the capacitor.

The locus phasor diagram of the impedance **Z** is shown in Fig. 4.10 for an *RLC* series circuit. Note **Z** shown as a complex number

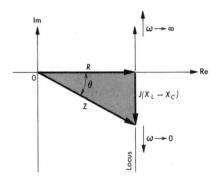

FIG. 4.10 *Locus of the impedance phasor as a function of frequency for an RLC series circuit.*

which has a locus along the vertical line Re **Z** = *R*. A locus phasor diagram showing **I** and **E** is given in Fig. 4.11. In each of these diagrams, resonance occurs when the phase angle θ is zero. Notice that when θ is zero the current is maximum and the impedance is minimum.

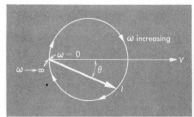

4.5 THE CONCEPT OF Q

FIG. 4.11 *Locus of the current phasor as a function of frequency for an RLC series circuit.*

The phenomenon of resonance in a physical system is important to engineers concerned with communication systems because resonant circuits are effective filters. A signal voltage at the same frequency as the resonant frequency of the circuit produces a current in the circuit many times greater than that produced by an alternating voltage of the same magnitude but of a frequency very different from resonance. As mentioned in Sec. 4.4, this is the basis of tuning a radio or television receiver; the desired signals are tuned in, and the undesired signals are rejected.

Example 4.3

Two signals e_1 and e_2 are of equal amplitude. One has a frequency of 1,000 kc, and one is 900 kc. Together they excite an RLC series circuit which is at resonance at 1,000 kc. Since $e_{in} = e_1 + e_2$, to find the output voltage e_o we use the superposition principle and find the response for e_1 and e_2 separately.

The resonant frequency of the circuit is, from Fig. 4.12,

$$\omega_0 = \frac{1}{\sqrt{LC}} = \frac{1}{\sqrt{0.2538 \times 10^{-3} \times 100 \times 10^{-12}}}$$
$$= 6.28 \times 10^6 \text{ radians/sec}$$

or

$$f_0 = \frac{\omega_0}{2\pi} = 10^6 \text{ cycles/sec}$$

which is the frequency of e_1. Then E_{01}, the circuit response to e_1 only, is the same as the input voltage e_1.

$$E_{01} = 0.707(0.1) = 0.0707 \text{ volt rms}$$

At 900 kc,

$$Z = \sqrt{R^2 + \left(\omega L - \frac{1}{\omega C}\right)^2}$$

$$= \sqrt{\begin{bmatrix} 100^2 + \left(2\pi \times 900 \times 10^3 \times 0.2538 \times 10^{-3} \\ - \dfrac{1}{2\pi \times 900 \times 10^3 \times 100 \times 10^{-12}}\right)^2 \end{bmatrix}}$$

$$= 1.26 \times 10^3 \text{ ohms}$$

The output voltage resulting from e_2 only is

$$E_{02} = \frac{E_2}{Z} R$$
$$= \frac{0.707 \times 0.1}{1.26 \times 10^3} \times 100 = 0.00561 \text{ volt rms}$$

The ratio of the output voltages caused by e_1 to the output voltage caused by e_2 is

$$\frac{0.0707}{0.00561} = 12.6$$

Thus signal e_1 produces 12.6 times the voltage output signal e_2 produces, which is $12.6^2 = 159$ times the **power** output produced by e_2.

Resonance is sometimes a phenomenon to be avoided. Vibrations are examples of responses of mechanical systems. A vibrating system has a natural or resonant frequency which is sometimes called the critical frequency. If the system is excited at the critical

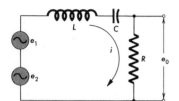

FIG. 4.12 *The RLC tuned circuit of Example 4.3.* $L = 0.2538$ mh, $C = 100 \mu\mu f$, $R = 100$ ohms, $E_{1m} = E_{2m} = 0.2$ volt.

frequency, the magnitude of the vibrations may become excessive. This is the reason a marching group of men break step when crossing a bridge; the frequency of their steps in unison may be near the critical frequency of the bridge and could cause vibrations of excessive amplitude and bridge collapse.

The sharpness of current-versus-frequency response shown in Fig. 4.9 can be described by a quantity known as the quality factor, or Q, of the circuit. The general definition of Q is arbitrarily taken to be

$$Q = 2\pi \frac{\text{maximum energy stored/cycle}}{\text{energy dissipated/cycle}} \tag{4.47}$$

In order to find the Q of a circuit, the maximum energy stored and the energy dissipated per cycle can be calculated and substituted into Eq. (4.47). The maximum energy stored in the inductor carrying an alternating current is

$$W_m = \frac{LI_m{}^2}{2} \tag{4.48}$$

and the energy dissipated per cycle in R is

$$\begin{aligned} W_{dis} &= \int_0^{1/f} p \, dt = \int_0^{1/f} Ri^2 \, dt \\ &= \int_0^{1/f} R(I_m \sin \omega t)^2 \, dt \\ &= \frac{RI_m{}^2}{2f} \end{aligned} \tag{4.49}$$

where f is the frequency and $1/f$ is the period of the sine wave. Substituting Eqs. (4.48) and (4.49) into Eq. (4.47) gives the Q for the RLC series circuit of

$$Q = 2\pi \frac{LI_m{}^2/2}{RI_m{}^2/2f} = 2\pi f \frac{L}{R}$$

or

$$Q = \frac{\omega L}{R} \tag{4.50}$$

For the circuit at resonance,

$$Q_0 = \frac{\omega_0 L}{R} \tag{4.51}$$

where a high-Q circuit is characterized by $R \ll \omega_0 L$.

Also at resonance

$$\omega_0 = \frac{1}{\sqrt{LC}} \quad \text{or} \quad L = \frac{1}{\omega_0{}^2 C} \tag{4.52}$$

Substituting Eq. (4.52) into Eq. (4.51) gives

$$Q_0 = \frac{1}{\omega_0 R C} \tag{4.53}$$

which is another expression for Q_0 independent of L, and the high-Q circuit is characterized by $R \ll 1/\omega_0 C$.

The half-power frequency terms defined by Eqs. (4.45) and (4.46) can be expressed in terms of Q_0 by substituting Eqs. (4.51) to (4.53) into Eqs. (4.45) and (4.46). Thus

$$\omega_2 = \frac{\omega_0}{2Q_0} + \frac{1}{2}\sqrt{\left(\frac{\omega_0}{Q_0}\right)^2 + 4\omega_0{}^2} \tag{4.54}$$

and

$$\omega_1 = -\frac{\omega_0}{2Q_0} + \frac{1}{2}\sqrt{\left(\frac{\omega_0}{Q_0}\right)^2 + 4\omega_0{}^2} \tag{4.55}$$

Let $\omega_2 - \omega_1$ define the bandwidth of the circuit. Then from Eqs. (4.54) and (4.55),

$$\omega_2 - \omega_1 = \frac{\omega_0}{Q_0} \tag{4.56}$$

where Eq. (4.56) shows the bandwidth proportional to the resonant frequency ω_0 and inversely proportional to Q_0.

Example 4.4

The Q of the RLC circuit of Example 4.3 at the resonant frequency of 1,000 kc is

$$Q_1 = \frac{\omega_0 L}{R} = \frac{2\pi \times 10^6 \times 0.2538 \times 10^{-3}}{100} = 15.8$$

The bandwidth is

$$\omega_2 - \omega_1 = \frac{2\pi \times 10^6}{15.8} = 3.94 \times 10^5 \text{ radians/sec}$$

$$f_2 - f_1 = \frac{3.94 \times 10^5}{2\pi} = 6.33 \times 10^4 = 63.3 \text{ kc}$$

4.6 POWER AND ENERGY CONSIDERATIONS

Instantaneous power being delivered to any circuit is the product of the instantaneous terminal voltage and the instantaneous current, as stated in Eq. (1.17).

$$p = vi$$

If the voltage and current of Eq. (1.17) are both constant, the instantaneous power is equal to the product of the constant voltage and current. Since the instantaneous power does not vary with time, it is identical to the average power delivered to the circuit.

Now let us consider the power being delivered to an impedance by a sinusoidal-voltage source. Let

$$v = V_m \sin \omega t \tag{4.57}$$

$$I = I_m \sin (\omega t - \theta) \tag{4.58}$$

Substituting Eqs. (4.57) and (4.58) into Eq. (1.17) yields

$$p = V_m I_m \sin \omega t \sin (\omega t - \theta) \tag{4.59}$$

The identity

$$\sin (x - y) = \sin x \cos y - \cos x \sin y$$

enables us to write Eq. (4.59) in the form

$$p = V_m I_m \sin \omega t (\sin \omega t \cos \theta - \cos \omega t \sin \theta) \tag{4.60}$$

where Eq. (4.60) is an expression for instantaneous power being delivered to the circuit. From Eq. (4.60) we can obtain an expression for average power by the method of averaging illustrated in Chap. 2. Further manipulation of Eq. (4.60), however, enables us to obtain average power without having to perform the integration. Using the identities

$$\sin^2 x = \tfrac{1}{2}(1 - \cos 2x)$$

and

$$\sin x \cos x = \tfrac{1}{2} \sin 2x$$

we can write Eq. (4.60) as

$$p = \frac{V_m I_m}{2} [(1 - \cos 2\omega t) \cos \theta - \sin 2\omega t \sin \theta] \tag{4.61}$$

$$p = \frac{V_m I_m}{2} [\cos \theta - (\sin 2\omega t \sin \theta + \cos 2\omega t \cos \theta)]$$

$$= \frac{V_m I_m}{2} \cos \theta - \frac{V_m I_m}{2} \cos (2\omega t - \theta) \tag{4.62}$$

Notice that the first term on the right side of Eq. (4.62) is a constant, being proportional to the cosine of the phase angle θ. The second term on the right is a sinusoid of twice the frequency of the voltage and current. The average value of a sinusoid taken over an integral number of cycles is zero. Therefore we can express the average power as the constant term only in Eq. (4.62). Thus,

$$P_a = \frac{V_m I_m}{2} \cos \theta \tag{4.63}$$

Expressing V_m and I_m in terms of their rms values,

$$P_a = VI \cos \theta \tag{4.64}$$

where V and I are rms values of voltage and current.

We might have expected the average power of an a-c circuit to be the product of rms voltage and rms current only. Equation (4.64) shows that another term, the cosine of the phase angle, is also a factor in determining average power. Indeed, the term $\cos \theta$ is defined as the "power factor" of the circuit. A purely resistive circuit has a phase angle between voltage and current of zero. For the ideal resistor, the power factor is unity, and the average power is the product of rms voltage and rms current. On the other hand, a pure reactance has a phase angle of $\pm 90°$. Its power factor is zero, and the average power delivered to it is zero. Between these two extremes are the circuits containing both resistance and reactance with a power factor somewhere between zero and unity.

Figure 4.13 shows instantaneous power as a function of time for three examples. In Fig. 4.13a is an ideal resistor, with voltage and current in phase with each other. Notice that the instantaneous power is always positive or zero. The average power P_a is shown, and the instantaneous power is a sinusoid about P_a, at twice the frequency of voltage and current. In Fig. 4.13b the load is inductive reactance. The current lags the voltage by 90°, and the instantaneous power swings negative for one-half cycle and then positive for one-half cycle. Notice that the average power in this case is zero, and the frequency of the instantaneous power is again twice the frequency of the applied voltage. In Fig. 4.13c is an example of a resistor and an inductive reactor in series. Notice that the average power is not zero. The instantaneous power swings negative during short intervals in the period of the power wave, but it is positive over much longer intervals. Thus the area under the instantaneous-power wave is positive, the average value of which is shown as P_a.

The significance of negative instantaneous power is that of direction of power flow. Since positive power represents the rate at which electric energy is being delivered from the generator to the circuit, negative power must be the rate at which electric energy

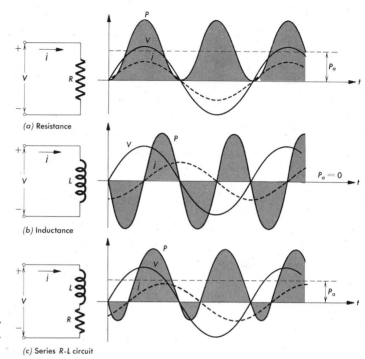

(a) Resistance

(b) Inductance

FIG. 4.13 *Voltage, current, and power as functions of time for (a) resistance, (b) inductance, and (c) a series RL circuit.*

(c) Series R-L circuit

is flowing away from the circuit to the generator. The presence of an energy-storage device, such as an inductor or a capacitor, makes it possible for the direction of power flow to be reversed. Thus in Fig. 4.13b and c are examples of energy being stored in energy-storage elements during part of a cycle and then being sent back to the electric-energy source during the other part of the cycle.

The product of rms voltage and rms current by itself is sometimes called "apparent power." This is the product of the magnitudes of the rms **V** and **I** phasors shown in Fig. 4.14. Notice that the average real power, $VI \cos \theta$, is the product of V and the component of current in phase with it, which is $I \cos \theta$. The units used to measure apparent power are volt-amperes, and, of course, average real power is measured in watts.

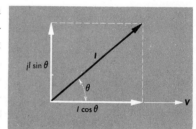

FIG. 4.14 *Phasor diagram showing power-factor angle, or phase angle, θ.*

Example 4.5

An inductor possesses some internal resistance in its windings, and can be represented by an equivalent circuit consisting of 0.0225 henry of inductance and 12.7 ohms resistance in series. The inductor is connected to a sinusoidal voltage source of 220 volts rms, 800 cycles/sec.

4.6 Power and Energy Considerations **117**

1. Find the current in the inductor and its phase angle with respect to the applied voltage.

   2. Find the Q of the inductor.

   3. Find the average power delivered to the inductor.

1. Using voltage as a reference,

$$V = 220 + j0$$

$$Z = R + j\omega L = 12.7 + j2\pi \times 800 \times 0.0225$$

$$= 12.7 + j113 \text{ ohms}$$

$$I = \frac{V}{Z} = \frac{220 + j0}{12.7 + j113} = \frac{220\epsilon^{j0}}{113.4\epsilon^{j83.6°}} = 1.94\epsilon^{-j83.6°} \qquad \text{amp rms}$$

Thus the rms current is 1.94 amp, lagging the applied voltage by 83.6°.

$$\text{2. } Q = \frac{\omega L}{R} = \frac{2\pi \times 800 \times 0.0225}{12.7} = \frac{113}{12.7} = 8.9$$

This is not a very high Q, since the ratio of reactance to resistance is only 8.9.

$$\text{3. } P_a = VI \cos \theta = 220 \times 1.94 \times \cos(-83.6°)$$
$$= 220 \times 1.94 \times 0.1112$$
$$= 47.6 \text{ watts}$$

As a check, use $P_a = I^2R$, where I is the rms current.

$$P_a = 1.94^2 \times 12.7 = 47.6 \text{ watts}$$

SUMMARY

Impedance is defined as the ratio of voltage to current when the current is an exponential function. Since a sinusoid is closely related to the exponential function, impedance to sinusoidal currents can also be defined as the ratio of voltage to current when both are sinusoids. In a series circuit, the sum of the impedances of each element is the total impedance of the circuit. Table 4.1 summarizes the impedances of the various elements.

Reactance is defined for an inductive or capacitive circuit excited by a sinusoidal voltage as the magnitude of the impedance; this is the ratio of the maximum voltage to maximum current, or the ratio of the rms voltage to the rms current. For the inductor, reactance [see Eq. (4.12)] is

$$X_L = \omega L \qquad \text{ohms}$$

and for the capacitor [Eq. (4.18)]

$$X_C = \frac{1}{\omega C} \quad \text{ohms}$$

Impedance to alternating current is the ratio of phasor voltage to phasor current; the impedance of an RL circuit in complex form [Eq. (4.24)] is

$$Z = R + j\omega L \quad \text{ohms}$$

and the impedance of an RC circuit [Eq. (4.31)] is

$$Z = R - j\frac{1}{\omega C} \quad \text{ohms}$$

An RLC series circuit has an impedance magnitude [Eq. (4.37)] of

$$Z = \sqrt{R^2 + \left(\omega L - \frac{1}{\omega C}\right)^2} \quad \text{ohms}$$

and an impedance angle [Eq. (4.36)] of

$$\theta = \tan^{-1}\frac{\omega L - 1/\omega C}{R}$$

Resonance occurs in an RLC series circuit when the power factor of the circuit is unity or when terminal voltage and current are in phase. At resonant frequency the impedance is a minimum and is equal to R. Resonant frequency of an RLC series circuit is expressed by Eq. (4.39),

$$\omega_0 = \frac{1}{\sqrt{LC}} \quad \text{radians/sec}$$

The limits of the passband when the RLC series circuit is used as a filter are expressed by Eqs. (4.45) and (4.46),

$$\omega_2 = \frac{R}{2L} + \frac{1}{2}\sqrt{\left(\frac{R}{L}\right)^2 + \frac{4}{LC}} \quad \text{radians/sec}$$

and

$$\omega_1 = -\frac{R}{2L} + \frac{1}{2}\sqrt{\left(\frac{R}{L}\right)^2 + \frac{4}{LC}} \quad \text{radians/sec}$$

Defining Q of a system in oscillation as in Eq. (4.47)

$$Q = 2\pi \frac{\text{maximum energy stored/cycle}}{\text{energy dissipated/cycle}}$$

the Q of an RLC series circuit is shown by Eq. (4.50) to be

$$Q = \frac{\omega L}{R}$$

If Q_0 is the Q at the resonant frequency of an RLC series circuit, the bandwidth of the circuit used as a filter [Eq. (4.56)] is

$$\omega_2 - \omega_1 = \frac{\omega_0}{Q_0} \qquad \text{radians/sec}$$

FURTHER READING

Steady-state circuit analysis is treated extensively in textbooks on circuits published during the first half of the twentieth century. Kerchner and Corcoran, *Alternating-current Circuits*, 3d ed. (John Wiley & Sons, Inc., New York, 1951), is an excellent reference devoted to the sinusoidal steady-state tradition. William H. Middendorf, *Analysis of Electric Circuits* (John Wiley & Sons, Inc., New York, 1956), chaps. 6, 9, and 10, and Fich and Potter, *Theory of A-C Circuits* (Prentice-Hall, Inc., Englewood Cliffs, N.J., 1958), chap. 3, are two helpful references.

PROBLEMS

4.1 Plot point by point $v_1 = 60 \sin 100t$ and $v_2 = 80 \sin (100t + 45°)$ as functions of time. For each instant of time, add v_1 and v_2 to find $v_1 + v_2$. Does the sum appear to be sinusoidal? From your plot, determine the maximum value of the sum and the phase of the sum with respect to v_1.

4.2 Using phasors, determine the maximum value of the sum of v_1 and v_2 defined in Prob. 4.1. Also, find the phase difference between the sum of v_1 and v_2 and v_1 alone. How do these results compare with the results of Prob. 4.1?

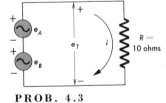

PROB. 4.3

4.3 Two voltage generators are connected in series as shown in the figure. They both generate sinusoidal voltages of 100 cycles/sec. The peak value of one, e_A, is 150 volts, and the peak value of the other, e_B, is 200 volts. Voltage e_A is 60° ahead of e_B in time. (a) What is the maximum value of the sum e_T? (b) What is the rms value of e_T? (c) What is the phase of e_T with respect to e_A?

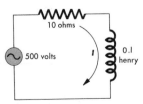

PROB. 4.4

4.4 A series circuit consisting of a 1,000-ohm resistor and a 0.1-henry inductor is connected as shown in the figure to a sinusoidal voltage source of 500 volts rms, 1,000 cycles/sec. *Find:* (a) the reactance of L in ohms;

(b) the complex impedance; (c) the impedance magnitude; (d) the phasor current, using voltage as a reference; (e) the rms current; (f) the rms voltage across the resistor; (g) the rms voltage across the inductor; (h) the phase angle between generator voltage and current.

4.5 A constant-voltage sine-wave generator feeds energy into an unknown load as shown in the illustration. The generator voltage and the current it supplies are $e = 452 \sin 377t$, $i = 105 \sin (377t - 27.3°)$. The unknown load can be represented by an equivalent circuit consisting of a resistor R and a reactor X in series. Find R and X. Is X inductive or capacitive?

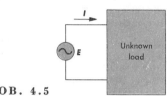

PROB. 4.5

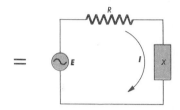

4.6 The electrical characteristics of an a-c induction motor can be represented approximately by a series equivalent circuit shown in the figure, where R_s and L_s are inherent in the machine and R_L represents the mechanical output of the motor. Suppose that $R_L = 12.2$ ohms, $R_s = 0.76$ ohm, and $L_s = 0.0216$ henry. The terminal voltage is 220 volts rms. Find: (a) power output of the motor in watts; (b) power factor; (c) motor efficiency (the ratio of power in R_L to the total power). The frequency is 60 cps.

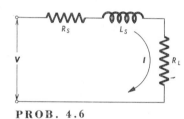

PROB. 4.6

4.7 A series circuit containing R, L, and C is connected to an a-c-voltage source. The circuit and constants are given in the illustration. (a) Find the rms current. (b) If an rms-reading voltmeter were connected across R, what would it read? (c) What is the rms voltage across L? Across C? $R = 100$ ohms, $L = 1$ henry, $C = 0.05$ µf, $\omega = 5,000$ radians/sec, and $E_m = 3,000$ volts.

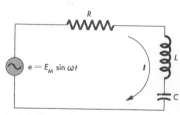

PROB. 4.7

4.8 Refer to the RLC series circuit of Prob. 4.7. Assume that R, L, and C and the applied voltage are the same, but that the frequency is adjustable. (a) Find the resonant frequency of the circuit. (b) If the frequency of the voltage source is adjusted to the resonant frequency of the circuit, find the rms current in the circuit. (c) If the circuit is excited at its natural resonant frequency, as in (b), find the rms voltage across R, L, and C.

4.9 Write the integrodifferential equation for the circuit of Prob. 4.7. Differentiate this equation once to get rid of the integral, so that the equation is a differential equation. Then verify that $i = A \cos nt + B \sin nt$ satisfies the differential equation. A, B, and n are constants. Find the specific value of n which satisfies the differential equation.

4.10 A series RLC circuit with $R = 500$ ohms and $L = 1$ henry is excited by a sinusoidal-voltage generator of frequency $f = 1,000$ cycles/sec. The capacitor is adjustable between 0.005 and 0.100 μf. Plot a curve of impedance magnitude versus capacitance for this circuit.

4.11 A series RLC circuit with $L = 1$ henry and $C = 1$ μf is excited by a voltage generator of variable frequency. Find the resonant frequency, and plot Z as a function of frequency for at least two octaves on each side of resonance for: (a) $R = 100$ ohms, (b) $R = 500$ ohms, (c) $R = 1,000$ ohms.

4.12 The RLC circuit of Prob. 4.7 is used as a filter, with an input voltage containing several different frequencies. Consider the output of the filter to be the voltage across R. (a) Find the Q of the circuit at resonance. (b) Find the upper and lower half-power frequencies.

4.13 A tennis ball is dropped from 10 ft and bounces 6.2 ft. What is the Q of the tennis ball?

4.14 A 5-μf capacitor has a Q of 100. Find the value of R in series with the capacitor.

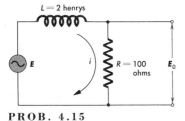

PROB. 4.15

4.15 In the figure an RL series circuit is excited by a 100-volt source with adjustable frequency. (a) Plot E_0 (the rms voltage across R) as a function of frequency. (b) Derive an expression for the frequency at which the output voltage is 0.707 times the output voltage at zero frequency.

4.16 The circuit of Prob. 4.15 can be thought of as a low-pass filter; the low frequencies are passed, but the high frequencies are attenuated. Suppose that all frequencies above 1,000 cycles/sec must be attenuated and that 1,000 cycles/sec is the frequency at which the output voltage is 0.707 of the input voltage. If $L = 2$ henrys, find a value of R that establishes the cutoff frequency at 1,000 cycles/sec.

4.17 An LC series circuit ($C = 1$ μf, $L = 1$ henry) is subjected to a variable-frequency driving voltage. Plot: (a) the reactance of C as a function of frequency; (b) the reactance of L as a function of frequency; (c) the impedance as a function of frequency.

4.18 An inductor L and a resistor R are connected in parallel to a sinusoidal-voltage source E and frequency ω. Find an equivalent series combination of resistance and reactance.

$$\text{COMPLETE SOLUTIONS}$$
$$\text{OF SERIES CIRCUITS}$$

5.1 INTRODUCTION

The natural response of a physical system is a function of the system parameters, but the coefficients of the natural-response terms depend upon the initial conditions at the instant when the system becomes excited. The natural response is found from the homogeneous form of the differential equation, obtained by letting the exciting function of the system differential equation be zero. Natural response of electric circuits was discussed in Chap. 3, and the general homogeneous second-order equation [Eq. (3.56)] was written

$$\frac{d^2x}{dt^2} + 2\omega_n\zeta\frac{dx}{dt} + \omega_n^2x = 0$$

where the dependent variable x must be of the form

$$x = A_1\epsilon^{p_1t} + A_2\epsilon^{p_2t}$$

in order to satisfy Eq. (3.56). The constants A_1 and A_2 are arbitrary constants, and p_1 and p_2 are the roots of the characteristic equation

$$p^2 + 2\omega_n\zeta p + \omega_n^2 = 0$$

The steady-state solution of the circuit, discussed in Chap. 4, satisfies the differential equation with an exponential exciting function. Thus a sinusoidal exciting function is represented by $\epsilon^{j\omega t}$, and a constant, or direct, exciting function is represented by ϵ^{pt} when $p = 0$. Sinusoidal steady-state solutions and d-c steady-state solutions are of major importance in steady-state analysis.

In this chapter we consider the complete solution of circuits in which both the natural response and the steady-state response are of importance. The complete solution of the differential equation is the sum of the natural response and the steady-state response. Of course, the complete solution must also satisfy the differential equation, just as the natural response must satisfy the homogeneous equation and the steady-state solution must satisfy the complete equation with its exciting function. The steps required to find the complete solution are:

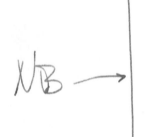

1. Find the steady-state solution; this can often be done by using impedance without actually writing the differential equation of the circuit.

2. Write and solve the homogeneous form of the circuit differential equation to find the natural response with arbitrary constants.

3. Add the steady-state solution and the natural response, and evaluate the arbitrary constants from a knowledge of the initial conditions.

The balance of this chapter is devoted to the complete solution of circuits by applying the three steps outlined above.

5.2 STEP INPUT TO AN RL CIRCUIT

The step input, which is the input obtained when a constant-voltage source is connected to the circuit, is now applied to an RL circuit. In this example shown in Fig. 5.1, the switch is closed at $t = 0$, connecting the battery or constant exciting voltage E to the circuit. The steady-state solution can be found conveniently from the circuit differential equation

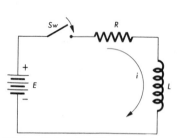

FIG. 5.1 *An RL series circuit with step input of voltage.*

$$L\frac{di}{dt} + Ri = E \tag{5.1}$$

Since the exciting function is the constant voltage E, we expect the steady-state current to be constant. The circuit impedance is $Z(p) = R$, and the steady-state current is

$$i_s = \frac{E}{R} \tag{5.2}$$

The natural response is obtained from the circuit differential equation by writing the differential equation in the homogeneous form and solving it as described in Chap. 3. Then from Eq. (3.13)

$$L\frac{di}{dt} + Ri = 0$$

and the assumed form of the natural response is the exponential form shown in Eq. (3.14),

$$i_n = A\epsilon^{pt}$$

where p is evaluated by substituting Eq. (3.14) into Eq. (3.13) as done in Sec. 3.4. Thus [Eq. (3.17)]

$$p = -\frac{R}{L}$$

The complete solution is the sum of the steady-state response and the natural response, or

$$i = i_s + i_n \tag{5.3}$$

which can be written

$$i = \frac{E}{R} + A\epsilon^{-(R/L)t} \tag{5.4}$$

Equation (5.4) is the complete solution of Eq. (5.1) for all values of the arbitrary constant A. To find the particular value of A which satisfies the initial conditions of this problem, we recognize that, at $t = 0$, $i = 0$, and under this constraint we solve Eq. (5.4) for A. Then, at $t = 0$, Eq. (5.4) becomes

$$0 = A + \frac{E}{R} \tag{5.5}$$

from which

$$A = -\frac{E}{R} \tag{5.6}$$

and the complete solution can be written

$$i = \frac{E}{R}(1 - \epsilon^{-(R/L)t}) \tag{5.7}$$

The two terms in Eq. (5.7) are the steady-state current and the natural-response current. These terms are plotted separately in Fig. 5.2, and their sum is the complete solution of the circuit problem. The time constant of the solution is the time constant of the natural response, or $\tau = L/R$.

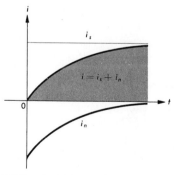

FIG. 5.2 *Steady-state and transient current add to form the complete solution of the RL circuit* [Eq. (5.7)].

5.2 **Step Input to an RL Circuit** 125

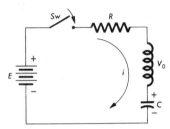

FIG. 5.3 An RC series circuit
with step input and initial charge
V_0 on C.

Another example of a complete solution is obtained by considering the RC series circuit of Fig. 5.3, where V_0 is the initial voltage on the capacitor. The switch is closed at $t = 0$, connecting the constant exciting voltage E to the circuit. The steady-state current $i_s = 0$, since the capacitor impedance to the direct voltage is infinite. The natural response of the circuit is obtained from the homogeneous form of the circuit equation,

$$iR + \left(\frac{1}{C}\int_0^t i\,dt + V_0\right) = E \tag{5.8}$$

which, when differentiated with respect to time, becomes the homogeneous equation

$$R\frac{di}{dt} + \frac{1}{C}i = 0 \tag{5.9}$$

The solution of Eq. (5.9) is the natural response containing the arbitrary constant A, or

$$i_n = A\epsilon^{-t/RC} \tag{5.10}$$

and the sum of the steady-state response and natural response is

$$i = A\epsilon^{-t/RC} \tag{5.11}$$

To evaluate the arbitrary constant A in Eq. (5.11), we seek to constrain Eq. (5.11) in such a manner that it satisfies the circuit at the instant after the switch is closed. At $t = 0+$, the voltage across R is $E - V_0$, and the current through R is

$$I_0 = \frac{E - V_0}{R}$$

Substituting $t = 0$ and I_0 into Eq. (5.11) and solving for A gives

$$A = \frac{E - V_0}{R} \tag{5.12}$$

and the complete solution is written

$$i = \frac{E - V_0}{R}\epsilon^{-t/RC} \tag{5.13}$$

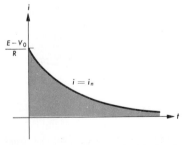

The complete solution, consisting of $i_s = 0$ and i_n of Eq. (5.10), is plotted in Fig. 5.4, where it is assumed that $E > V_0$. The time constant of the current is the time constant of the natural response, or $\tau = RC$.

5.3 STEP INPUT TO RLC SERIES CIRCUIT

The repetition of the steps outlined in Sec. 5.1 and utilized in Sec. 5.2 for an RL and an RC circuit is now made for the RLC series circuit when a step input is applied. The circuit is shown in Fig. 5.5, and V_0 is again the voltage on the capacitor before the switch is closed. The steady-state component of current is zero, since the impedance of the capacitor to direct current is infinite. In the steady state, the voltage across R is zero, and therefore the current i_s must be zero.

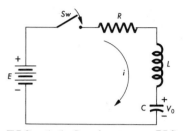

FIG. 5.5 *Step input to an RLC series circuit.*

To find the natural response, we first write the circuit integro-differential equation

$$L\frac{di}{dt} + Ri + \frac{1}{C}\int_0^t i\,dt + V_0 = E \qquad (5.14)$$

Differentiating Eq. (5.14) with respect to time, we can eliminate the integral term and form the homogeneous equation

$$L\frac{d^2i}{dt^2} + R\frac{di}{dt} + \frac{1}{C}i = 0 \qquad (5.15)$$

After dividing through by L, we can write the characteristic equation

$$p^2 + \frac{R}{L}p + \frac{1}{LC} = 0 \qquad (5.16)$$

We test the roots of the characteristic equation; assuming that the roots are real and unequal, we can write the natural response of the circuit in the form [Eq. (3.37)]

$$i_n = A_1\epsilon^{p_1t} + A_2\epsilon^{p_2t}$$

where [Eq. (3.34)]

$$p_1 = -\frac{R}{2L} + \sqrt{\frac{R^2}{4L^2} - \frac{1}{LC}}$$

and [Eq. (3.36)]

$$p_2 = -\frac{R}{2L} - \sqrt{\frac{R^2}{4L^2} - \frac{1}{LC}}$$

Or instead, if the roots of Eq. (5.16) are complex conjugates, the natural response is a damped sinusoid of the form [Eq. (3.53)]

$$i_n = \epsilon^{-\alpha t}(B_1 \cos \omega t + B_2 \sin \omega t)$$

where $-\alpha$ is the real part of p and ω is the imaginary part, or

$$-\alpha = -\frac{R}{2L}$$

and

$$\omega = \sqrt{\frac{1}{LC} - \frac{R^2}{4L^2}}$$

The arbitrary constants in Eq. (3.53) are B_1 and B_2. At the instant after the switch is closed, the current $I_0 = 0$, since it cannot increase instantaneously through the inductor. Also at that instant the capacitor voltage has not yet changed from V_0. Then, at $t = 0+$, from Eq. (5.14) we have

$$L\frac{di}{dt} + V_0 = E \tag{5.17}$$

$$\left.\frac{di}{dt}\right|_{t=0} = \frac{E - V_0}{L} \tag{5.18}$$

Thus for this second-order system we have established the initial values of I_0 and $di/dt|_{t=0}$.

To evaluate the arbitrary constants [assuming the damped sinusoidal response of Eq. (3.53)], we first substitute $i = 0$ at $t = 0$ into Eq. (3.53), which results in

$$B_1 = 0 \tag{5.19}$$

Then we differentiate Eq. (3.53) with respect to time, substitute in $t = 0$ and Eq. (5.18), and we have a second equation in the two arbitrary constants B_1 and B_2. Then

$$\frac{di}{dt} = \epsilon^{-\alpha t}(-B_2\alpha - B_1\omega) \sin \omega t + (-B_1\alpha + B_2\omega) \cos \omega t \tag{5.20}$$

and, at $t = 0$,

$$-B_1\alpha + B_2\omega = \frac{E - V_0}{L} \tag{5.21}$$

Solving Eqs. (5.21) and (5.19) simultaneously gives

$$B_2 = \frac{E - V_0}{L\omega} \quad \text{and} \quad B_1 = 0 \tag{5.22}$$

Then the complete solution, the sum of the natural response and the steady-state response, is expressed by

$$i = \epsilon^{-(R/2L)t} \frac{E - V_0}{L \sqrt{1/LC - R^2/4L^2}} \sin\left(\sqrt{\frac{1}{LC} - \frac{R^2}{4L^2}} \, t\right)$$

(5.23)

and is plotted in Fig. 5.6. The frequency of the sinusoid term is

$$\omega = \sqrt{\frac{1}{LC} - \frac{R^2}{4L^2}} \qquad \text{radians/sec} \qquad (5.24)$$

and the time constant of the exponential term is

$$\tau = \frac{2L}{R} \qquad (5.25)$$

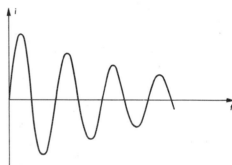

FIG. 5.6 *Response of underdamped RLC circuit excited by a unit step.*

The complete solution [Eq. (5.23)], as plotted in Fig. 5.6, is interesting in that the current oscillates as a damped sinusoid and eventually approaches zero when the circuit is excited by a step voltage. The overdamped solution of the form expressed by Eq. (3.37) shows the sum of two exponential terms as the response when the circuit is excited by the step voltage.

Example 5.1

A spring with constant K suspends a mass M which can move vertically without friction. The mass is initially at rest at $X = 0$. Then, at $t = 0$, a constant downward force is applied to the mass. The steady-state response is a displacement x_s at which the spring force is identically equal to the applied force F and the velocity is zero. Then $Kx_s = F$, or

$$x_s = \frac{F}{K}$$

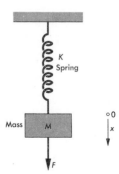

FIG. 5.7 *Spring and mass subject to a step force F (Example 5.1).*

The natural response x_n is obtained by writing the system differential equation

$$M \frac{d^2x}{dt^2} + Kx = F$$

from which the homogeneous equation is written,

$$M \frac{d^2x}{dt^2} + Kx = 0$$

Assuming a natural response of the form

$$x = A_1 \epsilon^{p_1 t} + A_2 \epsilon^{p_2 t}$$

where p is evaluated from the characteristic equation

$$Mp^2 + K = 0$$

or

$$p = \pm j \sqrt{\frac{K}{M}}$$

the natural response can be written

$$x_n = A_1 \epsilon^{j\sqrt{(K/M)}\,t} + A_2 \epsilon^{-j\sqrt{(K/M)}\,t}$$

Recalling that $\epsilon^{j\omega t} = \cos \omega t + j \sin \omega t$,

$$x_n = B_1 \cos \sqrt{\frac{K}{M}}\,t + B_2 \sin \sqrt{\frac{K}{M}}\,t$$

The complete solution is

$$x = x_s + x_n$$

or

$$x = \frac{F}{K} + B_1 \cos \sqrt{\frac{K}{M}}\,t + B_2 \sin \sqrt{\frac{K}{M}}\,t$$

To evaluate the arbitrary constants B_1 and B_2, we recognize that, at $t = 0+$, $x = 0$, and substituting these values for t and x into the solution gives

$$0 = \frac{F}{K} + B_1$$

or

$$B_1 = -\frac{F}{K}$$

Also at $t = 0+$, $dx/dt = 0$, and the derivative of the solution is

$$\frac{dx}{dt} = -B_1 \sqrt{\frac{K}{M}} \sin \sqrt{\frac{K}{M}}\,t + B_2 \sqrt{\frac{K}{M}} \cos \sqrt{\frac{K}{M}}\,t$$

Then

$$0 = B_2 \sqrt{\frac{K}{M}}$$

or

$$B_2 = 0$$

The complete solution with arbitrary constants evaluated then becomes

$$x = \frac{F}{K}\left(1 - \cos\sqrt{\frac{K}{M}}\,t\right)$$

which is plotted in Fig. 5.8. The frequency of the oscillations is $\omega = \sqrt{K/M}$.

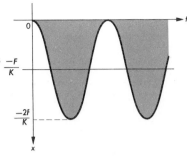

FIG. 5.8 *Solution of the undamped spring-mass system of Fig. 5.7.*

5.4 SINUSOIDAL INPUT TO *RL* AND *RC* CIRCUITS

A sinusoidal voltage exciting an *RL* or *RC* circuit produces a steady-state current which is also sinusoidal and whose magnitude and phase angle can be found from the circuit impedance as discussed in Chap. 4. The magnitude of the steady-state current is found from

$$I_m = \frac{E_m}{Z} \qquad (5.26)$$

where E_m is the maximum value of the sinusoidal exciting voltage and $Z = \sqrt{R^2 + X^2}$. The phase angle of the steady-state current with respect to the sinusoidal exciting voltage is

$$\theta = -\tan^{-1}\frac{X}{R} \qquad (5.27)$$

where X is positive for inductive reactance and negative for capacitive reactance. In other words, θ is negative and the current lags the voltage if the reactance is inductive, and θ is positive and the current leads the voltage if the reactance is capacitive. For the sinusoidal exciting voltage

$$e = E_m \sin(\omega t + \phi) \qquad (5.28)$$

the steady-state current expressed as a function of time is

$$i_s = \frac{E_m}{Z}\sin(\omega t + \phi + \theta) \qquad (5.29)$$

The natural response of an *RL* or *RC* circuit must be exponential in form and can be found from the circuit differential equation or characteristic equation. In Eqs. (3.18) and (3.27), respectively, we saw that the natural response of *RL* and *RC* circuits was

$$i_n = A\epsilon^{-(R/L)t}$$

$$i_n = A\epsilon^{-t/RC}$$

where A is an arbitrary constant in each case and must be evaluated to satisfy the initial conditions. The complete solution, from Eq. (5.3), is

$$i = i_s + i_n$$

or

$$i_{RL} = \frac{E_m}{Z} \sin (\omega t + \phi + \theta) + A\epsilon^{-(R/L)t} \qquad (5.30)$$

and

$$i_{RC} = \frac{E_m}{Z} \sin (\omega t + \phi + \theta) + A\epsilon^{-t/RC} \qquad (5.31)$$

where Eqs. (5.30) and (5.31) are for RL and RC circuits, respectively, ϕ is the angle on the sine wave at which the switch is closed, a.id Z is the sinusoidal impedance $Z = \sqrt{R^2 + X^2}$. The arbitrary constants are evaluated by substituting the initial current and $t = 0$ into Eqs. (5.30) and (5.31) and solving for A.

Example 5.2

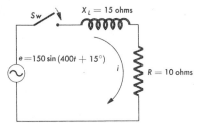

FIG. 5.9 *RL series circuit of Example 5.2.*

The RL circuit of Fig. 5.9 is connected to a sinusoidal-voltage source by closing switch Sw at $\phi = 15°$. The initial current is $I_0 = 0$ at $t = 0$. The steady-state solution is found first.

$$i_s = \frac{150}{\sqrt{10^2 + 15^2}} \sin (400t + 15° + \theta) \qquad \text{amp}$$

where

$$\theta = -\tan^{-1} \frac{15}{10} = -56.3°$$

Numerically, then,

$$i_s = 8.33 \sin (400t - 41.3°) \qquad \text{amp}$$

The natural response is of the form

$$i_n = A\epsilon^{-(R/L)t} \qquad \text{amp}$$

where L is found from $X_L = \omega L = 15$ to be

$$L = \frac{15}{400} = 0.0375 \text{ henry}$$

Then

$$i_n = A\epsilon^{-(10/0.0375)t} = A\epsilon^{-267t} \qquad \text{amp}$$

and the complete solution is

$$i = i_s + i_n$$

$$= 8.33 \sin (400t - 41.3°) + A\epsilon^{-267t} \qquad \text{amp}$$

To evaluate A, let $i = 0$ at $t = 0$. Then

$$0 = 8.33 \sin (-41.3°) + A$$

or

$$A = +8.33 \sin (-41.3°) = -8.33(0.660) = +5.50$$

The complete solution can now be written

$$i = 8.33 \sin (400t - 41.3°) + 5.50\epsilon^{-267t} \qquad \text{amp}$$

The time constant of the natural response is

$$\tau = \tfrac{1}{267} = 0.00375 \text{ sec}$$

After five time constants, where $5\tau = 0.01875$ sec, the natural response has decayed and become negligible, and the steady-state response can be considered to be the complete solution.

5.5 SINUSOIDAL INPUT TO AN *RLC* SERIES CIRCUIT

The RLC series circuit excited by a sinusoidal input voltage [Eq. (5.28)]

$$e = E_m \sin (\omega t + \phi)$$

presents interesting variations in the forms of the complete solution. The steady-state current is found as in preceding sections,

$$i_s = \frac{E_m}{Z} \sin (\omega t + \phi + \theta)$$

where from Eqs. (4.37) and (4.36), respectively,

$$Z = \sqrt{R^2 + \left(\omega L - \frac{1}{\omega C}\right)^2}$$

and

$$\theta = - \tan^{-1} \frac{\omega L - 1/\omega C}{R}$$

The frequency of the sinusoidal steady-state current is the same as the frequency of the exciting voltage, being ω of Eqs. (5.28) and (5.29). But the natural response, if underdamped, has a natural frequency which is determined only by the relative values of the parameters R, L, and C and which may be quite different from the steady-state frequency.

The form of the natural response is determined from the roots of the characteristic equation and the inequalities of Eqs. (3.38) to (3.40). If the roots are real and unequal, the natural response is the sum of two exponentials

$$i_n = A_1 \epsilon^{p_1 t} + A_2 \epsilon^{p_2 t} \tag{5.32}$$

where [Eqs. (3.34) and (3.36), respectively]

$$p_1 = -\frac{R}{2L} + \sqrt{\frac{R^2}{4L^2} - \frac{1}{LC}}$$

$$p_2 = -\frac{R}{2L} - \sqrt{\frac{R^2}{4L^2} - \frac{1}{LC}}$$

and the complete solution is

$$i = \frac{E_m}{Z} \sin (\omega t + \phi + \theta) + A_1 \epsilon^{p_1 t} + A_2 \epsilon^{p_2 t} \tag{5.33}$$

The arbitrary constants A_1 and A_2 are evaluated from the initial conditions. If $i = 0$ at $t = 0$, then substituting this information into Eq. (5.33) gives one algebraic equation in the two unknowns A_1 and A_2. Then

$$0 = -\frac{E_m}{Z} \sin (\phi + \theta) + A_1 + A_2$$

or

$$A_1 + A_2 = -\frac{E_m}{Z} \sin (\phi + \theta) \tag{5.34}$$

For another algebraic equation in A_1 and A_2, we differentiate Eq. (5.33) with respect to time and substitute the initial derivative and $t = 0$ into the resulting expression. The derivative at $t = 0$ is obtained from the circuit differential equation

$$L\frac{di}{dt} + Ri + \frac{1}{C} \int_0^t i \, dt + V_0 = E_m \sin (\omega t + \phi) \tag{5.35}$$

where, at $t = 0$ and $i = 0$,

$$L\frac{di}{dt} + V_0 = E_m \sin \phi$$

or

$$\left.\frac{di}{dt}\right|_{t=0} = \frac{E_m \sin \phi - V_0}{L} \tag{5.36}$$

Differentiating Eq. (5.33) with respect to time results in

$$\frac{di}{dt} = \frac{E_m\omega}{Z}\cos(\omega t + \phi + \theta) + A_1 p_1 \epsilon^{p_1 t} + A_2 p_2 \epsilon^{p_2 t} \qquad (5.37)$$

Substituting Eq. (5.36) and $t = 0$ into Eq. (5.37) gives the second algebraic equation in A_1 and A_2, namely,

$$A_1 p_1 + A_2 p_2 = -\frac{E_m\omega}{Z}\cos(\phi + \theta) + \frac{E_m \sin \phi - V_0}{L} \qquad (5.38)$$

Now, to solve Eqs. (5.34) and (5.38) simultaneously, it is convenient first to recognize that the right-hand side of each equation is a constant; thus Eqs. (5.34) and (5.38) can be written

$$A_1 + A_2 = D_1 \qquad (5.39)$$

$$p_1 A_1 + p_2 A_2 = D_2 \qquad (5.40)$$

where

$$D_1 = -\frac{E_m}{Z}\sin(\phi + \theta) \qquad (5.41)$$

and

$$D_2 = -\frac{E_m\omega}{Z}\cos(\phi + \theta) + \frac{E_m \sin \phi - V_0}{L} \qquad (5.42)$$

Now solving Eqs. (5.39) and (5.40) simultaneously for A_1 and A_2 as functions of D_1 and D_2 we have

$$A_1 = \frac{D_1 p_2 - D_2}{p_2 - p_1} \qquad (5.43)$$

and

$$A_2 = \frac{D_2 - p_1 D_1}{p_2 - p_1} \qquad (5.44)$$

Thus Eq. (5.33) is a complete solution for any possible initial conditions, but for the particular initial conditions specified, namely, $i = 0$ at $t = 0$, Eqs. (5.43) and (5.44) are the values of the arbitrary constants. The time constants in this example are $1/p_1$ and $1/p_2$. After five or more time constants, the exponential terms have effectively vanished, and the steady-state current can be considered the solution of the circuit.

5.6 IMPULSE RESPONSE

The response of a circuit to a step input of voltage has been discussed in Secs. 5.2 and 5.3. Step-input response consists of the natural response and the steady-state response, the latter being the response to a constant exciting voltage. But suppose that the step input is followed a time T later by another step input of opposite sign but equal magnitude, as shown in Fig. 5.10. The exciting voltage that results is a rectangular pulse of width T and magnitude E. The solution of circuits excited by a pulse of this form is straightforward. First the solution of the circuit excited by the step voltage starting at $t = 0$ is obtained. This is the solution for the interval $0 < t \leq T$. Then the "initial" conditions at $t = T$ are evaluated, and the solution is obtained for those "initial" condi-

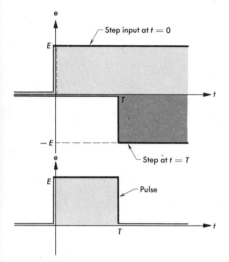

Step input at $t = 0$

Step at $t = T$

Pulse

FIG. 5.10 *Two voltage steps producing a rectangular pulse.*

tions for $t > T$ when the exciting voltage is zero. An example of this procedure can be followed to solve one of the problems at the end of the chapter.

Of considerable interest also as an exciting function is the *impulse* function, and the response of the circuit excited by an impulse. We define an impulse as a rectangular pulse of duration T, magnitude K/T, and area K, when $T \rightarrow 0$. A unit impulse is defined for $K = 1$. The impulse has interesting properties; its duration is infinitesimal, its magnitude approaches infinity, and its area is K. Although impulses do not ordinarily occur exactly in nature, there are several phenomena which are approximately equivalent to an impulse. We are familiar with the force of a blow with a hammer or the force of the kick of a gun; these are very nearly impulse functions.

Now suppose that an *RL* circuit is excited by an impulse of voltage. We first approximate the impulse by two step functions of voltage, the sum of which produces the impulse. The first step voltage initiates a current of the form

$$i = \frac{K/T}{R}(1 - \epsilon^{-(R/L)t}) \tag{5.45}$$

which becomes

$$I_T = \frac{K}{TR}(1 - \epsilon^{-RT/L}) \tag{5.46}$$

at $t = T$. Now we let $T \to 0$, and I_T becomes an indeterminant of the form $0/0$. Differentiating the numerator and denominator of Eq. (5.46) with respect to T according to L'Hospital's rule, and then letting $T \to 0$, we have

$$I_T = \frac{K}{L} \tag{5.47}$$

Thus the current $i = K/L$ expressed by Eq. (5.47) can be considered the initial current of the circuit at the instant after the impulse has passed. The differential equation after the impulse is

$$L\frac{di}{dt} + Ri = 0$$

with initial current $I_0 = K/L$, and the solution is

$$i = \frac{K}{L}\epsilon^{-(R/L)t} \tag{5.48}$$

When an impulse is the exciting function of a physical system, energy is stored in the system by the impulse. The system response, then, is merely the natural response with the initial conditions determined by the impulse.

Example 5.3

A mass of 4 kg is initially at rest on a horizontal plane (Fig. 5.11). It is struck by a hammer with a blow that can be considered as a force impulse of 12 newton-sec. The friction force is assumed to be viscous with friction constant $B = 8$ kg/sec. After the hammer blow at $t = T$, the velocity is

$$V_i = \frac{K}{BT}(1 - \epsilon^{-(B/M)T})$$

Differentiating numerator and denominator with respect to time and then letting $T \to 0$, we have

$$V_i = \frac{K}{M}$$

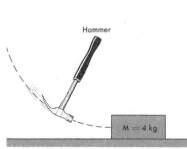

Hammer

$M = 4$ kg

FIG. 5.11 *An impulse delivered to mass M.*

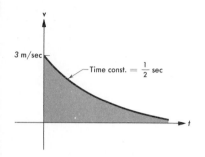

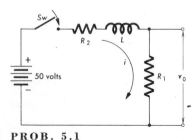

FIG. 5.12 *Velocity versus time for the mass of Fig. 5.11.*

PROB. 5.1

The velocity after the impulse is the solution of the equation

$$M \frac{dv}{dt} + Bv = 0$$

with the initial velocity of K/M. Then

$$v = \frac{K}{M} \epsilon^{-(B/M)t}$$

which can be written with numerical constants

$$v = 3\epsilon^{-2t} \qquad \text{m/sec}$$

which is sketched in Fig. 5.12.

SUMMARY

The complete solution of a physical system that can be described by a differential equation consists of two components: (*a*) the natural response, and (*b*) the steady-state response. If the system has no external exciting function, its steady-state response is zero and the complete solution is the natural response only.

An electric circuit excited by a step voltage or a sinusoidal voltage has a complete solution which is the sum of the steady-state current and the natural response, or [Eq. (5.3)]

$$i = i_s + i_n$$

The steady-state response can be evaluated by impedance concepts developed in Chap. 4 for sinusoidal or constant exciting voltages. The natural response is obtained by methods outlined in Chap. 3. The natural-response term in Eq. (5.3) contains arbitrary constants which must be evaluated by substituting into the solution the initial conditions of the circuit.

The impulse response is obtained from the natural response of the circuit after finding the initial conditions established by the impulse. The impulse can be considered as a rectangular pulse of width T and magnitude K/T as $T \rightarrow 0$. The area under the impulse function is K.

PROBLEMS

5.1 A step input of 50 volts is applied to the RL circuit shown by closing switch Sw in the illustration. Find v_0 as a function of time, if $R_1 = 1,000$, $R = 2,000$, and $L = 1$.

5.2 In the figure the capacitor with an initial charge of $Q_0 = 10^{-3}$ coulomb is part of an RC circuit excited by a step voltage. Find the current i as a function of time after the switch is closed.

5.3 The voltage applied to a series RL circuit has been constant at 500 volts for a long time. At $t = 0$ the voltage is suddenly raised to 800 volts. Find i as a function time if $R = 100$ ohms and $L = 2$ henrys.

5.4 Capacitor C_1 in the figure is charged to 100 volts before switch Sw is closed; the initial charge on C_2 is zero. At $t = 0$ the switch is closed. (a) Find i as a function of time. (b) Find the voltage across C_2 as a function of time.

5.5 The RLC series circuit of Fig. 5.5 is connected to a voltage source of $E = 200$ volts at $t = 0$ by closing Sw. If $L = 0.1$ henry, $C = 10$ μf, and $R = 1{,}000$ ohms, find i as a function of time. Evaluate all arbitrary constants. $v_0 = 0$.

5.6 Repeat Prob. 5.5 when R has been reduced to 100 ohms.

5.7 Substitute Eq. (5.4) into Eq. (5.1) to verify that Eq. (5.4) satisfies Eq. (5.1) for all values of A.

5.8 Substitute Eq. (5.7) into Eq. (5.1) to verify that Eq. (5.7) satisfies the differential equation [Eq. (5.1)].

5.9 The circuit shown in the illustration is in a steady state when switch Sw is closed at $t = 0$. Find i as a function of time after $t = 0$.

5.10 The constant-voltage source of Prob. 5.9 is replaced by a sinusoidal voltage of $E_m \sin \omega t$. The switch is closed at $t = 0$; find i as a function of time.

5.11 The circuit shown in the figure is initially in a steady-state condition with the switch Sw open. At $t = 0$ the switch is closed. (a) Find the current i before the switch is closed. (b) Find the current i a long time after the switch is closed. (c) Find i as a function of time after the switch is closed.

5.12 A rectangular voltage pulse of 100 volts magnitude and 0.2 sec duration excites the RC circuit shown in the illustration. (a) Find i as a function of time both during the pulse and after the pulse has passed. (b) Find e_o as a function of time after $t = 0$.

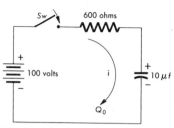

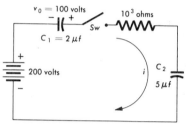

PROB. 5.2

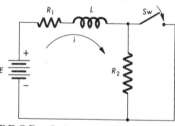

PROB. 5.4

PROB. 5.9

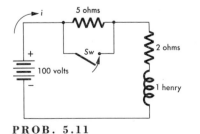

PROB. 5.11

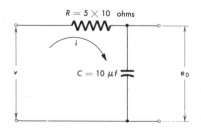

100 volts

0.2 sec

PROB. 5.12

Problems **139**

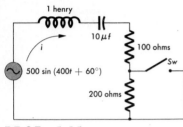

PROB. 5.15

5.13 The *RLC* series circuit of Fig. 5.5 is connected to a voltage source $e = 150 \sin(\omega t + 45°)$ at $t = 0$. If $L = 0.1$ henry, $C = 10\ \mu f$, and $R = 1{,}000$ ohms, find i as a function of time. Evaluate all arbitrary constants. $\omega = 100$ rad./sec.

5.14 An impulse of voltage is applied to the *RC* circuit of Prob. 5.12. The area under the impulse is 40 volt-sec. Find i as a function of time after the impulse has passed.

5.15 The *RLC* circuit shown in the illustration is in the steady state when *Sw* is opened at $t = 0$. Find i as a function of time after this event.

PARALLEL AND SERIES-PARALLEL CIRCUITS

6

6.1 INTRODUCTION

The circuits considered in the first five chapters have generally been series circuits; we have been interested in their steady-state response, in their natural response, and in the complete solution, which is the sum of steady-state and natural responses. Now we seek to extend our horizons by applying our present knowledge of circuit theory to parallel and series-parallel circuits. It is reasonable to expect that Kirchhoff's laws form the basis for formulating circuit equations and that natural response and steady-state response, as well as complete solutions, can be found by the methods that have already been developed.

The nature of the circuit problem dictates the kind of solution one must find. Under some conditions the complete solution may be needed; the complete solution tells the circuit response immediately after switching action, as well as after the steady state has been reached. The steady-state solution alone is sometimes sufficient, and the natural response by itself is also useful in circuit analysis. In this chapter we sometimes seek one kind of solution and sometimes another. The student must first determine which solution is adequate and then proceed to find it; there is no need to find the complete solution when only the frequency of the natural response is called for. Or the steady-state solution has no significance if the circuit is destroyed by the switching transient.

6.2 CIRCUIT ELEMENTS IN PARALLEL— ADMITTANCE

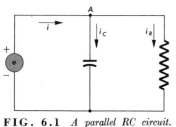

FIG. 6.1 *A parallel RC circuit.*

Kirchhoff's current law is the basis for the formulation of circuit equations of parallel elements. Consider the parallel circuit of Fig. 6.1, where the generator is the source of the arbitrary driving current i. At node A, the sum of the current at any instant is, by Kirchhoff's current law, zero. According to the directions of currents assigned in Fig. 6.1, then,

$$i_C + i_R = i \tag{6.1}$$

and

$$C\frac{de}{dt} + \frac{1}{R}e = i \tag{6.2}$$

Equation (6.2) is a first-order nonhomogeneous differential equation with arbitrary exciting current i.

If the exciting voltage e is a sinusoid, and only the sinusoidal steady-state solution is needed, Kirchhoff's current law applied to the circuit yields the phasor equation

$$\frac{\mathbf{E}}{1/j\omega C} + \frac{\mathbf{E}}{R} = \mathbf{I} \tag{6.3}$$

where $\mathbf{E}$ and $\mathbf{I}$ are the phasor exciting voltage and current, respectively. Observe in Eq. (6.3) that $1/j\omega C$ is the complex impedance of the capacitor and R is the impedance of the resistor. The complex *admittance*, denoted by $\mathbf{Y}$, can be written

$$\mathbf{Y} = \frac{1}{\mathbf{Z}} \tag{6.4}$$

where the complex admittance of the capacitor in Eq. (6.3) is $\mathbf{Y}_c = j\omega C$ and the admittance of the resistor is $1/R$. Then

$$\mathbf{E}\left(\frac{1}{R} + j\omega C\right) = \mathbf{I} \tag{6.5}$$

where the term in the parentheses of Eq. (6.5) is the parallel admittance of the circuit. The complex admittances of the two branches add to become the total admittance of the parallel circuit, just as series complex impedances add in a series circuit.

The parallel RLC circuit driven by a current source i is shown in Fig. 6.2. Equating the currents leaving the junction or node marked A to the currents entering A according to Kirchhoff's current law gives

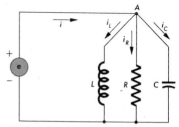

$$C\frac{de}{dt} + \frac{e}{R} + \frac{1}{L}\int_0^t e\,dt + I_0 = i \tag{6.6}$$

which can be made into a second-order differential equation by differentiating each term with respect to time.

FIG. 6.2 *Parallel RLC circuit.*

If the voltage e of Fig. 6.2 is a sinusoid, the steady-state equation in phasor form can be obtained from Kirchhoff's current law.

$$\frac{E}{1/j\omega C} + \frac{E}{R} + \frac{E}{j\omega L} = I \tag{6.7}$$

where E and I are phasor quantities. By factoring, Eq. (6.7) can be written

$$E\left(\frac{1}{R} + j\omega C + \frac{1}{j\omega L}\right) = I \tag{6.8}$$

where the term in the parentheses is the complex admittance of the parallel circuit.

The complete solution of Eq. (6.2) or (6.6) requires a knowledge of the nature of the exciting current i. For instance, if i is a step of magnitude I, then the solution of Eq. (6.2) is the sum of the steady-state response IR and the natural response, or

$$e = IR(1 - \epsilon^{-t/RC}) \tag{6.9}$$

The solution of Eq. (6.6) can be obtained by first differentiating the equation with respect to time. If i is a step of magnitude I, then Eq. (6.6) becomes

$$C\frac{d^2e}{dt^2} + \frac{1}{R}\frac{de}{dt} + \frac{1}{L}e = 0 \tag{6.10}$$

which is a second-order homogeneous equation. The solution of this form of homogeneous equation is described in Sec. 3.6.

6.3 SINUSOIDAL STEADY-STATE SOLUTIONS OF PARALLEL CIRCUITS

The sinusoidal steady-state solution of a parallel circuit of several circuit elements can be obtained in terms of the complex impedance of each element or the complex admittance of each element.

Ohm's law in the sinusoidal steady state, a consequence of the impedance and admittance concept, is

$$\mathbf{I} = \frac{\mathbf{E}}{\mathbf{Z}} = \mathbf{EY} \qquad (6.11)$$

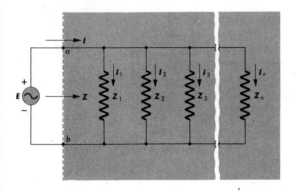

FIG. 6.3 *Parallel combination of n impedances.*

The circuit shown in Fig. 6.3 contains n impedances in parallel. By Kirchhoff's current law we can write

$$\mathbf{I} = \mathbf{I}_1 + \mathbf{I}_2 + \mathbf{I}_3 + \cdots + \mathbf{I}_n$$

or

$$\mathbf{I} = \frac{\mathbf{E}}{\mathbf{Z}_1} + \frac{\mathbf{E}}{\mathbf{Z}_2} + \frac{\mathbf{E}}{\mathbf{Z}_3} + \cdots + \frac{\mathbf{E}}{\mathbf{Z}_n} \qquad (6.12)$$

The impedance seen at terminals a–b is

$$\mathbf{Z} = \frac{\mathbf{E}}{\mathbf{I}} = \frac{1}{1/\mathbf{Z}_1 + 1/\mathbf{Z}_2 + 1/\mathbf{Z}_3 + \cdots + 1/\mathbf{Z}_n} \qquad (6.13)$$

and the admittance is the reciprocal of the impedance, or

$$\mathbf{Y} = \frac{\mathbf{I}}{\mathbf{E}} = \frac{1}{\mathbf{Z}_1} + \frac{1}{\mathbf{Z}_2} + \frac{1}{\mathbf{Z}_3} + \cdots + \frac{1}{\mathbf{Z}_n}$$

$$= \mathbf{Y}_1 + \mathbf{Y}_2 + \mathbf{Y}_3 + \cdots + \mathbf{Y}_n \qquad (6.14)$$

Notice that the circuit admittance as seen at the terminals is the sum of the admittances of each branch of the circuit.

Example 6.1

Find the complex impedance of the parallel RC circuit of Fig. 6.1 as seen by the generator. Express this impedance as the sum of a real and an imaginary term.

$$\mathbf{Z} = \frac{1}{\mathbf{Y}} = \frac{1}{1/R + j\omega C}$$

Rationalize the denominator.

$$\mathbf{Z} = \frac{1}{1/R + j\omega C}\frac{1/R - j\omega C}{1/R - j\omega C}$$

$$= \frac{1/R - j\omega C}{(1/R)^2 + \omega^2 C^2}$$

$$= \frac{R - j\omega C R^2}{1 + \omega^2 C^2 R^2} = \frac{R}{1 + \omega^2 C^2 R^2} - j\frac{\omega C R^2}{1 + \omega^2 C^2 R^2}$$

Example 6.2

Find the complex impedance of the two parallel paths in the circuit of Fig. 6.4, and express $\mathbf{Z}$ as the sum of a real part and an imaginary part.

$$\mathbf{Z} = \frac{1}{1/\mathbf{Z}_1 + 1/\mathbf{Z}_2}$$

where

$$\mathbf{Z}_1 = R + j\omega L$$

$$\mathbf{Z}_2 = \frac{1}{j\omega C}$$

$$\mathbf{Z} = \frac{1}{1/(R + j\omega L) + j\omega C} = \frac{R + j\omega L}{1 - \omega^2 LC + j\omega CR}$$

$$= \frac{R + j\omega L}{(1 - \omega^2 LC) + j\omega CR}\frac{(1 - \omega^2 LC - j\omega CR)}{(1 - \omega^2 LC - j\omega CR)}$$

$$= \frac{R - \omega^2 LCR + \omega^2 LCR + j(\omega L - \omega^3 L^2 C - \omega CR^2)}{(1 - \omega^2 LC)^2 + (\omega RC)^2}$$

$$= \frac{R + j\omega(L - R^2 C - \omega^2 L^2 C)}{(1 - \omega^2 LC)^2 + (\omega RC)^2}$$

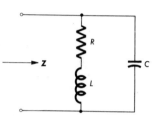

FIG. 6.4 *Series-parallel circuit of Example 6.2.*

Example 6.3

Find the complex admittance of a series RL circuit, and express $\mathbf{Y}$ as the sum of a real part and an imaginary part.

$$\mathbf{Y} = \frac{1}{\mathbf{Z}}$$

$$= \frac{1}{R + j\omega L} = \frac{R - j\omega L}{R^2 + (\omega L)^2} = \frac{R}{R^2 + (\omega L)^2} - j\frac{\omega L}{R^2 + (\omega L)^2}$$

The real part of admittance is called *conductance*, designated G, and the imaginary part is known as *susceptance*, designated B. If $Z = R + jX$ in a series circuit,

$$Y = \frac{1}{Z} = \frac{1}{R + jX}$$

$$= \frac{R - jX}{R^2 + X^2} = \frac{R}{R^2 + X^2} - j\frac{X}{R^2 + X^2} \tag{6.15}$$

where the conductance $G = R/(R^2 + X^2)$ and the susceptance $B = X/(R^2 + X^2)$. Notice that the sign of the imaginary term in Eq. (6.15) is opposite to the sign of the imaginary term of the impedance. Thus, if Z is written

$$Z = R + jX$$

then ,

$$Y = G + jB \tag{6.16}$$

The units of G and B are the reciprocal of resistance and reactance units, called "mhos," which have dimensions of amperes per volt.

6.4 PARALLEL RESONANCE

Inductance and capacitance in parallel, when excited by a sinusoidal exciting voltage, possess interesting frequency characteristics. Since inductive reactance is proportional to frequency and capacitive reactance is inversely proportional to frequency, a frequency exists at which the voltage and current from the generator are in phase; at this frequency a form of resonance occurs just as for the LC series circuit. But circuit impedance near parallel resonance behaves exactly opposite to the way series resonance behaves, and hence this phenomenon is sometimes termed "antiresonance."

Consider a parallel combination of resistance, inductance, and capacitance as shown in Fig. 6.2. The generator is a sinusoidal-voltage source whose frequency is adjustable; so the voltage, current, admittance, and impedance can be studied. The complex admittance can be written, from Eq. (6.8),

$$Y = \frac{1}{R} + j\left(\omega C - \frac{1}{\omega L}\right) \tag{6.17}$$

and the magnitude of Y is

$$Y = \sqrt{\left(\frac{1}{R}\right)^2 + \left(\omega C - \frac{1}{\omega L}\right)^2} \qquad (6.18)$$

Equation (6.18) is remarkably similar to the impedance equation for an RLC series circuit [Eq. (4.37)].

$$Z = \sqrt{R^2 + \left(\omega L - \frac{1}{\omega C}\right)^2}$$

At the frequency at which $\omega L = 1/\omega C$, both the admittance of Eq. (6.18) and the impedance of Eq. (4.37) have minimum values which increase as the frequency increases or decreases from $\omega = 1/\sqrt{LC}$. The admittance of the parallel RLC circuit is plotted as a function of frequency in Fig. 6.5. The impedance, or

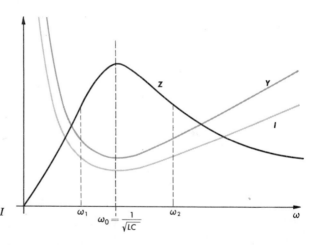

FIG. 6.5 *Parallel resonance showing Z, Y, and I versus ω.*

reciprocal admittance, is also shown. Notice that, since $Y = I/E$, for constant E the current I is proportional to Y. In Fig. 6.5 it is shown that I as a function of frequency reaches a minimum at the resonant frequency ω_0 when the exciting voltage is constant. Inspection of Eq. (6.18) shows that Y (and therefore I) is zero at resonant frequency if R is infinite. Thus, at resonance, both the admittance and the current are inversely proportional to R.

If the exciting current is constrained to be a sinusoid, the voltage across a parallel RLC combination is maximum at the resonant frequency, since impedance is maximum at resonant frequency. In fact, when the exciting current is a sinusoid of constant amplitude, the voltage E is proportional to the impedance Z. It is possible to define upper and lower half-power frequencies for this circuit just as was done for the series resonant circuit in Sec. 4.6. If the cutoff or half-power frequencies are defined as those frequencies on each side of resonance at which the voltage (for a constant sinusoidal exciting current) is 0.707 times the voltage at resonance, then

$$\frac{1}{0.707R} = \sqrt{\frac{1}{R^2} + \left(\omega C - \frac{1}{\omega L}\right)^2}$$ (6.19)

Solving Eq. (6.19) for ω gives

$$\omega = \pm\sqrt{\frac{A}{2} \pm \sqrt{\frac{A^2}{4} - \frac{1}{L^2 C^2}}}$$ (6.20)

where

$$A = \left(\frac{2}{LC} + \frac{1}{R^2 C^2}\right)$$

The two positive frequencies represented by Eq. (6.20) are shown as ω_1 and ω_2 in Fig. 6.5, and resonant frequency is $\omega_0 = 1/\sqrt{LC}$ radians/sec.

6.5 LOOP EQUATIONS FOR SERIES-PARALLEL CIRCUITS

An electric network often requires more than one equation to describe it by Kirchhoff's laws. Consider the circuit shown in Fig. 6.6, in which the current in each element has been defined. Kirch-

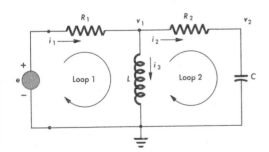

FIG. 6.6 *A series-parallel circuit with three branch currents* i_1, i_2, *and* i_3.

hoff's voltage law is the basis for writing

$$R_1 i_1 + L\frac{di_3}{dt} = e$$

$$R_2 i_2 + \frac{1}{C}\int i_2\, dt - L\frac{di_3}{dt} = 0$$

(6.21)

around the two loops shown, and Kirchhoff's current law allows us to write the currents in each branch as

$$i_1 = i_2 + i_3$$

(6.22)

Solving Eq. (6.22) for i_3 and substituting it into Eqs. (6.21) results in

$$R_1 i_1 + L\frac{d(i_1 - i_2)}{dt} = e$$

$$R_2 i_2 + \frac{1}{C}\int i_2\, dt + L\frac{d(i_2 - i_1)}{dt} = 0$$

(6.23)

Equations (6.23) are identical to the equations which result from an identical circuit in which the currents have been defined as shown in Fig. 6.7, where $i_1 - i_2 = i_3$. The currents i_1 and i_2 of

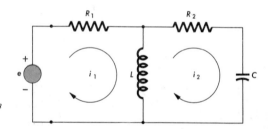

FIG. 6.7 *Series-parallel circuit of Fig. 6.6 with two loop currents defined.*

Fig. 6.7 are known as "loop" currents. By defining loop currents as shown, the required number of equations needed for a solution of the circuit is reduced from three to two. Notice that there are only two unknown currents, i_1 and i_2, and two simultaneous equations [Eqs. (6.23)], whereas three equations [Eqs. (6.21) and (6.22)] are required when branch currents defined in Fig. 6.6 are used.

Loop equations can be written for circuits in the sinusoidal steady state. It is necessary only to assign positive direction to the currents as they are defined in the loops and to make sure that at least one loop current passes through each circuit element.

6.5 *Loop Equations for Series-parallel Circuits* 149

Example 6.4

The ladder network shown in Fig. 6.8 is excited by voltage **E**. Loop currents are arbitrarily defined in the clockwise direction. Kirch-

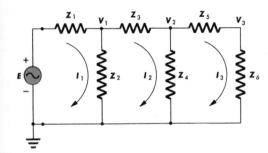

FIG. 6.8 *Ladder network of Example 6.4.*

hoff's voltage law is the basis for the following equations,

$$\mathbf{Z}_1\mathbf{I}_1 + \mathbf{Z}_2(\mathbf{I}_1 - \mathbf{I}_2) = \mathbf{E}$$

$$\mathbf{Z}_3\mathbf{I}_2 + \mathbf{Z}_4(\mathbf{I}_2 - \mathbf{I}_3) + \mathbf{Z}_2(\mathbf{I}_2 - \mathbf{I}_1) = 0 \tag{6.24}$$

$$\mathbf{Z}_5\mathbf{I}_3 + \mathbf{Z}_6\mathbf{I}_3 + \mathbf{Z}_4(\mathbf{I}_3 - \mathbf{I}_2) = 0$$

which can be written in the factored form

$$(\mathbf{Z}_1 + \mathbf{Z}_2)\mathbf{I}_1 - \mathbf{Z}_2\mathbf{I}_2 = \mathbf{E} \tag{6.25}$$

$$-\mathbf{Z}_2\mathbf{I}_1 + (\mathbf{Z}_2 + \mathbf{Z}_3 + \mathbf{Z}_4)\mathbf{I}_2 - \mathbf{Z}_4\mathbf{I}_3 = 0 \tag{6.26}$$

$$-\mathbf{Z}_4\mathbf{I}_2 + (\mathbf{Z}_4 + \mathbf{Z}_5 + \mathbf{Z}_6)\mathbf{I}_3 = 0 \tag{6.27}$$

Notice that, in the three equations above, the coefficient for each loop current is the total series impedance which that loop current sees in the particular loop for which the equation was written. For instance, in Eq. (6.25), $\mathbf{I}_1$ sees $\mathbf{Z}_1$ plus $\mathbf{Z}_2$ in its path around the first loop, and $\mathbf{I}_2$ sees $\mathbf{Z}_2$ in the opposite direction to $\mathbf{I}_1$.

Example 6.5

A resistive network with a constant-voltage source is shown in Fig. 6.9. Each resistor is shown with its value in ohms. Kirchhoff's voltage law allows us to write

$$8I_1 - 2I_2 - I_3 = 10 \tag{6.28}$$

$$-2I_1 + 15I_2 - 6I_3 = 0 \tag{6.29}$$

$$-I_1 - 6I_2 + 12I_3 = 0 \tag{6.30}$$

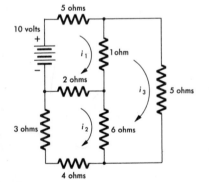

FIG. 6.9 *Resistive network of Example 6.5.*

Notice that, in Eq. (6.28) representing the upper left-hand loop, 8 ohms is the total resistance seen in that loop by I_1, 2 ohms is seen by I_2 in that loop, and 1 ohm is seen by I_3.

The solution of the algebraic system of equations follows the well-known Cramer's rule, where the various currents are expressed as the ratio of two determinants.

$$I_1 = \frac{\begin{vmatrix} 10 & -2 & -1 \\ 0 & 15 & -6 \\ 0 & -6 & 12 \end{vmatrix}}{\begin{vmatrix} 8 & -2 & -1 \\ -2 & 15 & -6 \\ -1 & -6 & 12 \end{vmatrix}} = 1.35 \text{ amp}$$

$$I_2 = \frac{\begin{vmatrix} 8 & 10 & -1 \\ -2 & 0 & -6 \\ -1 & 0 & 12 \end{vmatrix}}{\begin{vmatrix} 8 & -2 & -1 \\ -2 & 15 & -6 \\ -1 & -6 & 12 \end{vmatrix}} = 0.282 \text{ amp}$$

$$I_3 = \frac{\begin{vmatrix} 8 & -2 & 10 \\ -2 & 15 & 0 \\ -1 & -6 & 0 \end{vmatrix}}{\begin{vmatrix} 8 & -2 & -1 \\ -2 & 15 & -6 \\ -1 & -6 & 12 \end{vmatrix}} = 0.253 \text{ amp}$$

Loop currents can be defined around any closed path in the circuit, but they are usually drawn around each rectangle, or "window." One or more loop currents must pass through each circuit element if enough loops are defined to provide the number of independent equations needed to solve the circuit. The choice of how to define loop currents is an arbitrary one, but it must be made before the circuit equations are written.

6.6 NODE EQUATIONS
FOR SERIES-PARALLEL CIRCUITS

Instead of defining loop currents for a circuit, we can define node voltages and write Kirchhoff's current-law equations about each node. With the example of Fig. 6.6 as a basis, two voltages marked v_1 and v_2 are instantaneous values defined with respect to the ground reference potential. The two Kirchhoff's current-law equations are

$$\frac{v_1 - e}{R_1} + \frac{1}{L}\int_0^t v_1\, dt + I_0 + \frac{v_1 - v_2}{R_2} = 0$$

(6.31)

$$\frac{v_2 - v_1}{R_2} + C\frac{dv_2}{dt} = 0$$

where I_0 is the initial current through the inductor L. Then Eqs. (6.31) can be written

$$\frac{v_1}{R_1} + \frac{v_1}{R_2} + \frac{1}{L}\int_0^t v_1\, dt - \frac{v_2}{R_2} = \frac{e}{R_1} - I_0$$

(6.32)

$$\frac{-v_1}{R_2} + \frac{v_2}{R_2} + C\frac{dv_2}{dt} = 0$$

The simultaneous solution of the two equations above yields the voltages v_1 and v_2, but simultaneous differential-equation solutions will not be attempted yet.

Node equations for impedance networks excited by sinusoidal voltages also follow from Kirchhoff's current law. Consider the following example, which utilizes the same circuit as Example 6.4.

Example 6.6

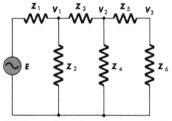

FIG. 6.10 *Impedance network for node equations.*

In the circuit shown in Fig. 6.10, we have defined the potential V_1, V_2, and V_3 with respect to the reference. By equating the sum of the currents away from each node to zero and by using the impedance of each element, Eqs. (6.33) result.

$$\frac{V_1 - E}{Z_1} + \frac{V_1}{Z_2} + \frac{V_1 - V_2}{Z_3} = 0$$

$$\frac{V_2 - V_1}{Z_3} + \frac{V_2}{Z_4} + \frac{V_2 - V_3}{Z_5} = 0$$

(6.33)

$$\frac{V_3 - V_2}{Z_5} + \frac{V_3}{Z_6} = 0$$

Using $Y = 1/Z$ and arranging terms, Eqs. (6.33) can be written

$$(Y_1 + Y_2 + Y_3)V_1 - Y_3V_2 = EY_1$$

$$-Y_3V_1 + (Y_3 + Y_4 + Y_5)V_2 - Y_5V_3 = 0$$

(6.34)

$$-Y_5V_2 + (Y_5 + Y_6)V_3 = 0$$

The above two sets of equations are equivalent descriptions of the circuit.

Example 6.7

To find the voltage V_2 in the d-c circuit shown in Fig. 6.11, first write the circuit equations.

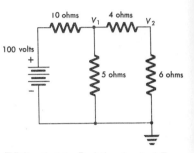

$$\frac{V_1 - 100}{10} + \frac{V_1}{5} + \frac{V_1 - V_2}{4} = 0$$

$$\frac{V_2 - V_1}{4} + \frac{V_2}{6} = 0$$

or

$$(\tfrac{1}{10} + \tfrac{1}{5} + \tfrac{1}{4})V_1 - \tfrac{1}{4}V_2 = 10$$

$$-\tfrac{1}{4}V_1 + (\tfrac{1}{4} + \tfrac{1}{6})V_2 = 0$$

FIG. 6.11 *Resistive circuit of Example 6.7.*

or

$$0.55V_1 - 0.25V_2 = 10$$

$$-0.25V_1 + 0.42V_2 = 0$$

Solving the above system of algebraic equations simultaneously by using Cramer's rule,

$$V_2 = \frac{\begin{vmatrix} 0.55 & 10 \\ -0.25 & 0 \end{vmatrix}}{\begin{vmatrix} 0.55 & -0.25 \\ -0.25 & 0.417 \end{vmatrix}} = \frac{2.5}{0.231 - 0.0625} = 14.8 \text{ volts}$$

Node equations with node voltages as the variables are equivalent to loop equations with loop currents as the variables, since current through each element can be found from the voltage across each element, and vice versa. A circuit with several parallel elements lends itself nicely to solution by node voltages, since there are fewer node voltages and hence fewer node equations than loop currents and loop equations. The choice of whether to use node equations or loop equations may depend upon the number of nodes or loops, and therefore upon the number of simultaneous equations that must be solved.

6.7 POLYPHASE VOLTAGE SOURCES

A polyphase circuit is one which contains two or more sinusoidal voltage sources of the same frequency but of different phase. The main use of polyphase circuits is for the distribution and utilization of electric power, where polyphase power systems have some real advantages over single-phase systems. In particular, a three-phase system, which is the polyphase system most often used, has the following advantages when compared with a single-phase system: (a) the efficiency of transmission of three-phase power is higher, and (b) the efficiency, cost, and construction of three-phase voltage generators and motors all favor the three-phase machine. Some of these advantages will become apparent in later chapters; for the present we are concerned with circuit aspects of the three-phase system.

The electric-power industry generates three-phase power for transmission to centers where the power is used. The transmission of electric power is generally accomplished by a three-wire line, though sometimes a fourth line at ground potential is also used. Utilization of three-phase power occurs either through three-phase loads or through single-phase loads connected to two of the three-phase lines. Thus three-phase and single-phase loads can operate separately and simultaneously from a three-phase line.

An electromechanical three-phase voltage generator is known as an "alternator," or "alternating-voltage generator." One machine produces the three voltages simultaneously, and the voltages each have the same magnitude but are 120° out of phase with each other. Consider the three single-phase voltage generators represented in Fig. 6.12a; assume that the generated voltages are

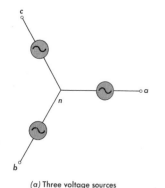

(a) Three voltage sources

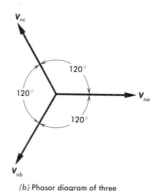

(b) Phasor diagram of three single-phase sources

FIG. 6.12   *Three-phase voltage source.*

120° apart in phase as shown in Fig. 6.12b. Generator A produces an emf represented in the phasor diagram as $\mathbf{V}_{na}$. Lagging $\mathbf{V}_{na}$ by 120° is voltage $\mathbf{V}_{nb}$ produced by generator B, and lagging $\mathbf{V}_{na}$ by 240° (leading it by 120°) is $\mathbf{V}_{nc}$ of generator C. Each of these voltages, referred to as "phase voltages," is measured with respect to the neutral, or common, terminal n of each generator. Using n

as the reference, or zero, potential, each of the phase voltages is represented by a phasor of equal magnitude 120° apart in phase from the others. Notice that the phasor sum of the three phase voltages in Fig. 6.12*b* is zero.

Terminals *a*, *b*, and *c* are line terminals, and to them is connected the network constituting the load. The load sees only the voltages between terminals *a*, *b*, and *c*; these are known as "line voltages," in contrast to the phase voltages $\mathbf{V}_{na}$, $\mathbf{V}_{nb}$, and $\mathbf{V}_{nc}$ produced by each generator. Line voltage $\mathbf{V}_{ab}$ is the voltage between terminals *a* and *b*. Likewise $\mathbf{V}_{bc}$ and $\mathbf{V}_{ca}$ are the line voltages between terminals *b* and *c* and terminals *c* and *a*, respectively. But the line voltage $\mathbf{V}_{ab}$ is the phasor sum of the phase voltages $\mathbf{V}_{an}$ and $\mathbf{V}_{nb}$. Since $\mathbf{V}_{an} = -\mathbf{V}_{na}$, then

$$\mathbf{V}_{ab} = -\mathbf{V}_{na} + \mathbf{V}_{nb} = \mathbf{V}_{an} + \mathbf{V}_{nb}$$

as shown in the phasor diagram of Fig. 6.13. Likewise

$$\mathbf{V}_{bc} = -\mathbf{V}_{nb} + \mathbf{V}_{nc} = \mathbf{V}_{bn} + \mathbf{V}_{nc}$$

and

$$\mathbf{V}_{ca} = -\mathbf{V}_{nc} + \mathbf{V}_{na} = \mathbf{V}_{cn} + \mathbf{V}_{na}$$

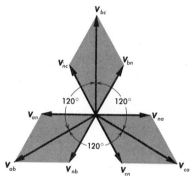

FIG. 6.13 *Phasor diagram of phase and line voltages of Y-connected three-phase source.*

The three line voltages $\mathbf{V}_{ab}$, $\mathbf{V}_{bc}$, $\mathbf{V}_{ca}$ are all shown in the phasor diagram of Fig. 6.13 as the sum of their appropriate phase voltages. Notice that, just as the three phase voltages $\mathbf{V}_{na}$, $\mathbf{V}_{nb}$, and $\mathbf{V}_{nc}$ are 120° apart, so also are the three line voltages·$\mathbf{V}_{ab}$, $\mathbf{V}_{bc}$, and $\mathbf{V}_{ca}$. Furthermore, the line voltages are not in phase with the phase voltages; for example, $\mathbf{V}_{ab}$ leads $\mathbf{V}_{an}$ by 30° and lags $\mathbf{V}_{nb}$ by 30°.

In the above example we have defined line voltages as $\mathbf{V}_{ab}$, $\mathbf{V}_{bc}$, and $\mathbf{V}_{ca}$. We could just as well have defined them as $\mathbf{V}_{ba}$, $\mathbf{V}_{cb}$, and $\mathbf{V}_{ac}$, in which case they would have occurred on the phasor diagrams 180° from where they now appear in Fig. 6.13.

The three-phase generators shown in Fig. 6.12*a* are connected with a common node in a manner that is often referred to as a Y connection, because of the similarity with the letter Y. It is possible to connect them in a manner corresponding to the Greek letter Δ (delta), in which case the line voltages and the phase voltages correspond. In Fig. 6.14 are shown the three generators connected delta, and the corresponding phasor diagram shows the identity of the phase voltages and the line voltages. In the Y connection, Kirchhoff's current law tells us that the phase current is the same as the line current. For the delta connection, however, the line current is the phasor sum of two phase currents.

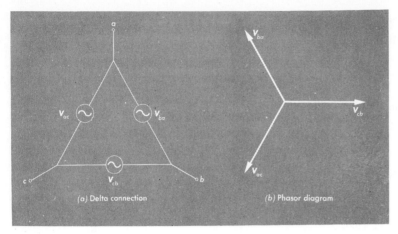

(a) Delta connection   (b) Phasor diagram

FIG. 6.14 *Three-phase delta-connected source.*

In Fig. 6.14, the three generators are connected around a closed loop, suggesting the possibility of current flowing around the loop through the generators. But if we add the three generated voltages around the loop, $\mathbf{V}_{cb} + \mathbf{V}_{ba} + \mathbf{V}_{ac}$, as shown in Fig. 6.14b, the phasor sum is zero, indicating there can be no circulating current around the loop of the delta.

Consider again the Y connection of voltage sources of Fig. 6.12a and the phasor diagram of Fig. 6.13. Observe that each of the line voltages $\mathbf{V}_{ab}$, $\mathbf{V}_{bc}$, and $\mathbf{V}_{ca}$ is equal in magnitude if the phase voltages $\mathbf{V}_{na}$, $\mathbf{V}_{nb}$, and $\mathbf{V}_{nc}$ are equal in magnitude. To find out how the line voltages compare with the phase voltages in magnitude and phase, consider the line voltage $\mathbf{V}_{ca}$, which is the phasor sum of phase voltages $\mathbf{V}_{na}$ and $\mathbf{V}_{cn}$. Phase voltage $\mathbf{V}_{nc}$ leads $\mathbf{V}_{na}$ by 120°, but $\mathbf{V}_{cn}$ lags $\mathbf{V}_{na}$ by 180° − 120°, or 60°; this 60° angle is bisected by the phasor sum of $\mathbf{V}_{na}$ and $\mathbf{V}_{cn}$, which is $\mathbf{V}_{ca}$. Then $\mathbf{V}_{na}$ leads $\mathbf{V}_{ca}$ by 30°, and $\mathbf{V}_{cn}$ lags $\mathbf{V}_{ca}$ by 30°. The component of $\mathbf{V}_{na}$ in phase with $\mathbf{V}_{ca}$ is $\mathbf{V}_{na} \cos 30°$, and the component of $\mathbf{V}_{cn}$ in phase with $\mathbf{V}_{ca}$ is $\mathbf{V}_{cn} \cos 30°$. Since $\mathbf{V}_{na}$ and $\mathbf{V}_{cn}$ are equal in magnitude and $\cos 30°$ is $\sqrt{3}/2$, then $\mathbf{V}_{ca}$ is equal to $2V_{na}\sqrt{3}/2$. Since V_{ca} is the magnitude of the line voltage and V_{na} is the magnitude of the phase voltage,

$$V_{\text{line}} = \sqrt{3}\, V_{\text{phase}} \tag{6.35}$$

for the Y connection.

By using complex algebra, the three-phase line voltages, such as those shown as phasors in Fig. 6.14b, can be expressed in conventional ways. For instance, $\mathbf{V}_{cb}$ can be expressed in polar form as $V_{cb}\epsilon^{j0°}$, with $\mathbf{V}_{ac} = V_{ac}\epsilon^{j240°}$ and $\mathbf{V}_{ba} = V_{ba}\epsilon^{j120°}$. The phasors can also be expressed in rectangular form.

6.8 THREE-PHASE CIRCUITS

In the preceding section, we saw how three voltage sources 120° apart in phase can be connected either delta or Y to provide the three-wire three-phase voltage source commonly used in power systems today. Now we investigate some methods for solving three-phase circuits connected to these voltage sources.

First, it should be obvious that a single impedance connected between two wires of the three-wire system represents a single-phase load to the system. This is shown in Fig. 6.15a, where Z_1 is connected between lines a and b and represents a single-phase (two-terminal) load on lines a and b. Furthermore, a second impedance, Z_2, can be connected between conductors b and c of the system, resulting in a second single-phase load. The third impedance, Z_3, completes the delta with three single-phase loads which now constitute the three-phase delta load on the system. Notice that Z_1, Z_2, and Z_3 each has only two terminals; so each constitutes the load on one phase of the system. But the three impedances together constitute a three-phase delta load.

Suppose that the voltage generators constituting the three-phase source are connected Y and that the neutral terminal n is available. Then impedances can be connected across each generator, as Z_a is across generator A from a to n in Fig. 6.16. The

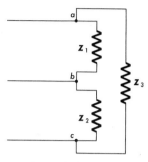

(a) Three single-phase loads

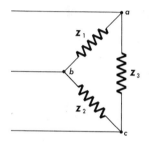

(b) Delta-connected three-phase load

FIG. 6.15 *Three single-phase loads make a three-phase delta load.*

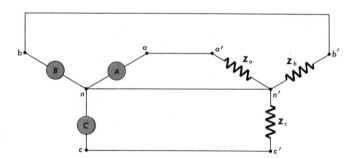

FIG. 6.16 *Three single-phase loads with a neutral make a Y-connected three-phase load.*

three impedances constitute a three-phase Y load with a neutral. Notice that four wires are shown. The line joining the generator neutral to the load neutral is unnecessary and can be removed. This would result in a three-wire three-phase system with a Y load.

It is always possible to solve three-phase-circuit problems by using Kirchhoff's laws and writing algebraic equations to be solved simultaneously. Phasor diagrams are helpful for keeping in mind the phase positions of the voltages and currents. Often the three-phase circuit can be solved as three single-phase circuits; this approach is used in Example 6.8 for a load connected delta.

Example 6.8

A three-phase voltage source is represented by the voltage phasors shown in Fig. 6.17a. The load is connected delta and is balanced,

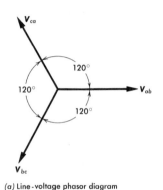

(a) Line-voltage phasor diagram

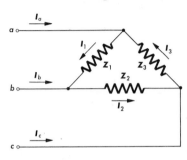

(b) Delta load

FIG. 6.17 *A three-phase delta load.*

and $\mathbf{Z}_1 = \mathbf{Z}_2 = \mathbf{Z}_3 = 10\epsilon^{j45°}$ ohms. The rms value of the line voltage is 220 volts. First, phase currents are found in phasor form.

$$\mathbf{I}_1 = \frac{\mathbf{V}_{ab}}{\mathbf{Z}_1} = \frac{220\epsilon^{j0°}}{10\epsilon^{j45°}} = 22\epsilon^{-j45°} \qquad \text{amp rms}$$

$$\mathbf{I}_2 = \frac{\mathbf{V}_{bc}}{\mathbf{Z}_2} = \frac{220\epsilon^{j240°}}{10\epsilon^{j45°}} = 22\epsilon^{j195°}$$

$$\mathbf{I}_3 = \frac{\mathbf{V}_{ca}}{\mathbf{Z}_3} = \frac{220\epsilon^{j120°}}{10\epsilon^{j45°}} = 22\epsilon^{j75°}$$

Next, phasor line currents are found from the appropriate phasor sum of the phase currents.

$$\mathbf{I}_a = \mathbf{I}_1 - \mathbf{I}_3 = 22\epsilon^{-j45°} - 22\epsilon^{j75°}$$

$$= 22[\cos(-45°) + j\sin(-45°)] - 22(\cos 75° + j\sin 75°)$$

$$= 22(0.707 - j0.707) - 22(0.259 + j0.966)$$

$$= (15.55 - j15.55) - (5.70 + j21.24)$$

$$= 9.85 - j36.79$$

$$= 38.1\epsilon^{-j75°} \qquad \text{amp rms}$$

Phasor line currents I_b and I_c can also be found by the same procedure.

$$I_b = I_2 - I_1 = 38.1\epsilon^{j165°}$$
$$I_c = I_3 - I_2 = 38.1\epsilon^{j45°}$$

The magnitude of the line currents is thus seen to be $\sqrt{3}$ times the magnitude of the phase current. The line currents are all equal in magnitude but spaced 120° apart in phase.

The above example shows how a three-phase delta circuit connected to a three-phase voltage source can be solved by finding phase currents in each impedance as a single-phase circuit and then adding appropriate phase currents to find line currents. This method can be used for delta loads regardless of whether the load is balanced or not, that is, whether or not Z_1, Z_2, and Z_3 are equal. But if the three-phase voltage source is connected to a Y load, each line current is equal to its corresponding phase current. Furthermore, if the Y load is unbalanced, so that $Z_a \neq Z_b \neq Z_c$ in Fig. 6.16, and the neutral of the voltage source is not connected to the neutral of the load, then the voltage across each phase is not known. Kirchhoff's voltage law provides a system of equations which can be solved for line (and phase) currents, from which the phase voltages can be found.

Consider the unbalanced Y circuit of Fig. 6.18b, excited by a balanced three-phase voltage source whose voltages are represented

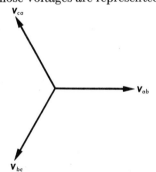 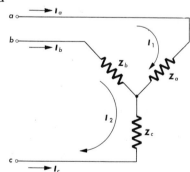

FIG. 6.18 *A Y-connected three-phase load.* (a) Line-voltage phasor diagram   (b) Wye load with loop currents defined

by the phasors in Fig. 6.18a. The loop currents I_1 and I_2 are defined as shown and are related to the three line (and phase) currents by

$$I_1 = I_a$$
$$I_2 - I_1 = I_b \qquad\qquad (6.36)$$
$$I_2 = -I_c$$

Line voltage can be expressed by

$$\mathbf{V}_{ab} = V_L \epsilon^{j0°}$$
$$\mathbf{V}_{bc} = V_L \epsilon^{j240°} \qquad (6.37)$$
$$\mathbf{V}_{ca} = V_L \epsilon^{j120°}$$

The two loop equations can now be written by Kirchhoff's law,

$$\mathbf{V}_{ab} = \mathbf{I}_1(\mathbf{Z}_a + \mathbf{Z}_b) - \mathbf{I}_2\mathbf{Z}_b$$
$$\mathbf{V}_{bc} = -\mathbf{I}_1\mathbf{Z}_b + \mathbf{I}_2(\mathbf{Z}_b + \mathbf{Z}_c) \qquad (6.38)$$

Solving for $\mathbf{I}_1$ and $\mathbf{I}_2$,

$$\mathbf{I}_1 = \frac{\begin{vmatrix} \mathbf{V}_{ab} & -\mathbf{Z}_b \\ \mathbf{V}_{bc} & \mathbf{Z}_b + \mathbf{Z}_c \end{vmatrix}}{\begin{vmatrix} \mathbf{Z}_a + \mathbf{Z}_b & -\mathbf{Z}_b \\ -\mathbf{Z}_b & \mathbf{Z}_b + \mathbf{Z}_c \end{vmatrix}} = \frac{\mathbf{V}_{ab}(\mathbf{Z}_b + \mathbf{Z}_c) + \mathbf{V}_{bc}\mathbf{Z}_b}{\mathbf{Z}_a\mathbf{Z}_b + \mathbf{Z}_a\mathbf{Z}_c + \mathbf{Z}_b\mathbf{Z}_c} \qquad (6.39)$$

$$\mathbf{I}_2 = \frac{\begin{vmatrix} \mathbf{Z}_a + \mathbf{Z}_b & \mathbf{V}_{ab} \\ -\mathbf{Z}_b & \mathbf{V}_{bc} \end{vmatrix}}{\mathbf{Z}_a\mathbf{Z}_b + \mathbf{Z}_b\mathbf{Z}_c + \mathbf{Z}_c\mathbf{Z}_a} = \frac{\mathbf{V}_{bc}(\mathbf{Z}_a + \mathbf{Z}_b) + \mathbf{V}_{ab}\mathbf{Z}_b}{\mathbf{Z}_a\mathbf{Z}_b + \mathbf{Z}_b\mathbf{Z}_c + \mathbf{Z}_c\mathbf{Z}_a} \qquad (6.40)$$

Example 6.9

In the circuit of Fig. 6.18 let $V_{ab} = V_{bc} = V_{ca} = 200$ volts, $\mathbf{Z}_a = 10\epsilon^{j0°}$, $\mathbf{Z}_b = 5\epsilon^{j0°}$, and $\mathbf{Z}_c = 20\epsilon^{j45°}$. Then the loop equations can be written from Eqs. (6.38),

$$200\epsilon^{j0°} = (10\epsilon^{j0°} + 5\epsilon^{j0°})\mathbf{I}_1 - 5\epsilon^{j0°}\mathbf{I}_2$$
$$200\epsilon^{j240°} = -5\epsilon^{j0°}\mathbf{I}_1 + (5\epsilon^{j0°} + 20\epsilon^{j45°})\mathbf{I}_2$$

Then

$$\mathbf{I}_1 = \frac{\begin{vmatrix} 200\epsilon^{j0°} & -5\epsilon^{j0°} \\ 200\epsilon^{j240°} & 5\epsilon^{j0°} + 20\epsilon^{j45°} \end{vmatrix}}{\begin{vmatrix} 10\epsilon^{j0°} + 5\epsilon^{j0°} & -5\epsilon^{j0°} \\ -5\epsilon^{j0°} & (5\epsilon^{j0°} + 20\epsilon^{j45°}) \end{vmatrix}}$$

$$= \frac{1,000\epsilon^{j0} + 4,000\epsilon^{j45°} + 1,000\epsilon^{j240°}}{50\epsilon^{j0°} + 200\epsilon^{j45°} + 100\epsilon^{j45°}}$$

$$= \frac{\left\{ \begin{aligned} &1,000 + 4,000(\cos 45° + j \sin 45°) \\ &+ 1,000(\cos 240° + j \sin 240°) \end{aligned} \right\}}{50 + 300(\cos 45° + j \sin 45°)}$$

$$= \frac{1,000 + 2,830 + j2,830 - 500 - j866}{50 + 212 + j212}$$

$$= \frac{3,330 + j1,964}{262 + j212} = 11.4 - j1.69 \text{ amp}$$

The solution of $\mathbf{I}_2$ is left as a problem for the student.

6.9 POWER IN THREE-PHASE CIRCUITS

The electric power delivered to a three-phase load can be found by treating each phase of the load as a single-phase circuit. Then

$$p = p_1 + p_2 + p_3 \qquad (6.41)$$

where p is the instantaneous power being delivered to the three-phase load and p_1, p_2, and p_3 are the instantaneous powers of each phase. Being interested mainly in the average power of the circuit in the steady state, we can write

$$P = P_1 + P_2 + P_3 \qquad (6.42)$$

where P is the average three-phase power and P_1, P_2, and P_3 are averages of the power in each phase. If the load is connected delta as shown in Fig. 6.17b, then Eq. (6.42) can be written

$$P = V_{ab}I_1 \cos \theta_1 + V_{bc}I_2 \cos \theta_2 + V_{ca}I_3 \cos \theta_3 \qquad (6.43)$$

where V_{ab}, V_{bc}, and V_{ca} are the rms line voltages, I_1, I_2, and I_3 the rms phase currents, and θ_1, θ_2, and θ_3 are the power-factor angles of each phase.

When the three-phase load is connected Y as in Fig. 6.14b, the three-phase average power can be written

$$P = V_{an}I_a \cos \theta_1 + V_{bn}I_b \cos \theta_2 + V_{cn}I_c \cos \theta_3 \qquad (6.44)$$

where V_{an}, V_{bn}, and V_{cn} are rms phase voltages, I_a, I_b, and I_c are rms phase (and line) currents, and θ_1, θ_2, and θ_3 are power-factor angles of each phase.

Average power delivered to a *balanced* three-phase load can be calculated readily from the phasor diagram of the circuit. A balanced delta load can be represented by Fig. 6.17b if $\mathbf{Z}_1 = \mathbf{Z}_2 = \mathbf{Z}_3$, and the balanced three-phase line voltage is represented by the phasor diagram of Fig. 6.17a, reproduced in Fig. 6.19. The phase currents $\mathbf{I}_1$, $\mathbf{I}_2$, and $\mathbf{I}_3$ each lags its respective phase voltage by the angle θ. Since the rms value of each phase voltage is the same and each phase current has the same rms value, then from Eq. (6.43)

$$P = 3V_{\text{phase}}I_{\text{phase}} \cos \theta \qquad (6.45)$$

For the delta load the line voltages and phase voltages are identical. Line current is formed as the phasor sum of two phase currents;

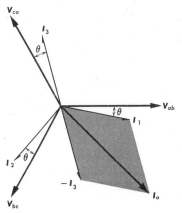

FIG. 6.19 *Phasor diagram for finding average power in a three-phase circuit.*

thus

$$\mathbf{I}_a = \mathbf{I}_1 - \mathbf{I}_3$$

From the geometry of Fig. 6.19, the angle between $\mathbf{I}_1$ and $-\mathbf{I}_2$ is 60°, and therefore the magnitude of $\mathbf{I}_a$ is

$$I_a = 2I_1 \cos 30°$$

or

$$I_a = \sqrt{3}\, I_1$$

Since I_a is a line current and I_1 is a phase current,

$$I_{\text{line}} = \sqrt{3}\, I_{\text{phase}} \tag{6.46}$$

Writing Eq. (6.45) in terms of line values, then,

$$P = \sqrt{3}\, V_{\text{line}} I_{\text{line}} \cos \theta \tag{6.47}$$

Thus, for a balanced delta load, average three-phase power can be found by substituting line voltage, line current, and power factor into Eq. (6.47). But, for an unbalanced three-phase load, average power can be obtained only from Eqs. (6.43) and (6.44). It can also be shown that, for a balanced three-phase Y load, Eq. (6.47) gives the average power delivered to the load.

The measurement of power delivered to a balanced three-phase load can be accomplished by means of two wattmeters connected so that each sees one line voltage and one line current. (Wattmeters are discussed in Appendix 1). Figure 6.20a shows the man-

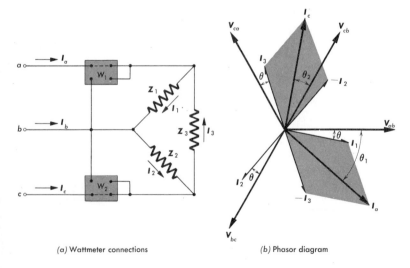

(a) Wattmeter connections   (b) Phasor diagram

FIG. 6.20 *Measuring three-phase power by two wattmeters.*

ner in which two wattmeters are connected. Wattmeter 1 reads W_1 and wattmeter 2 reads W_2, where

$$W_1 = V_{ab}I_a \cos \theta_1$$
$$W_2 = V_{cb}I_c \cos \theta_2$$
(6.48)

where θ_1 and θ_2 are the phase angles between $\mathbf{V}_{ab}$ and $\mathbf{I}_a$ and $\mathbf{V}_{cb}$ and $\mathbf{I}_c$, respectively, as shown in the phasor diagram of Fig. 6.20b. The wattmeters read the average values of the voltage–current–power-factor product of Eqs. (6.48). By some trigonometric manipulation of Eqs. (6.48) we shall show that the sum of the two wattmeter readings is equal to the average three-phase power expressed by Eq. (6.47).

From the phasor diagram (Fig. 6.20b),

$$\theta_1 = 30° + \theta$$

$$\theta_2 = 30° - \theta$$

where θ is the phase angle or power-factor angle of each single-phase load impedance. Adding Eqs. (6.48) together gives

$$W_1 + W_2 = V_{ab}I_a \cos (30° + \theta) + V_{cb}I_c \cos (30° - \theta)$$
$$= V_{ab}I_a (\cos 30° \cos \theta - \sin 30° \sin \theta)$$
$$+ V_{cb}I_c(\cos 30° \cos \theta + \sin 30° \sin \theta) \quad (6.49)$$

But for a balanced load and a balanced voltage source $I_a = I_c$ and $V_{ab} = V_{cb}$. Therefore

$$W_1 + W_2 = V_{ab}I_a\sqrt{3} \cos \theta$$

and since V_{ab} is the line voltage and I_a is the line current,

$$W_1 + W_2 = V_{line}I_{line}\sqrt{3} \cos \theta \quad (6.50)$$

Thus the sum of the two wattmeter readings is the three-phase average power delivered to the load.

The derivation of three-phase power delivered to a balanced delta load culminated in Eq. (6.50), and the derivation can be repeated for a Y load with the same result: if the wattmeters are connected as shown in Fig. 6.20a, their sum is the three-phase power regardless of whether the load is connected delta or Y. Furthermore, it can be shown that the sum of the two wattmeter readings gives the average three-phase power even if the load is not balanced. This is a convenient way to measure three-phase power; by using the two-wattmeter method, three-phase power can be measured from the line voltages and currents. Thus three watt-meters, one for each phase, are not needed.

SUMMARY

When solutions of parallel and series-parallel circuits are required, the admittance concept is a useful one. Complex admittance $\mathbf{Y}$ can be expressed as in Eq. (6.4),

$$\mathbf{Y} = \frac{1}{\mathbf{Z}}$$

and the total admittance of several parallel elements is the sum of the admittances of each element, as seen from Eq. (6.14).

$$\mathbf{Y}_t = \mathbf{Y}_1 + \mathbf{Y}_2 + \mathbf{Y}_3 + \cdots$$

Parallel resonance occurs in a parallel RLC circuit when the terminal voltage and current are in phase. The admittance of the parallel circuit [Eq. (6.17)] is

$$\mathbf{Y} = \frac{1}{R} + j\left(\omega C - \frac{1}{\omega L}\right)$$

and resonant frequency occurs where

$$\omega C - \frac{1}{\omega L} = 0$$

at which

$$\mathbf{Y} = \frac{1}{R}$$

Loop equations employing Kirchhoff's voltage law provide systems of simultaneous equations for circuit solutions. It is often convenient to define the loop around the "windows," or small rectangular areas, of the circuit, but at least one loop current must pass through each circuit element. If separate branch currents are defined for each branch, then additional current equations at each node are required to provide enough equations for the simultaneous solution of the branch currents.

Kirchhoff's current law provides a system of equations which can be solved simultaneously for the node voltages as the variables.

Three-phase circuits can sometimes be solved as three single-phase circuits. When a three-phase Y circuit is balanced so that the phase currents are equal, then

$$V_{\text{line}} = \sqrt{3}\, V_{\text{phase}}$$

and

$$I_{\text{line}} = I_{\text{phase}}$$

A balanced delta circuit is characterized by

$$V_{\text{line}} = V_{\text{phase}}$$

$$I_{\text{line}} = \sqrt{3}\, I_{\text{phase}}$$

Average power in a balanced three-phase circuit is

$$P = \sqrt{3}\, V_{\text{line}} I_{\text{line}} \cos\theta$$

and can be measured by the two-wattmeter method illustrated by Fig. 6.20a.

FURTHER READING

The publications cited at the end of Chap. 4 contain excellent reference chapters for the material presented here. In addition, J. B. Walsh and K. S. Miller, *Introductory Electric Circuits* (McGraw-Hill Book Company, Inc., New York, 1960), chap. 5, ties together many of the ideas presented here in the present chapter and the preceding chapter.

PROBLEMS

6.1 Verify that

$$Z = \frac{Z_1 Z_2}{Z_1 + Z_2}$$

for a parallel combination of Z_1 and Z_2, where Z is the parallel equivalent.

6.2 Find the parallel equivalent impedance Z for three impedances in parallel shown in the figure.

6.3 Find: (a) the undamped natural frequency; (b) the natural frequency; (c) the damping ratio of Eq. (6.10) in terms of R, L, and C.

6.4 In terms of R, L, and C, find the conditions for: (a) damped oscillatory response and (b) overdamped response of Eq. (6.10).

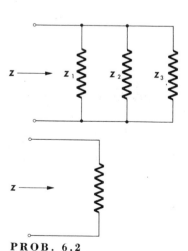

PROB. 6.2

6.5 Find the phase angle of the current **I** with respect to the sinusoidal voltage **E** for the *RL* parallel circuit shown in the illustration.

6.6 Plot the magnitude of the admittance and impedance for the parallel *RLC* circuit shown in the figure for four octaves each side of resonance. Let $L = 0.01$ henry, $C = 0.01$ μf, and (*a*) $R = 2,000$, (*b*) $R = 20,000$ ohms.

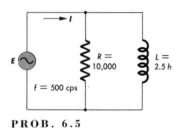

PROB. 6.5

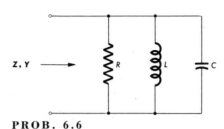

PROB. 6.6

6.7 Express the three phasors of Fig. 6.12 as sinusoids. Then plot sinusoidal voltages as functions of time for the three line voltages, assuming that each has a peak value of 100 volts. Verify that the sum of the three line voltages is zero at $\omega t = 0°$, $\omega t = 20°$, $\omega t = 90°$, and $\omega t = 150°$.

6.8 Find I_2 in Example 6.9.

6.9 Complete the derivation of Eq. (6.20), which gives the half-power frequencies for a parallel *RLC* circuit.

6.10 Prove that Eq. (6.47) gives the average power delivered to a balanced three-phase Y load.

6.11 A 10-ohm resistor, a capacitor with 10 ohms reactance, and an inductor with 10 ohms reactance are connected Y to a balanced 220-volt three-phase line. Find the power delivered to the Y load.

6.12 Repeat Prob. 6.11 for a delta load.

6.13 Three equal impedances of $5 + j10$ ohms are connected Y to a 220-volt three-phase line. Find: (*a*) line current; (*b*) phase voltage; and (*c*) average power of the load.

6.14 Three equal impedances of $5 + j10$ ohms are connected delta to a 220-volt three-phase line. Find: (*a*) phase current; (*b*) phase voltage; (*c*) line current; and (*d*) average power of the load.

6.15 Write sinusoidal steady-state loop equations for the circuit shown in the illustration, and solve for I_2 as a function of **E**, Z_1, Z_2, and Z_3.

6.16 Solve for I_1 in the d-c steady-state circuit shown in the figure. The resistor values are shown in ohms.

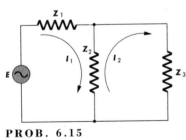

PROB. 6.15

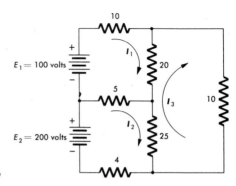

PROB. 6.16

6.17 Define node voltages for the circuit shown in the illustration, and write a system of node equations for the circuit. Solve for the voltage across R_2.

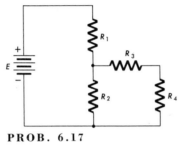

PROB. 6.17

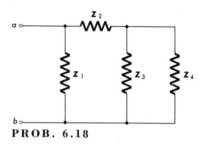

PROB. 6.18

6.18 Find the impedance $\mathbf{Z}$ seen looking in at the terminals a–b of the circuit shown in the illustration.

7

ELECTRIC NETWORKS

7.1 EQUIVALENT CIRCUITS

In preceding chapters we investigated the solution of electric circuits and networks, some of which consisted of several elements connected in series-parallel combinations. Now the concept of equivalence between two networks will be introduced and explored. If two circuits are equivalent, a complex one may be replaced by a simple one for analytical purposes to simplify the solution of the complex network; this is the reason for establishing equivalent-circuit concepts.

To define what we mean by equivalence in the sinusoidal steady state, consider the passive network of electric-circuit elements inside a box as shown in Fig. 7.1a. The actual number, nature, and configuration of the elements are unknown. All that is known is what can be measured at the two terminals marked a and b. A sinusoidal voltage $\mathbf{E}$ of radian frequency ω is connected to the terminals, and the steady-state current I and phase angle θ are measured. A complex impedance $\mathbf{Z}$ can now be defined at frequency ω as measured between the two terminals.

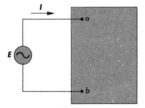

(a) An unknown circuit

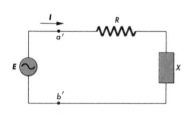

(b) Equivalent impedance

FIG. 7.1 *The concept of equivalence.*

$$\mathbf{Z} = \frac{E}{I} \epsilon^{j\theta} \tag{7.1}$$

The impedance $\mathbf{Z}$ can be reproduced by a resistance R and a reactance X in series, as shown in Fig. 7.1b. Then the impedance Z in Fig. 7.1b is equivalent in magnitude and angle to the complex circuit in Fig. 7.1a at the frequency ω. Two passive circuits are said to be equivalent at a given frequency if, for equal sinusoidal voltages connected to their terminals, the current in each is equal and at the same phase angle with respect to the voltage. Thus two equivalent passive circuits exhibit the same impedance at their input terminals.

The network represented in the box in Fig. 7.1a need not be passive. The box may contain one or more voltage (or current) sources, in which case the voltage-current relationships at terminals a–b must be duplicated by the voltage-current relationships between terminals a'–b' for equivalence to be established. If an electric-energy source is present in the box, one is also required in Fig. 7.1b for equivalence to exist. Equivalence between active circuits is discussed in Secs. 7.4 and 7.5.

If all the elements of a complex network are known and it is desired to find the total current delivered by the generator to the network, the equivalent-circuit concept can be used. A simple equivalent circuit can be found by successively combining together impedances that are in series, and those which appear in parallel together, until a single resistance and a single series reactance remain. Consider the following example: A network consisting of several impedances, shown in Fig. 7.2a, is excited by a single sinusoidal generator E. Of interest is the current I being supplied

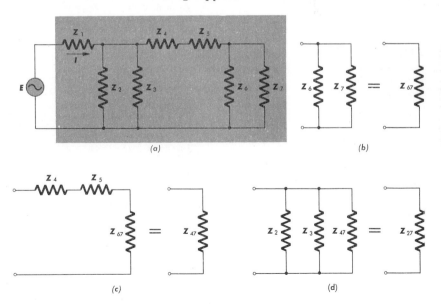

FIG. 7.2 *Reduction of series-parallel circuit to single impedance equivalent.*

by the generator to the network. As the circuit is shown here, it is convenient to start at the impedances farthest from the generator to combine them in series or parallel combinations. Impedances $\mathbf{Z}_6$ and $\mathbf{Z}_7$ in parallel are combined together to form an equivalent impedance $\mathbf{Z}_{67} = \mathbf{Z}_6\mathbf{Z}_7/(\mathbf{Z}_6 + \mathbf{Z}_7)$, as shown in Fig. 7.2b. Then $\mathbf{Z}_4$ and $\mathbf{Z}_5$ are added in series with $\mathbf{Z}_{67}$, as shown in (c), to find their equivalent, $\mathbf{Z}_{47} = \mathbf{Z}_4 + \mathbf{Z}_5 + \mathbf{Z}_{67}$. Next, $\mathbf{Z}_{47}$ is combined in parallel with $\mathbf{Z}_2$ and $\mathbf{Z}_3$ to find the equivalent impedance of that parallel combination, which we call $\mathbf{Z}_{27}$. This is shown in (d). Finally, $\mathbf{Z}_1$ and $\mathbf{Z}_{27}$ are added in series to find the final equivalent impedance containing one resistance and one reactance.

The admittance concept can be used to good advantage in this kind of network problem when parallel circuit elements must be combined. Remember that the admittances of parallel elements must be added to find the equivalent admittance of the parallel combination. Series impedances are added to find their equivalent impedance. These rules are demonstrated in the following example.

Example 7.1

To find $\mathbf{I}$ in the network shown, in Fig. 7.3, we first find the equivalent impedance seen by the generator. If

$$\mathbf{Z}_1 = 1 + j2 \qquad \mathbf{Z}_4 = 2 + j1$$

$$\mathbf{Z}_2 = 3 + j0 \qquad \mathbf{Z}_5 = 0 - j5$$

$$\mathbf{Z}_3 = \tfrac{1}{2} + j3$$

then

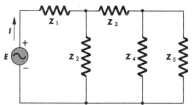

FIG. 7.3 *Series-parallel circuit to be reduced to an equivalent impedance.* $E = 10\epsilon^{j0} = 10 + j0.$

$$\mathbf{Y}_4 = G_4 + jB_4 = \frac{2}{2^2 + 1} - j\frac{1}{2^2 + 1} = \frac{2}{5} - j\frac{1}{5}$$

$$\mathbf{Y}_5 = 0 + j\tfrac{1}{5}$$

The admittance of $\mathbf{Z}_4$ and $\mathbf{Z}_5$ in parallel is $\mathbf{Y}_{45}$.

$$\mathbf{Y}_{45} = \mathbf{Y}_4 + \mathbf{Y}_5 = \tfrac{2}{5} - j\tfrac{1}{5} + 0 + j\tfrac{1}{5} = \tfrac{2}{5} + j0$$

$$\mathbf{Z}_{45} = \frac{1}{\mathbf{Y}_{45}} = \frac{5}{2} + j0$$

Add $\mathbf{Z}_3$ to $\mathbf{Z}_{45}$ to find $\mathbf{Z}_{3-5}$.

$$\mathbf{Z}_{3-5} = \tfrac{1}{2} + j3 + \tfrac{5}{2} + j0 = 3 + j3$$

Add $\mathbf{Y}_{3-5}$ and $\mathbf{Y}_2$ to find $\mathbf{Y}_{2-5}$.

$$\mathbf{Y}_{3-5} = \tfrac{1}{6} - j\tfrac{1}{6} \qquad \mathbf{Y}_2 = \tfrac{1}{3} + j0$$

$$\mathbf{Y}_{2-5} = \mathbf{Y}_{3-5} + \mathbf{Y}_2 = \tfrac{1}{6} - j\tfrac{1}{6} + \tfrac{1}{3} + j0 = \tfrac{1}{2} - \tfrac{1}{6}$$

$$\mathbf{Z}_{2-5} = \frac{1}{\mathbf{Y}_{2-5}} = \frac{1}{\frac{1}{2} - j\frac{1}{6}} \frac{\frac{1}{2} + j\frac{1}{6}}{\frac{1}{2} + j\frac{1}{6}}$$

$$= 1.8 + j0.6$$

The impedance seen by the generator is

$$\mathbf{Z}_{1-5} = \mathbf{Z}_1 + \mathbf{Z}_{2-5} = 1 + j2 + 1.8 + j0.6 = 2.8 + j2.6$$

$$\mathbf{I} = \frac{\mathbf{E}}{\mathbf{Z}_{1-5}} = \frac{10}{2.8 + j2.6} \frac{2.8 - j2.6}{2.8 - j2.6} = \frac{28 - j26}{2.8^2 + 2.6^2}$$

$$= \frac{28}{14.6} + j\frac{26}{14.6}$$

$$= 1.93 - j1.78 \text{ amp}$$

The procedure in the above example is laborious for complex networks, but the general method of attack is consistent and straight-forward.

7.2 THE PRINCIPLE OF SUPERPOSITION

The principle now known as "superposition" was first recorded by Bernoulli in 1755 and applied to water waves. In effect he found that the transmission of one surface wave through water does not affect the transmission of other waves simultaneously, and the net disturbance of several waves together is equal to the sum of the disturbances of each wave taken one at a time.

The principle of superposition applies to all linear relationships in which one quantity is proportional to another. One example is the series circuit shown in Fig. 7.4. If e_1 is zero, Ohm's law tells us that $i = e_2/R$. Or if e_2 is zero, we have $i = e_1/R$. Finally, if neither e_1 nor e_2 is zero, then $i = (e_1 + e_2)/R$. Thus it is evident in this example that, when the current is proportional to the voltage, the current when two voltages are present is equal to the sum of the currents found when each voltage is considered separately.

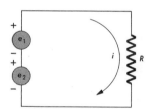

FIG. 7.4 *Series circuit illustrates the superposition principle.*

In more general terms, let

$$y_1 = mx_1$$

$$y_2 = mx_2$$

Then

$$y_1 + y_2 = m(x_1 + x_2)$$

where m is a constant, x an independent variable, and y is the dependent variable.

In contrast, suppose now that a nonlinear relationship exists between y and x. Let

$$y_3 = kx_3{}^2$$

$$y_4 = kx_4{}^2$$

Then

$$y_3 + y_4 \neq k(x_3 + x_4)^2$$
$$= k(x_3{}^2 + x_4{}^2)$$

Now we can state the superposition principle as it applies to electric circuits. The voltage-current relationships for linear circuit elements is the required linear relationship which applies not only for instantaneous values of voltage and current but also for the special case when sinusoidal values of voltages and currents are applied to linear impedance elements. The superposition principle applies to both these instances:

In any network consisting of voltage sources and linear-circuit elements, the instantaneous current flowing in any branch is the sum of the instantaneous currents which would flow if each voltage source were considered separately.

In any network consisting of sinusoidal-voltage sources and linear impedance elements, the steady-state current flowing in any branch is the phasor sum of the currents which would flow if each voltage source were considered separately.

Example 7.2

In the circuit shown in Fig. 7.5, Kirchhoff's laws can be used to verify that the current I_2 is the phasor sum of the current produced by E_1 with $E_2 = 0$ and that produced by E_2 with $E_1 = 0$.

The loop equations are

$$(Z_1 + Z_2)I_1 - I_2 Z_2 = E_1 - E_2$$

$$-Z_2 I_1 + (Z_2 + Z_3)I_2 = E_2$$

$$I_2 = \frac{\begin{vmatrix} Z_1 + Z_2 & E_1 - E_2 \\ -Z_2 & E_2 \end{vmatrix}}{\begin{vmatrix} Z_1 + Z_2 & -Z_2 \\ -Z_2 & Z_2 + Z_3 \end{vmatrix}} = \frac{E_2(Z_1 + Z_2) + (E_1 - E_2)Z_2}{(Z_1 + Z_2)(Z_2 + Z_3) - Z_2{}^2}$$

$$= \frac{E_1 Z_2 + E_2 Z_1}{Z_1 Z_2 + Z_1 Z_3 + Z_2 Z_3}$$

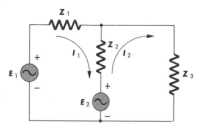

FIG. 7.5 *Circuit to verify superposition principle in Example 7.2.*

Now let I_{2a} be the current in the second loop if $E_2 = 0$. Then

$$I_{2a} = \frac{E_1 Z_2}{Z_1 Z_2 + Z_2 Z_3 + Z_1 Z_3}$$

Next, if $E_1 = 0$, let I_{2b} be the current in the second loop due to E_2. Then

$$I_{2b} = \frac{E_2 Z_2}{Z_1 Z_2 + Z_2 Z_3 + Z_1 Z_3}$$

Finally if neither E_1 nor E_2 is zero, then

$$I_2 = I_{2a} + I_{2b}$$

which illustrates the superposition principle.

7.3 EQUIVALENT T TRANSMISSION NETWORKS

If a network is considered to have two pairs of terminals to which can be connected voltage sources or load impedances, it can be thought of as a transmission network. Such a network is shown as a box in Fig. 7.6. The actual configuration of circuit elements in the box is arbitrary. We seek to show that, no matter what the configuration, for analytical purposes the network can be replaced at a single frequency by a T network consisting of three imped-ances.

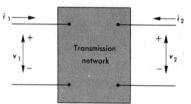

FIG. 7.6 *Four-terminal transmission network.*

Let v_1 and v_2 be the voltages between each pair of terminals and i_1 and i_2 be the currents in at each pair of terminals, as shown in Fig. 7.6. Of the four variables v_1, v_2, i_1, and i_2, only three are independent, and we can say that the voltages v_1 and v_2 are func-tions each of the currents i_1 and i_2.

$$v_1 = f_1(i_1, i_2)$$
$$v_2 = f_2(i_1, i_2) \tag{7.2}$$

Now, taking the total differential of Eqs. (7.2), we have

$$\Delta v_1 = \frac{\partial v_1}{\partial i_1} \Delta i_1 + \frac{\partial v_1}{\partial i_2} \Delta i_2 \tag{7.3}$$

$$\Delta v_2 = \frac{\partial v_2}{\partial i_1} \Delta i_1 + \frac{\partial v_2}{\partial i_2} \Delta i_2 \tag{7.4}$$

Since we have postulated that the transmission network is operat-ing in the sinusoidal steady state and is linear, we can replace the small increments in voltage and current by phasor values and write

Eqs. (7.3) and (7.4) as

$$V_1 = \frac{\partial V_1}{\partial I_1} I_1 + \frac{\partial V_1}{\partial I_2} I_2 \tag{7.5}$$

$$V_2 = \frac{\partial V_2}{\partial I_1} I_1 + \frac{\partial V_2}{\partial I_2} I_2 \tag{7.6}$$

But $\partial V_1/\partial I_1$ has the dimensions of an impedance, which we define as Z_{11}. Likewise, let $\partial V_2/\partial I_2 = Z_{22}$, $\partial V_1/\partial I_2 = Z_{12}$, and $\partial V_2/\partial I_1 = Z_{21}$. Now Eqs. (7.5) and (7.6) can be written

$$V_1 = Z_{11}I_1 + Z_{12}I_2 \tag{7.7}$$

$$V_2 = Z_{21}I_1 + Z_{22}I_2 \tag{7.8}$$

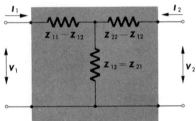

FIG. 7.7 *Equivalent T network for Fig. 7.6.*

Equations (7.7) and (7.8) can be recognized as the loop equations for the T network shown in Fig. 7.7, where $Z_{12} = Z_{21}$. To verify that $Z_{12} = Z_{21}$, we need only observe our definitions of Z_{12} and Z_{21} in partial derivative form and apply the reciprocity theorem. This theorem is stated without proof:

In any network consisting of linear circuit elements, if a voltage V_1 is applied between two terminals and the current I_2 is measured in any branch, then their ratio is the same as the ratio obtained if the voltage V_1 and the current I_2 are interchanged.

Thus we have seen that any four-terminal network can be replaced at a given frequency by an equivalent T network.

Example 7.3

The π network shown in Fig. 7.8*b* is to be replaced by an equivalent T network shown in (*a*). For the networks to be equivalent, the impedance seen looking in at any two terminals of one network must be equal to the impedance looking in at the corresponding pair of

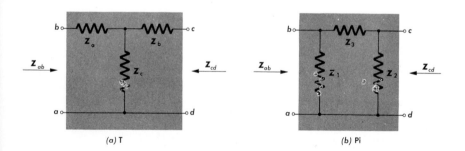

(a) T

(b) Pi

FIG. 7.8 *T and π equivalents.*

terminals of the other network when the other pairs of terminals are open.

π *network*   *T network*

$$\mathbf{Z}_{ab} = \frac{\mathbf{Z}_1(\mathbf{Z}_2 + \mathbf{Z}_3)}{\mathbf{Z}_1 + \mathbf{Z}_2 + \mathbf{Z}_3} \qquad\qquad \mathbf{Z}_{ab} = \mathbf{Z}_a + \mathbf{Z}_c$$

$$\mathbf{Z}_{bc} = \frac{\mathbf{Z}_3(\mathbf{Z}_1 + \mathbf{Z}_2)}{\mathbf{Z}_1 + \mathbf{Z}_2 + \mathbf{Z}_3} \qquad\qquad \mathbf{Z}_{bc} = \mathbf{Z}_a + \mathbf{Z}_b$$

$$\mathbf{Z}_{cd} = \frac{\mathbf{Z}_2(\mathbf{Z}_1 + \mathbf{Z}_3)}{\mathbf{Z}_1 + \mathbf{Z}_2 + \mathbf{Z}_3} \qquad\qquad \mathbf{Z}_{cd} = \mathbf{Z}_b + \mathbf{Z}_c$$

Equating the terminal impedances of the π network to the terminal impedances of the T network and solving for $\mathbf{Z}_a$, $\mathbf{Z}_b$, and $\mathbf{Z}_c$ in terms of $\mathbf{Z}_1$, $\mathbf{Z}_2$, and $\mathbf{Z}_3$, we see that, for the T network,

$$\mathbf{Z}_{ab} + \mathbf{Z}_{bc} - \mathbf{Z}_{cd} = 2\mathbf{Z}_a$$

Then, solving for $\mathbf{Z}_a$ and substituting in $\mathbf{Z}_{ab}$, $\mathbf{Z}_{bc}$, and $\mathbf{Z}_{ca}$ from the π network,

$$\mathbf{Z}_a = \frac{\mathbf{Z}_1\mathbf{Z}_3}{\mathbf{Z}_1 + \mathbf{Z}_2 + \mathbf{Z}_3}$$

Likewise

$$\mathbf{Z}_b = \frac{\mathbf{Z}_2\mathbf{Z}_3}{\mathbf{Z}_1 + \mathbf{Z}_2 + \mathbf{Z}_3}$$

and

$$\mathbf{Z}_c = \frac{\mathbf{Z}_1\mathbf{Z}_2}{\mathbf{Z}_1 + \mathbf{Z}_2 + \mathbf{Z}_3}$$

Thus, if $\mathbf{Z}_a$, $\mathbf{Z}_b$, and $\mathbf{Z}_c$ have values as shown in the above expressions, the T network is equivalent to the π network.

7.4 THÉVENIN'S THEOREM

An extremely useful equivalent-circuit theorem stated by Thévenin in 1887 applies to circuits containing sinusoidal-voltage sources as well as passive circuit elements. This theorem can be stated as follows:

Any two-terminal network of linear impedance elements and sinusoidal-voltage sources ·is equivalent at a single frequency to an ideal voltage source $\mathbf{E}$ *in series with an impedance* $\mathbf{Z}$, *where* $\mathbf{E}$ *is the open-circuit voltage between the two terminals and* $\mathbf{Z}$ *is the impedance looking in at the two terminals with voltage sources replaced by zero impedances.*

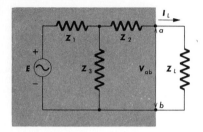

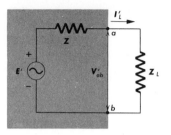

(a) Active T network   (b) Circuit equivalent to (a)   **FIG. 7.9** *Thévenin's equivalent circuit.*

To visualize the use of this theorem, consider the circuit of Fig. 7.9a, which is driven by a single voltage source **E**. Thévenin's equivalent circuit is shown in Fig. 7.9b; the new voltage generator **E'** is obtained from Fig. 7.9a, where, by voltage-divider action, the open-circuit voltage between terminals a and b is

$$\mathbf{E'} = \frac{\mathbf{Z}_3}{\mathbf{Z}_1 + \mathbf{Z}_3}\,\mathbf{E}$$

and the impedance seen looking in at terminals a and b is

$$\mathbf{Z} = \mathbf{Z}_2 + \frac{\mathbf{Z}_1\mathbf{Z}_3}{\mathbf{Z}_1 + \mathbf{Z}_3}$$

Thus an active circuit of four elements has been replaced by a circuit of two elements. The behavior at the terminals a–b and a'–b' is the same for the two equivalent circuits, independent of the value of $\mathbf{Z}_L$ connected across the terminals.

The verification of Thévenin's theorem for a network with a single voltage source follows from the verification that Fig. 7.9b is equivalent to Fig. 7.9a. In Sec. 7.3 it was shown that, at any one frequency, a four-terminal network can be replaced by an equivalent T network; therefore the active T network of Fig. 7.9a is equivalent to any four-terminal network with a voltage generator connected across one pair of terminals. Thévenin's theorem is verified when the equivalence of Fig. 7.9a and b is shown for any arbitrary load impedance $\mathbf{Z}_L$ connected to their terminals. Equivalence is demonstrated by showing that, when the load impedance $\mathbf{Z}_L$ is connected across terminals a–b of each circuit, the voltage between the terminals and the current at the terminals are equal for the two circuits. Since the two circuits must be equivalent for all values of $\mathbf{Z}_L$, let $\mathbf{Z}_L$ become very large approaching infinity. Then

$$\mathbf{V}_{ab} = \mathbf{E}\,\frac{\mathbf{Z}_3}{\mathbf{Z}_1 + \mathbf{Z}_3} = \mathbf{V}'_{ab}$$

and therefore

$$E' = E\frac{Z_3}{Z_1 + Z_3} \tag{7.9}$$

Now, if we let Z_L be zero, then $V_{ab} = 0$, and in **Fig.** 7.9*b*

$$I_L' = \frac{E'}{Z} = \frac{EZ_3}{Z(Z_1 + Z_3)} \tag{7.10}$$

In Fig. 7.9*a*,

$$I_L = \frac{1}{Z_2}\frac{E[Z_2Z_3/(Z_2 + Z_3)]}{Z_1 + Z_2Z_3/(Z_2 + Z_3)} \tag{7.11}$$

Since I_L must equal I_L' for the two circuits to be equivalent, we equate Eqs. (7.10) and (7.11).

$$\frac{EZ_3}{Z(Z_1 + Z_3)} = \frac{EZ_2Z_3}{Z_2(Z_1Z_2 + Z_2Z_3 + Z_1Z_3)} \tag{7.12}$$

Solving Eq. (7.12) for Z, we have

$$Z = \frac{Z_1Z_2 + Z_2Z_3 + Z_1Z_3}{Z_1 + Z_3}$$

$$= \frac{Z_1Z_3}{Z_1 + Z_3} + Z_2 \tag{7.13}$$

Notice that, in Eq. (7.9), E' is the open-circuit voltage seen looking in to the left at terminals *a–b* of Fig. 7.9*a*. Likewise, the impedance Z in Eq. (7.13) is the impedance seen looking in at the same terminals, with the voltage generator E replaced with zero impedance. Thus we have verified that, if Z and E' in Fig. 7.9*b* have the values expressed in Eqs. (7.9) and (7.13), then circuit of Fig. 7.9*b* is equivalent to that of Fig. 7.9*a*.

Example 7.4

Thévenin's equivalent circuit for the d-c network shown in Fig. 7.10*a* must have a voltage source equal to the open-circuit voltage at

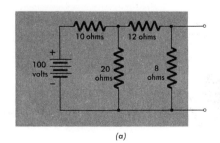

FIG. 7.10 *Thévenin's equivalent (Example 7.4).*

(a)   (b)

the terminals in Fig. 7.10a. Then

$$E' = \left(\frac{8}{8 + 12} \times \frac{10}{10 + 10} \right) 100 = 20 \text{ volts}$$

Looking in at the terminals a–b with the battery short-circuited the resistance seen is

$$R = \frac{\left(\dfrac{10 \times 20}{10 + 20} + 12 \right) 8}{\left(\dfrac{10 \times 20}{10 + 20} + 12 \right) + 8} = 5.59 \text{ ohms}$$

Then the circuit in Fig. 7.10b is Thévenin's equivalent to the circuit of Fig. 7.10a.

Thévenin's equivalent circuits can be found in exactly the same way when more than one voltage source is present even though our verification of Thévenin's theorem applied to the special case when only one was present. Proof of this statement follows from the superposition principle.

7.5 NORTON'S THEOREM

Just as Thévenin's theorem shows how to find a simple series equivalent for an active network, so Norton's theorem shows how to find a simple parallel equivalent:

Any two-terminal network of linear impedance elements and voltage sources is equivalent at a single frequency to an ideal current source $\mathbf{I}'$ in parallel with an impedance $\mathbf{Z}$. The current source $\mathbf{I}'$ is the current at the terminals when they are short-circuited, or $\mathbf{I}' = \mathbf{E}'/\mathbf{Z}$, and the impedance $\mathbf{Z}$ is the impedance seen looking in at the terminals with the voltage sources replaced by zero impedances.

Norton's theorem can be verified by showing that the Norton's equivalent circuit is truly equivalent to the Thévenin's equivalent circuit, the two circuits being shown in Fig. 7.11. For the two

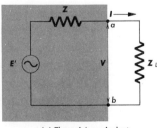

(a) Thevenin's equivalent

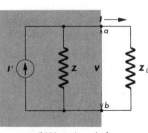

(b) Norton's equivalent

FIG. 7.11 *Constant-voltage and constant-current equivalent circuits.*

circuits shown in Fig. 7.11 to be equivalent, their terminal voltages must be equal when identical load impedances Z_L are connected to the terminals a–b of each circuit. The terminal voltage of the Thévenin's equivalent circuit is, from Fig. 7.11a,

$$V = \frac{E'Z_L}{Z + Z_L} \tag{7.14}$$

Terminal voltage at the Norton's equivalent circuit (Fig. 7.11b) is

$$V = IZ_L = \left(\frac{E'}{Z} - \frac{V}{Z}\right) Z_L \tag{7.15}$$

Solving Eq. (7.15) for terminal voltage V gives

$$V = \frac{E'Z_L}{Z + Z_L} \tag{7.16}$$

which is identical to Eq. (7.14). Thus the terminal voltages of the two circuits are equal when a load impedance Z_L is connected across the output terminals of each circuit; therefore the currents through the load impedances are equal, and the two circuits are equivalent.

Example 7.5

The Thévenin's equivalent circuit in Example 7.4 is shown in Fig. 7.12a. Since any active network can be represented by Thévenin's

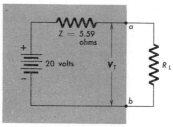

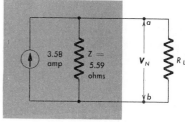

FIG. 7.12 *Equivalent circuits of Example 7.5.*

(a) Thevenin's equivalent   (b) Norton's equivalent

equivalent, we can represent any active network by Norton's equivalent also. The short-circuit current in the Thévenin's equivalent is $I = 20/5.59 = 3.58$ amp, found by short-circuiting the terminals in Fig. 7.12a; this is the current of the current generator of Norton's equivalent in Fig. 7.12b. The shunt impedance across the current generator is 5.59 ohms, equal to the series impedance of the Thévenin's equivalent.

To verify the equivalence of Fig. 7.12a and b, the voltage across R_L must be equal in each circuit, and the current through R_L must be equal in each circuit. Of course, since R_L has the same resistance in each circuit, it is necessary only to show that the terminal voltage (or the current) is the same in each circuit. In Fig. 7.12a, the Thévenin's circuit,

$$V = 20\,\frac{R_L}{5.59 + R_L}$$

and, in Fig. 7.12b, the Norton's equivalent,

$$V = 3.58\left(\frac{5.59R_L}{5.59 + R_L}\right) = 20\,\frac{R_L}{5.59 + R_L}$$

Thus we have verified that, for any value of R_L, the terminal voltages (voltage across R_L) are the same for the two circuits.

7.6 MAXIMUM POWER TRANSFER

Practical voltage sources inherently possess internal impedance which can be represented in series with an ideal impedance-free voltage source. In addition to the internal impedance of the generator, the impedance of the lines connecting the generator to its load may also be appreciable. Lumping together the internal impedance of the generator and the series impedance of the transmission lines connected to the load, and calling the lumped impedance $\mathbf{Z}_g$, we find $\mathbf{Z}_g$ in series with the load impedance in Fig. 7.13. Suppose now we consider how to extract the maximum amount of power from a given generator and transmission line; what value of load impedance $\mathbf{Z}_L$ results in a maximum amount of power being delivered to $\mathbf{Z}_L$?

Since

$$\mathbf{I} = \frac{\mathbf{E}}{\mathbf{Z}_g + \mathbf{Z}_L}$$

the average power delivered to $\mathbf{Z}_L$ is

$$P = I^2 R_L$$

where R_L is the resistive component of $\mathbf{Z}_L$.

As a special case, if $\mathbf{Z}_g$ and $\mathbf{Z}_L$ are ideal resistors R_g and R_L, respectively,

$$P = \frac{E^2 R_L}{(R_g + R_L)^2} \tag{7.17}$$

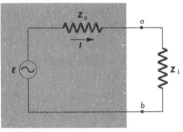

FIG. 7.13 *To illustrate maximum power transfer*

To find the maximum power as we let R_L take any value, we differentiate P with respect to R_L and set the derivative equal to zero.

$$\frac{dP}{dR_L} = E^2 \frac{(R_g + R_L)^2 - 2R_L(R_g + R_L)}{(R_g + R_L)^4} = 0 \qquad (7.18)$$

Equation (7.18) reduces to

$$R_g{}^2 + 2R_g R_L + R_L{}^2 - 2R_L R_g - 2R_L{}^2 = 0$$

and

$$R_g{}^2 - R_L{}^2 = 0$$

or $\qquad\qquad\qquad\qquad\qquad\qquad\qquad\qquad\qquad\qquad (7.19)$

$$R_L = R_g$$

Thus, for maximum power transfer, load resistance R_L must equal the resistance in series with the generator R_g.

A plot of power delivered to R_L as a function of R_L (E and R_g are constant) is shown in Fig. 7.14. Obviously, the power is zero

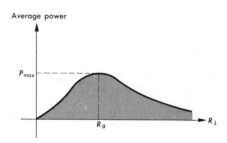

FIG. 7.14 *Power-versus-load-resistance curve.*

for $R_L = 0$ and also for $R_L = \infty$. At $R_L = R_g$, the load power is maximum.

If $\mathbf{Z}_g$ and $\mathbf{Z}_L$ also have reactance terms X_g and X_L as well as resistance terms R_g and R_L, respectively, the average power delivered to $\mathbf{Z}_L$ can be expressed as

$$P = \frac{E^2 R_L}{(R_L + R_g)^2 + (X_L + X_g)^2} \qquad (7.20)$$

Now if $X_L = -X_g$, Eq. (7.20) reduces to Eq. (7.17), and we can expect the power transfer to $\mathbf{Z}_L$ to be a maximum.

The maximum-power-transfer theorem can be stated as follows:

Maximum power is absorbed by a load impedance $\mathbf{Z}_L$ connected to a series combination of a voltage generator and a series impedance

$\mathbf{Z}_g$, when the load impedance is the complex conjugate of the series impedance, that is, when the resistive components of $\mathbf{Z}_L$ equals the resistive component of $\mathbf{Z}_g$, but the reactive component of $\mathbf{Z}_L$ is equal and opposite in sign to the reactive component of $\mathbf{Z}_g$.

Maximum power transfer is not always the goal of a power-transmission system. The voltage generator may not be capable of supplying the maximum power without overheating, and efficiency is only 50 per cent under maximum-power-transfer conditions. Electric-power systems never operate for maximum power transfer because of the low efficiency and because they are generally constant-voltage systems, which cannot tolerate high voltage drops between generated voltage and load. But in communication systems maximum power transfer is usually desirable. For instance, in a telephone system it is desirable to have the receiver "matched" to the microphone so that there is maximum power transferred from the microphone to the receiver.

Example 7.6

A 100-volt generator has an internal impedance $\mathbf{Z}_g$ of $2 + j1$ ohms. For maximum power transfer to the load impedance $\mathbf{Z}_L$, $\mathbf{Z}_L$ must be $2 - j1$ ohms, and the power delivered to $\mathbf{Z}_L$ is

$$P_L = I^2 R_L = \frac{100^2}{(2+2)^2} \times 2 = 1,250 \text{ watts}$$

No other value of $\mathbf{Z}_L$ will consume more power from a given $\mathbf{E}$ and $\mathbf{Z}_g$.

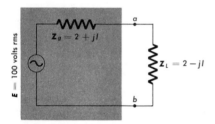

FIG. 7.15 *Circuit illustrating maximum power transfer (Example 7.6.)*

7.7 COUPLED CIRCUITS

Two electric circuits are said to be "coupled" if a current in one produces a current or voltage in the other. The circuits described by two or more loop-current equations are examples of coupled circuits. Figure 7.16 is a simple example of a coupled circuit which can be described by Kirchhoff's voltage-law equations,

$$(\mathbf{Z}_1 + \mathbf{Z}_3)\mathbf{I}_1 - \mathbf{Z}_3\mathbf{I}_2 = \mathbf{E} \tag{7.21}$$

$$-\mathbf{Z}_3\mathbf{I}_1 + (\mathbf{Z}_2 + \mathbf{Z}_3 + \mathbf{Z}_4)\mathbf{I}_2 = 0 \tag{7.22}$$

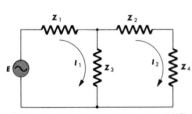

FIG. 7.16 *A coupled circuit with the common element.*

Notice that the impedance $\mathbf{Z}_3$ appears in both Eqs. (7.21) and (7.22) and that by means of $\mathbf{Z}_3$ the two loops are coupled together.

A coupled circuit is often used in communications circuits to improve the power transfer from a generator to a load. Suppose that we want to deliver power to a load impedance Z_L but that the generator has an internal impedance Z_g. A T network of pure reactances can be used to couple the generator to the load, as shown in Fig. 7.17. Reactances are used because they are not energy-dissipating elements. By the maximum-power-transfer theorem, if the impedance Z_{in} seen looking in at terminals a–b

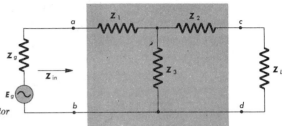

FIG. 7.17 *A T network to transfer power from generator E_g to load Z_L.*

is made equal to Z_g, then maximum power will be delivered by the generator. Then

$$Z_g = Z_1 + \frac{Z_3(Z_2 + Z_L)}{Z_2 + Z_3 + Z_L} \qquad (7.23)$$

where Z_1, Z_2, and Z_3 are pure reactances.

When the circuit is not in the steady state, Eqs. (7.21) and (7.22) must be written as differential equations. Suppose that we have a coupled network as shown in Fig. 7.18, identical to Fig. 7.16, with each circuit element made up of resistance, inductance, or capacitance. The system of integrodifferential equations, written from Kirchhoff's voltage law, is

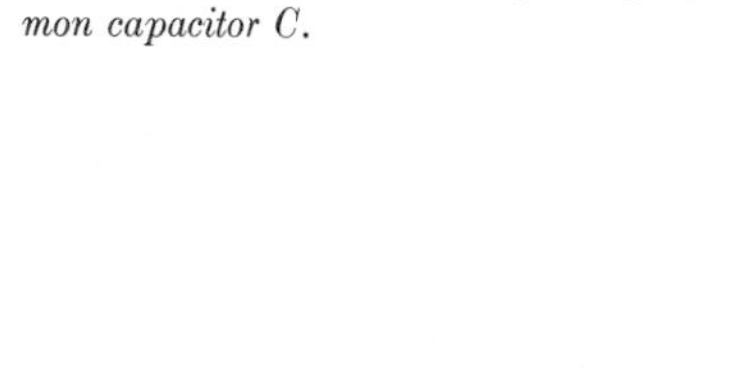

FIG. 7.18 *Circuit coupled by common capacitor C.*

$$L_1 \frac{di_1}{dt} + \frac{1}{C} \int i_1 \, dt - \frac{1}{C} \int i_2 \, dt = e_g$$

$$-\frac{1}{C} \int i_1 \, dt + \frac{1}{C} \int i_2 \, dt + L_2 \frac{di_2}{dt} + R_L i_2 = 0$$

$$(7.24)$$

or, after differentiation,

$$L_1 \frac{d^2 i_1}{dt^2} + \frac{1}{C} i_1 - \frac{1}{C} i_2 = \frac{de_g}{dt}$$

$$-\frac{1}{C} i_1 + L_2 \frac{d^2 i_2}{dt^2} + R_L \frac{di_2}{dt} + \frac{1}{C} i_2 = 0$$

$$(7.25)$$

Notice that the element C is common to each equation and is the only common element, just as in Eqs. (7.21) and (7.22) Z_3 was common to both equations. Coupled circuits lead to simultaneous equations for their solution, as demonstrated by Eqs. (7.21) and (7.22) and by Eqs. (7.25.)

7.8 INDUCTIVELY COUPLED CIRCUITS

In Sec. 1.12 it was shown that mutual inductance M is the proportionality constant relating an emf induced in one circuit to the rate of change of current in another, or [Eq. (1.31)]

$$v_1 = M \frac{di_2}{dt}$$

where v_1 is the voltage induced in one circuit and i_2 is the changing current in the other circuit. Consider the two coils represented in Fig. 7.19, coupling the voltage generator e to the load resistance

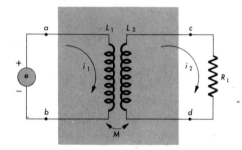

FIG. 7.19 *Mutual inductance couples circuit of i_1 to circuit of i_2.*

R_L. There is no physical connection between the two loops except for the magnetic field which couples them. The coil in the first loop has a self-inductance L_1 and is coupled to the second coil by the mutual inductance M. The second loop has a self-inductance L_2 and is likewise coupled to the first loop by M. The loop equations are

$$L_1 \frac{di_1}{dt} \pm M \frac{di_2}{dt} = e \qquad (7.26)$$

$$\pm M \frac{di_1}{dt} + L_2 \frac{di_2}{dt} + R_L i_2 = 0 \qquad (7.27)$$

Notice the ambiguity in the sign of M; reference to Fig. 7.20 is of assistance in resolving the ambiguity. If i_1 is increasing, the voltage caused by the self-inductance L_1 tends to oppose the increasing current with the polarity shown. Now, if i_2 is increasing, the sign of the emf induced in loop 1 by i_2 depends upon the direc-

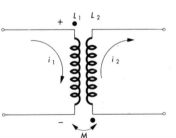

FIG. 7.20 *Dots used to indicate whether M is + or −.*

tion of the winding of the coil of L_2. If we define the positive direction of i_2 as indicated by the arrow, and if an increasing i_2 induces an emf in the first loop of the same polarity as the increasing i_1 causes in the first loop, then the sign of the mutual-inductance terms in Eqs. (7.26) and (7.27) are the same sign as the sign of the self-inductance terms.

The dots marking one side of each coil are used to determine the sign of the mutual term. The dots are to be interpreted in the following manner: If the positive direction of i_1 is into the dot terminal of the first coil and the positive direction of i_2 is into the dot terminal at the second coil, then the mutual-inductance term $M \, di_2/dt$ is the same sign as the self-inductance term $L \, di_1/dt$; if positive i_2 is defined as coming *out* of the dot terminal in the second loop and positive i_1 is *in* at the dot terminal of loop 1, then $M \, di_2/dt$ must be opposite in sign to $L \, di_1/dt$. These rules can be extended to the second loop as well. If i_2 is defined in a positive direction going into the circuit at the dot terminal of the second loop, and i_1 is defined in a positive direction as going *in* at the dot terminal in its loop, then $M \, di_1/dt$ must carry the same sign in the loop equation of the second loop as the $L \, di_2/dt$ term.

Loop equations for the circuit of Fig. 7.20 can be written in impedance terms if the exciting voltage is sinusoidal.

$$j\omega L_1 \mathbf{I}_1 + j\omega M \mathbf{I}_2 = \mathbf{E}$$

$$j\omega M \mathbf{I}_1 + (R_L + j\omega L_2)\mathbf{I}_2 = 0$$

(7.28)

Equations (7.28) can be solved simultaneously for $\mathbf{I}_1$ and $\mathbf{I}_2$ algebraically.

Examination of Eqs. (7.28) indicates a possible equivalent circuit in which the two loops are connected; this equivalent circuit, for which Eqs. (7.28) also apply, is shown in Fig. 7.21. In Fig. 7.21 the inductance marked M is a self-inductance of a magnitude M henrys. The impedance of the circuit seen looking from the

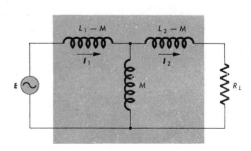

FIG. 7.21   *T equivalent of inductively coupled circuit of Fig. 7.19.*

generator is $\mathbf{E}/\mathbf{I}_1$ and can be found by solving Eqs. (7.28) simultaneously.

$$\mathbf{I}_1 = \frac{\begin{vmatrix} \mathbf{E} & j\omega M \\ 0 & R_L + j\omega L_2 \end{vmatrix}}{\begin{vmatrix} j\omega L_1 & j\omega M \\ j\omega M & R_L + j\omega L_2 \end{vmatrix}} \tag{7.29}$$

$$\mathbf{I}_1 = \frac{\mathbf{E}(R_L + j\omega L_2)}{\omega^2(M^2 - L_1 L_2) + j\omega L_1 R_L} \tag{7.30}$$

and

$$\mathbf{Z} = \frac{\mathbf{E}}{\mathbf{I}_1} = \frac{\omega^2(M^2 - L_1 L_2) + j\omega L_1 R_L}{R_L + j\omega L_2} \frac{R_L - j\omega L_2}{R_L - j\omega L_2} \tag{7.31}$$

$$\mathbf{Z} = \frac{\omega^2 M^2 R_L + j\omega(L_1 R_L{}^2 - \omega^2 L_2 M^2 + \omega^2 L_1 L_2{}^2)}{R_L{}^2 + \omega^2 L_2{}^2} \tag{7.32}$$

The impedance seen by the generator in Fig. 7.21, as represented by Eq. (7.32), is, of course, the same as the impedance seen by the generator in Fig. 7.19 when excited by a sinusoidal voltage.

SUMMARY

Two two-terminal circuits are equivalent if, when each is excited by the same voltage, the terminal current of each circuit is identical. Thus, when two circuits are equivalent, the voltage-current relationships at their terminals are identical.

The principle of superposition applies to linear networks only:

In any network consisting of voltage sources and linear-circuit elements, the instantaneous current flowing in any branch is the sum of the instantaneous currents which would flow if each voltage source were considered separately.

A transmission network is one with two pairs of terminals; at a single frequency any transmission network can be represented by an equivalent T or π network.

Thévenin's theorem is useful for finding an equivalent circuit of a linear circuit containing sinusoidal voltage sources:

Any two-terminal network of linear impedance elements and sinusoidal-voltage sources is equivalent at a single frequency to a voltage source $\mathbf{E}'$ *in series with an impedance* $\mathbf{Z}$*, where* $\mathbf{E}'$ *is the open-circuit voltage between the two terminals and* $\mathbf{Z}$ *is the impedance looking in at the two impedances with voltage sources replaced by zero impedances.*

Norton's theorem shows how to find a current-source equivalent:

Any two-terminal network of linear impedance elements and voltage sources is equivalent at a single frequency to a current source $\mathbf{I}'$ in parallel with an impedance $\mathbf{Z}$. The current source $\mathbf{I}$ is the current at the terminals when they are short-circuited, and the impedance $\mathbf{Z}$ is the impedance seen looking in at the terminals with voltage sources replaced by zero impedances.

The maximum-power-transfer theorem shows how a load impedance can obtain maximum power from a generator and series impedance:

Maximum power is absorbed by a load impedance connected to a series combination of a voltage generator and a series impedance when the load impedance is the complex conjugate of the series impedance.

Coupled circuits are circuits which contain elements common to two loop currents or which are equivalent to such circuits. Thus a circuit containing mutual inductance is a coupled circuit and is equivalent to a T network of self-inductance (Fig. 7.21).

FURTHER READING

The superposition theorem, the reciprocity theory, Thévenin's theorem, Norton's theorem, and the maximum-power-transfer theorem are all explained further in H. H. Skilling, *Electrical Engineering Circuits* (John Wiley & Sons, Inc., New York, 1957), chap. 11, and in W. H. Middendorf, *Analysis of Electric Circuits* (John Wiley & Sons, Inc., New York, 1956), chap. 18. See also J. B. Walsh and K. S. Miller, *Introductory Electric Circuits* (McGraw-Hill Book Company, Inc., New York, 1960), chap. 5.

PROBLEMS

7.1 Reduce the circuits shown in the illustration to equivalent impedances containing not more than a single resistance and a single reactance in series. In each circuit the exciting voltage is sinusoidal.

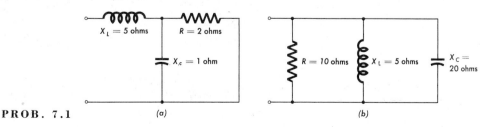

PROB. 7.1   (a)   (b)

7.2 Reduce the circuits shown in the figure to simple parallel equivalent circuits containing not more than a single resistance and a single reactance in parallel.

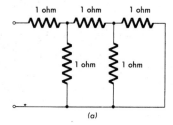

(a)

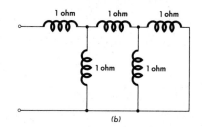

(b)

PROB. 7.2

7.3 Verify the superposition theorem for the circuit shown in the illustration. First assume that only E_1 is present and $E_2 = 0$. Find I_1 and I_2. Then let $E_1 = 0$ and find I_1 and I_2 when only E_2 is present. Finally, find I_1 and I_2 when both E_1 and E_2 are present in the circuit.

7.4 Find an equivalent T network for the network given in the illustration between E and R_L.

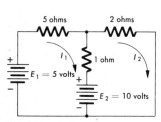

PROB. 7.3

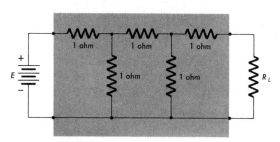

PROB. 7.4

7.5 Using Thévenin's theorem, find the equivalent circuit containing a single voltage source and series impedance for the circuits shown in the figure.

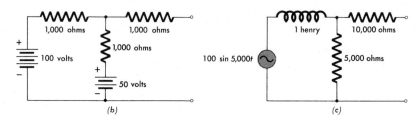

PROB. 7.5

7.6 Find the Norton's equivalent circuit for the networks in Prob. 7.5. (see the figure).

7.7 In the circuit shown in the illustration $Z_L = 25 + j40$. It is desired to transfer the maximum possible power from the generator to the load impedance Z_L. (a) Find the impedance Z necessary to accomplish maximum power transfer. (b) What is the maximum power that can be delivered to Z_L? (c) If Z is a transmission network, how much power is lost in transmission?

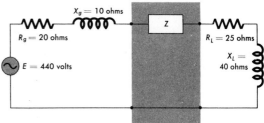

PROB. 7.7

7.8 The inductively coupled circuit of Fig. 7.19 has $L_1 = 1.0$ henry, $L_2 = 1.5$ henrys, and $M = 0.25$ henry. If the generator voltage is sinusoidal of a frequency of 400 cycles/sec and a magnitude of 100 volts rms, find the emf induced in L_2 by I_1.

7.9 Refer to Prob. 7.8 for L_1, L_2, M, f, and E in Fig. 7.19. Find the ratio of **E** to I_1 seen by the generator if $R_L = 1,000$ ohms.

7.10 The T network of Fig. 7.17 consists of $Z_1 = 100 + j100$, $Z_2 = 100 + j100$, and $Z_3 = 400 + j0$. The internal impedance of the generator is 50 ohms resistance, and $E_g = 100$ volts rms. The load impedance Z_L is adjusted for maximum power transfer. What is the maximum power that can be delivered to the load?

7.11 The T network of Fig. 7.17 consists of $Z_1 = 100 + j100$, $Z_2 = 100 + j100$, and $Z_3 = 400 + j0$, with $Z_g = 50 + j0$ and $E_g = 100$ volts. Find Thévenin's equivalent circuit for the T network and generator. Then, using Thévenin's equivalent circuit, find the current I_L in the load impedance $Z_L = 500 + j100$.

7.12 For the values of Z_1, Z_2, Z_3, Z_g, Z_L, and E_g given in Prob. 7.11, write loop equations for the circuit of Fig. 7.17, and solve for the current I_L through Z_L. Check with the value of I_L found in Prob. 7.11.

7.13 A series circuit consisting of resistance R, inductance L, and capacitance C is excited by a sinusoidal-voltage generator $e = E_m \sin \omega_1 t$. Find a parallel combination of resistance, inductance, and capacitance that is equivalent to the series combination at the radian frequency ω_1.

7.14 Refer to the circuit for Prob. 7.3. Write a node equation for the voltage at the node above the 1-ohm resistor, and solve for this node voltage.

8

NONLINEAR RESISTIVE CIRCUITS

8.1 INTRODUCTION

A resistor can be defined as a circuit element which observes Ohm's law; the voltage across the element is directly proportional to the current through the element. A resistor is also characterized by its ability to convert electric energy into heat energy and its inability to store energy as inductors and capacitors do. In this chapter we consider resistors which do *not* observe Ohm's law yet which observe all other characteristics of resistance. The voltage-current characteristics of non-Ohmic resistors are not straight lines through the origin as in Fig. 1.7; yet they produce heat according to Joule's law. Furthermore, the voltage across the non-Ohmic resistance is a function of the current only, and not a function of the integral or derivative of the current as with capacitors and inductors. This more general description of resistance applies to many useful devices, and the solution of circuits containing these devices is the subject of this chapter.

Non-Ohmic resistive devices may still be linear. Our definition of a linear resistive element for this chapter must be extended to mean that the relation between the voltage and current is characterized by a straight line. More specifically, we can define a linear-resistive-circuit element as one described by a linear algebraic equation of the form

$$v = m_1 i + b_1 \tag{8.1}$$

or

$$i = m_2 v + b_2 \tag{8.2}$$

where m_1 and m_2 are the slopes of the curves and b_1 and b_2 are the intercepts of the curves with the axes of the dependent variable, as shown in Fig. 8.1. In Fig. 8.1a, the current i is the independent

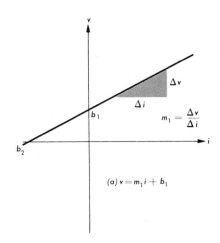

(a) $v = m_1 i + b_1$

(b) $i = m_2 v + b_2$

FIG. 8.1 *Examples of linear characteristic curves.*

variable, and voltage v is the dependent variable; in Fig. 8.1b, v is plotted as the independent variable, and i is the dependent variable. Both curves represent the same linear element, and therefore the slope of the curve in (b) is the reciprocal of the slope in (a). For the *characteristic curves* of Fig. 8.1 to represent Ohmic resistance, they must pass through the origin with b_1 and b_2 equal to zero.

The constant m_1 in Eq. (8.1) and Fig. 8.1a has the dimensions of resistance, and b_1 has the dimensions of voltage. Conversely, m_2 in Eq. (8.2) and Fig. 8.1b has the dimensions of conductance, or reciprocal resistance, and b_2 is current. The voltage-current or current-voltage characteristic curve is a common way to describe a resistive-circuit element. Some examples of linear-circuit elements and combinations of linear-circuit elements are shown in Fig. 8.2b to e, with their voltage-versus-current characteristics plotted in (a). Each of the characteristic curves shown can be represented by Eq. (8.1). Notice that the curve marked (b) in Fig. 8.2a represents a

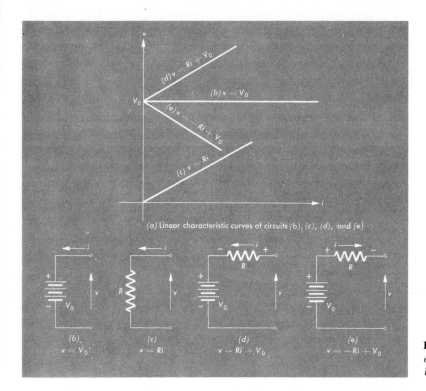

(a) Linear characteristic curves of circuits (b), (c), (d), and (e)

(b),
$v = V_0$

(c)
$v = Ri$

(d)
$v = Ri + V_0$

(e)
$v = -Ri + V_0$

FIG. 8.2 *Characteristic curves of a battery, resistor, and series combinations of the two.*

constant voltage V_0. For this curve, the constant b_1 in Eq. (8.1) is equal to V_0, and $m_1 = 0$. The curve representing the resistance in Fig. 8.2c is shown with $b_1 = 0$ and $m_1 = R$, the resistance of the element. In Fig. 8.2d is a series combination of the constant-voltage source V_0 and the resistance R. The direction of positive current i in R is such as to make the two voltages V_0 and iR have the same sign, so that they add algebraically. The positive-current in the circuit of Fig. 8.2e is of a direction such that V_0 and iR are opposite in sign, and thus the iR term carries a minus sign.

Linear elements and combinations of elements lend themselves nicely to algebraic solutions in the steady state. There are many circuit elements, however, which are resistive in nature but cannot be described by linear algebraic equations of the form of Eqs. (8.1) and (8.2). These nonlinear elements can be described by voltage-versus-current or current-versus-voltage characteristic curves which are not straight lines. Often, too, an analytic function approximating the characteristic curves can be found. But nonlinear circuits—circuits containing one or more nonlinear elements—are inherently more difficult to solve analytically than circuits consisting entirely of linear elements.

8.2 SOME NONLINEAR CHARACTERISTICS

Figure 8.2b to e gives examples of some voltage-current characteristics that are linear. Examples of characteristic curves of some nonlinear devices are shown in Fig. 8.3. An electron tube known as a "vacuum diode" has a characteristic as shown in Fig. 8.3a,

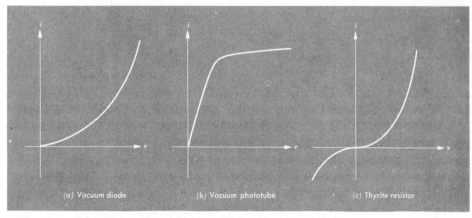

(a) Vacuum diode   (b) Vacuum phototube   (c) Thyrite resistor

FIG. 8.3 *Examples of nonlinear current-versus-voltage characteristics.*

and a vacuum phototube with constant illumination has a characteristic the shape of which is shown in Fig. 8.3b. A thyrite resistor is characterized by the curve in Fig. 8.3c. In none of these examples does a single linear resistor approximate the shape of the curve. Characteristic curves such as those shown in Fig. 8.3 can be obtained experimentally by measuring the current through the device for various voltages applied between the terminals of the device. Since many of these devices are manufactured in large quantities, their characteristic curves are often published in catalogues or handbooks so that the user does not have to find the characteristic curves by measurement.

Nonlinear characteristics such as those shown in Fig. 8.3 can often be approximated by one or more algebraic forms. For instance, the curve in Fig. 8.3b can be approximated by three straight lines, as in Fig. 8.4. Each of these straight lines can be represented by an equation of the form of Eqs. (8.1) and (8.2) and a

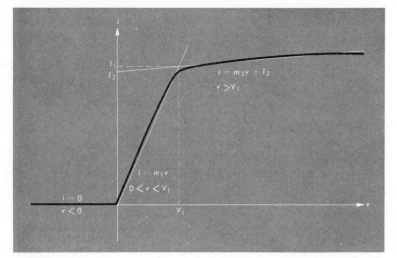

FIG. 8.4 *Linear approximation of curve of Fig. 8.3b.*

statement concerning the limits between which the equation applies, as shown in Fig. 8.4 and Eqs. (8.3).

$$i = 0 \qquad\qquad v < 0$$
$$i = m_1 v \qquad\quad 0 < v < V_1 \qquad\qquad (8.3)$$
$$i = m_2 v + I_2 \qquad v > V_1$$

Example 8.1

The characteristic curve shown in Fig. 8.5 is concave upward and can be approximated for positive voltages by three straight lines

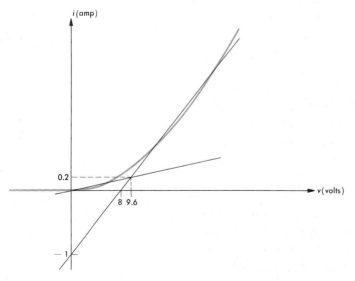

FIG. 8.5 *Linear approximation of a non-linear characteristic explained in Example 8.1.*

whose equations are

$$i = 0 \qquad\qquad v < 0$$

$$i = 0.025v \qquad\qquad 0 < v < 10$$

$$i = 0.125v - 1.0 \qquad\qquad v > 10$$

If this device is connected in the circuit shown in Fig. 8.6, let us find the steady-state current that results, using the linear approximation. First, we find the region on the linear curve where the device is operating. If we assume that $i = 0.025$ amp, there is a 25-volt drop in R and a 10-volt drop in the nonlinear resistance. Since these two drops add up to only 35 volts and 50 volts is applied from the battery, the actual current must be greater than 0.25 amp. Thus the nonlinear element is operating on a portion of the curve approximated by the equation

$$i = 0.125v - 1.0$$

which can be written

$$v = 8.0i + 8.0$$

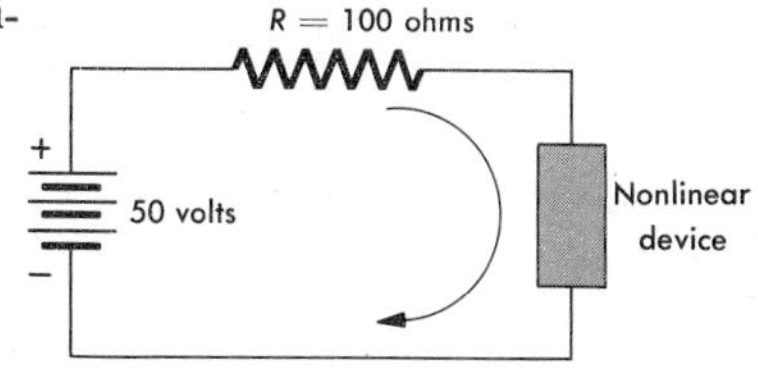

By Kirchhoff's voltage law the voltage across R plus the voltage across the nonlinear element must be 50 volts. Then

$$100i + (8.0i + 8.0) = 50$$

Solving for i,

$$i = {}^{42}\!/_{108} = 0.389 \text{ amp}$$

Circuit elements which can be represented over limited portions of their voltage-current characteristic curves by linear characteristics are often referred to as "piecewise linear" elements. The vacuum-phototube characteristic, represented by Fig. 8.4, and the vacuum diode of Fig. 8.5 are examples of piecewise linear elements. By resolving nonlinear elements into piecewise linear approximations we have a powerful tool for solving nonlinear problems by linear theory.

FIG. 8.6 Nonlinear circuit of Example 8.1.

8.3 GRAPHICAL SOLUTION OF LINEAR CIRCUITS

The graphical solution of a resistive circuit is merely an application of Kirchhoff's laws and the observance of the voltage-current relationship of each element. As an example, consider the circuit

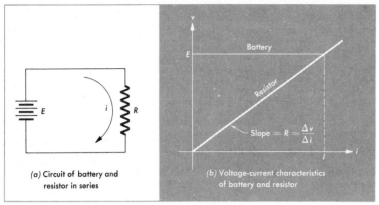

(a) Circuit of battery and resistor in series

(b) Voltage-current characteristics of battery and resistor

FIG. 8.7 *Graphical solution of a linear resistive current.*

shown in Fig. 8.7*a*, consisting of an ideal battery of constant voltage E and an Ohmic resistor R in series. The characteristic of the resistor is shown in Fig. 8.7*b* as a straight line through the origin with a positive slope. The characteristic of the voltage source is also shown in Fig. 8.7*b* as a straight line with zero slope. At the point of intersection of these two curves, Kirchhoff's voltage and current laws are satisfied. At the intersection, the current through the resistor is equal to the battery current, and the voltage drop across the resistor is equal to the battery voltage E. Then the current I, read on the graph at the intersection of the two curves, is the circuit current.

Next, considering the same problem again, we plot the voltage v as the independent variable and i as the dependent variable, as shown in Fig. 8.8. Now the characteristic curve of the resistor R has a slope $\Delta i / \Delta v = 1/R$, and the characteristic curve of the battery has an infinite slope. The intersection of the two curves shows the current I at which Kirchhoff's laws are satisfied.

Another method requires the characteristic curve of both the resistor and battery in series to be plotted. The voltage v, in this case, is the voltage seen between the terminals a–b of the series combination, as shown in Fig. 8.9*a*. Suppose that an adjustable load resistor is connected between the terminals so that the current i can be varied. If $i = 0$, then $v = E$, as shown on the characteristic curve of Fig. 8.9*b*. For any current i,

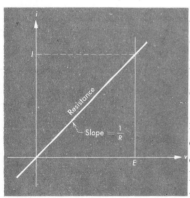

FIG. 8.8 *Current-voltage characteristics for battery and resistor of Fig. 8.7a.*

$$v = E - iR \qquad (8.4)$$

Suppose that $v = 0$, which can be accomplished by short-circuiting the terminals a–b in Fig. 8.9*a*. Then $E = iR$, or $i = E/R$. From

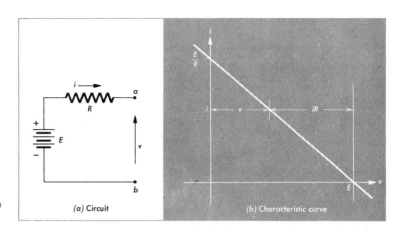

FIG. 8.9 *Direct voltage in series with a resistor.*

(a) Circuit (b) Characteristic curve

the two points $i = 0$, $v = E$, and $v = 0$, $i = E/R$, a straight line can be drawn which represents the characteristic for the battery and series-resistor combination and which is often called the "load line." Observe that the sum of the voltage drop across the terminals, v, when added to the voltage across the resistor R equals the battery voltage E for any value of current i. Now, if the terminal voltage becomes zero, the intersection of the battery-and-resistor characteristic with the zero-voltage coordinate occurs at $i = E/R$.

As another example, suppose that another resistor R_2 is connected between the terminals a–b of Fig. 8.9a, as shown in Fig. 8.10a. The characteristic of the resistor R_2 is, by Ohm's law, a straight line through the origin with slope of $1/R_2$, as shown in Fig.

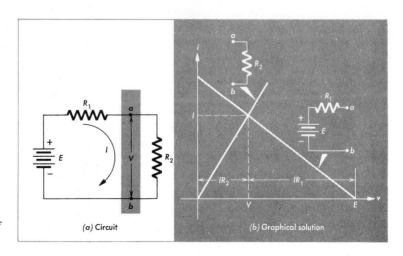

FIG. 8.10 *Graphical solution of a series circuit.*

(a) Circuit (b) Graphical solution

8.10*b*. This is the current-voltage characteristic on looking to the right from terminals *a–b* in Fig. 8.10*a*. The current-voltage characteristic of the circuit to the left of terminals *a–b* is identical to Fig. 8.9*b* and is also shown in Fig. 8.10*b*. At the intersection of these two characteristic curves, the current through R_2 is equal to the current through R_1 and the battery. Furthermore, the voltage drop across R_2 is equal to the battery voltage minus the voltage drop in R_1. Therefore, both Kirchhoff's laws are satisfied at this operating point on the characteristic curves, from which we can determine the current I, the voltage across R_1, and the voltage across R_2, as shown in Fig. 8.10*b*.

A similar technique can be used to solve parallel circuits. Suppose that two resistors are in parallel and connected to a series battery and resistor combination as shown in Fig. 8.11*a*. The

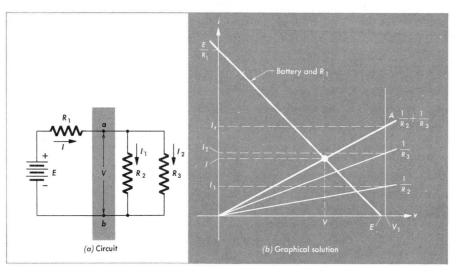

(a) Circuit (b) Graphical solution

FIG. 8.11 *Graphical solution of series-parallel resistive circuit.*

characteristic of the battery and R_1, as seen in looking to the left from the terminals *a–b*, is shown in Fig. 8.11*b* with a slope of $1/R_1$. Looking to the right from *a–b*, we see R_2 and R_3 in parallel. This parallel combination can be simplified to a single characteristic equivalent to the parallel combination of R_2 and R_3. At any arbitrary voltage, the total current through the parallel combination is the sum of the currents through R_2 and R_3. Graphically, then, an arbitrary voltage V_1 is chosen and the total current found by adding the currents in R_2 and R_3 at this voltage. This gives one point at A on the new equivalent characteristic of the parallel combination of R_2 and R_3. The origin is another point necessary to determine the straight-line characteristic of R_2 and R_3 in parallel. The equivalent characteristic of the parallel combination of R_2 and R_3 is now drawn, connecting the origin and point A. Notice that, for any arbitrary voltage v across terminals a–b, the total current $I_t = I_1 + I_2$. The intersection of these two characteristics (the battery-and-R_1 characteristic and the parallel R_2-and-R_3 characteristic) indicates a current I in Fig. 8.11b which satisfies Kirchhoff's current law and a terminal voltage V which satisfies Kirchhoff's voltage law.

Another way to solve graphically the series-parallel circuit of Fig. 8.11a is to place the terminals as shown in Fig. 8.12a. The

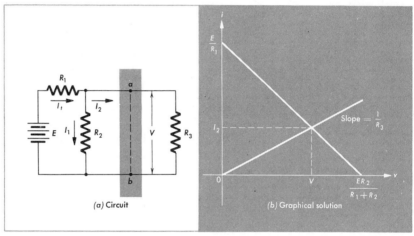

(a) Circuit   (b) Graphical solution

FIG. 8.12 *Another graphical solution of the series-parallel circuit.*

characteristic of R_3 alone is seen in looking to the right of terminals a–b. Looking to the left, we see R_2 in parallel with the series combination of R_1 and the battery. When the current at the terminals a–b is zero, the voltage at the terminals of this parallel combination is $E[R_2/(R_1 + R_2)]$. When the voltage across the terminals is zero, the short-circuit condition, then the current out of the terminals is E/R_1. These two points determine the characteristic of the circuit to the left of terminals a–b. The intersection of this characteristic with the characteristic for R_3 shows the terminal current I_2, which flows through R_3, and V, which is the voltage between the terminals or across R_3.

Still another solution of the same problem can be obtained by choosing terminals a–b across the battery. A vertical line at $V = E$

is the battery characteristic, as shown in Fig. 8.13*b*. The characteristics for R_2 and R_3 are added together in parallel as before by
adding the currents through each for a common voltage across

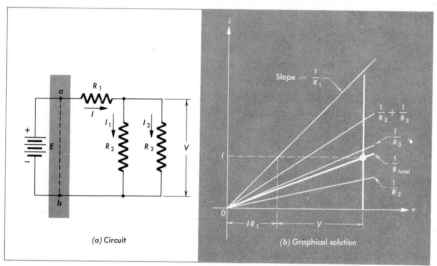

(a) Circuit   (b) Graphical solution

FIG. 8.13 *Still another graphical solution of the series-parallel circuit.*

them. Then the characteristic for R_1 is added in series with the
$R_2 + R_3$ characteristic by adding voltages at some arbitrary current I_1. The intersection of the composite characteristic for R_1 in
series with the parallel combination of R_2 and R_3 and the battery
characteristic shows current I as the terminal current and E as the
terminal voltage. In addition, the voltage across R_1, R_2, and R_3
can be identified as shown in Fig. 8.13*b*.

In summary, we can say that graphical solutions can be obtained by the following steps: (*a*) Break the circuit in two, and
draw voltage-current or current-voltage characteristics for each
half of the circuit seen looking into the circuit at the two sides of
the break. (*b*) The intersection of these two characteristics shows
the voltage across the circuit at the break terminals and the current
at the break terminals. (*c*) Once the voltage and current at the break
terminals are located, other voltages and currents can be obtained
from the graph between intersections of appropriate characteristics.

8.4 NONLINEAR CIRCUITS

If the current-versus-voltage characteristic for a nonlinear-circuit
element is known, the same graphical methods as discussed in the
previous section can be used to solve a circuit containing the non-

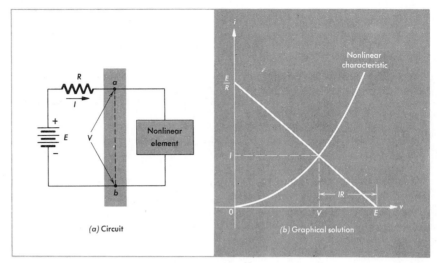

(a) Circuit (b) Graphical solution

FIG. 8.14 *Graphical solution of a nonlinear series circuit.*

linear element. Figure 8.14a shows a series circuit containing a nonlinear resistive element in series with a linear resistor and a battery. The characteristic of the nonlinear element is shown in Fig. 8.14b, together with the characteristic of the battery-resistor series combination. At the intersection of the two curves, Kirchhoff's laws are satisfied, and the current I and voltage V are determined. Notice the similarity between this example and that of Fig. 8.10.

Another example is the circuit of Fig. 8.15a. This circuit contains a linear resistor in parallel with the nonlinear resistive

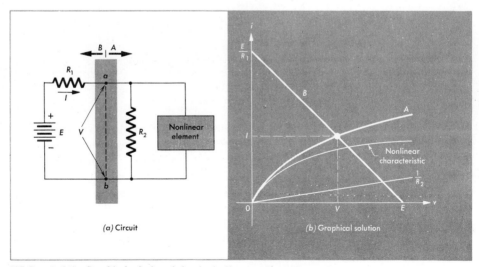

(a) Circuit (b) Graphical solution

FIG. 8.15 *Graphical solution of circuit of a linear and a nonlinear element.*

element. Notice that the characteristic of the nonlinear element is combined with R_2 by adding the currents for any given voltage, resulting in the curve marked A. Curve B is the familiar series battery-and-resistor characteristic, and its intersection with A shows the current I and the voltage V at the terminals a–b.

Example 8.2

Two d-c generators, symbolized by G_1 and G_2, are connected in parallel to supply current to load resistor R_L. The resistance of the power line between the generators and R_L is represented by R_1. The voltage-current characteristics of the two generators are represented by the two curves marked G_1 and G_2 in Fig. 8.16b. The

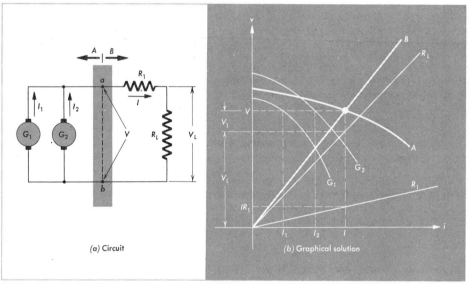

(a) Circuit   (b) Graphical solution

FIG. 8.16 *Graphical solution of parallel d-c-generator circuit (Example 8.2).*

composite characteristic of the two generators in parallel is found by adding the currents of the two generators for several arbitrary voltages across the generators' terminals and thus locating the curve marked A. The characteristics of the two resistors R_1 and R_L are shown, and they are added in series to produce the composite characteristic of the two, marked B. The intersection of the curves marked A and B indicates that current I is being supplied to the load by the generators, and V is the terminal voltage of the two generators in parallel. The voltage across R_L is marked V_L, and the voltage drop in the transmission line represented by R_1 is marked V_1, where

$V_1 = IR_1$. Generator G_1 supplies current I_1, generator G_2 supplies current I_2 to the load, and $I_1 + I_2 = I$, the total load current.

When the driving voltage is not constant, solutions that apply for a particular instant in time can be obtained by the graphical methods previously discussed. It is necessary only to determine a number of these solutions at various instants in time and then plot them as a function of time. For each solution at each instant, it is necessary to use the exciting voltage as it is at that particular instant.

The circuit shown in Fig. 8.17d shows a sinusoidal-voltage generator e exciting a linear resistor R_L and a nonlinear resistive

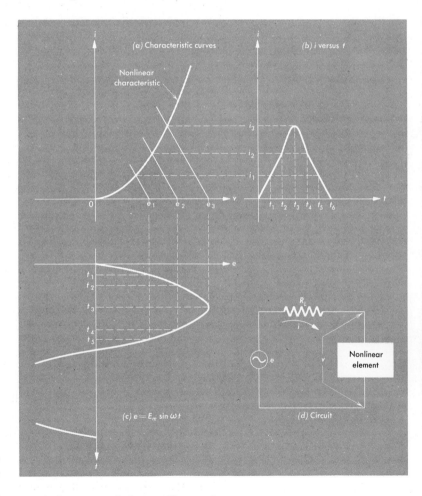

FIG. 8.17 *Graphical solution for sinusoidal driving voltage.*

element in series. The characteristic curve of the nonlinear element is shown in Fig. 8.17a. Superimposed on the nonlinear characteristic curve are characteristic curves for the generator and linear resistor R_L in series, taken at various instants in time. At t_1, the generator voltage is e_1 from the plot of the sinusoidal generator voltage in Fig. 8.17c. At e_1 in Fig. 8.17a, the linear characteristic curve with slope $-1/R_L$ is drawn. Its intersection with the characteristic curve of the nonlinear element satisfies Kirchhoff's laws and indicates that current i_1 is flowing at that instant in time. At t_2, the generator voltage is e_2, the load line or characteristic for the generator, R_L is drawn with the same slope, and it is found that i_2 is the resulting current. This is continued, and for each instant in time, the current is plotted in Fig. 8.17b. Finally the current points in Fig. 8.17b are connected with a smooth curve, and we have a plot of the nonsinusoidal circuit current as a function of time.

8.5 ALGEBRAIC SOLUTIONS

Resistive elements that are not linear can sometimes be approximately described by a simple analytic function. For instance, the voltage-current characteristic of a thermionic diode, under certain restrictions and approximations, can be shown to be

$$i = Kv^{3/2} \qquad 0 < v$$

$$= 0 \qquad v < 0 \tag{8.5}$$

where v is the anode-to-cathode voltage across the diode, i is the current, and K is a constant, dependent on electrode dimensions, etc. An equivalent expression is

$$v = \left(\frac{i}{K}\right)^{2/3} = K_1 i^{2/3} \tag{8.6}$$

where $K_1 = (1/K)^{2/3}$.

The thermionic diode whose voltage-current characteristic is described by Eqs. (8.5) and (8.6) can also be described approximately by an infinite power series of the form

$$i = a_0 + a_1 v + a_2 v^2 + a_3 v^3 + \cdots \tag{8.7}$$

where the a terms are all constants which usually diminish in magnitude as the subscript integers increase. Often the first three terms of Eq. (8.7) are adequate for a first approximation of the current-versus-voltage characteristic. If the current-versus-voltage characteristic of Fig. 8.17a can be described by the first three terms of Eq. (8.7), and if the diode is connected in series with a linear resistor as in Fig. 8.17d, then Kirchhoff's voltage law allows us to write

$$e - iR = v_n \tag{8.8}$$

where v_n is the voltage across the nonlinear element. Substituting the first three terms of Eq. (8.7) into Eq. (8.8) and collecting terms, we have

$$e - Ra_0 - Ra_1 v_n - Ra_2 v_n{}^2 = v_n \tag{8.9}$$

or

$$v_n{}^2 + \left(\frac{a_1}{a_2} + \frac{1}{Ra_2}\right)v_n + \left(\frac{a_0}{a_2} - \frac{e}{Ra_2}\right) = 0 \tag{8.10}$$

which is a quadratic in v_n. The solution of Eq. (8.10) is routine with the use of the quadratic equation.

Example 8.3

A thermionic diode has a characteristic curve plotted in Fig. 8.18b. It is connected in series with a 1,000-ohm resistor and a 100-volt d-c source in the circuit in Fig. 8.18a. Analytically, we shall find the

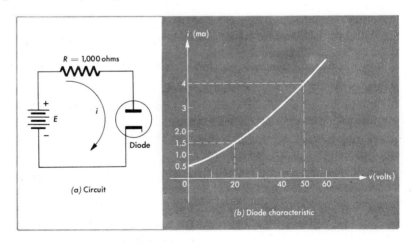

FIG. 8.18 *Power-series analytical approximation (Example 8.3).*

(a) Circuit

(b) Diode characteristic

first three terms of a power-series expansion of three terms to represent the characteristic and shall then solve the circuit algebraically. We note that, at $v = 0$, $i = 0.5$ ma, which must be the value of a_0 in Eq. (8.7). Then we arbitrarily locate two more points on the curve, choosing points at $v = 20$ volts, $i = 1.5$ ma, and $v = 50$ volts, $i = 4$ ma. Since each of these points must satisfy Eq. (8.7), we can write the first three terms, neglecting higher-order terms. Then

$$1.5 = 0.5 + 20a_1 + 20^2a_2$$

$$4 = 0.5 + 50a_1 + 50^2a_2$$

Solving these equations simultaneously for a_1 and a_2, we proceed as follows:

$$20a_1 + 400a_2 = 1.0$$

$$50a_1 + 2{,}500a_2 = 3.5$$

Using Cramer's rule,

$$a_1 = \frac{\begin{vmatrix} 1.0 & 400 \\ 3.5 & 2{,}500 \end{vmatrix}}{\begin{vmatrix} 20 & 400 \\ 50 & 2{,}500 \end{vmatrix}} = \frac{2{,}500 - 1{,}400}{50{,}000 - 20{,}000} = \frac{1{,}100}{30{,}000} = 0.0367$$

$$a_2 = \frac{\begin{vmatrix} 20 & 1.0 \\ 50 & 3.5 \end{vmatrix}}{\begin{vmatrix} 20 & 400 \\ 50 & 2{,}500 \end{vmatrix}} = \frac{70 - 50}{30{,}000} = \frac{20}{30{,}000} = 0.000667$$

Then

$$i = 0.5 + 0.0367v + 0.000667v^2 \qquad \text{ma}$$

Substituting i into Eq. (8.9) yields, for $E = 100$ and $R = 1{,}000$,

$$100 - 0.5 - 0.0367v_n - 0.000667v_n{}^2 = v$$

or

$$0.000667v_n{}^2 + 1.0367v_n - 99.5 = 0$$

Solving for v_n,

$$v_n = \frac{-1.0367 \pm \sqrt{1.0367^2 + 4(99.5)(0.000667)}}{2(0.000667)}$$

$$= 90.5 \text{ volts}$$

We discard the possible negative v, since the equations apply only for positive values.

From the above example it is apparent that greater accuracy can be obtained by using more terms in the power-series expansion. However, more terms in the power-series expansion means higher-order algebraic equations to solve, which increases the effort required for the solution.

8.6 SUCCESSIVE APPROXIMATION A METHOD OF SOLUTION

A nonlinear-resistive-circuit element incorporated in an otherwise linear circuit renders the analytical solution of that circuit more difficult than if only linear elements were present. Often approximation methods are used to solve nonlinear circuits, such as the solution described in the previous section. Successive approximation is also a useful technique. It can be carried on to any degree of accuracy desired.

Suppose that a nonlinear element such as a thermionic diode is connected in series with a linear resistor and battery as shown in Fig. 8.19. The voltage across the diode is expressed by Eq. (8.6). Kirchhoff's voltage law yields the equation

$$E = Ri + K_1 i^{2/3} \qquad (8.11)$$

where E, R, and K_1 are known constants. To find i, we guess a value of i and see whether or not it satisfies the equation. If our assumed value is such as to make the right side of Eq. (8.11) less than E, it is too small and a larger value can be tried. Conversely, if we guess a value of current which makes $Ri + K_1 i^{2/3}$ greater than E, we try a smaller value. After several trials, the value of i which very nearly satisfies the equation can be found.

A systematic method for accomplishing these successive trials for various values of current i is desirable to minimize labor. A tabulation of the solution is convenient, as shown in the following example.

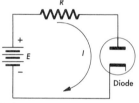

FIG. 8.19 *A nonlinear resistive circuit.*

Example 8.4

A thermionic diode is used in a series circuit, as shown in Fig. 8.19, where $E = 100$ volts, $R = 100$ ohms, and $K = 70$. To find i, a tabulation of terms can be made as in Table 8.1, and the first value of i is tried. We seek to have $Ri + K_1 i^{2/3} = E$, or $100i + 70i^{2/3} = 100$. Notice that the first trial of $i = 1.0$ makes $100i + 70i^{2/3} = 170$, which obviously indicates that i must be less than 1 amp to satisfy the equation. The second trial of $i = 0.5$ results in $100i + 70i^{2/3} = 94.1$, which indicates that i must be greater than 0.5 to satisfy the equation. Once i is bracketed, other successive trials put closer limits on i. Notice that the fourth trial very nearly satisfies the equation.

TABLE 8.1

Trial	i	$i^{3/5}$	Ri	$K_1 i^{3/5}$	$Ri + K_1 i^{3/5}$
1	1.00	1.000	100.0	70.0	170.0
2	0.50	0.630	50.0	44.1	94.1
3	0.60.	0.711	60.0	49.7	109.7
4	0.54	0.663	54.0	46.4	100.4

SUMMARY

Graphical methods of solution of linear and nonlinear resistive circuits are applications of Kirchhoff's laws. Voltage-current or current-voltage characteristics of each resistor and voltage (or current) source must be known. Then the characteristic curves of the various elements are combined in series or in parallel as necessary until values of voltage and current satisfying Kirchhoff's laws are found. Often it is convenient to break the circuit into two two-terminal circuits and combine the characteristics in each until a single composite characteristic is found for each half of the complete circuit; the intersection of these two composite characteristics satisfies Kirchhoff's laws, for only at the intersection are the two terminal currents identical and the two terminal voltages identical.

When the characteristics of resistive elements in series are combined to find the characteristic of the single resistor equivalent to the series combination, by Kirchhoff's law the same current flows through each series resistor. Thus, for an arbitrary current common to all the series resistors, the voltage across each element can be added graphically. Conversely, parallel elements all have the same voltage across them; the one-resistor equivalent to two or more resistors in parallel is obtained by assuming arbitrary voltages, adding the currents through each parallel resistor at that voltage, and thus locating points on the characteristic of the one-resistor equivalent. When only linear characteristics are added, another linear characteristic results, which can be obtained from only two points. (Review the example represented by Figs. 8.11 to 8.13.)

Piecewise linear approximations to nonlinear characteristics can be used to reduce a nonlinear-circuit problem to a linear one. Caution must be exercised in determining which linear portion on the curve must be used for the problem solution (Example 8.1).

Power-series approximations to nonlinear characteristic curves are useful if sufficient accuracy can be obtained by the use of terms of the power series up to and including the second-order term. A quadratic equation results and must be solved if only terms up to the second order are included (see Example 8.3).

Successive approximation is also a useful method for solving nonlinear algebraic equations. Successive "guesses" are necessary, each guess being substituted into the equation to see whether or not the equation is satisfied. Careful tabulation is helpful if the effort required is to be kept to a minimum.

PROBLEMS

8.1 Three resistors, $R_1 = 100$, $R_2 = 50$, and $R_3 = 200$ ohms, are all connected in series. Using the graphical method, plot current-versus-voltage characteristics for these resistors, and find a single resistor that is equivalent to the series combination. Check your results algebraically.

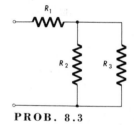

PROB. 8.3

8.2 The three resistors in Prob. 8.1 are connected in parallel. Using the graphical method, find the single resistor that is equivalent to the parallel combination of R_1, R_2, and R_3. Check your results analytically.

8.3 R_2 and R_3 of Prob. 8.1 are connected in parallel, and R_1 is connected in series with them as shown in the figure. By the graphical method, find a single resistor that is equivalent to the series-parallel combination. Check your graphical results analytically.

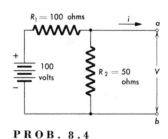

PROB. 8.4

8.4 Find the current-versus-voltage characteristic of the circuit shown in the illustration, as seen in looking in at terminals a–b.

8.5 A 200-ohm resistor is connected across terminals a–b in Prob. 8.4. Find the current through this resistor and the voltage across it by the graphical method. Check your result analytically.

8.6 A particular thyrite resistor shown in the illustration has a characteristic which can be described by $i = 4.000v^2$, where v is in volts and i is in milliamperes. It is connected in series with a linear resistor of 300 ohms and a direct-voltage source of 160 volts. Plot the thyrite-resistor characteristic, and find graphically the current through and the voltage across the thyrite resistor.

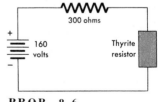

PROB. 8.6

8.7 A vacuum phototube has a characteristic as shown in the figure, where the parameter is illumination in lumens. It is connected in series with a sensitive relay whose coil is represented by 50 megohms of resistance. The d-c-supply source is 200 volts. (*a*) Find the current through the phototube when the illumination is 0.04 lumen. (*b*) If the relay closes at 2 μa, find the illumination necessary to cause the relay to close. (c) After the relay has closed, the current through the relay coil must be reduced to 1 μa to open the relay. Find the illumination necessary to cause this to happen. What is the voltage across the phototube when this occurs?

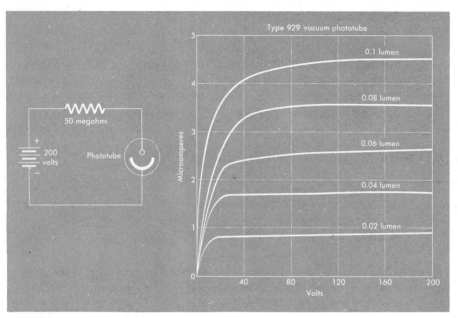

PROB. 8.7

8.8 The circuit of Prob. 8.6 is modified by connecting a 100-ohm linear resistor in parallel with the thyrite resistor. Solve this circuit graphically for the voltage across the thyrite resistor and the current through the thyrite resistor. What is the current through the 300-ohm resistor?

8.9 A vacuum phototube (type 929) has constant illumination of 0.06 lumen. Its characteristic is given in Prob. 8.7, and it is used in the same circuit as that of Prob. 8.7. Using a piecewise linear approximation, solve for the current through the phototube.

8.10 Repeat Prob. 8.9, using the power-series approximation and disregarding third- and higher-order terms. Does this particular curve lend itself to accurate solutions by this method?

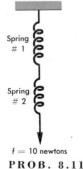

PROB. 8.11

8.11 Two linear springs are fastened in "series" as shown in the figure. Their characteristics can be expressed by $d_1 = 0.012f_1$, $d_2 = 0.030f_2$, where d is the deflection in meters and f is the force in newtons. Plot these individual characteristic curves, and find the total deflection of the two springs by graphical means (neglect the weight of the springs).

8.12 The two springs of Prob. 8.11 are connected in parallel as shown in the figure and constrained so that each spring always has the same deflection as the other. A force of 20 newtons extends the springs. Find the deflection d.

8.13 In the illustration a linear spring has constraints on it so that, when it has been extended 0.10 m, it cannot be extended farther no matter what the force. Its characteristic can be expressed by $d_1 = 0.0075f_1$, $0 < f < 13.33$, $d_1 = 0.10$, $13.33 < f$. This spring is connected in series with a spring that is linear and whose characteristic is $d_2 = 0.0032f_2$ for all practical values of f_2. Find the total deflection for a force of 15 newtons.

8.14 In the illustration a third spring is connected in parallel to the two in Prob. 8.13, and its characteristic is expressed by $d_3 = 0.010f_3$, $0 < f < 20$, $d_3 = 0.2$, $20 < f$. (a) What force f is required to produce a total deflection of 0.175 m? (b) What deflection does a force of 25 newtons produce?

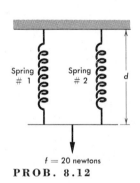

$f = 20$ newtons

PROB. 8.12

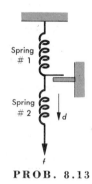

f

PROB. 8.13

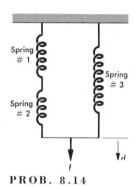

f

PROB. 8.14

8.15 The current-voltage characteristic curve for a 6H6 diode can be plotted from the following data:

v, volts	-1	0	5.0	10	15	20	25
i, ma	0	0.5	5.0	11.5	20.0	30.0	41.0

The diode is connected to a 30-volt battery in series with a 1,000-ohm linear resistor. Find the diode current.

8.16 The 6H6 diode of Prob. 8.15 is connected to a sinusoidal-voltage source of $e = 25 \sin 377t$ in series with a linear 500-ohm resistor. (a) Plot the diode current as a function of time. (b) Find the average value of the diode current.

8.17 The circuit shown in the figure consists of the 6H6 diode of Prob. 8.15, linear resistors, and a constant-voltage source. Find the battery current I and the diode current I_b.

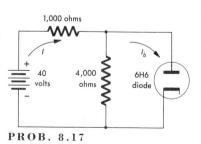

PROB. 8.17

9

ELECTRON PHYSICS

9.1 ELECTRONICS

At one time the science of electronics had to do almost exclusively with devices which employed the passage of electric charges through a vacuum or through a gas. Accordingly, vacuum tubes, fluorescent lights, phototubes, etc., are examples of electronic devices. One characteristic common to the two-terminal electronic devices is the nonlinearity of their voltage-current characteristic curves. Yet some present-day devices possessing the necessary nonlinear characteristics rely on conduction of current through solid semiconductor material. Then electronics must also include devices composed of any material which possesses the necessary nonlinear characteristics. Three- and four-terminal transmission, or input-output, electronic devices are characterized by their ability to amplify. The vacuum tube is the classical example, but now semiconductor devices called "transistors" perform amplification and are considered to be electronic devices. Indeed, it is difficult to define "electronics" without leaving out some present or future form of electronic device. With this possible oversight in mind, electronics can be defined as the science and technology concerned with the conduction of current through a gas or vacuum or through semiconductor material; the voltage-current characteristic curve of a two-terminal electronic device must be nonlinear, or the device must have the ability to amplify. It is conceivable that future electronic devices will have the necessary characteristics obtained from conduction in other kinds of materials.

From another point of view, electronics can be thought of as the science and technology concerned with the collection, processing, and distribution of information; it includes communication systems, automatic control systems, instrumentation, and computers. Nonlinear impedances and amplifying circuits are necessary in these kinds of systems.

In this chapter we consider the fundamental physics of electron devices, including conduction in a vacuum and in semiconductor materials. Following chapters are concerned with the actual voltage-current relationships at the terminals of electronic instruments and the application of these instruments as circuit elements in electric circuits.

9.2 THE ELECTRIC FIELD

Whenever positive and negative electric charges are separated from each other and concentrated in separate locations, an electric field is established in the region between and around the separated charges. The presence of the electric field is determined by the force on a separate electric charge placed in the field. The electric-field intensity is defined as the force on a unit of positive charge placed in the electric field. Since force is a vector quantity, electric-field intensity is also a vector quantity; at every point in the electric field the field intensity possesses both magnitude and direction.

As an example of an electric field, consider the vicinity of the charge $+Q_1$ concentrated at point A in Fig. 9.1, with the charge $-Q_1$ at infinity. In order to establish the presence of the electric field in the vicinity of A, we place an exploring positive charge of 1 coulomb at position B a distance r from A and measure the force on the exploring charge. The force per unit charge is observed to be of the magnitude

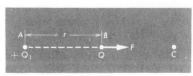

FIG. 9.1 *Charge Q_1 at A causes force F on exploring positive charge at B.*

$$\mathcal{E} = \frac{Q_1}{4\pi\epsilon r^2} \qquad \text{newtons/coulomb} \qquad (9.1)$$

in the radial direction away from A, as shown in Fig. 9.1. The constant ϵ in Eq. (9.1) is a function of the material between and surrounding the charges and is known as "permittivity." If the experiment is performed in air or in a vacuum or "free space," the permittivity is

$$\epsilon_0 = \frac{1}{36\pi \times 10^9} = 8.85 \times 10^{-12} \text{ farad/m} \qquad (9.2)$$

The permittivity or dielectric constant of several common materials is shown in Table 1.4. The electric-field intensity at point B is the force in newtons on one coulomb of positive charge as given by Eq. (9.1) and shown in Fig. 9.1. Electric-field intensity is symbolized by $\mathcal{E}$ as in Eq. (9.1).

If a charge Q is placed at position B in Fig. 9.1, the force on the other charge is observed to have a magnitude

$$F = \frac{Q_1 Q}{4\pi \epsilon r^2} \qquad \text{newtons} \qquad (9.3)$$

Equation (9.3) is the well-known Coulomb's law. The direction of the forces is that of attraction if Q_1 and Q are of opposite sign and that of repulsion if Q_1 and Q are the same sign. Since Eq. (9.1) gives $\mathcal{E}$, the force on a unit positive charge, and Eq. (9.3) shows the force on the charge Q being proportional to charge Q, substituting Eq. (9.1) into Eq. (9.3) results in

$$F = \mathcal{E}Q \qquad \text{newtons} \qquad (9.4)$$

Thus, by Eq. (9.4), the force on a charge Q in an electric field $\mathcal{E}$ is proportional to the electric-field intensity and the magnitude of the charge.

The two equations (9.1) and (9.3) give the force in the vicinity of Q_1 as a function of permittivity, a property of the material or space surrounding the charge. It is convenient to define an electric-field quantity which is independent of the permittivity of the material. Thus, Eq. (9.1) can be written

$$D = \frac{Q_1}{4\pi r^2} \qquad \text{coulombs/m}^2 \qquad (9.5)$$

where

$$D = \epsilon \mathcal{E} \qquad (9.6)$$

Notice that D in Eq. (9.5) is independent of permittivity and has the dimensions of charge divided by area. D is known as "electric-flux density"; it is a vector-field quantity with the same direction as the direction of the field intensity.

From electric-flux density, the concept of electric flux can be developed. Notice that the units of D in Eq. (9.6) represent an area density and that, when D is multiplied by an area, the product is in coulombs; this product we call "electric flux." If r is chosen in Eq. (9.5) such that $4\pi r^2 = 1$ m^2, then $D = Q_1$ coulombs/m^2 and the flux through the area of the sphere of radius r is 1 coulomb. Thus, the net electric flux through a closed area is equal to the charge enclosed in that area. Electric flux, symbolized by ψ, is a scalar quantity; it has magnitude and direction but is distributed over a surface and cannot be defined at a point in space. The direction of the electric flux is the direction of the electric-field intensity, i.e., the direction of force on a positive charge.

In Chap. 1, the potential difference between two points in volts was defined as the work required to move a coulomb of positive charge through the electric field between the two points. If the charge is moved in a direction opposite to the electric field, mechanical work is done on the charge and the potential increases. The potential difference in going from C to B in Fig. 9.1 is the work done to move a coulomb of charge from C to B, or

$$E_{BC} = -\int_{r_C}^{r_B} \mathcal{E}\, dr \qquad \text{volts} \tag{9.7}$$

where r_B is the distance from point B to Q_1, r_C is the distance from point C to Q_1, and dr is an incremental distance in the radial direction along line CB. Substituting Eq. (9.1) into Eq. (9.7) gives

$$E_{BC} = -\int_{r_C}^{r_B} \frac{Q_1}{4\pi\epsilon r^2}\, dr = +\frac{Q_1}{4\pi\epsilon}\left(\frac{1}{r_B} - \frac{1}{r_C}\right) \qquad \text{volts} \tag{9.8}$$

Equations (9.7) and (9.8) are force-times-distance equations similar to Eq. (1.11).

Another field configuration of simple geometry is the space between two infinite parallel-plane electrodes on which charges of opposite sign are distributed uniformly. A square section of these infinite planes is shown in Fig. 9.2, where ρ is the uniform surface-charge density in coulombs per square meter. The electric flux between the planes is in the direction from the positive charges on A to the negative charges on B, represented by the lines between the charges. The flux density in the space between the electrodes is equal to the charge density on the surface of the electrodes, or $D = \rho$. Then the electric-field strength in the space between the planes has a magnitude of

$$\mathcal{E} = \frac{\rho}{\epsilon} \qquad \text{volts/m} \tag{9.9}$$

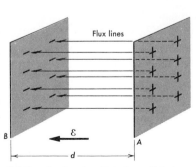

FIG. 9.2 *A section of parallel-plane electrodes uniformly but oppositely charged.*

and is uniform everywhere between the plates. A positive charge placed anywhere in the region between the plates experiences a force in the direction toward the negatively charged plate and away from the positively charged plate, and the direction of the electric field is from right to left in Fig. 9.2. Since ε is everywhere uniform in the region between the plates, the voltage between the plates is the product of electric-field intensity and the spacing, found from Eq. (1.11) [or Eq. (9.7)], is

$$E = \varepsilon d \qquad \text{volts} \tag{9.10}$$

Another configuration of electric field is produced by a straight line of charge with an equal but opposite charge at infinity. In Fig. 9.3, the charged line is located at A and extends into the paper with a uniform charge density of $+\lambda$ coulombs/m. To find the electric-flux density D at a distance r from the line charge, it is convenient to examine one unit length of the line charge. It is assumed that the lines representing coulombs of electric flux originate on positive charges and terminate on negative charges; therefore, the flux extends radially outward from the charged line and terminates on charges at infinity. A charge of $+\lambda$ coulombs exists on any 1-m length of the line, and therefore λ coulombs of flux emanate from the line. At a distance r from the line, the area through which the flux passes is $2\pi r$, and therefore

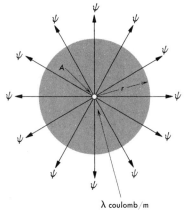

λ coulomb/m

FIG. 9.3 *Line charge at A directed into the paper, with λ coulombs/m.*

$$D = \frac{\lambda}{2\pi r} \tag{9.11}$$

and

$$\varepsilon = \frac{\lambda}{2\pi r \epsilon} \tag{9.12}$$

Notice from Eq. (9.12) that the field intensity has a magnitude that is inversely proportional to the distance from the line, r. The direction of the electric field is radially outward, away from the positive charges of the line and toward the negative charges at infinity.

It is interesting to compare the electric-field equations for the point charge, the line charge, and the plane charge [Eqs. (9.1), (9.12), and (9.9)]. For the point charge, the electric-field intensity is inversely proportional to the *square* of the distance from the charge. The field intensity about the line charge is inversely proportional to the *distance* from the line, and the field intensity between parallel charged plates of large area is *independent* of the distance from the planes. Many other field configurations are encountered, but these three represent the simplest geometries possible.

9.3 MOTION OF ELECTRONS IN A VACUUM

An electric charge in an electric field has a force exerted on it by the field. If the charge is free to move in the field, energy can be transferred from the field to the charge. Consider now the action of uniform electric field described by Eq. (9.9) upon an electron placed in that field. Assume that the region in the electric field is evacuated so that no gas molecules interfere with the motion of the electron. Two forces act upon the electron; they are the force of the electric field and the inertia force attributed to the mass of the electron. Equating the magnitudes of these forces gives

$$\mathcal{E}e = m \frac{dv}{dt} \qquad (9.13)$$

where e is the charge on the electron, m is its mass, assumed constant, and dv/dt is the acceleration of the electron. Solving Eq. (9.13) for velocity v of the electron, and considering only velocity in the direction of the field,

$$v = \int_0^t \frac{e}{m} \mathcal{E} \, dt + V_0 \qquad (9.14)$$

where v is the velocity at time t and V_0 is the initial velocity at $t = 0$. Since e/m is a constant and we have assumed a uniform electric field where $\mathcal{E}$ is also constant, the integration of Eq. (9.14) can be performed, yielding

$$v = \frac{e}{m} \mathcal{E}t + V_0 \qquad (9.15)$$

The value of electronic charge and mass and the ratio of e/m have all been accurately determined by experiment. They are

$$e = 1.6021 \times 10^{-19} \text{ coulomb}$$

$$m = 9.1085 \times 10^{-31} \text{ kg}$$

$$\frac{e}{m} = 1.7589 \times 10^{11} \text{ coulombs/kg}$$

Distance traveled by the electron during time t in a uniform electric field can be found by integrating the velocity with respect to time. Then

$$x = \int_0^t v \, dt = \mathcal{E} \frac{e}{m} \frac{t^2}{2} + V_0 t \qquad \text{meters} \tag{9.16}$$

assuming that $x = 0$ at $t = 0$.

The energy which the electron extracts from the electric field can be found by integrating the force with respect to distance. Since $\mathcal{E}e$ is the force on the electron,

$$dW_e = F \, dx \qquad \text{joules} \tag{9.17}$$

where dW_e is an increment of energy of the electron and F is force as a function of distance x. Then by integration, substituting in the constant force for this special case of uniform field intensity,

$$W_e = \int_0^x \mathcal{E}e \, dx = \mathcal{E}ex \tag{9.18}$$

where W_e is the change in energy of the electron in moving the distance x. Substituting Eq. (9.16) into (9.18) yields

$$W_e = \frac{e^2 \mathcal{E}^2 t^2}{2m} + \mathcal{E}eV_0 t \tag{9.19}$$

which is the kinetic energy of the electron as a function of time. Obviously the change in kinetic energy expressed by Eq. (9.19) must be the difference between the energy after acquiring velocity v and the initial energy attributed to the initial velocity V_0, or

$$W_e = \tfrac{1}{2}mv^2 - \tfrac{1}{2}mV_0{}^2 \tag{9.20}$$

Substitution of Eq. (9.15) into Eq. (9.20) also results in Eq. (9.19). Thus, the kinetic energy extracted from the field by the electron can be found either from the kinetic-energy equation [Eq. (9.20)] or by integrating force with respect to distance.

As the electron falls through the electric field and gains kinetic energy, it loses potential energy at the same rate. The change in kinetic energy expressed by Eq. (9.20) is a measure of the voltage or potential difference through which the electron has fallen. A unit of energy, the electron volt, can be defined as the change in kinetic energy of an electron in falling through a potential difference of one volt. We have seen that, when 1 coulomb moves through a potential difference of 1 volt, the change in energy is 1 joule. Then

$$1 \text{ electron volt} = 1.6021 \times 10^{-19} \text{ joule}$$

Obviously the electron volt is not an mks unit, but it is a very convenient unit nevertheless.

The motion of electrons in a vacuum is a phenomenon present in all vacuum tubes. Some simple examples of electron motion in electric fields are illustrated in the following examples.

Example 9.1

An electron is released at the negative plane in the electric field established by two infinite parallel-plane electrodes. Initially the electron has zero velocity. The planes are separated by 0.7 m, and a potential difference of 1,000 volts is maintained between the plates.

To find the time required for the electron to travel from the negative plane to the positive plane, first find the strength of the electric field between them. The field is uniform, and

$$\mathcal{E} = \frac{1{,}000 \text{ volts}}{0.7 \text{ m}} = 1{,}428 \text{ volts/m}$$

Then solving Eq. (9.16) for t, and recognizing that the initial velocity $V_0 = 0$,

$$t = \sqrt{\frac{2mx}{\mathcal{E}e}} = \sqrt{\frac{2 \times 9.1085 \times 10^{-31} \times 0.7}{1{,}428 \times 1.6021 \times 10^{-19}}}$$

$$= 0.748 \times 10^{-7} \text{ sec}$$

The velocity of the electron as a function of time is

$$v = \frac{e}{m} \mathcal{E}t$$

$$= 1.7589 \times 10^{11} \times 1{,}428t$$

$$= 2.510 \times 10^{14}t \quad \text{m/sec}$$

and the distance traveled as a function of time is

$$x = \mathcal{E} \frac{e}{m} \frac{t^2}{2} = 1.255 \times 10^{14}t^2 \quad \text{meters}$$

The velocity with which the electron strikes the positive plate is

$$v_s = 2.510 \times 10^{14} \times 0.748 \times 10^{-7} = 1.880 \times 10^7 \text{ m/sec}$$

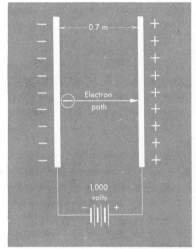

FIG. 9.4 *Motion of electron between parallel-plane electrodes of Example 9.1.*

Example 9.2

An electron starts from rest and is accelerated through 1,000 volts in the x direction, after which it enters a vertical electric field of 2×10^3 volts/m. The velocity of the electron after falling through 1,000 volts is seen from Example 9.1 to be 1.880×10^7 m/sec.

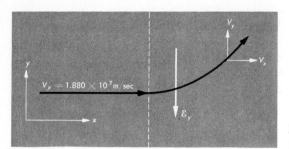

FIG. 9.5 *Electron deflected by vertical electric field (Example 9.2).*

The velocity after entering the vertical electric field can be obtained in two components, v_x and v_y. The x component of velocity remains unchanged.

$$v_x = 1.880 \times 10^7 \text{ m/sec}$$

From $F_y = ma_y$,

$$v_y = \int_0^t \frac{\mathcal{E}_y e}{m} \, dt$$

$$= \frac{\mathcal{E}_y e}{m} t = 2 \times 10^3 \times 1.7589 \times 10^{11} t = 3.518 \times 10^{14} t$$

The net velocity v_s is the vector sum of v_x and v_y.

$$v_s = \sqrt{v_x{}^2 + v_y{}^2} = \sqrt{(1.880 \times 10^7)^2 + (3.518 \times 10^{14} t)^2}$$

At some particular instant in time, say, $t = 10^{-8}$ sec, v_s is

$$v_s = \sqrt{(1.880 \times 10^7)^2 + (3.518 \times 10^6)^2} = 1.91 \times 10^7 \text{ m/sec}$$

9.4 ELECTRONIC EMISSION

Valence electrons in the outermost orbit of conductor atoms are loosely bound to the atomic nuclei. Only a small amount of energy is required for the valence electrons to break the bonds holding them to the nuclei. Thermal energy in the conductor is adequate at normal temperatures to break the bonds of the outermost electrons and leave them unattached to any one nucleus. The free electrons thus produced within the conductor are able to move under the influence of an electric field superimposed upon the conductor to produce electric current. Without an external electric field, the free electrons move with random velocities and random directions and on the average do not produce current. But, in the presence of the field, the free, or conducting, electrons move with an average velocity in the direction opposite to the direction of the electric field and with an average velocity proportional to the field intensity.

Conducting electrons moving at random in a conductor come under the influence of several nuclei at once. Moving as they do in the region between the lattices of the crystal, they are attracted in several directions at once by the nearby atoms, and the net force on them is very nearly zero. But when the free electrons, moving at random among the atoms of the conductor, arrive at the surface of the conductor, the forces of attraction by the positive nuclei produce resultant forces on the free electrons normal to the conductor surface and directed toward the conductor. For a free electron to leave the conductor's surface, it must possess a component of velocity directed away from the surface of the conductor of sufficient magnitude to overcome the nuclear forces at the surface. Furthermore, once the electron leaves the surface, the conductor remains with a positive charge, tending to attract the electron back to the conductor. Thus, free electrons are able to move at random through the conductor but are bound somewhat to the conductor boundaries. Only those electrons with sufficient kinetic energy directed outward normal to the conductor surface ever leave the conductor, producing a phenomenon known as "electronic emission."

Emission of electrons can be encouraged by increasing the average kinetic energy of the free electrons in the conductor. Since the velocities of the free electrons in the conductor are distributed at random, some electrons possess more kinetic energy than others; there is a continuous range of velocities represented in a large sample of the free electrons. By increasing the average velocity of the electrons, the number of electrons arriving at the surface with sufficient energy to leave the surface is also increased. Therefore, to stimulate electronic emission, the average energy possessed by the free electrons must be increased.

The amount of energy which an electron must possess in order to overcome the surface forces of a conductor is known as the "work function" of the conductor. Work function is a function of the kind of conductor material, its purity, and the condition of its surface. Materials of low work functions are those of large atomic radii. Tungsten has a work function of 4.52 electron volts; copper, of 4.33 electron volts; and nickel, of 2.77 electron volts.

Energy can be added to the free electrons in a conductor by heating the conducting material, causing the atoms in a crystalline lattice to vibrate over wider amplitudes, and also increasing the mean velocity of the free electrons. By heating the conductor to a high temperature, electron emission from the conductor increases tremendously. When a hot conductor is employed in an electron tube, it becomes the cathode, or source of electrons in the tube. Electronic emission stimulated by high temperatures is known as "thermionic emission." Most electron tubes commonly used employ thermionic emission as a source of electrons in space.

Energy can be imparted to the free electrons in a conductor from light shining on the conductor. Some of the photons give up their energy to the free electrons, which then acquire sufficient energy to leave the surface of the conductor. In some materials the energy of the impinging photons is more readily absorbed by the free electrons in the conductor than in other materials. If the free electrons of the conductor readily absorb light energy, and if the potential barrier or work function at the surface of the conductor is low, then appreciable electronic emission can be obtained from light. This is known as "photoelectric emission" and has useful application in phototubes and other light-sensitive devices.

The extent to which a piece of conducting material emits thermal electrons is a function of the nature of the material, the temperature of the material, and the nature of its surface. In order to discuss thermionic emission in a quantitative manner, consider two metallic electrodes in an evacuated region, as shown in Fig. 9.6. The electrode marked "cathode" is heated to a high uniform temperature and emits electrons. The anode is maintained at a positive potential with respect to the cathode, thus establishing an electric field which attracts the emitted electrons to the anode. If all the electrons emitted by the cathode are attracted to the anode, then the current density of the cathode is given by

$$J = A_0 T^2 \epsilon^{-b_0/T} \qquad \text{amp/m}^2 \tag{9.21}$$

where A_0 is a constant, T is the temperature of the cathode in degrees Kelvin, and b_0 is a constant which depends for its value on the material of the cathode and its work function. Equation (9.21) is known as "Dushman's equation." If current density is plotted as a function of the temperature of the cathode, the current density is seen to increase very rapidly with temperature, as shown in Fig. 9.7 for tungsten.

The heating of the cathode is ordinarily accomplished by passing an electric current through the cathode or through a heating element adjacent to the actual cathode. The cathodes of most electron tubes commonly used today are of the indirectly heated variety. These cathodes consist of a metal sleeve coated with an oxide of barium, strontium, and calcium. Inside the metal sleeve,

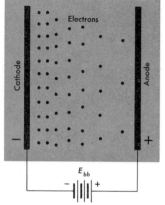

FIG. 9.6 *Parallel-plane electrodes consisting of a thermionic cathode and an anode in an evacuated chamber.*

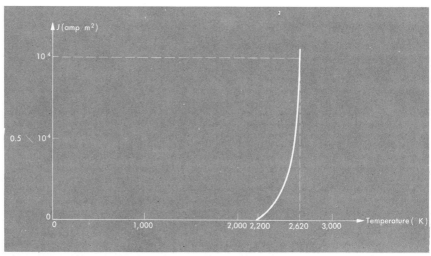

FIG. 9.7 *Current density versus temperature for a tungsten cathode.*

and insulated from it, is the heating element of the cathode. In-directly heated cathodes operate at about 1100°K at the surface of the cathode. Cathodes of a few electron tubes in common use, especially diodes, are directly heated. They consist of a thin wire or ribbon through which current is passed. There is a distributed voltage drop across the directly heated cathode, so that its po-tential is.not everywhere the same, as it is with the indirectly heated cathode. Directly heated cathodes are often oxide-coated, too. Oxide-coated cathodes are more efficient than cathodes of pure metallic materials or alloys; their emission current in amperes per watt of heating power is high compared with pure metallic cathodes such as tungsten.

Since electron tubes contain one electrode for the emission of electrons, the cathode, and one electrode for the capture of elec-trons, known as the "anode," it is obvious that the direction of **electron flow is from cathode to anode.** The anode is seldom oper-ated under conditions at which it emits electrons. If the anode is made negative with respect to the cathode, no current flows through the tube. The tube is essentially a one-way-current de-vice. Since the direction of current flow is defined as the direction of flow of positive charges in a circuit, the conventional current flow is from anode to cathode. This should not be confusing when one keeps in mind that positive charges moving in one direction are electrically equivalent to electrons moving in the opposite direction.

9.5 SPACE CHARGE

As large quantities of electrons leave a cathode, they form a distributed charge, known as "space charge," around the cathode. Electrostatic forces between electrons are repulsive forces. Thus, as additional electrons leave the cathode, they are acted upon by the space charge and experience a force which tends to drive them back into the cathode. Space charge tends to reduce the amount of electron current flowing from the cathode to the anode. If the potential of the anode is maintained sufficiently high with respect to the cathode, the electrons are accelerated continuously in their path toward the anode and the effect of the space charge is small. But if the anode potential is not sufficiently high, the electrons are in flight for a longer period of time, contributing to the space charge, and limiting the current.

Under space-charge conditions, the cathode current density is described by Child's law, which can be expressed

$$J = KE_b^{3/2} \qquad \text{amp/m}^2 \tag{9.22}$$

where K is a constant, E_b is the potential between anode and cathode in volts, and J is the current density in amperes per square meter. Child's law can be derived from the following assumptions: (a) the cathode is an infinite-plane electrode of uniform temperature everywhere; (b) the anode is an infinite plane parallel to the cathode and is maintained at a uniform positive potential difference with respect to the cathode; (c) space charge exists between the cathode and the anode, limiting the space current; and (d) the electric field at the surface of the cathode is zero. Dushman's equation [Eq. (9.21)] was derived on the assumption that all the space charge is withdrawn from the vicinity of the cathode as it forms. The condition of space charge, described by Child's law in Eq. (9.21), assumes that space charge exists near the cathode which limits the space current. Electron tubes are ordinarily operated in the space-charge-limited condition.

In the practical electron tube where infinite-parallel-plane electrodes are not possible, Child's law is still a reasonable approximation to the voltage-current relationship. The exponent of $3/2$ may not be exact for the various shapes of short, nearly cylindrical electrodes commonly used in vacuum tubes, but it is quite close. The current-versus-voltage characteristic for a vacuum diode consisting of an anode and a cathode can be obtained experimentally with the circuit shown in Fig. 9.8a. The battery voltage is shown adjustable so that anode-to-cathode potential difference can be varied. When the cathode is heated to its rated temperature, the anode-cathode voltage E_b and the anode current I_b are measured for various values of E_b. A plot of I_b versus E_b is shown in Fig. 9.8b. For small values of E_b, the current I_b increases according

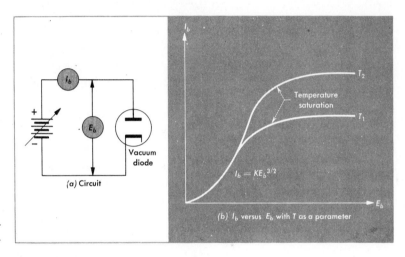

FIG. 9.8 *The current-versus-voltage characteristic of a vacuum diode.*

to Child's three-halves-power law, and the curve is concave upward. If the cathode is heated to temperature T_1, eventually the anode voltage becomes high enough to attract all the space-charge electrons emitted from the cathode and any increase in anode voltage causes no more increase in the current. This is known as "temperature saturation," shown by the horizontal part of the curve in Fig. 9.8b. At a higher temperature T_2, temperature saturation exists at a higher saturation current because more electrons can be emitted by the cathode at the higher temperature. Under conditions of temperature saturation, Dushman's equation describes the current density as a function of cathode temperature.

A plot of potential versus distance for the space between the cathode and the anode of a vacuum diode with parallel-plane electrodes is shown in Fig. 9.9 for the space-charge-limited condition. If no space charge is present, the electric-field intensity is uniform and the curve follows the straight line shown, where E_b is the anode-to-cathode voltage. The negative space charge tends to

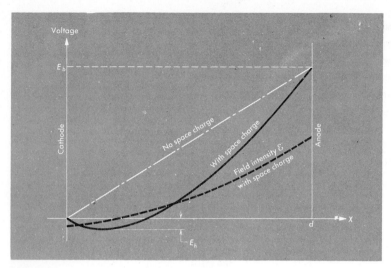

FIG. 9.9 *Potential versus distance for space-charge-limited vacuum diode with parallel-plane electrodes.*

reduce the potential everywhere between the two electrodes, and under space-charge conditions the curve is concave upward, as shown. A potential hump E_h must be crossed by the electrons if they are to reach the anode. The electric-field intensity as the derivative of potential with respect to distance is also shown. Notice that the electrons emitted from the cathode initially experience a force back toward the cathode but that after they cross the potential hump, the force is toward the anode.

9.6 SEMICONDUCTORS

A semiconductor is a solid which has a resistivity somewhere in between the resistivity of conductors and that of insulators. A conductor has a large number of conducting, or free, electrons, and its resistivity is of the order of 10^{-7} ohm-m. An insulator has very few charge carriers and a resistivity of the order of 10^{10} to 10^{16} ohm-m. Semiconductors are characterized by intermediate resistivities of the order of 1 ohm-m, and with relatively few charge carriers, the number being greatly influenced by the temperature of the semiconductor and the presence of light shining on it. Conductors and insulators are discussed in Sec. 1.4.

The semiconductors silicon and germanium in extremely pure form are known as "intrinsic" semiconductors. The atoms of these semiconductor elements are arranged in crystals, a crystal being an orderly array of atoms located in repetitive geometric patterns. A single crystal consists of a large number of atoms, and the high purity of intrinsic semiconductors requires that only about 1 atom or less in every 10^{10} atoms be an impurity atom. Germanium and silicon atoms have four valence electrons each, and therefore each atom shares four additional electrons from the neighboring atoms. A two-dimensional representation of germanium or silicon in crystalline form is shown in Fig. 9.10. Each atom, besides having its own four valence electrons which it shares with four neighboring atoms, shares one valence electron from each of the four adjacent atoms. The positive charges shown in Fig. 9.10 as +4 represent the nuclei together with the electrons in orbits inside the

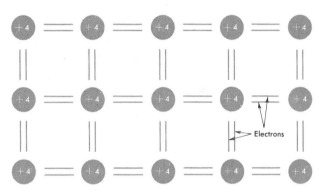

FIG. 9.10 *Two-dimensional representation of a semiconductor crystal of germanium or silicon.*

valence orbits. The valence electrons, each shared now by two atoms, are shown by minus signs. Each atom fills its valence orbit with eight electrons, four of which are its own and four of which are from neighboring atoms.

Each atom in Fig. 9.10 is bound to the four surrounding adjacent atoms by a covalent bond. At a temperature of 0°K (absolute zero), all the electrons in intrinsic germanium or silicon are tightly bound to each of two atoms. There are no free, or conducting, electrons, and therefore the semiconductor behaves like a perfect insulator. But if energy is added to one of the valence electrons by just the right amount, the electron can break its covalent bond and be free to drift among the atoms without being bound to any of them. Once it breaks loose, it is a free electron, capable of moving under the influence of an electric field and thus causing electric current.

When the temperature of the intrinsic semiconductor is raised above 0°K, the thermal energy is manifest in the thermal vibrations of the atoms about their mean lattice positions and in the vibration of the valence electrons. Some of the valence electrons in the various atoms acquire enough energy to break their covalent

bonds and become conducting electrons. But even at room temperature the number of free electrons is not large; about one conducting electron exists for every 10^9 atoms for germanium. When
an electron breaks its covalent bond and leaves the vicinity of its
atom, it leaves a positive charge behind. Recombination of charges
takes place at the same rate at which free electrons are produced,
and the average concentration of free electrons remains constant.
The positive charge left when the covalent bond is broken by the
removal of the electron is known as a "hole." At temperatures
above 0°K, both positive holes and free electrons are present in
equal numbers in semiconductor material; the material is always
electrically neutral. At any given temperature, the average rate
at which electrons free themselves from their bound positions is
exactly equal to the average rate at which the holes and the electrons recombine.

When an electric field is established within the semiconductor,
both holes and electrons migrate under its influence. The free
electrons drift with an average velocity proportional to the electric-
field intensity, but they move opposite to the direction of the field.
The holes, being positive charges, move in the same direction as
the field. The resulting electric current has two components, the
electron current and the current caused by the positive holes.
The tendency for electrons and holes to recombine still exists.
Recombination provides one way to visualize the apparent motion
of the holes. Suppose that an electron, freed from its valence
orbit in position A in Fig. 9.11, migrates to position B under the

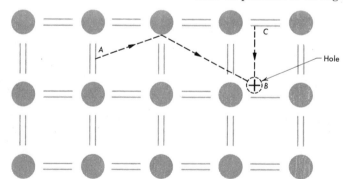

FIG. 9.11 *Motion of holes caused by mo-*
tion of free electrons and recombination or by mo-
tion of adjacent bound electrons.

influence of the electric field, suffering collisions with the atoms
in the lattices on the way. Suppose that there is a hole at B and
that the electron combines with the hole to neutralize the charge.
There is now a hole at position A previously occupied by the electron, and there is no hole at B because of recombination. Thus

there exists the effect of the electron moving to the right and the hole moving to the left. The conventional current moves in the direction of hole motion and consists of electron current and hole current.

The motion of holes is actually more subtle than the visualization of the previous paragraph indicates. While free electrons by recombination can produce apparent hole motion, bound electrons from adjacent atoms can also recombine with a hole to produce apparent hole motion. This is illustrated by Fig. 9.11 again, where the electron marked C moves into the hole at B, causing apparent hole motion from B to C. The electron at C does not receive the required energy to be freed from its covalent bond; it merely moves over to the adjacent hole. Motion of holes is accomplished, then, by two different mechanisms, both resulting from electron motion. First, the motion of free electrons and their recombination causes hole motion, and, second, the motion of bound electrons from adjacent atoms to fill the holes causes hole motion.

Electric charges free to move in a vacuum accelerate when an electric field is applied; the *acceleration* is directly proportional to the electric-field intensity. Holes and electrons in semiconductors experience collisions with atoms in the crystal lattices and tend to move at a *velocity* that is proportional to the electric-field strength. Then

$$V_a = \mu \mathcal{E} \qquad \text{m/sec} \tag{9.23}$$

where V_a is the average velocity of the charges, $\mathcal{E}$ is the electric-field intensity, and μ is the constant of proportionality known as "mobility." From Eq. (9.23) it is seen that mobility has units of meters per second for every volt per meter of field strength, or square meters per volt-seconds.

The measured mobility of electrons in a given intrinsic semiconductor is greater than the measured mobility of the holes. Mobilities of holes and electrons in silicon and germanium are given in Table 9.1. If n is the number of charge carriers per cubic

TABLE 9.1

	Mobility, m^2/volt-sec	
Charge carrier	Germanium	Silicon
Electron	0.360	0.120
Hole	0.170	0.025

meter, e is the charge on each carrier, and V_a is the average velocity of the charges, then from Eq. (1.1) the current density in amperes per square meter is

$$J = neV_a \qquad \text{amp/m}^2 \tag{9.24}$$

Current caused by motion of both electrons and holes must be added to give the total current, or

$$J_t = J_e + J_h \qquad \text{amp/m}^2 \tag{9.25}$$

Substituting Eq. (9.23) into Eq. (9.24) gives

$$J = ne\mu\mathcal{E} \qquad \text{amp/m}^2 \tag{9.26}$$

where $ne\mu$ is the electron or hole conductivity of the semiconductor, the reciprocal of the resistivity.

Example 9.3

A bar of intrinsic germanium at a temperature of $300°K$ has a free-electron density of 2.5×10^{13} electrons/cm³ or 2.5×10^{19} electrons/m³. If an electric field of 500 volts/m is superimposed upon the germanium, the electron current density can be calculated by Eq. (9.26).

$$J_e = n_e e \mu_e \mathcal{E}$$
$$= 2.5 \times 10^{19} \times 1.6 \times 10^{-19} \times 0.360 \times 500$$
$$= 720 \text{ amp/m}^2 = 0.0720 \text{ amp/cm}^2$$

Hole current density is

$$J_h = n_h e \mu_e \mathcal{E}$$

where $n_h = n_e$. Then

$$J_h = 2.5 \times 10^{19} \times 1.6 \times 10^{-19} \times 0.170 \times 500$$
$$= 340 \text{ amp/m}^2 = 0.0340 \text{ amp/cm}^2$$

The net current density J_T is

$$J_T = J_e + J_h = 720 + 340 = 1,060 \text{ amp/m}^2$$
$$= 0.1060 \text{ amp/cm}^2$$

Example 9.4

The number of free electrons in a copper conductor is approximately equal to the number of atoms in the conductor. In 1 cm³ of copper, the number of atoms is

$$n = \frac{N_0 d}{A} = 8.37 \times 10^{22} \text{ atoms/cc}$$

where N_0 is Avogadro's number ($N_0 = 6.025 \times 10^{23}$ atoms/g atom), d is the density (8.89 g/cm³), and A is the atomic weight ($A = 64$). Then suppose that 1 cc of copper is drawn out in a wire 100 cm long with a cross-sectional area of 0.01 cm². If 1 amp flows in the wire, the velocity of the free electrons must be

$$V_a = \frac{J}{ne}$$

where I is current, n is the number of charges per unit length, and e is the charge of the electron. Then

$$V_a = \frac{1}{8.37 \times 10^{22} \times 1.602 \times 10^{-19}}$$

$$= 7.46 \times 10^{-5} \text{ m/sec}$$

and the actual velocity of the free electrons is very slow.

9.7 *N*-TYPE AND *P*-TYPE SEMICONDUCTORS

The conductivity of the semiconductor elements germanium and silicon can be altered greatly by the addition of minute amounts of impurities into the crystalline structure. Consider an impurity atom which has five valence electrons, and suppose that each atom of the impurity takes the place of one of the semiconductor atoms in the crystal. Figure 9.12 illustrates the doping of germanium

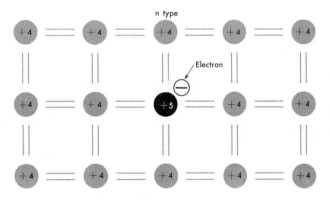

FIG. 9.12 *Two-dimensional representation of a semiconductor crystal doped with antimony with five valence electrons.*

with minute amounts of antimony. Only about 1 atom of antimony to every 10^7 or 10^8 atoms of germanium is present in the doped semiconductor crystal. The antimony atoms form covalent bonds with four adjacent germanium atoms, as the replaced germanium atoms did, but there is one surplus electron left over after the covalent bonds are formed. The surplus electron is not as tightly bound to its nucleus as are the electrons in the covalent bond; comparatively little energy is required to release it. At room temperature, nearly all the surplus electrons not incorporated in the covalent bonds have sufficient thermal energy to break the weak bond and become free electrons. Consequently, the conductivity of the crystal is greatly increased by the increase in the number of free electrons present.

The ratio of impurity atoms to germanium atoms is kept very low. For example, suppose that antimony is introduced into the germanium crystal at the rate of 1 atom of antimony to every 10^8 atoms of germanium. The total number of free, or conducting, electrons is the sum of those released from the antimony atoms and those produced thermally by the intrinsic germanium. If a sample of 10^{10} atoms is taken, we would find nearly 100 free electrons introduced into the semiconductor by the antimony atoms and about 5 present naturally in the intrinsic semiconductor at room temperature. Thus the number of charge carriers is increased by a factor of 20, and the conductivity is increased by a corresponding factor merely by adding the right kind of impurity at a ratio of 1 part in 10^8.

When a semiconductor has been doped with an impurity with five valence electrons, such as antimony or arsenic, it is said to be an "n-type" semiconductor. The crystalline structure is still electrically neutral, since in any given volume there is an equal number of positive and negative charges. But the number of free electrons has been increased by the number of impurity atoms added. Atoms with five valence electrons are known as donors, since they "donate" free electrons to the crystal. In an n-type semiconductor, the ratio of free electrons to holes is very large; the free electrons are called the "majority" carriers, and the holes are known as "minority" carriers.

Just as free electrons are added to a semiconductor by doping it with small amounts of impurities with five valence electrons, holes can be added to the semiconductor by doping it with small amounts of impurities possessing three valence electrons. Boron, gallium, and indium are examples of such impurities. When boron, with three valence electrons, is added in minute amounts to the crystalline structure of the semiconductor, there is a deficiency of one electron in the covalent bonds attaching the boron atom to the neighboring semiconductor atoms. The absence of the electron in the covalent bond is not in itself a hole, since the bond does not carry positive charge; but one electron from the covalent bond is missing. There is a tendency for an electron from a nearby atom to move over to fill the covalent bond, leaving a positive charge, or hole, behind. This is shown in Fig. 9.13, where the covalent bond

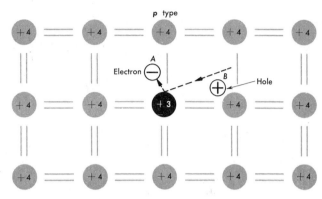

FIG. 9.13 *Hole production by doping with impurity with three valence electrons.*

at *A* is not filled until the electron at *B* moves over to fill it, leaving behind a hole. Once the hole is produced, it is free to drift in an electric field and contribute to the current in the semiconductor. A semiconductor that has been doped with minute amounts of impurities whose atoms have three valence electrons is known as a "*p*-type" semiconductor. Impurity atoms in *p*-type semiconductors are able to accept bound electrons from the surrounding atoms and are known as "acceptors." In *p*-type semiconductors, holes are the majority carriers, and electrons are the minority carriers.

It must be emphasized that in an intrinsic semiconductor, when a valence electron is released to become a free or conduction electron, a hole is also produced. Free electrons and holes are produced at an equal rate in intrinsic semiconductors by thermal action. In *p*-type material, holes are produced when a bound electron moves over to complete a covalent bond, as well as by thermal action in the intrinsic semiconductor atoms. In *n*-type material, conduction electrons are produced by thermal action from the intrinsic semiconductor atoms, as well as by the donor atoms. When an intrinsic semiconductor is doped by both donor and acceptor atoms, the free-electron density and hole density are both increased.

9.8 THE *P-N* JUNCTION

In the preceding section we saw how holes can be introduced into a semiconductor by the addition of a minute number of acceptor atoms to the crystalline structure as an impurity. Likewise, free electrons can be added to the intrinsic semiconductor by the introduction of small quantities of donor atoms into the crystalline structure. In either case the conductivity of the semiconductor was greatly increased by the addition of a small amount of impurity. At ordinary temperatures and with no electric field applied, the charge carriers move around at random. Increased temperatures cause increased mean velocities of the charge carriers.

Now assume that some *p*-type-semiconductor and some *n*-type-semiconductor materials are brought together to form a plane of contact with each other. The free electrons in the *n*-type material, moving at random velocities and in a random direction, have a tendency to diffuse across the *p-n* junction into the *p*-type material. Likewise, the holes in the *p*-type material, moving at random, tend to diffuse across the junction into the *n*-type material.

Diffusion is a deconcentrating process. The same laws govern diffusion of charges and diffusion of molecules that govern heat flow. If a metal bar is heated at one end, heat is conducted down the bar from the point of highest temperature toward points of least temperature and there is a tendency for the bar to acquire the same temperature throughout. If a container of oxygen and a container of nitrogen at the same temperature and pressure are connected together so that the two gases can mix, they will do so. Diffusion tends to make the concentration of the oxygen in both containers the same and the concentration of nitrogen in both containers the same. Diffusion is the same process that tends to cause the holes from the *p*-type material to seek to spread throughout the *n*-type material and the free electrons from the *n*-type material to seek to spread throughout the *p*-type material. Thus there is a flow of charges in the direction from the region of greatest concentration to the region of least concentration.

The diffusion process occurring across the semiconductor junction is hampered by the electrostatic forces that are developed as soon as there is a separation of charge across the junction. The *p*-type material and the *n*-type material by themselves are electrically neutral, even though a high concentration of holes occurs in *p*-type material and a high concentration of free electrons occurs in *n*-type material. When the holes diffuse across the junction into the *n*-type material and the electrons diffuse across into the *p*-type material, an electric field is developed by the separation of charges on the two sides of the junction. The *n* region is now positively charged, and the *p* region is now negatively charged, as shown in Fig. 9.14*a*. Once the junction is established, diffusion continues until the electric-field intensity is great enough to prevent further diffusion. The electric field established by the separation of charge across the junction is in a direction that tends to prevent more positive charges from the *p* region from leaving the *p* region and more electrons from the *n* region from leaving the *n* region, somewhat like space-charge limiting of current in a vacuum tube. It is not necessary to connect a voltage source across the junction to accomplish the charge separation shown; it is accomplished by diffusion alone.

Now consider what happens when an external voltage source is connected to the two sides of the *p-n* junction. If the *p* region is raised in potential with respect to the *n*-type material by means of an external voltage source, the electric field established by the battery across the junction overcomes the electric field caused by the charge separation (shown in Fig. 9.14) and the net field intensity is to the right, as shown in Fig. 9.15*a*. The diffusion process sustains a constant flow of charges across the junction. Conduction electrons from the battery flow into the *n*-type material and recombine with the holes from the *p*-type material as they diffuse across the junction. The separation of charges as illustrated in Fig. 9.14*b* is now impossible, since the holes diffusing across the junction combine with the conducting electrons, and the electrons diffusing across the junction are neutralized by the holes. Thus a steady current flows across the *p-n* junction, and the battery is said to be connected in the "easy-current" direction.

If the battery is connected in the direction shown in Fig. 9.15*b*, it establishes an electric field across the junction from the *n* to the *p* region as shown. This is the same direction as that when only the field due to charge separation was present, as in Fig. 9.14. The direction of the electric field prohibits further diffusion across the junction, and current flow across the junction is nil. A current-versus-voltage characteristic for a *p-n* junction is shown in Fig. 9.16; the static resistance in the easy-current direction in this ex-

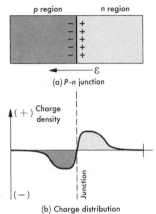

(a) *P-n* junction

(b) Charge distribution

FIG. 9.14   *The separation of charge across a p-n junction, and the field established.*

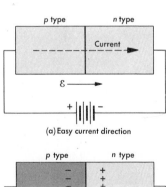

(a) Easy current direction

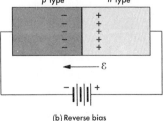

(b) Reverse bias

FIG. 9.15   *An external voltage source is connected to the p-n junction.*

9.8   The P-N Junction   235

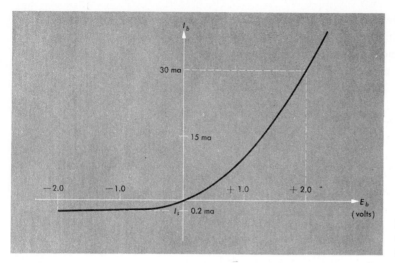

FIG. 9.16 *Current-versus-voltage characteristic curve for a typical p-n junction.*

ample is about 70 ohms at $E_b = 2$ volts, whereas the static resistance in the reverse direction is about 10,000 ohms at $E_b = -2$ volts. A slight current in the reverse direction is caused by the holes and electrons existing in the intrinsic semiconductor material. The thermally produced holes in the intrinsic material in the n region cross the junction in the easy-current direction, and the thermally produced electrons in the p region cross the junction in the easy-current direction. But since the thermally produced electron-hole pairs exist in concentrations very much smaller than the concentration of holes produced by acceptor atoms or electrons produced by donor atoms, the reverse current is many times smaller than the forward current.

Current saturation occurs when the junction is biased in the reverse direction because the rate at which the charge carriers are produced is a function only of temperature. When all the charge carriers are being drawn across the junction before they can recombine, increasing the junction reverse voltage does not increase the reverse current. Saturation current is shown in Fig. 9.16 as I_s. Junction current can be shown to be

$$I = I_s(\epsilon^{38.7V} - 1) \qquad \text{amp} \tag{9.27}$$

where I_s is the saturation current and V is the potential difference across the junction only, not including the IR drop in the semiconductor. V is positive in the forward direction and negative in the reverse direction. The constant 38.7 in the exponent is temperature-dependent and applies only at a room temperature of $300°K$.

SUMMARY

Electric-field intensity, represented by $\mathscr{E}$, is defined as the force on a unit positive charge. The electric field near a point charge Q_1 is found to be [Eq. (9.1)]

$$\mathscr{E} = \frac{Q_1}{4\pi\epsilon r^2} \qquad \text{volts/m, or newtons/coulomb}$$

where r is the distance from the charge. Electric-flux density D is always related to $\mathscr{E}$ by the constant of proportionality ϵ, or [Eq. (9.6)]

$$D = \epsilon\mathscr{E}$$

Electric-field intensity around a uniformly charged line is given by Eq. (9.12),

$$\mathscr{E} = \frac{\lambda}{2\pi\epsilon r} \qquad \text{volts/m}$$

where λ is charge per unit length on the line and r is the distance from the line. If a charge density $+\rho$ coulombs/m^2 is distributed uniformly over an infinite plane and $-\rho$ is distributed over a parallel plane, then, between the two planes, the electric-field intensity is [Eq. (9.9)]

$$\mathscr{E} = \frac{\rho}{\epsilon} \qquad \text{volts/m}$$

Electric charges free to move in a vacuum and subjected to an electric field experience an acceleration force caused by the field. Equating electric-field force to inertia force gives Eq. (9.13),

$$\mathscr{E}e = m\frac{dv}{dt}$$

which can be solved for velocity or distance in the direction of the electric force. The change in energy of an electric charge free to accelerate in an electric field is [Eq. (9.17)]

$$dW_e = F\,dx$$

where F is the electric force and dx is the differential distance in the direction of the electric force.

A thermionic cathode emits electrons at a rate which is a function of its temperature. If there is no effective space charge around the cathode, the emission current density is [Eq. (9.21)]

$$J = A_0 T^2 \epsilon^{-b_0/T} \qquad \text{amp/m}^2$$

where T is the cathode temperature in degrees Kelvin and A_0 and b_0 are constants. If the cathode is surrounded by space charge, the current density is limited to Eq. (9.22),

$$J = K E_b^{3/2} \qquad \text{amp/m}^2$$

where K is a constant and E_b is the voltage between the cathode and the anode.

Semiconductors are extremely pure crystals consisting of atoms with four valence electrons. Each atom is bound to four adjacent atoms by a covalent bond. When energy is added to the semiconductor, some of the electrons in the covalent bonds break loose, leaving behind a positive charge, or hole. In the presence of an electric field, both holes and electrons drift under the field forces, causing electric current.

Doping the semiconductor with atoms with five valence electrons has the effect of adding free, or conducting, electrons to the semiconductor, and the material is known as n-type material. Doping with atoms with three valence electrons has the effect of adding holes to the semiconductor; the semiconductor thus doped is known as p-type material. Current density in a semiconductor containing only one kind of charge carrier is given by Eq. (9.26),

$$J = n e \mu \mathcal{E} \qquad \text{amp/m}^2$$

where n is the density of the charge carriers, e is the charge on the carrier, μ is charge mobility, and $\mathcal{E}$ is the field strength. When charge carriers of both signs are present, the total current density is the sum of the current density caused by the positive charges in motion and the current density caused by the negative carriers in motion.

At a p-n junction, the process of diffusion causes the charge carriers to cross the junction. If the junction is biased in the reverse direction, the charge carriers diffuse across the junction and establish an electric field which prohibits further diffusion of carriers across the junction. If the junction is biased in the forward direction, the charge carriers recombine after they cross the junction and the diffusion process continues. Thus resistance in the forward direction is relatively low, while resistance in the reverse direction is high.

FURTHER READING

An excellent brief summary of semiconductor physics, written by Dr. Richard B. Adler, is found in L. B. Arguimbau, *Vacuum-tube Circuits and Transistors* (John Wiley & Sons, Inc., New York, 1956), chap. 4. G. F. Corcoran and H. W. Price, *Electronics* (John Wiley & Sons, Inc., New York, 1954), treat electric-field concepts in chap. 1, motion of charges in electric fields in chap. 2, and thermionic emission in chap. 3. Karl R. Spangenberg, *Fundamentals of Electron Devices* (McGraw-Hill Book Company, Inc., New York, 1957), treats ion motion in a vacuum in chap. 4, semi-conductors in chap. 6, junction effects in chap. 7, and electron emission in chap. 8.

PROBLEMS

9.1 Two parallel conducting plates, spaced 0.1 cm apart and with 0.5 m^2 area, are connected to a 100-volt battery. Find the force of attraction between the two plates.

9.2 A mass of 1 kg carrying a charge of $+1$ coulomb is inserted into a uniform electric field of 100 volts/m at zero velocity. After 2 sec, find: (*a*) acceleration, (*b*) velocity, (*c*) distance traveled, of the charge.

9.3 A uniformly charged line of $+10^{-4}$ coulombs/m produces an electric field into which is placed at zero velocity a mass of 10^{-10} kg carrying a charge of $+10^{-12}$ coulomb. After the charged mass has been free 1 sec, find its velocity and the distance traveled from its initial position at $r = 0.1$ cm.

9.4 An electron falls through a potential difference of 10^3 volts which gives it a velocity in the x direction of v_x. Then the electron enters a uniform field, also in the x direction, which decelerates the electron. Find the strength of the electric field needed to stop the electron in 1 m. Then derive an expression for velocity as a function of time for the electron in the decelerating field.

9.5 In the figure an electron with a velocity of 10^7 m/sec enters the field between two parallel-plane electrodes at an angle of 60°. The field between the planes is 2×10^3 volts/m. Find d, the distance the electron remains in the field before striking the lower plane.

9.6 An electron falls through a potential difference of 1,000 volts in the $+x$ direction and then through a potential difference of 500 volts in the

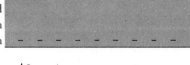

PROB. 9.5

$+y$ direction. Assuming the electron had zero initial velocity, find its final velocity and direction.

9.7 Using Dushman's equation, plot current density-versus-temperature for an oxide-coated cathode with $A_0 = 0.025$ and $b_0 = 12,500$. How does emission efficiency for the oxide-coated cathode compare with tungsten, whose current-density curve is shown in Fig. 9.7?

9.8 Plot forward current-versus-voltage for an n-p junction whose saturation current is $I_s = 1.2 \times 10^{-5}$ ma. Let the forward voltage take values from $V = 0$ to $V = 0.5$ volt.

9.9 Find the approximate velocity of the free electrons in an aluminum conductor with a cross-sectional area of 5×10^{-5} m^2 carrying 100 amp.

9.10 A round rod of intrinsic germanium 10 cm long and 2 cm in diameter is connected at the two ends of the bar to a 25-volt source of voltage. Find the current that flows in the bar.

9.11 Two concentric spheres of radii 1 cm and 3 cm have air dielectric separating them. Find the capacitance between the spheres, using $C = q/v$; place a charge q on one of the spheres, $-q$ on the other sphere, and find the voltage that results.

9.12 A certain junction diode has a saturation current I_s of 0.002 ma. The junction voltage is 0.01 volt. Find the junction current. Repeat for a junction current of -0.01 volt. Assume that the junction is at 300°K.

$$10$$

ELECTRONIC DEVICES

10.1 DIODE CHARACTERISTICS

A diode is a two-terminal nonlinear resistive device characterized
by low impedance to current flow in one direction and high impedance to current flow in the opposite direction. Only because of
the nonlinear nature of its current-versus-voltage characteristic is
the diode a valuable circuit element. There are two regions on the
nonlinear diode current-voltage characteristic which are exploited
in diode circuits. One is the region where the impedance changes
rapidly from a high to a low value as the current reverses its direction through the diode. The other region of use is in the region of
low impedance, where the current increases at an increasing rate
with respect to the voltage. Only the first region will be explored
in this chapter.

Vacuum diodes consist of two elements, a cathode and an
anode, or plate, sealed in an evacuated envelope of glass or metal.
A thermionic cathode, described in Sec. 9.4, generally provides the
emission of electrons. The second element, the anode, when maintained at a positive potential with respect to the cathode, establishes the electric field which attracts and collects the electrons
from the vicinity of the cathode. Under normal operating conditions the characteristic curve of a vacuum diode is as represented

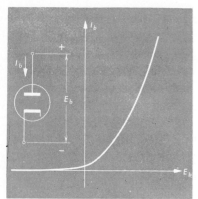

FIG. 10.1 *Current-versus-voltage characteristic of a vacuum diode.*

in Fig. 10.1, where I_b is the current through the diode and E_b is the voltage from cathode to anode across the diode. Notice that a very small current flows when E_b is zero. Some of the electrons when emitted from the cathode have sufficient velocity to penetrate the space charge surrounding the cathode and reach the anode even if the anode voltage is zero or even slightly negative with respect to the cathode; the small value of I_b when E_b is zero or slightly negative in Fig. 10.1 is attributed to these few high-energy electrons. The curve in Fig. 10.1 is concave upward and generally follows Child's law. When E_b becomes negative, I_b approaches zero and cannot reverse its direction. The impedance in this region approaches infinity. Current in the reverse direction through a vacuum diode is ordinarily impossible, since the anode cannot emit electrons under normal operating conditions.

A vacuum diode whose cathode utilizes photoelectric emission is known as a "phototube." The I_b-versus-E_b characteristic of a vacuum phototube is shown as a family of curves in Fig. 10.2,

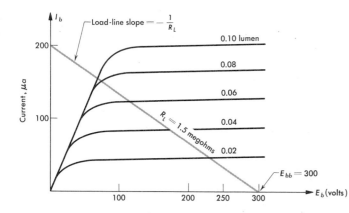

FIG. 10.2 *Current-versus-voltage characteristic of a vacuum phototube.*

where illumination in lumens is the parameter. For constant illumination, I_b increases as E_b increases until nearly all the electrons emitted from the cathode are collected by the anode. When all the emitted electrons are collected by the anode, any further increase in E_b causes no further increase in I_b; the saturation that results is similar to the temperature saturation of a vacuum diode shown in Fig. 9.8b. For a constant value of E_b above the saturation region, I_b is approximately proportional to the intensity of illumination. In Fig. 10.3, the phototube is shown in series with the large load resistance and a voltage source. The load line for the resistance and battery characteristic is shown in Fig. 10.2. Notice that E_b and I_b vary linearly with the degree of illumination.

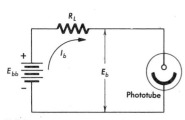

FIG. 10.3 *Phototube in series with load resistance R_L.*

Semiconductor junction diodes possess characteristics generally described by Fig. 9.16. The low-impedance direction for current flow in the junction diode is from the p-type material to the n-type material. The p-type material is analogous to the anode of a vacuum diode, and the n-type material is analogous to the cathode. But current flow in a semiconductor diode results from positive-charge (hole) motion *and* electron motion, whereas only electrons make up the current flow within a vacuum tube. Furthermore, the resistance of a semiconductor diode in the reverse current direction is finite and ordinarily of the order of 20 kilohms to 1 megohm, whereas for a vacuum diode the backward impedance is essentially infinite.

A diode is often used as an on-off device; that is, either it conducts or it does not conduct. In this application it is convenient to define an ideal diode as one having zero impedance in the forward direction and infinite impedance in the reverse direction. Obviously, vacuum diodes and transistor or semiconductor diodes only approximate this ideal, but when the diode is used in a high-impedance circuit, the approximation is a good one. The ideal diode I_b-versus-E_b characteristic is given in Fig. 10.4a, showing infinite

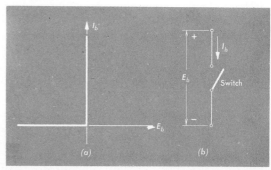

FIG. 10.4 *Ideal diode characteristic (a) and equivalent circuit (b).*

resistance in the reverse direction when E_b is negative and zero resistance in the forward direction when E_b tends to be positive. A switch has the same characteristics if the switch is open when the voltage across it is in the reverse direction and if it is closed when the voltage tends to be in the forward direction. The switch shown in Fig. 10.4b is equivalent to the ideal diode because it has the same current-versus-voltage characteristic as the diode.

Now consider the equivalent circuit of a diode whose resistance in the forward direction cannot be neglected. Assume that a linear approximation has been made to the actual characteristic, as shown in Fig. 10.5a. A resistance R_b possesses the characteristics of the

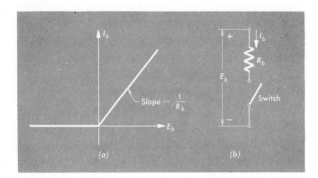

FIG. 10.5 *Linear diode approximation (a) and its equivalent circuit (b).*

diode in the forward direction, the value of R_b being the reciprocal of the slope of the linear approximation. In the reverse direction, the diode has the characteristics of an open circuit. An equivalent circuit is shown in Fig. 10.5b where the switch is open to represent negative values of plate voltage and the switch is closed when the diode is in the conducting region of positive plate voltage.

Another linear equivalent circuit for the semiconductor diode, used in circuits where the resistance in the reverse direction is not high enough to be considered infinite, is shown in Fig. 10.6a, where

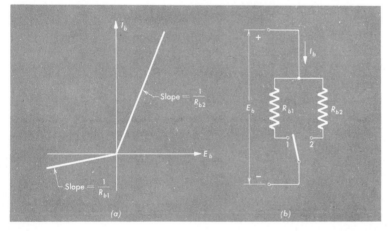

FIG. 10.6 *Linearized semiconductor diode characteristic (a) and equivalent circuit (b).*

R_{b1} is the resistance in the reverse direction and R_{b2} is the resistance in the forward direction. The equivalent circuit (Fig. 10.6b) shows two resistors R_{b1} and R_{b2} and a single-pole double-throw switch to make connection with the appropriate resistor.

Suppose now that a vacuum diode, which can be represented approximately by the linearized characteristic shown in Fig. 10.5a, is connected in series with a load resistor and an alternating-voltage source as shown in Fig. 10.7a. During the first half cycle of the sinusoidal driving voltage, the diode conducts in the forward direction and appears to have a resistance R_b. The equivalent circuit is shown in Fig. 10.7b, with the switch in the closed position. The current through the circuit, by Ohm's law, is

$$i_b = \frac{E_m}{R_b + R_L} \sin \omega t \qquad 0 < \omega t < \pi \qquad (10.1)$$

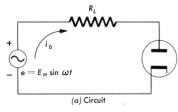

(a) Circuit

After $\omega t = \pi$, the supply voltage reverses, and the diode must be represented by an open switch. Then

$$i_b = 0 \qquad \pi < \omega t < 2\pi \qquad (10.2)$$

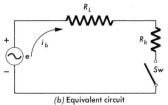

(b) Equivalent circuit

The voltage across the load resistor is proportional to the current and is

$$e_L = \frac{E_m R_L}{R_b + R_L} \sin \omega t \qquad 0 < \omega t < \pi$$

$$= 0 \qquad \pi < \omega t < 2\pi \qquad (10.3)$$

The switching action must be repeated each cycle; at $\omega t = 0, 2\pi, 4\pi, 6\pi, \ldots$, the switch must be closed, and, at $\omega t = \pi, 3\pi, 5\pi, 7\pi, \ldots$, the switch must be opened.

The diode characteristic shown in Fig. 10.1 suggests two ways for defining the resistance of the diode in the forward, or conducting, direction. First, the diode resistance can be defined as the ratio of the diode voltage to the current through the diode, or

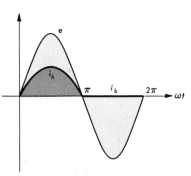

(c) Voltage and current versus ωt

FIG. 10.7 *A vacuum diode and load resistor excited by an alternating-voltage source.*

$$R_b = \frac{E_b}{I_b} \qquad (10.4)$$

where R_b is known as the "d-c," or "static," resistance of the diode. But it is often convenient to define a dynamic resistance that can, by Ohm's law, relate a differential change in plate voltage to a differential change in plate current. Dynamic plate resistance can be defined by

$$r_p \, dI_b = dE_b \qquad \text{or} \qquad r_p = \frac{dE_b}{dI_b} \qquad (10.5)$$

where r_p is the reciprocal of the slope of the diode characteristic curve. For the linearized diode characteristic of Fig. 10.5a, $R_b = r_p$, but only in certain special cases is this true. According to the definitions, R_b and r_p are both functions of the position on the curve for which they are obtained.

10.2 THE VACUUM TRIODE

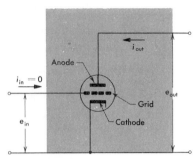

FIG. 10.8 *Schematic symbol for the vacuum triode.*

The vacuum and semiconductor diodes mentioned in the preceding section are two-terminal devices, and they can be described by static current-versus-voltage characteristic curves and by their static and dynamic resistances. Now we consider a vacuum diode to which has been added a third electrode between the cathode and anode. The new three-electrode vacuum tube is known as a "triode," and the third electrode is known as the "control grid," or simply the "grid." Figure 10.8 shows the schematic symbol for the triode as an input-output device with two pairs of terminals, the cathode common to both pairs. The control grid of the vacuum triode, situated between the cathode and the anode, is in a position to influence greatly the flow of electrons from cathode to anode. The grid controls the flow of electrons by altering the electric field in the space between the cathode and the anode. Thermal electrons emitted from the cathode experience the force of the electric field and either return to the cathode or pass the space charge and fall into the anode. Grid potential determines the rate at which the electrons pass the space-charge area, and therefore the cathode-to-anode electron current.

Consider now the electric field between the anode and cathode when the grid is not present. The potential difference between the cathode and anode is plotted in Fig. 10.9*a* for a vacuum diode with parallel electrodes. If some negative space charge is present in the interelectrode space, the potential-versus-distance curve is con-

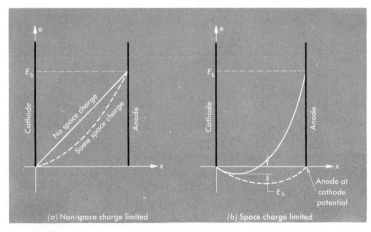

FIG. 10.9 *Potential-versus-distance curves for a parallel-plane diode.*

cave upward. When no space charge is present, the potential curve is linear for a diode with parallel-plane anode and cathode. In Fig. 10.9b the magnitude of the negative space charge between the electrodes has been greatly increased. The potential is negative near the cathode, and the field is therefore in a direction that tends to force electrons back toward the cathode. Only those electrons emitted with energy greater than E_h electron volts pass over the potential hump and then fall into the anode. If the anode voltage is reduced, the negative space charge increases even more, E_h becomes larger, and the electron current from cathode to anode is even further reduced. If the anode is at the same potential as the cathode, as shown also in Fig. 10.9b, the potential hump over which the emitted electrons must pass is so large that very few electrons are able to reach the anode.

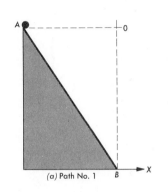

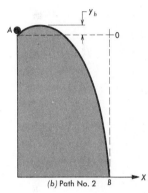

FIG. 10.10 *Mechanical analogy of Fig. 10.9.*

(a) Path No. 1

(b) Path No. 2

A mechanical analogy is shown in Fig. 10.10. Assume that round, smooth spheres such as marbles are released at A on a smooth path or chute. If the spheres are released with zero velocity on path 1, where the slope is always downhill, all of them roll down to position B, corresponding to the position of the anode. Neglecting friction, the potential through which the marbles fall is proportional to OB. This corresponds to the diode represented in the linear curve of Fig. 10.9a, where an electron constantly loses potential energy and gains kinetic energy as it travels from the cathode to the anode.

If path 2 is followed, a marble released at zero velocity at A never moves. A marble released at A with a velocity v directed along path 2 does not pass over the hump unless its initial kinetic energy $\frac{1}{2}Mv^2$ is greater than the potential energy Mgy_h, where M is the mass of the marble, g is the acceleration due to gravity, and y_h is the height of the hump over which it must pass. A critical velocity v_c can be defined above which the marble released at A has enough kinetic energy to cross the hump and travel to C but below which the marble returns to A. This mechanical analog of Fig. 10.10b corresponds to the field problem of a diode in Fig. 10.9b, where a potential hump E_h exists. Electrons, emitted with energy less than $E_h e$, do not pass the potential hump.

The function of the control grid in a vacuum triode is to control the average magnitude of the potential hump E_h over which the emitted electrons must pass. This is accomplished by placing a wire screen, the control grid, between the cathode and the anode as shown in Fig. 10.11. The potential of the control grid is es-

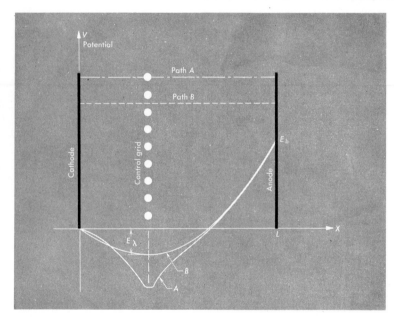

FIG. 10.11 *Potential versus distance between cathode and anode. Path B lies between grid wires, and path A passes through a grid wire.*

tablished by the external circuit to which it is connected. The grid is ordinarily maintained at a negative potential with respect to the cathode in order to prevent the grid from capturing electrons from the space charge. If we examine the potential distribution from anode to cathode along path B midway between the grid wires, it would be as shown by curve B in Fig. 10.11. The potential hump is not large, and those electrons which are emitted with sufficient velocity and follow path B pass over the potential hump and reach the anode. The electrons which follow a path nearer the grid wire have a larger hump to pass over, and fewer of these electrons reach the anode. The potential-versus-distance curve for path A which passes through a grid wire is shown in curve A (Fig. 10.11). The potential hump shown for path A is considerable. Thus, if the control grid is maintained at a high negative potential, most of the electrons which follow a path close to the grid wire are repelled back to the cathode and few reach the anode. Furthermore, if the control grid is made highly negative, the potential hump of curve B becomes more pronounced, too, and the average height of the potential hump becomes large. The electron flow from cathode to anode is controllable by the potential applied to the control grid: if the control-grid potential is highly negative, relatively few electrons arrive at the anode; if the control-grid potential is only slightly negative, the electron current to the anode is relatively high.

In order to describe the operation of a vacuum triode, certain voltages and currents must be defined. With the cathode as zero, or reference, potential, the average control-grid voltage is designated E_c, and the average anode voltage is designated E_b, as shown in Fig. 10.12. Average anode current is I_b, and the grid current I_c is negligible. Thus there are three variables needed to describe triode operation, and any one can be written as a function of the other two,

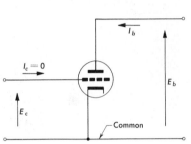

FIG. 10.12 *Definition of grid voltage and current and plate voltage and current.*

$$I_b = f(E_b, E_c) \tag{10.6}$$

or

$$E_c = f(I_b, E_b) \tag{10.7}$$

or

$$E_b = f(E_c, I_b) \tag{10.8}$$

Equations (10.6) to (10.8) suggest some characteristic curves which can be measured experimentally to describe the behavior of the vacuum triode. For example, in Eq. (10.6) if E_c is maintained constant, I_b is a function of E_b alone and can be plotted as such. For several values of constant E_c, I_b-versus-E_b curves are plotted in Fig. 10.13 for a typical triode. Notice that for $E_c = 0$ the I_b-versus-E_b curve roughly approximates that of a vacuum diode. As the control-grid voltage is made more negative, the I_b-versus-E_b characteristic curve shifts to the right, demonstrating that highly negative grid voltages tend to reduce the cathode current in the tube. The characteristic curves of Fig. 10.13 are known as "plate" characteristics. In this form the curves are convenient for graphical solutions of the plate, or anode, circuit.

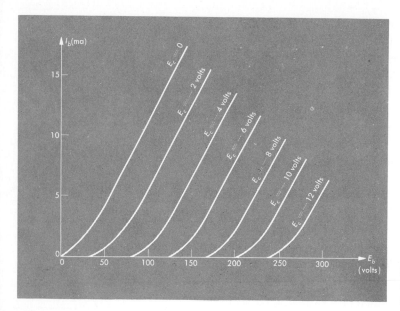

FIG. 10.13 *Plate characteristic curves for a typical triode I_b-versus-E_b curve with E_c a parameter.*

Another possible set of characteristic curves is shown in Fig. 10.14, where E_b is held constant and I_b is plotted as a function of E_c. For each value of E_b there exists a negative grid voltage known as the "cutoff bias" below which I_b is always zero. The phenomenon of cutoff can also be observed from the plate characteristic curves of Fig. 10.11, where, for any given value of E_b, there exists a value of E_c for which I_b is zero. Observe that, as the plate voltage becomes large, E_c must have a larger negative value in order to cut off the plate current. A third set of characteristic

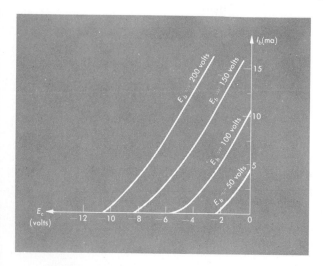

FIG. 10.14 *I_b-versus-E_c characteristic for a triode, with E_b as a parameter.*

curves (not shown) can be drawn with I_b as the parameter and E_c plotted as a function of E_b.

A circuit for obtaining experimental data from which to plot the various characteristic curves for the triode is shown in Fig. 10.15. The voltage of the direct-voltage source connected to the

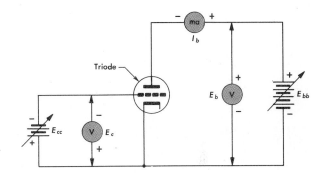

FIG. 10.15 *Schematic diagram of circuit for measuring triode characteristics.*

anode is designated E_{bb}, and the direct-voltage source connected to the grid is designated E_{cc}. In the circuit of Fig. 10.15, $E_{bb} = E_b$, and $E_{cc} = E_c$. The plate characteristic curve is obtained by adjusting E_c to a negative value and maintaining it constant while E_b is varied and several values of E_b and I_b are read from the instruments. Average characteristic curves for the various types of triodes are published in tube handbooks, which catalogue the characteristics of a large number of tubes. Characteristic curves for particular triodes of the same type vary somewhat from the average curves obtained from the tube handbook.

10.3 TRIODE PARAMETERS

In order to be able to use the vacuum triode as a circuit device, it is convenient to define some tube parameters which are useful in circuit analysis. In the study of the diode, it was convenient to define the dynamic plate resistance as the rate of change of plate voltage with respect to plate current [Eq. (10.5)]. For the triode a third variable E_c is involved. But the dynamic plate resistance of a triode can now be defined as the partial derivative of plate voltage with respect to plate current with grid voltage maintained constant, or

$$r_p = \frac{\partial E_b}{\partial I_b}\bigg|_{E_c=\text{const}} \qquad (10.9)$$

The value of r_p at any point on the plate characteristic curve is the reciprocal of the slope of the curve at that point. Thus, from the plate characteristic of Fig. 10.13, r_p can be found by taking increments of E_b and I_b along a curve of constant E_c. This is shown in Fig. 10.16, where r_p is obtained at point A on the curve by

$$r_p = \frac{\Delta E_b}{\Delta I_b}\bigg|_{Ec=\text{const}} \qquad (10.10)$$

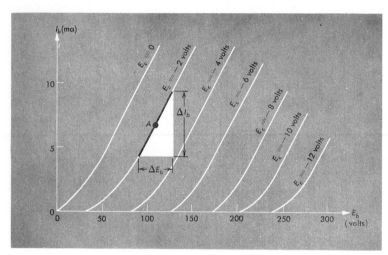

FIG. 10.16 *Obtaining the dynamic plate resistance from the plate characteristics.*

It is obvious that r_p is not a constant but varies from point to point on the characteristic curves. Yet, in a limited region on the curves, r_p may be considered to be constant.

Another parameter associated with a vacuum triode is the amplification factor, symbolized by μ. The amplification factor is a measure of the relative effectiveness of the anode voltage and the grid voltage in controlling anode current. The amplification factor is defined as the partial derivative of E_b with respect to E_c with I_b maintained constant, or

$$\mu = -\frac{\partial E_b}{\partial E_c}\bigg|_{Ib=\text{const}} \qquad (10.11)$$

The value of μ for a triode is very much greater than unity (perhaps 10 to 200). According to Eq. (10.11), for a small change in E_c, a larger change in E_b is necessary to keep I_b constant. The amplification factor is a dimensionless ratio, being a ratio of voltages. From the plate characteristic curves shown in Fig. 10.17, the amplification factor at point A is obtained approximately by con-

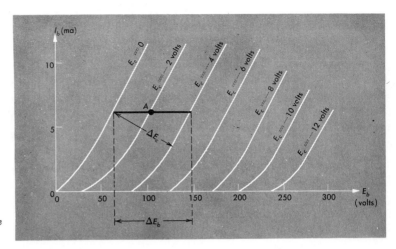

FIG. 10.17 *Obtaining μ from the plate characteristic.*

straining I_b to be constant, letting E_c vary over a range $E_c = 0$ to $E_c = -4$ volts, which is ΔE_c, and observing the variation in E_b, which is ΔE_b. Or, in differentials, μ is approximately

$$\mu \approx -\frac{\Delta E_b}{\Delta E_c}\bigg|_{I_b=\text{const}} \qquad (10.12)$$

The third parameter is called "transconductance," symbolized by g_m, and is defined by

$$g_m = \frac{\partial I_b}{\partial E_c}\bigg|_{E_b=\text{const}} \qquad (10.13)$$

Transconductance has the dimensions of conductance, which is the reciprocal of resistance. It is obtained approximately from the plate characteristic of Fig. 10.18 by constraining E_b to be constant

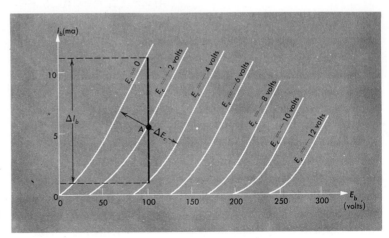

FIG. 10.18 *Obtaining g_m from the plate characteristic.*

and taking increments of E_c and I_b as shown in Fig. 10.16. Then,

$$g_m \approx \frac{\Delta I_b}{\Delta E_c}\bigg|_{E_b=\text{const}} \tag{10.14}$$

According to the definitions of the vacuum-tube parameters, r_p, μ, and g_m are not constant but depend on the point of operation on the characteristic curves. Yet over the region of the plate characteristic curves where the constant-E_c curves are nearly straight and parallel, the values of r_p, μ, and g_m tend to be fairly constant and not to change appreciably between nearby points. For this reason, as long as the tube is operated over the linear portion of the curves, the μ, r_p, and g_m of the tube are often considered to be constant.

10.4 TRIODE EQUIVALENT CIRCUITS

Whenever a dependent variable is a function of two or more independent variables, the total derivative is a useful concept for describing the function over a limited range of the variables. The three variables of the triode have been related by Eq. (10.6),

$$I_b = f(E_b, E_c)$$

The total derivative of Eq. (10.6) can be written

$$dI_b = \frac{\partial I_b}{\partial E_b} dE_b + \frac{\partial I_b}{\partial E_c} dE_c \tag{10.15}$$

or, in differentials,

$$\Delta I_b \approx \frac{\partial I_b}{\partial E_b} \Delta E_b + \frac{\partial I_b}{\partial E_c} \Delta E_c \tag{10.16}$$

The total differential of Eq. (10.16) shows that the change in I_b is equal to the rate at which I_b changes with respect to E_b times the change in E_b plus the rate at which I_b changes with respect to E_c times the change in E_c. The partial derivatives in Eqs. (10.15) and (10.16) are recognized from Eqs. (10.9) and (10.13) as $1/r_p$ and g_m. Substituting Eqs. (10.9) and (10.13) into Eq. (10.16) results in

$$\Delta I_b \approx \frac{1}{r_p} \Delta E_b + g_m \Delta E_c \tag{10.17}$$

Equation (10.17) shows that I_b increases when E_c increases (becomes less negative) for E_b constant and that I_b increases when

E_b increases and E_c is constant, on the assumption that r_p and g_m are constant.

Equation (10.17) is justification for establishing a linear equivalent circuit for the triode which is valid for small changes in the variables I_b, E_b, and E_c. Kirchhoff's current law requires two parallel paths to satisfy the right side of Eq. (10.17). Considering only the anode circuit of the triode, Eq. (10.17) is satisfied by the circuit in Fig. 10.19a consisting of a current generator $g_m \, \Delta E_c$ and a parallel resistance r_p.

Another possible equivalent circuit is obtained by similar reasoning, starting with Eq. (10.8),

$$E_t = f(E_c, I_b)$$

The total differential of Eq. (10.8) is written

$$\Delta E_b \approx \frac{\partial E_b}{\partial E_c} \Delta E_c + \frac{\partial E_b}{\partial I_b} \Delta I_b \qquad (10.18)$$

where by Eqs. (10.11) and (10.9), respectively,

$$-\frac{\partial E_b}{\partial E_c} = \mu$$

$$\frac{\partial E_b}{\partial I_b} = r_p$$

Then

$$\Delta E_b = -\mu \, \Delta E_c + r_p \, \Delta I_b \qquad (10.19)$$

Kirchhoff's voltage law applied to Eq. (10.19) requires a voltage generator $\mu \, \Delta E_c$ and series resistance r_p to make up the equivalent circuit shown in Fig. 10.19b. The two circuits shown in Fig. 10.19 are equivalent to each other, and either may be used to represent the vacuum triode for small changes in E_c, I_b, and E_b when the parameters μ, g_m, and r_p are considered constant.

The triode equivalent circuits of Fig. 10.19, derived for small increments of the three variables E_c, I_b, and E_b, are also applicable when small sinusoidal variations in E_c occur. The grid of the triode must always be maintained at a negative potential with respect to the cathode if the triode is to operate in the linear region where the equivalent circuits apply. If a small sinusoidal voltage is applied to the grid, an additional constant negative voltage known as "bias" must also be applied to the grid in order to keep it negative. The nomenclature of vacuum-tube voltages and currents has been standardized and can be defined with the help of

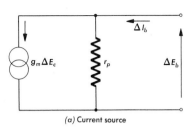

(a) Current source

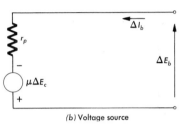

(b) Voltage source

FIG. 10.19 Equivalent circuits for a triode.

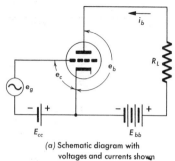

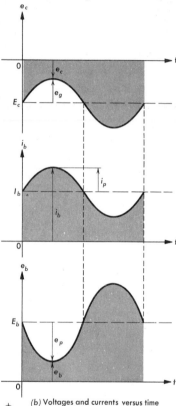

(a) Schematic diagram with voltages and currents shown

(b) Voltages and currents versus time

FIG. 10.20 *Standard nomenclature for vacuum-tube voltages and currents.*

Fig. 10.20a and b. In the grid circuit, E_{cc} is the constant-bias voltage source, e_g is the sinusoidal component of voltage applied to the grid, e_c is the instantaneous sum of the two, and E_c is the average, or d-c, value of the sum, or

$$e_c = E_c + e_g \tag{10.20}$$

The plate, or anode, current must always be in the same direction, but a sinusoidal component of plate current, designated i_p, can be superimposed upon a direct, or average, component of plate current, designated I_b, and the sum designated i_b, or

$$i_b = I_b + i_p \tag{10.21}$$

Figure 10.21 shows the triode plate characteristic on which has been drawn the load line $E_{bb} - i_b R_L$ for the resistive load of the circuit of Fig. 10.20a. The load line represents the locus of points of the three instantaneous triode variables e_c, i_b, and e_b. The instantaneous value of plate voltage e_b is

$$e_b = E_{bb} - i_b R_L \tag{10.22}$$

or

$$e_b = E_b + e_p \tag{10.23}$$

where E_b is the average, or d-c, value of the anode voltage and e_p is the sinusoidal component of anode voltage.

The operating point, or Q point, of the triode is that point on the characteristic curve where E_c, I_b, and E_b intersect, as shown in Fig. 10.21; it is the operating point when only a constant voltage E_c is applied to the grid. Now observe that, when operation is constrained to the load line in Fig. 10.21 and e_c is allowed to increase (become less negative), then i_b also increases. But because of the load resistance R_L, as i_b *increases*, e_b *decreases*, as shown by Eq. (10.20). Thus it appears from Figs. 10.20 and 10.21 that a sinusoidal component of grid voltage produces a sinusoidal component of anode current in phase with the grid voltage and a sinusoidal component of anode voltage 180° out of phase with the grid voltage.

Amplification, or gain, of an amplifier is defined as the ratio of the output quantity to the input quantity. If the input quantity of the amplifier circuit of Fig. 10.20a is considered to be the a-c component of the grid voltage, or e_g, and the output quantity is taken as e_p, then the voltage gain of the amplifier can be obtained from the ratio of the maximum values of e_p to e_g, obtained either graphically or analytically.

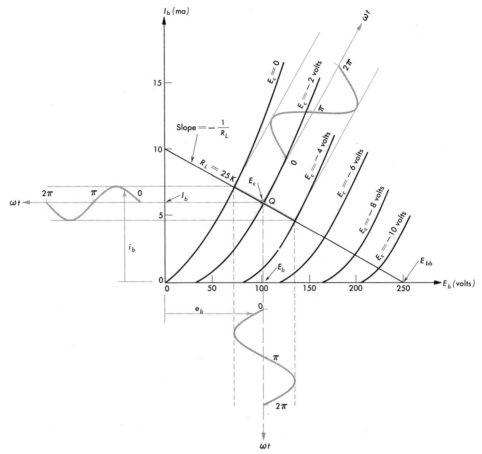

FIG. 10.21 *Operation of triode amplifier of Fig. 10.20a with sinusoidal signal $e_g = 2 \sin \omega t$ applied to the grid.*

Example 10.1

A 6J5 triode with a resistive load $R_L = 25,000$ ohms is operated with $E_c = -4$ volts and $E_{bb} = 250$ volts.

To find μ, g_m, and r_p in order to solve the equivalent circuits, first locate the Q point on the characteristic curves. Then, at the Q point shown in Fig. 10.23,

$$\mu = \frac{\Delta E_b}{\Delta E_c}\bigg|_{I_b=\text{const}} = -\frac{80}{-4} = 20.00$$

$$g_m = \frac{\Delta I_b}{\Delta E_c}\bigg|_{E_b=\text{const}} = \frac{0.0083}{4} = 0.002075 \text{ mho}$$

$$r_p = \frac{\Delta E_b}{\Delta I_b}\bigg|_{E_c=\text{const}} = \frac{80}{0.0083} = 9,630 \text{ ohms}$$

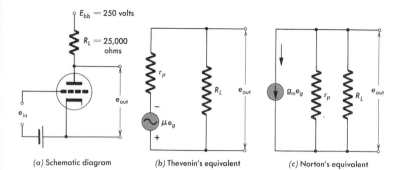

(a) Schematic diagram   (b) Thevenin's equivalent   (c) Norton's equivalent

FIG. 10.22 *An elementary triode amplifier.*

From Thévenin's equivalent circuit of Fig. 10.22b,

$$e_o = -e_g \frac{\mu R_L}{r_p + R_L}$$

and the gain is

$$\frac{e_o}{e_{in}} = \frac{-\mu R_L}{r_p + R_L} = \frac{-20.00(25,000)}{9,630 + 25,000} = -14.4$$

The negative gain merely indicates that the output voltage e_o is 180° out of phase with e_g, or e_{in}.

The solution of Norton's equivalent circuit of Fig. 10.22c gives

$$\frac{e_o}{e_{in}} = \frac{-g_m r_p R_L}{r_p + R_L} = \frac{-0.002075(9,630)(25,000)}{9,630 + 25,000}$$

$$= -14.4$$

Thus either Thévenin's equivalent or Norton's equivalent circuit for the vacuum triode gives the same voltage gain or amplification.

Direct graphical results can also be obtained from the characteristic curves and load line. Let the variation in the grid voltage e_g be 4 volts, from -2 to -6 volts. The resulting variation in plate voltage e_b is 103 to 161 volts, and e_p swings through a variation of $161 - 103 = 58$ volts. Then the voltage-gain magnitude is

$$|A| = \frac{e_o}{e_{in}} \doteq \frac{58}{4} = 14.5$$

corresponding to the gain found analytically from the equivalent circuits.

10.5 TETRODE AND PENTODE CHARACTERISTICS

The anode of a vacuum triode serves two purposes: it establishes the electric field through which the electrons from the cathode fall, and it captures the electrons after they pass through the electric

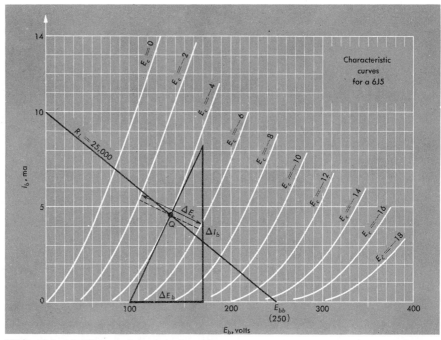

FIG. 10.23 *Characteristic curves for a 6J5.*

field. Because of the proximity of the anode and the control grid, appreciable interelectrode capacitance exists between them. If the triode is operated as an amplifier, the capactive reactance of the grid-to-plate capacitance becomes small at high frequencies and energy from the plate circuit is fed back to the grid circuit through the grid-to-plate capacitance. The voltage fed back from the plate to the grid through the interelectrode capacitance can, if in phase with the signal voltage applied to the grid, cause increased amplification by reinforcing the grid signal. Once sufficient feedback is established in phase with the grid voltage, the grid-signal voltage can be removed and the sinusoidal plate voltage or output voltage will continue even though there is no input to the amplifier. The triode under this condition is operating as an oscillator, producing a periodic output when no input signal is applied. But an amplifier should not oscillate; its output should be proportional to its input. In order to reduce the grid-to-plate interelectrode capacitance and also increase the amplification factor of the triode, a second grid is placed between the control grid and the anode. The second grid, known as the "screen" grid, is maintained at a constant positive potential with respect to the cathode and serves to establish the electric field at the surface of the cathode and in the vicinity of the control grid. Electrons released by the cathode fall toward the screen grid because of the electric field established by the screen. But the screen grid is not solid like the anode, and most of the electrons pass between the screen-grid wires and are collected by the plate. Because the screen is maintained at a constant voltage by a constant-voltage source, any variation in anode voltage has no appreciable effect on the screen voltage. Furthermore, the anode has no appreciable effect on the electric field established between the screen grid and the cathode, and therefore a variation in anode voltage has negligible effect on the control-grid voltage. Thus the screen grid serves as a screen between the control grid and the anode, reducing the grid-to-plate capacitance to a negligible amount. In addition, the amplification factor of the tube is increased tremendously by the addition of the screen grid; this is seen from Eq. (10.11), where an extremely large change in E_b is necessary to affect the tube current as much as a very small change in E_c does.

A vacuum tube with two grids (four elements) is known as a "tetrode." The anode, cathode, and control grid of a tetrode are ordinarily connected just as the triode is connected in Fig. 10.8; so the tube can be thought of as an input-output device. The screen grid is maintained at a constant positive potential with respect to the cathode. The wires making up the screen grid are aligned with the control-grid wires so that electrons passing between the control-grid wires tend to miss the screen-grid wires and fall into the anode, which is also positive. An appreciable screen-grid current does flow in spite of the alignment of the grid wires. But a change in anode potential does not affect the electric field in the vicinity of the control grid and therefore has little effect on the anode current. The amplification factor of a tetrode tends to be very large for this reason.

Plate characteristic curves for a tetrode are shown in Fig. 10.24 for a constant screen-grid potential E_{c2} maintained at +90 volts. Some interesting phenomena are indicated by the curves. If E_{c1} (the control-grid voltage) and E_{c2} are both held constant, then I_b is a function of E_b only. For low values of positive E_b, the current I_b is approximately proportional to E_b. The electrons have low kinetic energies when they arrive at the anode, and many are diverted and captured by the screen grid. As E_b increases from zero, fewer of the electrons are captured by the screen grid, more of them fall into the plate, and the plate current increases. This

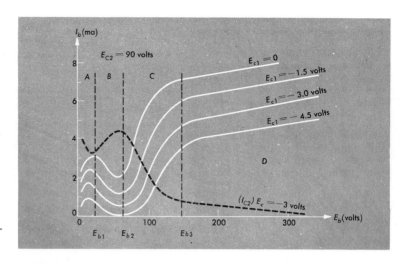

FIG. 10.24 I_b-versus-E_b characteristic curve for a tetrode.

is region A of Fig. 10.24, assuming that $E_{c1} = 0$ and $E_{c2} = +90$ volts. But when the anode voltage exceeds E_{b1} shown on the curve, some of the electrons arriving at the anode cause secondary emission at the anode by imparting their kinetic energy on impact to a free electron at the surface of the anode. The free electrons thus emitted from the anode are attracted to the more positive screen grid. As E_b increases further, the kinetic energy of the primary electrons from the cathode which strike the anode increases proportionately and the secondary emission at the anode increases. Secondary emission from the anode, causing electron-current flow from anode to screen grid, accounts for the negative slope of region B in Fig. 10.24. Region B demonstrates the negative-resistance characteristic of the tetrode; in this region, as E_b increases, I_b decreases. As E_b increases in region B, the anode emits more and more electrons, which flow to the screen grid. The net anode current I_b is the difference between the rate at which the anode captures primary electrons emitted thermally from the cathode and the rate at which secondary electrons are emitted from the anode.

In region C of Fig. 10.24, the anode has become sufficiently positive so that some of the secondary electrons are attracted back to the anode rather than the screen grid. The screenlike nature of the screen grid makes the electric field at the surface of the anode slightly irregular. Directly opposite the screen-grid wires, the electric field forces the secondary electrons emitted from the anode toward the screen. But at the surface of the anode and opposite the points midway between the screen wires, the electric field forces the secondary electrons toward the anode. As E_b increases in region C, more and more of the secondary electrons return to the anode. Finally in region D all the secondary electrons fall back to the anode, and the anode current is determined by the screen-grid potential and not the anode potential. As E_b increases in this region, I_b tends to remain nearly constant, since the anode is already capturing all the electrons which pass the screen grid. Anode potential in region D has practically no effect on the electric field in the vicinity of the control grid, and the field near the control grid determines I_b.

In order to minimize the effect of secondary emission in regions B and C of the tetrode, a third grid can be added in the region between the screen grid and the anode. The third grid, known as the "suppressor" grid because it suppresses secondary emission, is ordinarily maintained at cathode potential. The secondary electrons, on being emitted from the anode, are forced back to the anode by the field established between the suppressor grid and the anode. Thus the negative-resistance region of the tetrode shown in Fig. 10.24 is eliminated by the addition of the third grid. The three-grid five-element tube is known as a "pentode"; its I_b-versus-E_b characteristic curves are shown in Fig. 10.25 for $E_{c2} = 100$

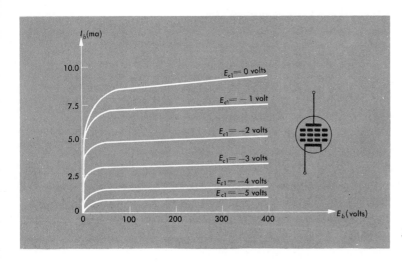

FIG. 10.25 *Plate characteristics for a pentode.* I_b-versus-E_b *curve with* $E_{c2} = 100$ *and* $E_{c3} = 0.$

volts and the suppressor-grid voltage $E_{c3} = 0$. The region of nearly parallel straight lines is the region in which the pentode is ordinarily operated. The linear operating region of the pentode extends much farther into the region of low E_b than does the operating region of the tetrode; this is the reason why pentodes are used much more than tetrodes.

10.6 TRANSISTORS

The *p-n* junction of doped semiconductor material discussed in Sec. 9.8 must rely on thermal electrons in the intrinsic materials for charge carriers causing conduction in the reverse direction across the junction. Conduction in the forward direction across the *p-n* junction utilizes holes and electrons injected into the semiconductor by the donor and acceptor atoms, and the concentration of these injected holes and electrons is much greater than the concentration of the thermal holes and electrons of the intrinsic material.

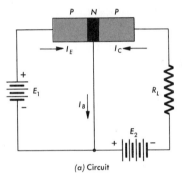

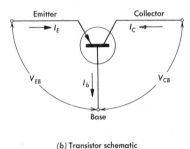

FIG. 10.26 *The p-n-p-junction transistor.*

(a) Circuit   (b) Transistor schematic

Conduction across a *p-n* junction in the reverse direction can be greatly increased by placing two junctions in tandem, as shown in Fig. 10.26*a*. The device represented here is known as a *p-n-p*-junction transistor, and it can also be represented symbolically as shown in Fig. 10.26*b*. In Fig. 10.26*a*, the left-hand *p-n* junction is biased in the forward direction by the battery marked E_1. The right-hand *n-p* junction is biased in the reverse direction by the battery marked E_2. Holes from the left-hand *p* region diffuse across the left *p-n* junction in the forward direction; a small voltage E_1 of the polarity shown can produce a relatively large forward current across this junction. If the *n* region is very thin, these holes from the left-hand *p* region diffuse right through the *n* region without recombining and cross the right-hand *n-p* junction in the reverse direction. By Kirchhoff's current law, current crossing the right-hand *n-p* junction is the same as the current in the load resistor R_L. A small change in the source voltage E_1 causes a large change in the current through the large load resistor

R_L, producing a large change in the voltage drop across R_L; this is the principle of voltage amplification in a transistor with common base.

The left-hand p region in Fig. 10.26a, biased in the forward direction with respect to the n region, is known as the "emitter," since it emits majority carriers (holes) into the middle (n) region. The thin section of n-type material in the middle is known as the "base," and the right-hand p region is called the "collector," since it captures the majority carriers given off by the emitter.

The schematic representation of the transistor shown in Fig. 10.26b uses the base potential as the reference, or ground, potential. Constant emitter voltage V_{EB} and collector voltage V_{CB} are measured with respect to the base. The direct emitter current I_E and the direct collector current I_C have positive directions as defined by the arrows; they add to produce the base current. The arrowhead on the emitter symbol indicates the direction of conventional current from the emitter, which is the direction of motion of the holes.

An n-p-n-junction transistor is shown in Fig. 10.27. The emitter is composed of n-type material, with electrons the majority

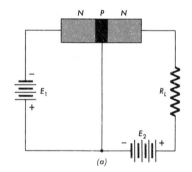

(a)

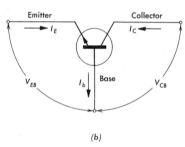

(b)

FIG. 10.27 *n-p-n-junction transistor and biasing potentials.*

carriers. Free electrons from the n-type material of the emitter diffuse across the left-hand n-p junction in the forward direction. The thickness of the p-type base is so small that most of the free electrons diffuse right on through the base and into the right-hand n-type material without recombining with the holes in the base. Thus, just as in the p-n-p-junction transistor, the majority carriers from the emitter diffuse across the emitter junction in the forward direction, cross the very thin base, and diffuse across the collector junction in the reverse direction. The emitter of the n-p-n transistor must be negative with respect to the base if the electrons are to cross the emitter-to-base junction in the forward direction.

The collector is positive with respect to the base so that electrons cross the base-to-collector p-n junction in the reverse direction.

Emitter current I_E shown in Figs. 10.26 and 10.27 is determined by the emitter voltage V_{EB} and the forward resistance of the emitter-to-base junction. Most of the emitter current also crosses the base-to-collector junction. The fraction of the majority-carrier emitter current which also flows in the collector circuit is defined as α, where

$$I_C = -\alpha I_E \qquad (10.24)$$

The value of α is less than unity but ordinarily greater than 0.9. From Kirchhoff's current law, the base current is, according to Fig. 10.27b,

$$I_B = I_E + I_C = (1 - \alpha)I_E = -\left(\frac{1}{\alpha} - 1\right)I_C \qquad (10.25)$$

Equations (10.24) and (10.25) apply for both p-n-p and n-p-n transistors; they relate constant or direct values of emitter, collector, and base currents.

10.7 TRANSISTOR CHARACTERISTICS

In the preceding section the transistor base was used as a reference from which emitter and collector voltages were defined. Furthermore, emitter and collector currents were defined, from which the base current could be obtained by Eq. (10.25). Thus, with the base as a reference, emitter voltage V_{EB}, collector voltage V_{CB}, emitter current I_E, and collector current I_C as defined in Figs. 10.26b and 10.27b are the four variables which describe the transistor characteristics. These variables can be represented by characteristic curves in a number of ways. If we consider the emitter-to-base terminals as the input terminals, emitter voltage-versus-emitter current can be plotted with one of the output, or collector, variables as a parameter. This is shown in Fig. 10.28a for a p-n-p transistor, with the collector voltage V_{CB} as the parameter. The collector, or output, variables I_{CB} versus V_{CB} are shown in Fig. 10.28b with I_E as the parameter. An n-p-n-junction transistor has similar characteristic curves, but with voltage and current polarities reversed.

The two curves of Fig. 10.28 are known as the "emitter" and "collector" characteristics of the common-base transistor. The

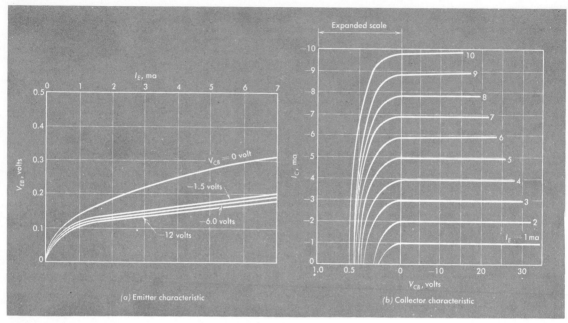

FIG. 10.28 *Characteristic curves for a p-n-p-junction transistor.*

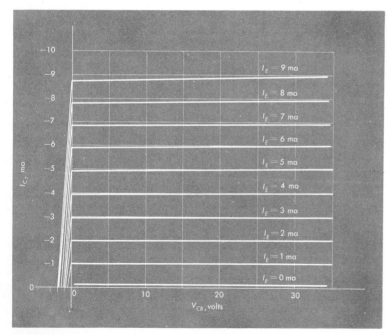

FIG. 10.29 *Linear approximation to the collector characteristic of a p-n-p-junction transistor.*

collector characteristics are nearly straight and parallel over much of the operating region, with some resemblance to the I_b-versus-E_b characteristics of a vacuum pentode. To a good approximation, the collector characteristics can be represented by a family of straight, parallel lines, as shown in Fig. 10.29. Notice that, when $I_E = 0$, the collector current is not quite zero; this is the current attributed to thermal holes and electrons crossing the base-to-collector junction in the reverse direction. This current we call I_{CO}; it is I_C when $I_E = 0$. From the idealized collector characteristic shown in Fig. 10.29, the collector current can be expressed approximately as

$$I_C = I_{CO} - \alpha I_E \tag{10.26}$$

where I_C and I_E are defined by Fig. 10.27b and α is a positive fraction. The value of I_{CO} is of the order of a few microamperes and can usually be neglected in calculating I_C.

Small-signal equivalent circuits can be found for a transistor in the same manner as the equivalent circuit was found for the vacuum triode. Of the four transistor variables V_{EB}, I_E, V_{CB}, and I_C, any three of them are independent. Then we can write

$$I_E = f_1(V_{EB}, V_{CB}) \tag{10.27}$$

$$I_C = f_2(V_{EB}, V_{CB}) \tag{10.28}$$

$$V_{EB} = f_3(I_E, I_C) \tag{10.29}$$

$$V_{CB} = f_4(I_E, I_C) \tag{10.30}$$

where each variable is shown as a function of two other variables. Taking the total differentials of each of the above equations results in

$$\Delta I_E = \frac{\partial I_E}{\partial V_{EB}} \Delta V_{EB} + \frac{\partial I_E}{\partial V_{CB}} \Delta V_{CB} \tag{10.31}$$

$$\Delta I_C = \frac{\partial I_C}{\partial V_{EB}} \Delta V_{EB} + \frac{\partial I_C}{\partial V_{CB}} \Delta V_{CB} \tag{10.32}$$

$$\Delta V_{EB} = \frac{\partial V_{EB}}{\partial I_E} \Delta I_E + \frac{\partial V_{EB}}{\partial I_C} \Delta I_C \tag{10.33}$$

$$\Delta V_{CB} = \frac{\partial V_{CB}}{\partial I_E} \Delta I_E + \frac{\partial V_{CB}}{\partial I_C} \Delta I_C \tag{10.34}$$

Now observe that $\partial I_E/\partial V_{EB}$, $\partial I_C/\partial V_{CB}$, $\partial I_E/\partial V_{CB}$, and $\partial I_C/\partial V_{EB}$ all have the dimensions of admittance. If we assume that these partial derivatives are constant, then we can define

$$y_{11} = \frac{\partial I_E}{\partial V_{EB}} \qquad y_{12} = \frac{\partial I_E}{\partial V_{CB}}$$

$$\text{(10.35)}$$

$$y_{22} = \frac{\partial I_C}{\partial V_{CB}} \qquad y_{21} = \frac{\partial I_C}{\partial V_{EB}}$$

Substituting Eqs. (10.35) into Eqs. (10.31) and (10.32), and letting the differential voltages ΔV_{EB} and ΔV_{CB} be designated by v_{eb} and v_{ec}, respectively, and the differential currents ΔI_E and ΔI_C by i_e and i_c, then

$$i_e = y_{11}v_{eb} + y_{12}v_{cb} \qquad \text{(10.36)}$$

$$i_c = y_{21}v_{eb} + y_{22}v_{cb} \qquad \text{(10.37)}$$

Equations (10.36) and (10.37) must be satisfied by the transistor equivalent circuit we seek. Although v_{eb}, v_{cb}, i_e, and i_c are small increments or changes in voltage and current, and not d-c components, Eqs. (10.36) and (10.37) apply when v_{eb}, v_{cb}, i_e, and i_b are small sinusoidal components of voltage and current as well.

Next, observe that $\partial V_{EB}/\partial I_E$, $\partial V_{EB}/\partial I_C$, $\partial V_{CB}/\partial I_E$, and $\partial V_{CB}/\partial I_C$ in Eqs. (10.33) and (10.34) all have dimensions of impedance. If these derivatives are assumed to be constant for small variations in V_{EB} and V_{EC}, then we can define

$$z_{11} = \frac{\partial V_{EB}}{\partial I_E} \qquad z_{12} = \frac{\partial V_{EB}}{\partial I_C}$$

$$\text{(10.38)}$$

$$z_{22} = \frac{\partial V_{CB}}{\partial I_C} \qquad z_{21} = \frac{\partial V_{CB}}{\partial I_E}$$

Again designate ΔV_{eb} and ΔV_{cb} in Eqs. (10.33) and (10.34) as v_{eb} and v_{cb} and ΔI_E and ΔI_C as i_e and i_c, respectively. Then substituting Eqs. (10.38), v_{eb}, v_{cb}, i_e, and i_c, into Eqs. (10.33) and (10.34) yields

$$v_{eb} = z_{11}i_e + z_{12}i_c \qquad \text{(10.39)}$$

$$v_{cb} = z_{21}i_e + z_{22}i_c \qquad \text{(10.40)}$$

Here again, Eqs. (10.39) and (10.40), derived for increments or changes in v_{eb}, v_{cb}, i_e, and i_c, are valid also for small sinusoidal components of these voltages and currents. A transistor equivalent circuit must satisfy Eqs. (10.39) and (10.40) for small sinusoidal variations in v_{eb}, v_{cb}, i_e, and i_c.

The transistor can be represented by the "black box" shown in Fig. 10.30 and Eqs. (10.36), (10.37), (10.39), and (10.40) for small variations in v_{eb} and v_{cb}, i_e, and i_c. Equations (10.36) and (10.37) are satisfied by the active circuit shown in Fig. 10.31a and consisting of two current generators $y_{12}v_{cb}$ and $y_{21}v_{eb}$ and two admittances y_{11} and y_{22}. Equations (10.39) and (10.40) are satisfied by the active circuit shown in Fig. 10.31b, where $z_{12}i_c$ and $z_{21}i_e$ are voltage sources. These two small-signal equivalent circuits of Fig. 10.31 are, of course, equivalent to each other. Once the parameters y_{11}, y_{12}, y_{21}, and y_{22} or z_{11}, z_{12}, z_{21}, and z_{22} are determined for the transistor, the appropriate small-signal equivalent circuit converts the transistor problem to a circuit problem. The only coupling between the left-hand and the right-hand parts of each equivalent circuit is by means of the current or voltage generators in each circuit.

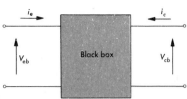

FIG. 10.30 *"Black box" representation of the transistor.*

It is sometimes convenient to simplify the equivalent circuits shown in Fig. 10.31 by reducing to one the number of generators shown in each. This can be done by rewriting Eqs. (10.36) and (10.37) in an equivalent form and then recognizing the circuits which are represented by the new equations equivalent to Eqs. (10.36) and (10.37). By adding and subtracting $y_{12}v_{eb}$ to the right-hand side of Eqs. (10.36) and (10.37) we have

$$i_e = (y_{11} + y_{12})v_{eb} + (v_{eb} - v_{cb})(-y_{12}) \qquad (10.41)$$

$$i_c = y_{12}v_{eb} + y_{22}v_{cb} + (y_{21} - y_{12})v_{eb} \qquad (10.42)$$

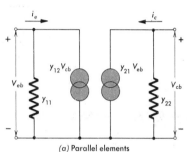

(a) Parallel elements

which are recognized as the nodal equations for the circuit of Fig. 10.32a. Likewise, Eqs. (10.39) and (10.40) can be modified by adding and subtracting $z_{12}i_e$ to the right-hand side of each.

$$v_{eb} = (z_{11} - z_{12})i_e + z_{12}(i_e + i_c) \qquad (10.43)$$

$$v_{cb} = z_{12}i_e + z_{22}i_c + (z_{21} - z_{12})i_e \qquad (10.44)$$

Equations (10.43) and (10.44) are recognized as the loop equations for the circuit of Fig. 10.32b. Obviously the two circuits of Fig.

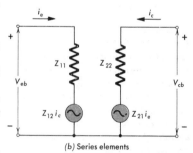

(b) Series elements

FIG. 10.31 *Active circuit equivalents of a transistor for small signals.*

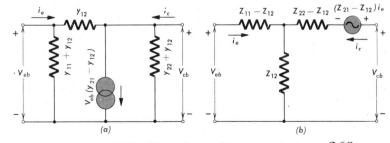

FIG. 10.32 *One-generator small-signal equivalent circuits for a transistor.*

(a)

(b)

10.7 Transistor Characteristics **269**

10.32 must be equivalent to each other; these two equivalent circuits are one-generator equivalents to the transistor for small sinusoidal signals.

It should be emphasized that the equivalent circuits of Fig. 10.32 are valid only for *changes* in voltages and currents, or for small a-c components, and not for constant, or d-c, components; this is a consequence of the use of the total differential to obtain Eqs. (10.31) to (10.34). The differential voltages and currents can be replaced by small sinusoidal voltages and currents which are changing with time, but they cannot be replaced by constant voltages and currents.

The one-generator small-signal equivalent circuits of Fig. 10.32 can be modified to simplify them for the grounded-base nomenclature. Assume that the transistor is used to amplify low-frequency signals. Let

$$r_e = z_{11} - z_{12}$$

$$r_b = z_{12}$$

$$r_c = z_{22} - z_{12}$$

$$r_m = z_{21} - z_{12}$$

(10.45)

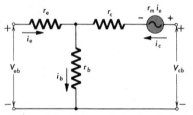

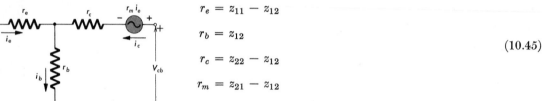

FIG. 10.33 *Small-signal equivalent circuit for grounded-base transistor.* $r_e + r_b$ *is the input (emitter) resistance when the output, or collector, is open.* $r_c + r_b$ *is collector resistance when emitter is open.* r_b *is the ratio of emitter voltage to collector current when emitter circuit is open.* r_m *is the ratio of collector voltage to emitter current with the collector circuit open.*

Then substituting Eqs. (10.45) into Eqs. (10.43) and (10.44) results in

$$v_{eb} = r_e i_e + r_b(i_e + i_c)$$ (10.46)

$$v_{cb} = r_c i_c + r_b(i_c + i_e) + r_m i_e$$ (10.47)

The equivalent circuit represented by Eqs. (10.46) and (10.47), similar to Fig. 10.32b, is shown in Fig. 10.33. A further modification of Fig. 10.33 can be made to replace the series combination of r_c and the voltage generator $r_m i_e$ with Norton's equivalent parallel combination of r_c and a current generator αi_e. Justification for the current generator αi_e will not be given here, but the modified circuit is shown in Fig. 10.34.

The transistor equivalent circuits developed in this section illustrate a general procedure for obtaining equivalent circuits for four-terminal networks. Many other equivalent circuits can be obtained; some will be developed in Chap. 11. It must be emphasized that the equivalent circuits are valid only when the changes in input (emitter) voltage and current are small so that the transistor is always operated on that part of its characteristic curves which is linear and evenly spaced.

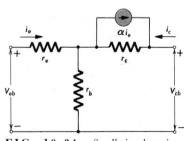

FIG. 10.34 *Small-signal equivalent circuit with grounded base using current generator* αi_e.

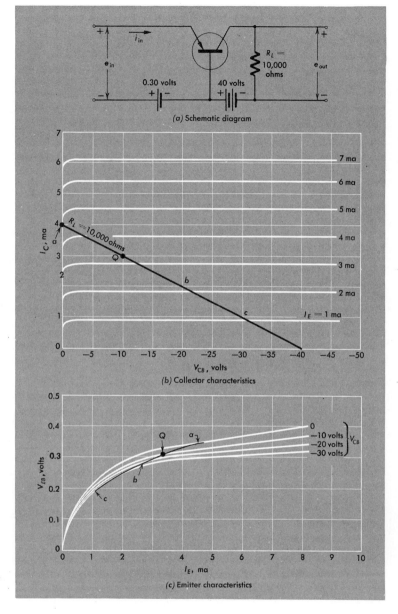

(a) Schematic diagram

(b) Collector characteristics

(c) Emitter characteristics

FIG. 10.35 *Finding transistor parameters.*

Example 10.2

A certain *p-n-p*-junction transistor, used in the circuit shown in Fig. 10.35a, has characteristics as shown in Fig. 10.35b and c. The load line in the collector circuit is drawn first. Then the operating line is determined in the emitter circuit by locating points on the emitter characteristic corresponding to V_{CB} and I_E taken from the collector load line; these points are shown as a, b, c, and Q. The emitter Q point is determined at the point where $V_{EB} = 0.3$ volt intersects the emitter operating line. From the emitter Q point, $I_E = 3.3$ ma is determined and transferred to the collector characteristic; the collector Q point is determined by the intersection of the collector load line with $I_E = 3.3$ ma.

Transistor parameters can now be determined at the operating points. For instance,

$$z_{11} = \frac{\Delta V_{EB}}{\Delta I_E}\bigg|_{V_{CB}=\text{const}} = 31 \text{ ohms}$$

where z_{11} is the slope of the emitter characteristic at the emitter Q point.

$$z_{22} = \frac{\Delta V_{CB}}{\Delta I_C}\bigg|_{I_E=\text{const}} = 500 \text{ kilohms}$$

where z_{22} is the reciprocal of the slope of the collector characteristic at the collector Q point.

$$z_{12} = \frac{\Delta V_{EB}}{\Delta I_C}\bigg|_{I_E=\text{const}} = 67 \text{ ohms}$$

z_{12} is the above ratio where ΔI_C is taken between $V_{CB} = 0$ and $V_{CB} = -30$ from the collector characteristic with $I_E = 3.3$ ma and where ΔV_{EB} comes from the emitter characteristic for $I_E = 3.3$ ma with V_{CB} varying from 0 to -30 volts.

$$z_{21} = \frac{\Delta V_{CB}}{\Delta I_E}\bigg|_{V_{EB}=\text{const}} = 16{,}700 \text{ ohms}$$

z_{21} is obtained from the emitter characteristic by constraining $V_{EB} = 0.3$ volt and finding ΔI_E as V_{CB} takes values from 0 to -20 volts. Then, for this example,

$$r_e = z_{11} - z_{12} = -36 \text{ ohms}$$

$$r_b = z_{12} = 67 \text{ ohms}$$

$$r_c = z_{22} - z_{12} \approx 500 \text{ kilohms}$$

$$r_m = z_{21} - z_{12} \approx 16{,}700 \text{ ohms}$$

10.8 THE CATHODE-RAY TUBE

A visual display of information can be accomplished by means of the cathode-ray tube such as is used in television receivers, radar scopes, and laboratory instruments. The cathode-ray tube performs three functions. First, it accelerates and focuses electrons into a beam. Then it causes the beam to be deflected by an amount proportional to an external applied voltage or current. Finally it converts the position of the beam into an optical display by means of a fluorescent screen.

The cathode-ray tube is a vacuum tube; if gas molecules interfere with the beam path, the beam is scattered. The electron gun, which produces the electron beam, consists of an indirectly heated cathode K, a grid G, and two accelerating anodes A_1 and A_2, as shown in Fig. 10.36. The accelerating anodes are maintained

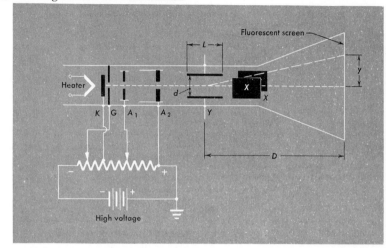

FIG. 10.36 *The cathode-ray tube.*
K = cathode, G = grid, A_1 and A_2 = accelerating anodes, Y = vertical-deflection plates, and X = horizontal-deflection plates.

at high positive potentials with respect to the cathode, A_2 being more positive than A_1. Anodes A_1 and A_2 are shaped with symmetry about the axis of the tube, and the electric field between them serves to focus the electrons into a beam. The kinetic energy which the electrons possess when they pass through the second anode must equal the potential energy lost by the electron in falling from the cathode to the anode. If V_a is the anode potential with respect to the cathode, then, equating kinetic and potential energies, we have

$$\tfrac{1}{2}mv^2 = V_a e \tag{10.48}$$

where e and m are the charge and mass of the electron, respectively, and v is its velocity. Solving for velocity gives

$$v = \sqrt{\frac{2V_a e}{m}} = 5.91 \times 10^5 \sqrt{V_a} \qquad \text{m/sec} \tag{10.49}$$

when V_a is in volts.

The grid of the cathode-ray tube is maintained at a potential slightly negative with respect to the cathode. Just as in a vacuum triode, the grid of the cathode-ray tube controls the electron current arriving at the anode. By adjusting the potential of the grid, the rate at which electrons pass the grid is controlled, and the intensity of the spot made by the electrons on the fluorescent screen is adjusted.

The deflection system utilizes either a magnetic field or an electric field to deflect the electron beam. In Fig. 10.36, electro-static deflection is used. At Y, two parallel horizontal-deflection plates produce between themselves a uniform electric field in the vertical direction, and the electron beam passing through this field is bent in a vertical plane. Likewise, the deflection plates at X are vertical, and they produce between themselves a uniform horizontal electric field. The electron beam is bent in a horizontal plane when it passes between the X deflection plates. The analysis of beam deflection can be accomplished by considering that a voltage V_y is placed on the vertical-, or Y, deflection plates, establishing an electric field of intensity V_y/d, where d is the spacing between the plates. Suppose that the electron beam enters the field between the deflection plates with a velocity v_z along the z axis as given by Eq. (10.49). The time during which an individual electron of velocity v_z is in the field while passing between the plates is L/v_z, where L is the length of the deflection plates. When the beam leaves the deflection plates, the vertical component of velocity [Eq. (9.15)] is

$$v_y = \frac{e}{m} \mathcal{E}_y t + V_0 \qquad \text{m/sec}$$

where e/m is the charge-to-mass ratio of the electron, $\mathcal{E}_y$ is the electric-field intensity between the plates, t is the time during which an electron is between the plates, and V_0, the initial velocity in the y direction, is zero. Then

$$v_y = \frac{e}{m} \frac{V_y}{d} \frac{L}{v_z} = 1.759 \times 10^{11} \frac{V_y L}{d v_z} \qquad \text{m/sec} \qquad (10.50)$$

and the component of velocity along the z axis of the tube is given by Eq. (10.49),

$$v_z = 5.91 \times 10^5 \sqrt{V_a} \qquad \text{m/sec}$$

Substituting Eq. (10.49) into Eq. (10.50) yields

$$v_y = 2.974 \times 10^5 \frac{V_y L}{d \sqrt{V_a}} \qquad \text{m/sec} \qquad (10.51)$$

If the distance from the deflection plates to the screen is D and the deflection of the beam on the screen is Y, then, by similar triangles,

$$\frac{v_y}{v_z} = \frac{Y}{D} \tag{10.52}$$

Substituting Eqs. (10.49) and (10.51) into Eq. (10.52) gives

$$\frac{Y}{D} = \frac{V_y L}{2 \, d V_a} \tag{10.53}$$

or

$$Y = \frac{V_y L D}{2 \, d V_a} \quad \text{meters} \tag{10.54}$$

Equation (10.54) shows that the deflection of the beam on the screen is directly proportional to V_y, the voltage between the deflection plates. Thus, by measuring Y, it is possible to determine the voltage on the deflection plates, and the cathode-ray tube can be used as a voltmeter.

The cathode-ray tube, used in an instrument known as the cathode-ray oscillograph or oscilloscope, is an extremely versatile laboratory instrument. By means of the oscillograph, periodic voltages can be made to appear stationary on the screen. A saw-tooth voltage wave, shown in Fig. 10.37, of the same frequency as the periodic voltage is applied to the horizontal-deflection plates (the plates which accomplish horizontal deflection). The horizontal deflection of the beam is proportional to the instantaneous voltage of the saw-tooth wave; therefore the beam sweeps at a uniform rate across the screen in the horizontal direction, returning to the starting position almost instantaneously, and sweeping again. The vertical deflection is proportional to the instantaneous voltage on the vertical-deflection plates. The net effect is a volt-age-versus-time plot on the screen of the voltage applied to the vertical-deflection plates. A periodic nonelectric quantity can also be observed by first converting it to an analogous voltage and then viewing the voltage on the screen. Figure 10.38 shows the pattern on the screen when the saw-tooth sweep voltage of Fig. 10.37 is applied to the horizontal plates and a sinusoidal voltage is applied to the vertical plates. The beam moves horizontally at a constant rate while tracing out the sinusoid. The return right-to-left path of the beam is almost instantaneous, and the cycle is repeated over and over again. The appearance on the screen is a stationary sine wave of voltage traced out at the frequency of the sine wave.

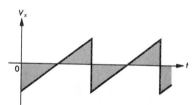

FIG. 10.37 *Saw-tooth sweep voltage applied to horizontal-deflection plates of a cathode-ray tube.*

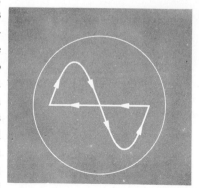

FIG. 10.38 *Trace of a sinusoidal voltage of the same frequency as saw-tooth sweep voltage.*

SUMMARY

A diode is a two-terminal nonlinear device. Its I_b-versus-E_b characteristic can be approximated by straight lines over various regions of the curve, and therefore the diode can be approximated over the linear regions by combinations of resistors, batteries, and switches. Static resistance of a diode is merely the ratio of the diode voltage to current, or [Eq. (10.4)]

$$R_b = \frac{E_b}{I_b} \quad \text{ohms}$$

Dynamic resistance for a diode is the rate of change of plate voltage to plate current, or [Eq. (10.5)]

$$r_p = \frac{dE_b}{dI_b}$$

A triode is a three-element vacuum tube which has the ability to amplify; a transistor is a three-element semiconductor device which also has the ability to amplify. Triode characteristics are described best by I_b-versus-E_b curves with grid voltage as a parameter. The three variables in a vacuum triode are plate voltage, plate current, and grid voltage. These three variables define three tube parameters, amplification factor μ, plate resistance r_p, and transconductance g_m [Eqs. (10.9), (10.11), and (10.13)].

$$r_p = \frac{\partial E_b}{\partial I_b}\bigg|_{E_c = \text{const}} \quad \text{ohms}$$

$$\mu = -\frac{\partial E_b}{\partial E_c}\bigg|_{I_b = \text{const}}$$

$$g_m = \frac{\partial I_b}{\partial E_c}\bigg|_{E_b = \text{const}} \quad \text{mhos}$$

When a triode is operated as an amplifier, it is convenient to use for analysis an equivalent circuit consisting of a resistor r_p in series with a generator μe_g, where e_g is the small sinusoidal signal applied to the grid of the triode. The Norton equivalent circuit is also useful. Analysis of the amplifier circuit then becomes a circuit problem.

The transistor variables defined with respect to the base are emitter voltage and current and collector voltage and current.

When used as an amplifier, the transistor can also be reduced to a small-signal equivalent circuit containing only one generator; two possible such equivalent circuits are shown in Fig. 10.30. The basis for deriving the small-signal equivalents of the triode and the transistor is the total derivative. The variables are defined, the total derivative is taken, and the equivalent circuit is recognized from the total derivative.

The cathode-ray tube provides visual display of voltages connected to its deflection plates. Deflection of the electron beam is directly proportional to the voltages applied to the deflection plates, and therefore deflection is a measure of these applied voltages.

FURTHER READING

Linear models and equivalent circuits of transistors and vacuum triodes are discussed extensively in H. J. Zimmermann and S. J. Mason, *Electronic Circuit Theory* (John Wiley & Sons, Inc., New York, 1959), chaps. 5 and 6, and in Jacob Millman, *Vacuum-tube and Semiconductor Electronics* (McGraw-Hill Book Company, Inc., New York, 1958), chaps. 7 to 10. The cathode-ray tube is discussed in the Millman book in chap. 2.

PROBLEMS

10.1 A certain vacuum-diode characteristic can be approximated by a 500-ohm linear resistor in the forward direction and an infinite resistance in the reverse direction. It is connected in series with a 1,000-ohm load resistor and a rectangular voltage source as shown in the figure.

(a) Find the instantaneous output voltage e_o.

(b) Find the average or d-c value of the output voltage.

(c) Find the rms value of the output voltage.

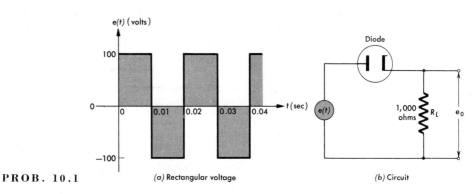

PROB. 10.1

(a) Rectangular voltage

(b) Circuit

10.2 A 50-volt battery is added to the circuit of Prob. 10.1 so that its constant voltage adds to that of the rectangular voltage source. Repeat parts a to c of Prob. 10.1.

10.3 A certain semiconductor diode has a characteristic which can be approximated by the linearized characteristic shown in the figure. A sinusoidal voltage $e_{in} = 200 \sin 1,000t$ is connected to the input of the diode and 2,500-ohm load resistor in series.

    (a) Find the rms current through R_L.

    (b) Find the direct current through R_L.

    (c) Find the instantaneous current through R_L as a function of time.

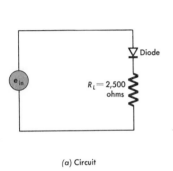

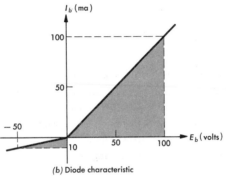

(a) Circuit   (b) Diode characteristic   **PROB. 10.3**

10.4 The plate characteristic of a 6J5 triode is shown in **Fig. 10.23**. The operating point is chosen at $E_c = -2$ volts, $I_b = 5$ ma. Find μ, g_m, and r_p at the operating point.

10.5 Draw a small-signal equivalent circuit for the 6J5 triode, using values of tube parameters found in Prob. 10.4. Show the triode equivalent circuit connected to a 10,000-ohm load resistor. Solve for the output voltage across the load resistor when the input voltage is $2 \sin \omega t$.

10.6 A certain transistor has the following parameters: $\alpha = 0.98$, $r_b = 500$ ohms, $r_m = 980,000$ ohms, $r_e = 25$ ohms, $r_c = 1$ megohm. A load impedance of $R_L = 10,000$ ohms is connected across the output (collector-to-base) of the common-base equivalent circuit. A current step of 1 ma is applied at the input (emitter). Find the output voltage across R_L.

10.7 A voltage step of 0.1 volt is applied to the input (emitter) of the common-base transistor amplifier of Prob. 10.6. Find the output voltage across R_L.

10.8 Find the collector parameters z_{21} and z_{22} of the 2N43 transistor whose characteristics are shown in Fig. 10.28b at the operating point $I_E = 4$ ma, $V_{CB} = -10$ volts.

10.9 A 6SK7 pentode is operated as a linear amplifier in the circuit shown in the illustration. The control grid is biased to -2.5 volts, and the screen grid is 150 volts positive with respect to the cathode.

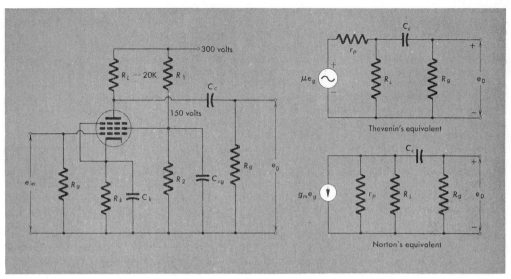

PROB. 10.9

(a) From the plate characteristic curve, find Thévenin's equivalent circuit for the pentode.

(b) From the plate characteristic curve, find Norton's equivalent circuit for the pentode.

(c) Assume that the screen current is negligible. Find the ratio of R_1 to R_2 to provide 150 volts to the screen grid.

10.10 A certain electromechanical device has a current-versus-voltage characteristic curve as shown in the figure; the parameter x is the mechanical position of the lever arm.

(a) Find Thévenin's equivalent circuit for the device.

(b) Find Norton's equivalent circuit for the device.

(c) Find the current i as a function of x if a 100-volt battery is connected across the terminals.

10.11 A strain-gauge element has a current-versus-voltage characteristic as shown in the illustration (p. 280), where the parameter s is strain, measured as a fraction of elongation of the strain-gauge element.

(a) Devise an equivalent circuit for the element.

(b) Devise a circuit using the strain-gauge element; make the current in your circuit a linear function of the strain on the element.

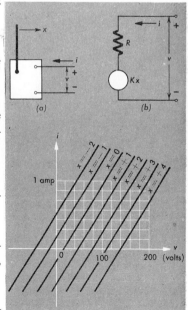

PROB. 10.10

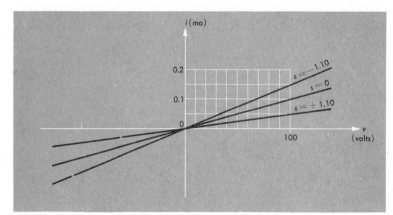

10.12 A certain pressure transducer has a current-versus-voltage characteristic as shown in the figure; the pressure P, measured in newtons per square centimeter, is the parameter.

(a) Find an approximate linear equivalent circuit for the transducer when the voltage is 10 volts and the pressure is 2.0 newtons/cm^2.

(b) Using the transducer in the circuit shown in (b) of the figure, solve for the current measured by the milliammeter. Use the approximate linear equivalent circuit found in part a.

(c) Find the current in the circuit shown graphically in (b) of the figure, and make a plot of pressure versus current.

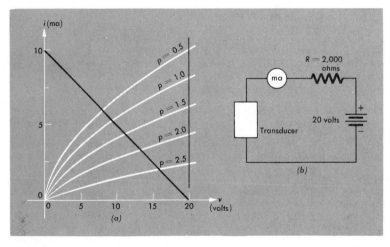

PROB. 10.12

10.13 The phototube characteristic shown in Fig. 10.2 applies to the tube used in the circuit of Fig. 10.3. Assume that $E_{bb} = 300$ volts and $R_L = 1.5$ megohms.

(a) Find an approximate equivalent circuit with illumination as the input variable or parameter.

(b) If the illumination varies between 0.02 and 0.06 lumens, over what range does the voltage across R_L vary? (This is the principle of reproducing sound recorded on film.)

10.14 The characteristic curves of a 6SJ7 pentode are shown in Fig. A1.4. Find the tube parameters μ, g_m, and r_p for the operating point $E_b = 80$ volts, $E_c = -3$ volts.

10.15 The sensitivity of a cathode-ray tube is defined as the ratio of deflection of the beam per volt applied to the deflection plates, in meters per volt. A cathode-ray tube uses 2,000 volts to accelerate the beam. The length L of the Y deflection plates is 0.05 m, and their spacing is 0.01 m. Distance D to the fluorescent screen is 0.25 m. Find the sensitivity of the Y deflection plates.

11

LINEAR OPERATION

11.1 INTRODUCTION

One of the major applications of three- and four-terminal electronic devices such as vacuum tubes and transistors is to provide amplification of time-varying voltages and currents. Amplification, or gain, can be defined quantitatively as the ratio of the output quantity to the input quantity. If the input quantity is a sinusoidal voltage, the voltage gain of the linear amplifier can be defined as

$$\mathbf{A}_v = \frac{\mathbf{V}_{\text{out}}}{\mathbf{V}_{\text{in}}} \qquad \text{or} \qquad \mathbf{V}_{\text{out}} = \mathbf{A}_v \mathbf{V}_{\text{in}} \tag{11.1}$$

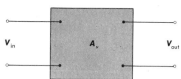

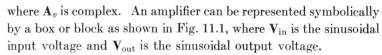

FIG. 11.1 *Linear amplifier terms.*

where $\mathbf{A}_v$ is complex. An amplifier can be represented symbolically by a box or block as shown in Fig. 11.1, where $\mathbf{V}_{\text{in}}$ is the sinusoidal input voltage and $\mathbf{V}_{\text{out}}$ is the sinusoidal output voltage.

If the input voltage is periodic but not a sinusoid, it can be represented by an infinite series of sinusoids of frequencies that are multiples of the fundamental frequency, as explained in Sec. 2.11. Each of the component frequencies of the signal can be considered separately in amplifier analysis, and the output voltage is then the superposition or summation of each input signal multiplied by the gain of the amplifier for the particular frequency. Amplifier analysis is simplified when only one frequency term is present. Thus it is convenient to assume that $\mathbf{V}_{\text{in}}$ is a sinusoid and to study the gain of the amplifier as a function of the frequency of V_{in}.

Amplifier gain is a function of frequency, just as impedance is a function of frequency. Distortion in an amplifier results when the gain is not real, finite, and constant for all frequencies. The output of an amplifier is an identical reproduction of the input when the gain of the amplifier is real, constant, and independent of frequency.

When the gain is not constant but varies with frequency, three kinds of distortion result. The gain, being complex, can be expressed in exponential form as

$$\mathbf{A}_v = A\epsilon^{j\theta} \tag{11.2}$$

where gain magnitude A and phase θ are both functions of frequency. Then the magnitude of the output voltage depends not only on the magnitude of the input voltage but also on the frequency of the input voltage. Thus, if several frequencies are impressed on the input of the amplifier, some frequencies are amplified more than others; this is known as "frequency distortion." With Eq. (11.1) used for magnitude only, the magnitude of the output voltage is the product of the input-voltage magnitude and the gain magnitude for that frequency.

A second kind of distortion results from the phase angle θ being a function of frequency. Phase distortion occurs when signals are shifted in phase by the amplifier by an amount that varies with frequency. The third kind of distortion results from the nonlinear nature of electronic devices, causing frequencies to appear at the output which do not occur at the input. This is known as "amplitude" or "nonlinear" distortion, and its cause is explained in Chap. 12. In a sense, nonlinear distortion can be thought of as resulting from infinite gain for certain frequencies, where an output can occur with no input.

Amplifiers are often classified according to the nature of the signal which they must amplify. Each kind of signal requires a range or spectrum of frequencies to represent it by the predominant terms in its Fourier-series expansion, as explained in Sec. 2.11. Therefore the amplifier, to amplify the signal without frequency distortion, must have constant gain over a frequency range which corresponds to that of the signal. If the frequency range is a narrow one, a narrow-band amplifier is used. Broad-band amplifiers have frequency ranges adequate to amplify signals which possess widely separated frequencies. When extremely low frequencies or even constant voltages must be amplified, an amplifier is required which has constant gain over the low frequencies and at zero frequency. Thus, amplifiers are classified according to the range of frequencies they must amplify, and their design depends upon the frequency requirements.

Besides gain and frequency requirements, input and output impedance of the amplifier must also be considered for maximum power transfer. A common-base transistor amplifier gives good voltage gain, but its input impedance is low, and too much power is required to drive it. Therefore, the common emitter amplifier, which has about the same voltage gain but requires much less signal-power input, is more practical for most applications. The grounded-cathode triode amplifier has a high voltage gain, but its output impedance is high and maximum power cannot be transferred to a low impedance load. The cathode-follower amplifier, discussed in Chap. 13, has a voltage gain less than unity, but its output impedance is low and it can operate into low-impedance loads with maximum power transfer.

In this chapter only a few of the possible amplifier circuits will be discussed. The emphasis must be on principles rather than variety. Voltage gain as a function of frequency is considered for a triode amplifier and for a transistor amplifier. Some biasing problems are also discussed. But detailed analysis of the multitude of amplifier circuits is left to the references mentioned at the end of the chapter.

11.2 ELEMENTARY TRIODE AMPLIFIER

An elementary triode amplifier circuit is shown in Fig. 11.2a, along with the two equivalent circuits, shown in (b) and (c), which were derived in Chap. 10. The signal to be amplified is represented by

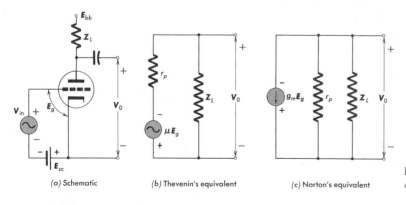

(a) Schematic   (b) Thevenin's equivalent   (c) Norton's equivalent

FIG. 11.2   *The elementary triode amplifier with impedance load* $\mathbf{Z}_L$.

V_{in}, and given the control-grid circuit shown in Fig. 11.2a,

$$E_g = V_{in} \tag{11.3}$$

where E_g is the sinusoidal component of the voltage applied to the control grid. The sinusoidal component of output voltage is represented by V_o. The equivalent circuits apply only for the changing, or a-c, components of the plate voltage and current. When the d-c component of plate voltage is eliminated from the equivalent circuit,

$$E_p = V_o \tag{11.4}$$

where E_p is the alternating component of the plate voltage.

The solution of the equivalent circuits in Fig. 11.2b and c follows in a straightforward manner. Thévenin's equivalent is easily solved for I_p, giving

$$I_p = \frac{-\mu E_g}{r_p + Z_L} \tag{11.5}$$

from which

$$V_o = I_p Z_L = \frac{-\mu E_g Z_L}{r_p + Z_L} \tag{11.6}$$

Dividing Eq. (11.6) through by E_g and substituting Eq. (11.3) gives

$$\frac{V_o}{V_{in}} = A_v = \frac{-u Z_L}{r_p + Z_L} \tag{11.7}$$

where A_v is the voltage gain or amplification of the stage and Z_L is the load impedance.

The solution of Fig. 11.2c is obtained by recognizing that the current generator $g_m E_g$ feeds its current through the parallel combination of r_p and Z_L. Then the output voltage is

$$V_o = -g_m E_g \frac{r_p Z_L}{r_p + Z_L} \tag{11.8}$$

and

$$\frac{V_o}{V_{in}} = A_v = \frac{-g_m r_p Z_L}{r_p + Z_L} \tag{11.9}$$

Since Eqs. (11.7) and (11.9) are obtained from two equivalent circuits, they must both be equivalent to each other. Therefore, from Eqs. (11.7) and (11.9), we verify that

$$\mu = g_m r_p \tag{11.10}$$

The two gain equations for the triode amplifier [Eqs. (11.7) and (11.9)], show that the gain is a function of the load impedance Z_L. But Z_L is a function of frequency, and therefore gain is also a function of frequency. For Z_L to be independent of frequency, it must be resistive. If $Z_L = R_L$, the gain expressed by Eq. (11.7) is real and independent of frequency. The minus signs on the gain equations indicate a phase shift of 180° between the output voltage and the input voltage, when $Z_L = R_L$.

If the load impedance contains a reactive component, the magnitude and phase of the impedance are both functions of frequency. From Eq. (11.7) it follows that the gain is also complex for complex Z_L and that the gain magnitude and phase angle are both functions of frequency.

Ordinarily the design of a vacuum-tube amplifier requires that a choice of the value of Z_L be made. It is obvious from Eqs. (11.7) and (11.9) that maximum gain occurs when Z_L is very large compared with r_p. Passing to the limit, as Z_L approaches infinity, the gain approaches the amplification factor μ of the triode as a limit.

11.3 BIASING OF VACUUM TUBES

Ordinarily when a vacuum tube is operated in the linear region, the control grid must always be maintained at a negative potential with respect to the cathode. A constant negative voltage is therefore applied to the control grid, superimposed upon which is the signal-voltage input to the amplifier. The direct voltage applied to the grid is known as the grid-bias voltage. It may be applied by means of a battery such as is shown in Fig. 11.2a, or it may be applied in other ways. However it is applied, for linear operation the direct bias voltage must maintain the grid negative with respect to the cathode at all times.

Cathode biasing is a convenient way to eliminate the bias battery and achieve the necessary grid-bias voltage. Cathode biasing is illustrated in Fig. 11.3, where R_K and C_K, both in parallel, are connected in the cathode circuit of the triode. The value of R_K is chosen so that the average voltage drop across R_K is equal to the desired grid-bias voltage E_c. Then

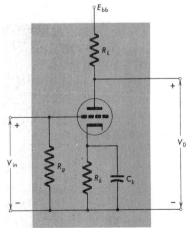

FIG. 11.3 *Cathode biasing by means of R_K and C_K.*

$$R_K = \frac{E_c}{I_b}$$

(11.11)

and the voltage drop across R_K makes the cathode positive with respect to the control grid or the control grid negative with respect to the cathode.

The cathode capacitor C_K in Fig. 11.3 serves as a filter to maintain the voltage drop across R_K constant. The time constant $R_K C_K$ must be large compared with the period of the lowest frequency being amplified to maintain the bias relatively constant. Or, from another point of view, the reactance of C_K must be much less than the resistance R_K for the lowest frequency being amplified. As a rule of thumb, let

$$R_k \gg \frac{1}{\omega_L C_k} \tag{11.12}$$

where ω_L is the lowest frequency being amplified. The equivalent circuit for the triode amplifier shows R_K and C_K replaced by a short circuit, since, for all a-c signals, C_K appears to be a negligible reactance.

The control grid and cathode of the triode represent the elements of a small capacitor C_{gk}. High-energy electrons emitted from the cathode may be picked up by the control grid even though the grid is maintained at a negative potential. If no resistive path connects the control grid to the cathode, the high-energy electrons from the cathode build up a charge on C_{gk} which tends to increase the bias of the triode. In order to allow the charge on C_{gk} to leak off, a grid resistor R_g is connected from grid to ground as shown in Fig. 11.3. The signal-voltage input to the amplifier now appears across R_g, and R_g also serves to provide the resistive path from grid to cathode necessary to maintain the desired grid bias.

Example 11.1

Suppose that the amplifier shown in Fig. 11.3 must have -5 volts bias on the grid and that the average plate current is 10 ma. Then the cathode resistor must be

$$R_K = \frac{5}{0.010} = 500 \text{ ohms}$$

If the lowest frequency which the amplifier must amplify is 100 cycles/sec, the cathode capacitor must satisfy the inequality

$$\frac{1}{\omega_L C_K} \ll R_K \quad \text{or} \quad C_K \gg \frac{1}{\omega_L R_K}$$

The inequality is satisfied if

$$C_K = \frac{10}{\omega_L R_K} = \frac{10}{2\pi \times 100 \times 500} = 31.8 \ \mu f$$

A cathode capacitor of 20 to 50 μf would be satisfactory.

11.4 RC COUPLING

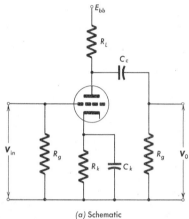

(a) Schematic

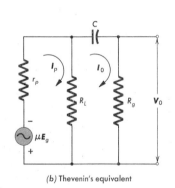

(b) Thevenin's equivalent

FIG. 11.4 *RC coupling between two amplifier stages in cascade.*

The output voltage of the triode amplifier shown in Fig. 11.2a or 11.3 actually contains a large direct-voltage component which is not part of the input signal. Since a capacitor has infinite impedance at zero frequency, it can be used to block out the direct component of the output voltage. Figure 11.4 shows a coupling capacitor C_c used to connect the output of one amplifier stage to the input of the following stage. In Fig. 11.4, $\mathbf{V}_o$ is the output of the first amplifier stage, and $\mathbf{V}_o$ is also the input to the following stage. The network consisting of R_L, R_g, and C_c must be considered in calculating the gain of the amplifier stage.

The equivalent circuit shown in Fig. 11.4b contains the RC coupling circuits consisting of R_g and C_c. The solution of this circuit for $\mathbf{V}_o$ follows from the solution of series-parallel circuits discussed in Chap. 6.

If we choose to solve the equivalent circuit of Fig. 11.4b for $\mathbf{V}_o$ by writing loop currents, the loop currents can be defined as $\mathbf{I}_p$ and $\mathbf{I}_o$ as shown in the figure. The loop-currents equations then can be written

$$(r_p + R_L)\mathbf{I}_p - R_L\mathbf{I}_o = -\mu\mathbf{E}_g \tag{11.13}$$

$$-R_L\mathbf{I}_p + \left(R_L + R_g - \frac{j}{\omega C_c}\right)\mathbf{I}_o = 0 \tag{11.14}$$

By Cramer's rule,

$$\mathbf{I}_o = \frac{\begin{vmatrix} r_p + R_L & -\mu\mathbf{E}_g \\ -R_L & 0 \end{vmatrix}}{\begin{vmatrix} r_p + R_L & -R_L \\ -R_L & R_L + R_g - \dfrac{j}{\omega C_c} \end{vmatrix}} \tag{11.15}$$

which, after evaluating the determinants, can be written

$$\mathbf{I}_o = \frac{-\mu\mathbf{E}_g R_L}{(r_p + R_L)(R_L + R_g - j/\omega C_c) - R_L{}^2} \tag{11.16}$$

But $V_o = I_o R_g$, and the voltage gain of the amplifier stage follows from Eq. (11.16) as

$$A_v = \frac{-\mu R_L R_g}{r_p R_L + r_p R_g + R_L R_g - j[(r_p + R_L)/\omega C_c]} \tag{11.17}$$

Notice that the gain of the RC coupled amplifier is a function of frequency ω.

The use of RC coupling circuits between amplifier stages connected in cascade (the output of one connected to the input of the next) makes it possible for n identical stages connected in cascade to have a gain of nA_v, where A_v is the voltage gain of a single stage. The coupling capacitor C_c blocks the direct-voltage component of the output of the first stage, making it possible for the correct bias to be applied to the grid of the following stage. But the use of capacitors introduces reactance into the circuit, causing the gain to be a function of frequency.

11.5 FREQUENCY RESPONSE OF RC COUPLED AMPLIFIERS

The gain of an amplifier has been defined as the ratio of the output quantity to the input quantity, and in the preceding triode amplifiers the output and input quantities have been voltages. Thus Eq. (11.17) is a statement of the voltage gain of the RC coupled amplifier. Equation (11.17) is a complex equation; the gain $\mathbf{A}$ has a real and an imaginary part, or it can be expressed in polar form as having a magnitude and an angle associated with it. We consider now the magnitude of the gain as a function of frequency and the phase angle as another separate function of frequency.

The magnitude of the voltage gain of the RC coupled amplifier can be obtained from the complex gain equation [Eq. (11.17)] as

$$A_v = \frac{\mu R_L R_g}{\sqrt{(r_p R_L + r_p R_g + R_L R_g)^2 + \left(\dfrac{r_p + R_L}{\omega C_c}\right)^2}} \tag{11.18}$$

from the rule of complex algebra that the magnitude of the quotient of two complex numbers is the quotient of the magnitude of the two numbers. Observe from Eq. (11.18) that, as ω increases without bound, the gain approaches

$$A_o = \frac{u R_L R_{\sim}}{r_p R_L + r_p R_g + R_L R_g} \tag{11.19}$$

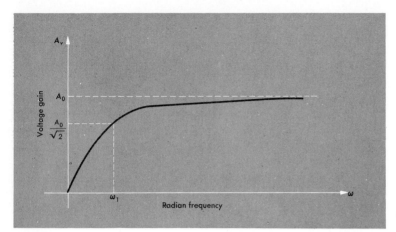

FIG. 11.5 *Gain magnitude as a function of frequency for RC coupled amplifier of Fig. 11.4.*

The high-frequency-gain magnitude expressed by Eq. (11.19) is a maximum gain for any frequency. It is an asymptotic value, approached as frequency increases without bound. A plot of gain magnitude versus frequency is shown in Fig. 11.5. A frequency ω_1 exists at which the gain is $1/\sqrt{2}$ times the high-frequency gain. Then the frequency at which

$$A_v = \frac{A_o}{\sqrt{2}} \tag{11.20}$$

is obtained from Eq. (11.18) as

$$\omega_1 = \frac{r_p + R_L}{C_c(r_p R_L + r_p R_g + R_L R_g)} \quad \text{radians/sec} \tag{11.21}$$

Notice that the cutoff frequency ω_1 is inversely proportional to the size of the coupling capacitor C_c. Notice also, from Eq. (11.18) and from Fig. 11.5, that, as the frequency approaches zero, the gain also approaches zero. The RC coupled amplifier discriminates against low frequency components of the signal, and the gain for the direct component is zero.

At relatively high frequencies, a triode-amplifier equivalent circuit different from that of Fig. 11.4 must be developed. At these high frequencies, the coupling capacitor represents a low reactance compared with R_g and can be considered a short circuit in the equivalent circuit shown in Fig. 11.6. But stray capacitance

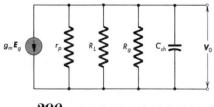

FIG. 11.6 *RC-coupled-amplifier equivalent circuit for high frequencies.*

exists between anode and cathode and between the grid and cathode of the stage following. All the stray capacitance has been lumped together and represented in Fig. 11.6 by C_{sh}. It is convenient to use the Norton's equivalent circuit for the triode because all the circuit elements of the equivalent circuits of Fig. 11.6 are in parallel.

The equivalent circuit for high frequencies for the RC coupled amplifier can easily be solved for the output voltage $\mathbf{V}_o$ as a function of the input voltage $\mathbf{V}_{in} = \mathbf{E}_g$. From Fig. 11.6, the current generator pumps a current $g_m \mathbf{E}_g$ through four impedance elements in parallel. In order to simplify the derivation, let

$$R' = \frac{r_p R_L R_g}{R_L r_p + R_L R_g + R_g r_p} \tag{11.22}$$

where R' is the parallel combination of r_p, R_L, and R_g. Then, solving for $\mathbf{V}_o$,

$$\mathbf{V}_o = -g_m \mathbf{E}_g \frac{R'/j\omega C_{sh}}{R' - j/\omega C_{sh}} \tag{11.23}$$

or

$$\mathbf{A}_v = \frac{\mathbf{V}_o}{\mathbf{V}_{in}} = \frac{-g_m R'}{1 + j\omega C_{sh} R'} \tag{11.24}$$

where the gain $\mathbf{A}_v$ is again a complex quantity. The gain magnitude can be expressed as

$$A_v = \frac{g_m R'}{\sqrt{1 + (\omega C_{sh} R')^2}} \tag{11.25}$$

From Eq. (11.25) it can be seen that, as ω approaches zero, in the limit the gain magnitude becomes

$$A_o = g_m R' \tag{11.26}$$

The gain-versus-frequency curve for the RC coupled amplifier for high frequencies is plotted from Eq. (11.25) in Fig. 11.7   Maximum

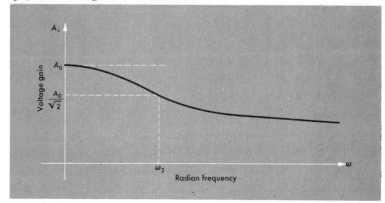

FIG. 11.7 *Gain-versus-frequency curve for the high-frequency equivalent circuit of Fig. 11.6.*

gain is seen to occur at zero frequency. There exists a frequency ω_2, known as the "upper cutoff" frequency, at which the gain is $1/\sqrt{2}$ times the low-frequency gain.

The upper cutoff frequency can be found from Eqs. (11.25) and (11.26). When the gain expressed by Eq. (11.25) has dropped to $1/\sqrt{2}$ times the low-frequency gain expressed by Eq. (11.26), the frequency at which this occurs is ω_2. Then

$$A_v = \frac{A_o}{\sqrt{2}} \tag{11.27}$$

from which, by solving Eq. (11.25) for ω_2,

$$\omega_2 = \frac{1}{R'C_{sh}} \tag{11.28}$$

According to Eq. (11.28), if ω_2 is to be kept as high as possible, C_{sh} must be kept to a minimum.

Equations (11.18) and (11.25) must not be construed to be contradictory. Keep in mind that Eq. (11.18) was derived for an equivalent circuit of the triode amplifier which applied for low frequencies and which did not account for the effects of the shunt capacitance. Equation (11.25), however, was derived for relatively high frequencies, where the reactance of C_c is very small compared with R_g, and where the reactance of C_{sh} is of the order of magnitude of R_g. At high frequencies, the reactance of C_c can be neglected, but the reactance of C_{sh} cannot. This kind of reasoning is common to most branches of engineering. A good engineer is one who recognizes which factors are important and which can be neglected. A solution of electronic circuits can often be greatly simplified by making reasonable approximations such as these. The solution of the triode-amplifier circuit including the effects of C_c and C_{sh} is straightforward but much more complex than the solution of these approximate equivalent circuits of Figs. 11.4b and 11.6.

The gain-versus-frequency curve for the triode amplifier when both low- and high-frequency effects are considered is shown in Fig. 11.8. The amplifier bandwidth is $\omega_2 - \omega_1$, and the gain of the amplifier is considered to be A_0. It is usually desirable for the amplifier to amplify with equal gain all frequencies in the pass-band from ω_1 to ω_2. For instance, a high-quality audio amplifier should amplify all audio frequencies between about 20 cycles/sec and 20,000 cycles/sec, this being approximately the frequency range of the human ear. Amplifiers for other applications have inherent frequency requirements also. In Chap. 14 we shall see

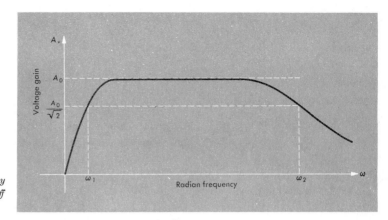

FIG. 11.8 *Gain-versus-frequency curve showing upper and lower cutoff frequencies ω_2 and ω_1.*

how operational amplifiers, especially designed so that the lower cutoff frequency is zero, have applications in electronic analog computers.

Example 11.2

One stage of an *RC* coupled amplifier consists of the circuit of Fig. 11.4a with a 6SF5 triode being used. Tube parameters are $\mu = 100$, $g_m = 1.5 \times 10^{-3}$ mho, and $r_p = 67,000$ ohms. The circuit components are $R_g = 10^6$ ohms, $R_L = 10^5$ ohms, $C_c = 0.01$ μf, and R_k is of such a value as to give -2 volts bias to the grid of the tube.

1. To find the midband gain, assume that the reactance of C_c is negligible compared with R_g and that the reactance of C_{sh} is very much larger than the parallel combination of r_p, R_L, and R_g. Then the equivalent circuit is as shown in Fig. 11.9a, and from the equivalent circuit the output voltage E_o can be written

$$E_o = \mu E_g \frac{R}{R + r_p}$$

where

$$R = \frac{R_L R_g}{R_L + R_g} = \frac{10^5 \times 10^6}{10^5 + 10^6} = 9.08 \times 10^4 \text{ ohms}$$

Then the midband gain is

$$A_o = \frac{E_o}{E_{in}} = \frac{\mu R}{R + r_p} = \frac{100 \times 9.08 \times 10^4}{9.08 \times 10^4 + 6.7 \times 10^4} = 57.6$$

2. At low frequencies the reactance of C_c is of the same order of magnitude as R_g, and the equivalent circuit is now as shown in Fig. 11.9b. The lower cutoff frequency is obtained from Eq. (11.21).

$$\omega_1 = \frac{r_p + R_L}{C_c(r_p R_L + r_p R_g + R_L R_g)}$$

$$= \frac{6.7 \times 10^4 + 10^5}{10^{-8}(6.7 \times 10^4 \times 10^5 + 6.7 \times 10^4 \times 10^6 + 10^5 \times 10^6)}$$

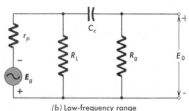

(a) Mid-frequency range

(b) Low-frequency range

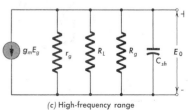

(c) High-frequency range

FIG. 11.9 *Equivalent circuits for the various frequency ranges.*

11.5 Frequency Response of RC Coupled Amplifiers **293**

Then

$$\omega_1 = 96.4 \text{ radians/sec} \qquad \text{and} \qquad f_1 = \frac{96.4}{2\pi} = 15.35 \text{ cycles/sec}$$

3. The upper cutoff frequency is obtained from the equivalent circuit which considers the reactance of the shunt capacitance C_{sh} to be small enough to be important and the reactance of C_c to be small enough to be negligible. If $C_{sh} = 250 \times 10^{-12}$ f, then, from Eq. (11.28),

$$\omega_2 = \frac{1}{R'C_{sh}}$$

where

$$R' = \frac{r_p R_L R_g}{R_L r_p + R_L R_g + R_g r_p}$$

$$= \frac{6.7 \times 10^4 \times 10^5 \times 10^6}{10^5 \times 6.7 \times 10^4 + 10^5 \times 10^6 + 10^6 \times 6.7 \times 10^4}$$

Then $R' = 3.87 \times 10^4$ ohms and

$$\omega_2 = \frac{1}{3.86 \times 10^4 \times 250 \times 10^{-12}} = 1.035 \times 10^5 \text{ radians/sec}$$

$$f_2 = \frac{1.035 \times 10^5}{2\pi} = 16{,}500 \text{ cycles/sec}$$

The amplifier bandwidth is 15.35 to 16,500 cycles/sec, which corresponds approximately to the audible range.

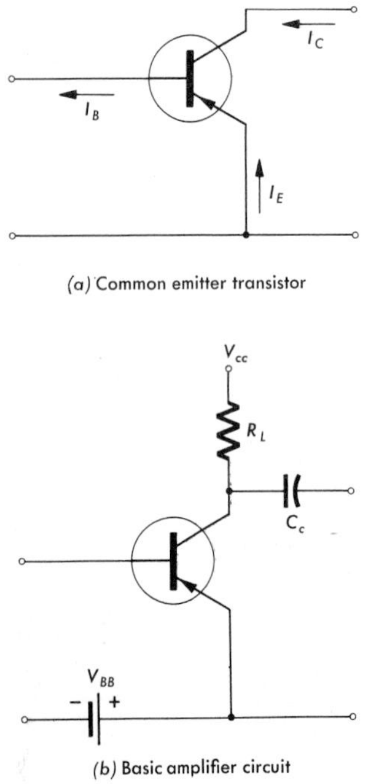

(a) Common emitter transistor

(b) Basic amplifier circuit

FIG. 11.10 *The common-emitter connection, p-n-p transistor.*

11.6 AN ELEMENTARY TRANSISTOR AMPLIFIER

In the preceding chapter, equivalent circuits for the common-base transistor amplifier were developed. The impedance seen in looking in between the emitter and base terminals is relatively low for the common-base transistor amplifier, and considerable signal power is required to drive the amplifier. An apparent improvement, requiring less signal power, is to ground the emitter of the transistor and apply the input signal between the base and the common emitter. This is shown in Fig. 11.10, where the input current is now the base current. From Fig. 11.10a,

$$I_B = I_E + I_C \tag{11.29}$$

where [Eq. (10.24)]

$$I_C \approx -\alpha I_E$$

The common-emitter connection for the transistor differs from the common-base connection only in that the emitter and base connections have been reversed. The convention established in Chap. 10 defining I_C, I_E, and I_B is used here in Fig. 11.10 for the common-emitter connection.

The analysis of the common-emitter transistor-amplifier circuit for voltage gain follows in a manner similar to the analysis of the vacuum triode. The amplifier circuit of Fig. 11.10b can be represented by the equivalent circuit shown in Fig. 11.11 where a medium frequency range has been assumed such that capacitive reactances, such as C_c and C_{sh} of the triode analysis, can be neglected. To solve for $\mathbf{V}_o$ as a function of $\mathbf{V}_{in}$, the loop-current equations can be written

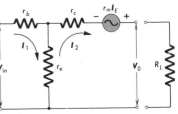

FIG. 11.11 *Equivalent circuit for common-emitter amplifier of Fig. 11.10b.*

$$(r_b + r_e)\mathbf{I}_1 - r_e\mathbf{I}_2 = \mathbf{V}_{in}$$
$$-(r_e - r_m)\mathbf{I}_1 + (r_e + r_c + R_L - r_m)\mathbf{I}_2 = 0$$

$$(11.30)$$

where $\mathbf{I}_E = \mathbf{I}_2 - \mathbf{I}_1$. Solving for the output current $\mathbf{I}_2$ by Cramer's rule,

$$\mathbf{I}_2 = \frac{\begin{vmatrix} r_b + r_e & \mathbf{V}_{in} \\ r_m - r_e & 0 \end{vmatrix}}{\begin{vmatrix} r_b + r_e & -r_e \\ r_m - r_e & r_e + r_c + R_L - r_m \end{vmatrix}}$$

$$= \frac{-\mathbf{V}_{in}(r_m - r_e)}{(r_b + r_e)(r_e + r_c + R_L - r_m) + r_e(r_m - r_e)} \qquad (11.31)$$

Upon recognizing that

$$\mathbf{V}_o = \mathbf{I}_2 R_L \qquad (11.32)$$

the ratio of output voltage to input voltage can be written as the voltage gain

$$\mathbf{A}_v = \frac{-(r_m - r_e)R_L}{r_b(r_e + r_c + R_L - r_m) + r_e(r_c + R_L)} \qquad (11.33)$$

where the minus sign on the gain equation indicates a phase shift between $\mathbf{V}_o$ and $\mathbf{V}_{in}$ of 180°.

Since r_b is ordinarily very small compared with the resistive parameters r_m, r_e, and r_c, Eq. (11.33) can be written approximately as

$$\mathbf{A}_v \approx \frac{-(r_m - r_e)R_L}{r_e(r_c + R_L)} \qquad (11.34)$$

11.6 An Elementary Transistor Amplifier **295**

Current gain is defined as the ratio of output current to input current. If Eqs. (11.30) are solved for both I_1 and I_2, the ratio of I_2 to I_1 is the current gain of the common-emitter amplifier circuit. Equation (11.31) gives I_2. Solving Eqs. (11.30) for I_1 gives

$$I_1 = \frac{V_{in}(r_e + r_c + R_L - r_m)}{(r_b + r_e)(r_e + r_c + R_L - r_m) + r_e(r_m - r_e)} \tag{11.35}$$

The current gain is therefore

$$A_i = \frac{I_2}{I_1} = \frac{-(r_m - r_e)}{r_e + r_c + R_L - r_m} \tag{11.36}$$

Current gain for the common-emitter amplifier is ordinarily very much greater than unity, but certainly not infinite. This is in contrast to the current gain of the vacuum triode, which is very nearly infinite.

In Chap. 10 the common-base transistor circuit was discussed, and in this chapter the common-emitter transistor circuit has been analyzed. The common-collector transistor circuit is also a useful circuit but will not be discussed here. A transistor can be used with any one of its three terminals grounded, and the amplifier characteristics will of course be different for the three basic figurations.

Input impedance to a common-emitter amplifier is the impedance seen at the input terminals and can be defined as $Z_{in} = V_{in}/I_1$ from Fig. 11.11. Then, from Eq. (11.35),

$$Z_{in} = r_b + r_e + \frac{r_e(r_m - r_e)}{r_e + r_c + R_L - r_m} \tag{11.37}$$

which reduces to

$$Z_{in} = r_b + \frac{r_e(r_c + R_L)}{r_e + r_c + R_L - r_m} \tag{11.38}$$

Output impedance is the impedance seen at the output terminals when no signal is applied to the input. Thus if $V_{in} = 0$, from Fig. 11.11 the output impedance seen by R_L is the ratio of V_o to $-I_2$. Writing loop equations, solving for I_2 as a function of V_o, and evaluating $-V_o/I_2$ gives

$$. Z_o = r_c - r_m + r_e\left(1 + \frac{r_m - r_e}{r_e + r_b + R_g}\right) \tag{11.39}$$

where R_g is the resistance of the generator connected to the input.

Graphical analysis of the common-emitter transistor-amplifier circuit follows from techniques discussed in Chaps. 8 and 10. The collector characteristic curves for the transistor show I_C versus V_{CE} for constant values of I_B; these curves tend to be similar to the collector characteristics for common-base connections but have more slope.

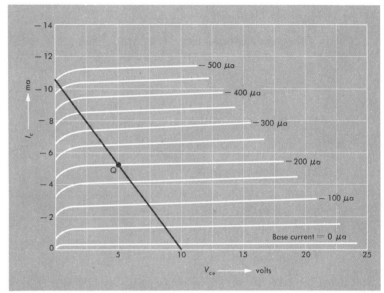

FIG. 11.12 *Collector characteristic curves for the CK722 transistor, common-emitter connection.*

The common-emitter amplifier circuit of Fig. 11.10*b* can be analyzed by drawing a load line for the appropriate collector supply voltage V_{CC} and the load resistor R_L. Figure 11.12 shows the collector characteristic for a CK722 *p-n-p* transistor. Manufacturer's data for the CK722 list average characteristics at 27°C as

$$r_e = 25 \text{ ohms} \qquad r_c = 2.0 \text{ megohms}$$

$$r_b = 350 \text{ ohms} \qquad r_m = 1.92 \text{ megohms}$$

$$\alpha = 0.96$$

and absolute maximum ratings of collector voltage as -22 volts and collector current as -10 ma.

Transistor-amplifier design includes choosing the direct voltage V_{CC} and R_L. This is usually done by first choosing an operating point, such as Q shown in Fig. 11.12, well within the maximum ratings of collector voltage and current. A load line drawn through Q must intersect the $I_C = 0$ coordinate at V_{CC}. Arbitrarily choosing $V_{CC} = 10$ volts, we then draw the load line. The slope of the load line is $-1/R_L$, from which $R_L = 1,160$ ohms.

In order to maintain the Q point in the position shown in Fig. 11.12, the base current must be maintained at -200 μa by an appropriate bias voltage. Suppose that the base current consists of a sinusoidal component and a direct component such that

$$I_b = (-200 + 100 \sin \omega t) \qquad \mu a$$

Then, from the curve of Fig. 11.12, the collector-to-emitter voltage V_{ce} varies about an average value of 5 volts, with a maximum at 7.25 and a minimum at 3.1 volts.

The base-to-emitter voltage required to furnish a base current of 200 μa can be obtained by Ohm's law once the input resistance of the amplifier is obtained. Since input impedance for the common-emitter circuit can be shown to be [Eq. (11.38)]

$$\mathbf{Z}_{in} = r_b + \frac{r_e(r_c + R_L)}{r_c - r_m + r_e + R_L}$$

with the manufacturer's average values used for r_b, r_e, r_c, and r_m and 1,160 ohms used for R_L, then

$$\mathbf{Z}_{in} = 975 \text{ ohms resistance}$$

Then the bias voltage necessary to furnish -200 μa base current is

$$V_{BB} = -2 \times 10^{-4} \times 975 = -0.1950 \text{ volt}$$

and

$$v_{in} = 0.0975 \sin \omega t$$

Voltage gain is

$$\mathbf{A}_v = \frac{\mathbf{V}_o}{\mathbf{V}_{in}}$$

which is approximately

$$\mathbf{A}_v \approx \frac{(7.25 - 3.1)/2}{0.0975} = 21.8$$

in magnitude. Some nonlinear distortion occurs in this example.

11.8 TRANSISTOR BIASING

It has been convenient to show the necessary bias voltages as separate batteries, such as in Fig. 11.10b, where V_{BB} is the bias battery for the base and V_{CC} is the collector supply voltage. Obviously, if several stages are connected in tandem, it would be inconvenient to use two separate batteries or voltage sources for each stage. Although the bias voltages can be supplied by separate voltage sources as in Fig. 11.10b, self-bias circuits are more desirable because they provide the necessary bias voltage and require only one voltage source. Cathode bias is, of course, an example of self-bias for a vacuum-tube amplifier.

Any circuit which applies a forward direct voltage across the emitter-to-base junction and a reverse direct voltage across the base-to-collector junction establishes normal polarities for transistor operation. The separate bias batteries of Fig. 11.10b, satisfy this requirement. So long as the transistor is operated near its rated operating temperature, the actual operating point coincides closely with the designed operating point on the load line. But transistor parameters are exceptionally sensitive to the temperature of the transistor junction. The product of instantaneous voltage across and current through a junction represents electric power converted to heat at the junction. Heat must be conducted away from the transistor as it is produced so that the temperature of the junction remains at a constant value not very much above room temperature. The transistor is normally fastened to the metal chassis, which serves as a heat sink, conducting the heat away from the transistor, and also serving to support the other circuit elements.

Most of the heating effect occurs at the collector junction, because collector current is nearly equal to the emitter current and collector-to-base voltage is very much greater than emitter-to-base voltage. Practical self-bias circuits provide the necessary operating voltages with only one voltage source. In addition, the self-bias circuit should provide a means for limiting the increase in emitter or collector current that may result from changing transistor parameters caused by increased operating temperatures of the junction.

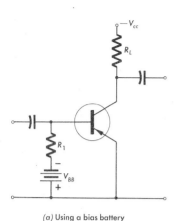

(a) Using a bias battery

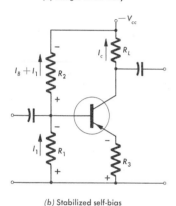

(b) Stabilized self-bias

FIG. 11.13 *Biasing common-emitter amplifier circuits for a p-n-p transistor.*

The self-bias transistor circuit shown in Fig. 11.13*b* provides operating-point stabilization. The operation of this circuit can be explained qualitatively as follows: R_1 and R_2 constitute a voltage divider which establishes the direct voltage of the transistor base. Base current flowing through R_2 is negligible compared with the current supplied through R_1 and R_2 by V_{CC}, and therefore the potential of the base remains essentially constant, independent of base current. Collector current I_C flows around the loop of R_L and R_3 and through r_e and r_c of the transistor. The collector resistance r_c is temperature-sensitive, decreasing with an increase in temperature. Since r_c is greater than R_3, R_L, and r_e put together, its effect on I_C is very great. Suppose that the temperature increases, decreasing r_c, and thus causing I_C to increase. An increase in the voltage across R_3 results, which, when added to the direct voltage across R_1, decreases the emitter-to-base bias voltage and decreases I_B and I_C. Thus temperature changes are compensated for, and I_C is made relatively insensitive to temperature changes.

If R_1 and R_2 are small, the input impedance of the amplifier is very low, thus loading the signal source. If R_3 is large, excessive power consumption in R_3 results. A workable value of R_3 is found by making the voltage drop across R_3 equal to $\frac{1}{3}V_{CC}$. Likewise, the voltage drop across R_L should be $\frac{1}{3}V_{CC}$. The voltage-divider resistors R_1 and R_2 must be chosen in a manner that provides appropriate bias voltage to the base of the transistor. Furthermore, the parallel combination of R_1 and R_2 must equal R_3. These rules of thumb can be followed to find appropriate values for all the circuit resistors in the stabilized self-bias transistor-amplifier circuit.

11.9 DIRECT-COUPLED AMPLIFIERS

Many applications exist for broad-band amplifiers whose low-frequency cutoff has been extended to zero frequency. Such an amplifier must amplify direct voltages in a manner such that the output voltage is always directly proportional to the input voltage. An extensive application for this type of amplifier is utilized in Chap. 14 in a study of electronic analog computers. Many other applications exist in instrumentation problems.

We have seen that for sinusoidal signals or for small step signals the gain of an amplifier can be predicted rather definitely, provided that the tube or transistor parameters do not change.

In order to extend the frequency range of an a-c amplifier to zero frequency, the coupling capacitor must be eliminated between these stages of the amplifier. In a practical circuit this may mean that the grid of one stage of a vacuum-tube direct-coupled amplifier must be operated at the same potential as the anode of the preceding stage, as shown in Fig. 11.14. Obviously the direct-voltage-supply problem for several stages thus cascaded is considerable.

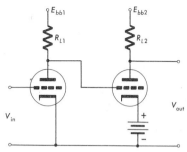

FIG. 11.14 *Direct-coupled triode amplifier.*

Direct-coupled amplifiers also have a tendency to be unstable; the gain of the several stages may drift with time. This is a consequence of temperature effects in the tubes or transistors and of aging of tubes or transistors. To some extent, drift can be corrected by feedback, which will be explained in Chap. 13.

Transistor direct-coupled amplifiers in cascade can overcome the direct-supply-voltage problem by alternate use of *n-p-n* and *p-n-p* transistors in the cascade. Figure 11.15 shows the collector of one transistor, representing its output voltage, connected directly to the base, or input, of the following stage. The first stage is a common-emitter connection, and the second stage is a common-collector connection. A single supply voltage is shown. Additional stages can be added if more gain is required. The drift problem in this transistor direct-coupled amplifier is still considerable, however.

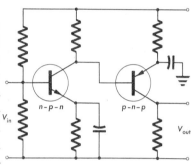

FIG. 11.15 *Direct-coupled transistor amplifier.*

Practical direct-voltage amplifiers often use choppers, which break the direct voltage into alternating voltage, amplify the alternating voltage, and then rectify it back to its amplified direct value. In this manner, the problem of conventional direct-coupled amplifiers is avoided. Mechanical choppers are available commercially which do the chopping and can also provide the rectification.

SUMMARY

Linear operation of an electronic device implies operation on the linear portion of its characteristic curves where the parameters are constant. As a consequence of linear operation, a linear equivalent circuit can be found to replace the electronic device for analysis purposes. Once the device has been reduced to an equivalent circuit, the entire circuit, including the device, can be analyzed.

It is convenient to simplify amplifier equivalent circuits by making approximations valid over various ranges of frequency.

For example, the RC coupled vacuum-tube amplifier can be analyzed for gain as a function of frequency at low frequencies where shunt capacitive reactance is very large with respect to r_p, R_L, and R_g and can be neglected but the reactance of C_c must be considered. For the frequency range thus defined, the voltage gain is [Eq. (11.17)]

$$\mathbf{A}_v = \frac{-\mu R_L R_g}{r_p R_L + r_p R_g + R_L R_g - j[(r_p + R_L)/\omega C_c]}$$

From Eq. (11.17), as the frequency increases, Eq. (11.17) approaches Eq. (11.19),

$$\mathbf{A}_o = \frac{-\mu R_L R_g}{r_p R_L + r_p R_G + R_L R_g}$$

and the range of frequencies for which the reactance of the coupling capacitor C_c can also be neglected is known as the midband range, or the middle range.

At relatively high frequencies, the analysis of an RC coupled amplifier can be simplified by recognizing that the reactance of C_c is negligible compared with R_g and that the reactance of the shunt capacitance C_{sh} is of the same order of magnitude as the parallel combination of r_p, R_L, and R_g. Then the voltage gain for the high-frequency range becomes [Eq. (11.24)]

$$\mathbf{A}_v = \frac{-g_m R'}{1 - j\omega C_{sh} R'}$$

where [Eq. (11.22)]

$$R' = \frac{r_p R_L R_g}{R_L r_p + R_L R_g + R_g r_p}$$

At middle frequencies, the gain A_o is given by Eq. (11.19).

The analysis of transistor amplifiers can also be made for the various frequency ranges, but when RC coupling is employed, the analysis is somewhat more complex. At middle frequencies when shunt capacitance can be neglected and the coupling reactance is negligible, the transistor-amplifier gain is approximately [Eq. (11.34)]

$$\mathbf{A}_v = \frac{-(r_m - r_e)R_L}{r_e(r_c + R_L)}$$

for the common-emitter circuit.

The upper and lower cutoff frequencies or half-power frequencies can be found from the complex form of the gain equations. For the RC coupled triode amplifier, the lower cutoff frequency is defined as that frequency at which the gain is $A_0/\sqrt{2}$, or [Eq. (11.21)]

$$\omega_1 = \frac{r_p + R_L}{C_c(r_p R_L + r_p R_g + R_L R_g)}$$

and the upper cutoff frequency is also defined as that frequency at which $A = A_0/\sqrt{2}$, or [Eq. (11.28)]

$$\omega_2 = \frac{1}{R' C_{sh}}$$

Input and output impedances of amplifier circuits can be found from the ratio of voltage to current at the input and output terminals. Input impedance is the complex ratio of voltage to current when a sinusoidal voltage is applied at the input terminals. Output impedance is the ratio of output voltage to output current at the output terminals when the input voltage is zero.

Biasing an electronic device means applying appropriate direct voltages to the various terminals. Ideally, only one voltage source should be used. Cathode bias of a vacuum tube utilizes a direct-voltage drop across the cathode resistor to maintain the grid negative with respect to the cathode. Common-emitter transistor biasing is often accomplished by a resistor in series with the emitter and a voltage divider in the base circuit.

FURTHER READING

Vacuum-tube amplifiers are discussed extensively in the literature. See, for example, E. J. Angelo, Jr., *Electronic Circuits* (McGraw-Hill Book Company, Inc., New York, 1958), chaps. 4 to 6; Samuel Seely, *Electron-tube Circuits*, 2d ed. (McGraw-Hill Book Company, Inc., New York, 1958), chaps. 3 and 4; and T. L. Martin, Jr., *Electronic Circuits* (Prentice-Hall, Inc., Englewood Cliffs, N.J., 1955), chaps. 3 and 4.

Transistor amplifiers are discussed in an elementary way in Milton S. Kiver, *Transistors in Radio, Television, and Electronics*, 2d ed. (McGraw-Hill Book Company, Inc., New York, 1959), chaps. 4 and 12. More detailed information is found in Richard B. Hurley, *Junction Transistor Electronics* (John Wiley & Sons, Inc., New York, 1958), chaps. 3 to 5 and others; and David DeWitt and Arthur L. Rossoff, *Transistor Electronics* (McGraw-Hill Book Company, Inc., New York, 1957), chap. 5.

PROBLEMS

11.1 Verify that the voltage gain expressed by Eq. (11.19) for the triode approaches the gain expressed by Eq. (11.7) for $\mathbf{Z}_L = R_L$, $R_g \gg r_p$, and $R_g \gg R_L$.

11.2 Show that Eq. (11.19) is equivalent to Eq. (11.26).

11.3 Find the magnitude of the voltage gain of the 6J5 triode of Fig. 11.2a when $E_{cc} = -4$ volts, $E_{bb} = 250$ volts, and $\mathbf{Z}_L$ is 12,000 ohms of pure resistance.

11.4 The amplifier of Prob. 11.3 must amplify a band of frequencies. from 200 to 5,000 cycles/sec. Find R_K and C_K to provide cathode bias, and choose R_g for the grid resistive path from grid to cathode.

11.5 The amplifier of Prob. 11.3 is modified such that $Z_L = 5,000 + j5,000$ at a frequency of $\omega = 10,000$ radians/sec. Find the magnitude of the voltage gain at that frequency and at $\omega = 10$ and $\omega = 100,000$ radians/sec.

11.6 Verify that Eq. (11.38) can be derived from Eq. (11.37).

11.7 Derive Eq. (11.39) for the output impedance of a common-emitter transistor amplifier.

11.8 A 6C4 triode is used in the circuit of Fig. 11.4. A plate supply voltage of $E_{bb} = 180$ volts is available. With $R_g = 1$ megohm find: (a) a load resistor R_L such that the gain is 8 for middle frequencies; (b) R_K necessary for a grid bias of -5 volts. See Fig. A1.2 for the characteristics of the 6C4.

11.9 Shunt capacitance C_{sh} is difficult to determine directly because it includes wiring capacitance. An amplifier using a 6C4 triode with $R_g = 1$ megohm, $R_L = 47,000$ ohms, $R_k = 5,000$ ohms, and $C_c = 1$ μf has an upper cutoff frequency of 70,000 cycles/sec. Find the shunt capacitance C_{sh}.

11.10 Power gain is the ratio of power output to power input. Derive an equation for the power gain of a common-emitter amplifier at middle frequencies from the equations of voltage gain and current gain.

11.11 An RC coupled amplifier has been built, but its upper cutoff frequency is too low. What effect does increasing R_L have on upper cutoff frequency and on midband gain? Explain.

11.12 A high-μ triode with amplification factor μ of 100 and plate resistance r_p of 75,000 ohms is used as the first stage of an RC coupled amplifier. The grid resistor of the stage following is $R_g = 0.5$ megohm, the lower cutoff frequency must be 50 cycles/sec, and the gain of the stage must be 50 at midband frequencies. Find the required load resistor R_L and the minimum value of the coupling capacitor C_c.

11.13 A 6C4 triode, whose characteristics are given in Fig. A1.2, is operated in the circuit shown in the figure. From the characteristic curve, locate the operating point, and find E_b and I_b. Then find a new value of R_L which provides the same operating point when $E_{bb} = 300$ volts. What is the gain if a small signal voltage is applied to the grid?

11.14 A type 6SJ7 pentode vacuum tube, whose characteristics are given in Fig. A1.4, is operated from a plate supply voltage $E_{bb} = 300$ volts and with a screen-grid voltage of 100 volts. The load resistor is 30,000 ohms, and the grid bias is -2 volts. Locate the operating point on the characteristic curves, and find the anode-to-cathode voltage E_b and the anode current I_b. If a sinusoidal signal of 2 volts peak to peak is applied to the grid, what is the signal output voltage, peak to peak?

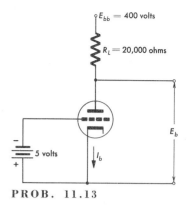

PROB. 11.13

11.15 A p-n-p transistor is used in the circuit shown in the illustration and has common-emitter collector characteristics also shown in the figure. The input impedance between the base and emitter is 8.0 ohms. Find the collector current I_C and the collector voltage V_{CE}. Also find the gain of the transistor circuit if a small signal voltage is inserted in series with the 0.32-volt bias battery.

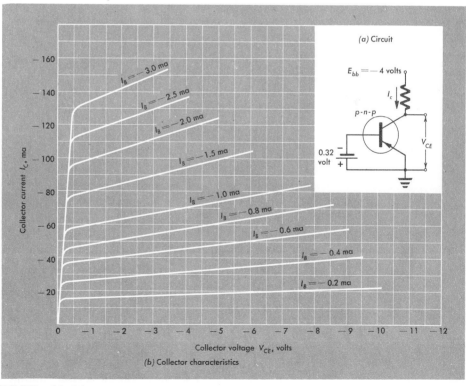

PROB. 11.15

12

NONLINEAR OPERATION

12.1 INTRODUCTION

An electronic device employed as an amplifier is an example of linear operation of the device, some examples of which were analyzed in Chap. 11. Linear operation requires that the electronic device be operated in the region where its characteristic curves are linear and parallel and its parameters are constant. Linear operation is only an approximation; the characteristic curves are never exactly straight, parallel, and equidistant. Nevertheless, operation can be very nearly linear, justifying our approximation.

In this chapter we take advantage of the nonlinear nature of the electronic device in circuits which are not basically amplifier circuits. Some examples of nonlinear operation are discussed which exploit the ability of the nonlinear instrument to distort or modify the shape of the input quantities to the circuit. Rectification, clipping, switching, modulation, and demodulation are some of the applications of electronic devices which take advantage of their nonlinear nature.

12.2 DIODES AS RECTIFIERS

The equivalent circuits of the diodes developed in Chap. 10 are now useful to show the rectification of alternating current to direct current or the conversion of alternating voltages to direct voltages.

Rectification is one of the major applications of diodes. In Fig. 10.7 is shown a single diode used as a half-wave rectifier and causing the current through the load resistor R_L to be unidirectional. To extend the analysis further, consider the half-wave rectifier circuit shown in Fig. 12.1a, consisting of the sinusoidal-voltage source e, the resistive load R_L, and the semiconductor diode. The equivalent circuit is shown in Fig. 12.1b, where R_{b1} is the diode equivalent resistance in the reverse direction and R_{b2} is the equivalent resistance in the forward direction. During the first π radians of the supply voltage e, the switch in the equivalent circuit is in position 2, during which time

$$i_L = \frac{E_m \sin \omega t}{R_{b2} + R_L} \qquad 0 \leq \omega t \leq \pi \qquad (12.1)$$

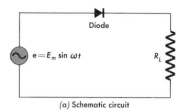

Diode

$e = E_m \sin \omega t$

R_L

(a) Schematic circuit

When $\omega t = \pi$, the switch is thrown to position 1 and, for the next one-half cycle,

$$i_L = \frac{E_m \sin \omega t}{R_{b1} + R_L} \qquad \pi \leq \omega t \leq 2\pi \qquad (12.2)$$

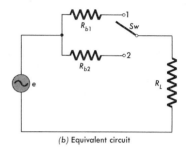

(b) Equivalent circuit

The current through the load resistor R_L is not unidirectional, but its d-c component, defined as its average value, is

$$I_a = \frac{1}{2\pi}\left(\int_0^\pi \frac{E_m \sin \omega t}{R_{b2} + R_L}\, d\omega t + \int_\pi^{2\pi} \frac{E_m \sin \omega t}{R_{b1} + R_L}\, d\omega t\right) \qquad (12.3)$$

where the first integral from zero to π is represented by the area under the current curve from zero to π and the second integral from π to 2π is represented by the area under the current curve from π to 2π. The evaluation of the integrals yields

$$I_a = \frac{E_m}{\pi}\left(\frac{1}{R_{b2} + R_L} - \frac{1}{R_{b1} + R_L}\right) \qquad (12.4)$$

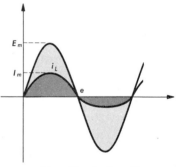

(c) e and i_L as functions of time

FIG. 12.1 *Analysis of a half-wave rectifier circuit.*

an expression for the direct current through the load resistor.

The rms current through the load resistor can be found in the usual way by taking the square root of the average or mean of the square of the current through R_L. Then

$$I_{rms} = \sqrt{\frac{1}{2\pi}\left[\int_0^\pi \left(\frac{E_m \sin \omega t}{R_{b2} + R_L}\right)^2 d\omega t + \int_\pi^{2\pi}\left(\frac{E_m \sin \omega t}{R_{b1} + R_L}\right)^2 d\omega t\right]}$$

$$(12.5)$$

which, upon evaluating the integrals, results in

$$I_{rms} = \frac{E_m}{2}\left(\frac{1}{R_{b2} + R_L} + \frac{1}{R_{b1} + R_L}\right) \qquad (12.6)$$

Equations (12.4) and (12.6) illustrate the fact that the rms value of a nonconstant function of time is greater than the average value of the function.

In order to increase the d-c value of the rectified sine wave, the full-wave rectifier circuit of Fig. 12.2a is often used. An equivalent circuit is shown in Fig. 12.2b, where the diode resistance in the reverse direction is assumed to be infinite and R_b is the diode resistance in the conducting direction. The transformer with the connection at the center of its secondary winding serves as a phase inverter, causing the voltage e_{ac} to be 180° out of phase with the voltage e_{bc}, as shown in Fig. 12.2c. When e_{ac} goes positive, diode a conducts and the switch must be in position a. During this interval from $\omega t = 0$ to $\omega t = \pi$, the instantaneous current through R_L can be expressed as

$$i_L = \frac{E_m \sin \omega t}{R_b + R_L} \qquad 0 \le \omega t \le \pi \tag{12.7}$$

During the second interval the switch is in position b, and the current through R_L is expressed by

$$i_L = \frac{-E_m \sin \omega t}{R_b + R_L} \qquad \pi \le \omega t \le 2\pi \tag{12.8}$$

The average value of the current is merely the average value of one half-cycle of a sine wave which, from Eq. (2.5), is

$$I_a = \frac{2}{\pi} \frac{E_m}{R_b + R_L} \tag{12.9}$$

Compare Eq. (12.9) with Eq. (12.4), and observe that, for a given maximum value of voltage E_m, the full-wave rectifier gives twice the direct current through R_L that the half-wave rectifier does, on the assumption that R_{b2} in Eq. (12.4) is infinite. By inspection, the rms value of current through the load resistor in Fig. 12.2 is the rms value of a sinusoidal current, or

$$I_{rms} = \frac{1}{\sqrt{2}} \frac{E_m}{R_b + R_L} \tag{12.10}$$

Again the rms value is greater than the average value.

The current through R_L in Fig. 12.2 is unidirectional, but it is not constant. If a constant current flow through R_L is required, a filter must be added to eliminate all but the direct component of current in R_L. In applications where only unidirectional current is required, such as electroplating and electrolysis, a rectifier such as that of Fig. 12.2 may prove to be satisfactory.

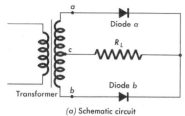

Diode a

R_L

Diode b

Transformer

(a) Schematic circuit

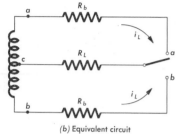

R_b

R_L

i_L

R_b

i_L

(b) Equivalent circuit

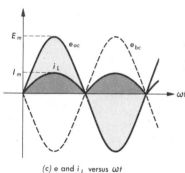

E_m

e_{ac} e_{bc}

I_m

i_L

ωt

(c) e and i_L versus ωt

FIG. 12.2 *Full-wave rectifier.*

12.3 RECTIFIERS WITH FILTERS

The half-wave and full-wave rectifiers of Figs. 12.1 and 12.2 produced current in their respective load resistors, which possess both
d-c and a-c components. In order to eliminate the a-c components
through R_L and leave only the constant, or d-c, component, a
filter must be added to the circuit. The simplest form of filter is a
capacitor, shown in Fig. 12.3a for a half-wave rectifier. The capaci-

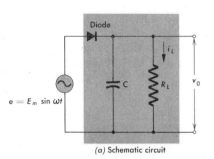

(a) Schematic circuit

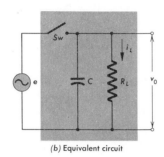

(b) Equivalent circuit

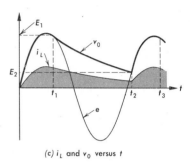

(c) i_L and v_0 versus t

FIG. 12.3 *Half-wave rectifier with capacitive filter.*

tor tends to charge when the voltage across the diode is in the forward direction; when the voltage across the diode is in the reverse
direction, the diode looks like an open circuit and the capacitor
tends to discharge through R_L. The equivalent circuit of Fig.
12.3b utilizes the switch Sw as the equivalent of the diode, a first
approximation explained in Sec. 10.1. The voltage from the
generator is shown in Fig. 12.3c, along with the load current i_L.
During the interval from $t = 0$ to $t = t_1$, switch Sw is closed and
the capacitor voltage v_o follows the generator voltage e. Then at
t_1 switch Sw opens because the voltage across the diode reverses,
and the capacitor discharges through R_L. Finally, at t_2, the generator voltage again establishes a forward potential across the diode,
and the capacitor charges again along the sinusoidal generator
voltage curve. In the steady state, then, the capacitor discharges
from E_1 to E_2 each cycle and recharges to E_1 each cycle, maintaining a unidirectional voltage across R_L which has a large d-c component.

During the time interval from zero to t_1 in Fig. 12.3c, the load
voltage v_o is

$$v_o = E_{\text{in}} \sin \omega t \qquad 0 < t < t_1 \qquad\qquad (12.11)$$

During the discharging period,

$$v_o = E_1(1 - \epsilon^{-(t-t_1)/R_LC}) \qquad t_1 < t < t_2 \qquad (12.12)$$

and again during the charging part of the cycle after t_2,

$$v_o = E_{\text{in}} \sin \omega t \qquad t_2 < t < t_3 \qquad (12.13)$$

One complete cycle of the steady state is described by Eqs. (12.12) and (12.13). In order to minimize the amount of capacitor discharge during the interval when the diode is nonconducting, the time constant R_LC must be kept large. With the load resistor R_L fixed, the capacitor is the filter element that must be kept as large as possible in order to minimize the amount of voltage variation during each cycle of steady-state operation. Obviously an infinite capacitor would give perfect filtering, since it would hold infinite charge and maintain constant voltage. But observe that the diode is conducting only during a short part of the complete cycle. The interval from t_2 to t_3 is the conducting interval of the diode, and this interval becomes smaller as the change in capacitor voltage $E_1 - E_2$ decreases. Thus, if C is made larger and larger, the diode conducts greater current for a lesser period of time during each cycle.

The principle on which the capacitor filter operates can be explained in terms of the voltage-current relationship for the capacitor [Eq. (1.35)]

$$v = \frac{1}{C} \int_0^t i \, dt + V_o$$

where V_o is the capacitor voltage at some initial time defined as $t = 0$ and v is the capacitor voltage at time t later. The integral term of Eq. (1.35) can be represented by the area under the current-versus-time curve. As t increases from zero, the interval of integration increases in proportion to time. The area under the current curve representing the charge on the capacitor is a function not only of the instantaneous current but also of the limits of integration. As the upper limit of integration t becomes small and approaches zero, the value of the integral also approaches zero and the capacitor voltage approaches V_o, the initial voltage at $t = 0$. The lower limit of integration $t = 0$ is arbitrary and can be defined for any instant for which an initial voltage V_o is known. Then the voltage an infinitesimal time t later than $t = 0$ can change only an infinitesimal amount from V_o. Thus it is often said that the voltage across a capacitor cannot change instantaneously (unless the capacitor current approaches infinity). Then Eq. (1.35) verifies that the voltage across a capacitor-filter circuit cannot change rapidly.

Just as a capacitor tends to prevent its voltage from changing rapidly, so an inductor tends to prevent its current from changing rapidly.

The voltage-current relationship for an inductor is [Eq. (1.30)]

$$v = L\frac{di}{dt}$$

where v is the voltage across the inductance and i is the current through the inductance. The current i can be expressed as

$$i = \frac{1}{L}\int_0^t v\,dt + I_0 \tag{12.14}$$

where I_0 is the inductor current at $t = 0$. In Eq. (12.14) the value of the integral can be represented by the area under the voltage-versus-time curve, and this area cannot increase instantaneously unless v approaches infinity. Thus it can be said that for a short interval of time the current through an inductor cannot change rapidly and therefore an inductor is a valuable current-filter element. If an inductor L is in series with a load resistor R_L in Fig. 12.3, the current through R_L and L tends to be held constant. Indeed, Lenz's law states that, when the current through the inductor changes, an emf is induced in the inductor which opposes the change in current.

Figure 12.4a and b shows two basic filter circuits. The rectified input voltage to the filter consists of the output from the a-c-voltage source and rectifier or diode combination of Figs. 12.1a or 12.2a. The output of the filter circuit is the voltage across the resistive load R_L and the current through R_L. An ideal filter provides pure direct voltage and direct current to R_L with no sinusoidal

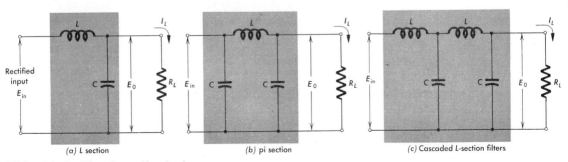

(a) L section   (b) pi section   (c) Cascaded L-section filters

FIG. 12.4 *Filters for rectifier circuits.*

components. In any practical filter circuit, small a-c components occur in the filter output. Usually the peak value of the alternating-voltage component must be less than 1 per cent of the direct voltage. If a given filter does not provide adequate filtering action, larger values of L and C can be used or a better filter circuit can be chosen.

The L-section filter, although not providing as much filtering action as the π-section filter, can be cascaded if necessary as in Fig. 12.4c to provide two or more sections of filters. The inductors L are wound on iron cores to provide large values of inductance.

A major application of the full-wave rectifier circuit and filter is the power supply capable of providing a direct voltage for vacuum-tube circuits. Such a power supply must ordinarily provide about 250 volts at 10 to 200 ma. For such a supply, filter inductors of about 10 henrys and capacitors of at least 10 μf provide good filtering action. Transistor power supplies must provide lower direct voltages of about 25 volts, although current requirements are often higher and larger capacitors and inductors are needed for the filter.

12.4 VACUUM TUBES AS SWITCHING DEVICES

An ideal diode with zero resistance in the forward direction and infinite resistance in the reverse direction behaves like a switch. In order to assure conduction, a diode must be biased in a forward direction. To cut off the current flow in a diode, it must be biased in a reverse direction. The half-wave rectifier circuit of Fig. 12.1 and the full-wave rectifier circuit of Fig. 12.2 can be thought of as switching circuits in which the diodes conduct in one direction and do not conduct when the voltage across them is in the reverse direction.

An example of a simple clipping circuit is shown in Fig. 12.5a. On the assumption of an ideal diode with zero resistance in the forward direction and infinite resistance in the reverse direction, the diode conducts only when $E_m \sin \omega t > E$. During conduction,

$$i_L = \frac{e - E}{R_L} = \frac{E_m \sin \omega t - E}{R_L}$$

$$\sin^{-1} \frac{E}{E_m} \leq \omega t \leq \left(180° - \sin^{-1} \frac{E}{E_m} \right) \qquad (12.15)$$

the switch closes when e reaches E and opens again when e becomes

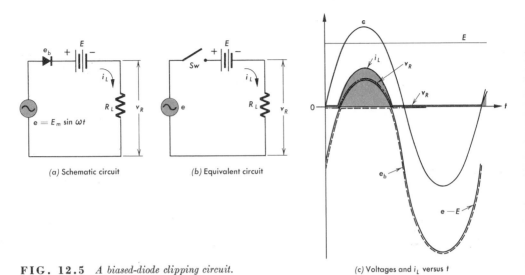

FIG. 12.5 *A biased-diode clipping circuit.*

(a) Schematic circuit   (b) Equivalent circuit

(c) Voltages and i_L versus t

less than E. Thus i_L is the top of a sine wave, and the voltage across R_L is the top of the applied sinusoidal voltage during the interval when the diode is conducting and zero otherwise. The voltage across the diode is the applied sinusoidal voltage with its top clipped off, shown as e_b in Fig. 12.5c. The voltage across R_L, v_R, is the top of the sine wave, also shown in the figure. At any instant, the sum of the voltages around the loop must be zero. Thus

$$e - E - e_b - v_R = 0 \qquad (12.16)$$

Another example of a clipping circuit is shown in Fig. 12.6a. Two identical diodes in series with identical voltage sources E are in parallel but are connected to conduct in opposite directions, as shown. The alternating-voltage source e is shown in Fig. 12.6b as a sine wave. As e increases from zero, there is no current in R_L

FIG. 12.6 *Two biased diodes clip top and bottom of sine wave.*

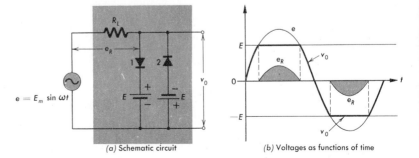

(a) Schematic circuit   (b) Voltages as functions of time

12.4   Vacuum Tubes as Switching Devices   313

and $v_o = e$. Eventually e exceeds E, making the voltage across diode 1 in the forward-conducting direction. Then, while $e > E$, diode 1 conducts and $v_o = E$. When $e < E$, diode 1 ceases to conduct and there is no voltage drop across R_L; during this interval, $v_o = e$. Then, when e becomes more negative than $-E$, diode 2 conducts and v_o is clamped at $-E$. Thus v_o is a sinusoid with the maximum and minimum values clipped off. The operation of this clipping circuit is not confined to sinusoidal input voltages; the maximum and minimum voltages of any input signal can be clipped at levels determined by the bias batteries marked E in Fig. 12.6a. In general, when the input voltage lies between $+E$ and $-E$, the output voltage follows the input voltage. But when the input voltage exceeds $\pm E$, the output voltage is clamped at $\pm E$.

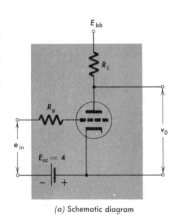

(a) Schematic diagram

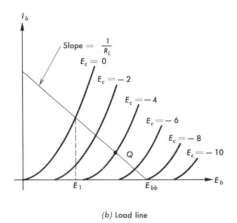

(b) Load line

FIG. 12.7 *A triode used as a clipper.*

A single triode can be used as a clipper to accomplish what the two diodes accomplish in Fig. 12.6. The triode clipper is shown in Fig. 12.7a, and the load line and characteristic curve are shown in Fig. 12.7b. Assume that the triode is biased to operate at $E_c = -4$. Any input voltage e_{in} in the range of ± 4 volts is amplified in a linear fashion. If the input voltage is more negative than -4 volts, e_c is more negative than -8 volts and the tube is cut off. Thus, no matter how much more negative the input voltage becomes, no current flows in the anode circuit and the output voltage v_o is clamped at E_{bb}. The triode has been driven to cutoff. In the other direction, suppose that the signal voltage is greater than $+4$ volts, in which case e_c can become greater than zero. As soon as the grid is driven positive, it attracts electrons from the cathode and becomes an anode. The plate resistance of the new diode formed by the grid and cathode is of the order of 1,000 ohms, and if

R_g is of the order of 1 megohm, it is virtually impossible to make the grid go positive. Therefore, no matter how much the signal input voltage may exceed +4 volts, the grid does not rise appreciably above $e_c = 0$ and the output voltage v_o is held at E_1. Thus the top of any signal exceeding +4 volts is cut off at +4 volts because of the diode action of the grid and cathode. It is possible to shift the Q point of the triode to any point on the load line between cutoff and $E_c = 0$. If the Q point is shifted to cutoff, all negative input voltages are clipped; if the Q point is shifted to $E_c = 0$, all positive input voltages are clipped. In addition to clipping, a polarity reversal occurs between e_{in} and v_o.

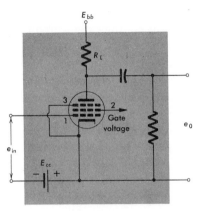

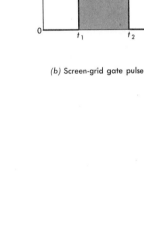

FIG. 12.8 *Pentode gate circuit.*   (a) Schematic circuit   (b) Screen-grid gate pulse

An electronic circuit sometimes known as a "gate" is a transmission circuit which allows a signal to pass when desired but does not allow the signal to pass otherwise. An example of a gate circuit is shown in Fig. 12.8, using a vacuum pentode RC coupled amplifier. The suppressor grid (grid 3) is connected to the cathode as usual. The screen grid (grid 2) is ordinarily connected to a constant voltage of about +100 volts in order to establish the electric field through which the electrons from the cathode must fall. If the screen-grid voltage is zero, the electric field is not established and electrons do not fall to the anode. In order to stop the output signal, it is necessary only to make the screen-grid voltage zero. In Fig. 12.8b, the rectangular pulse of voltage is +100 volts during the interval from t_1 to t_2 and is zero the rest of the time. If this pulse is applied to the screen grid, the input signal is amplified and appears at the output during the interval from t_1 to t_2 but there is no output signal otherwise. Thus the gate is open during the interval from t_1 to t_2, and it is closed the rest of the time. This kind of circuit has many applications in radar and telemetering systems.

12.5 AMPLITUDE MODULATION

In electrical communications, modulation is a process by which one signal, known as the "carrier," is caused to vary by another signal, known as the "modulating" signal. The carrier is either a direct voltage or current or a sinusoidal voltage or current. A carbon microphone is an example of a device which modulates a d-c carrier; the direct current from a battery is modulated when the resistance of the carbon granules of the microphone vary with time according to the acoustic pressure on the diaphragm of the microphone. A vacuum-tube or transistor amplifier is also a modulator; an input signal modulates the direct voltage or current from the power supply, producing a larger output signal.

Often in electrical communications the signal to be transmitted consists of frequencies in a range that is difficult or uneconomical to transmit. Radio communications is an example. For instance, if the signal to be transmitted lies in the frequency range 100 to 3,000 cycles/sec, it is difficult to obtain appreciable radiation from practical antennas at these frequencies. But at frequencies of 100,000 or 1,000,000 cycles/sec or even higher, radiation from practical antennas is easily accomplished. Therefore it is convenient to modulate a high-frequency carrier with the low audio-frequency signal and then transmit the modulated carrier through space. A carrier thus modulated carries with it the low-frequency signal, which can be extracted at the receiver by the process known as "demodulation," or "detection."

The process of modulation can be accomplished in several ways, depending upon the nature of the modulating signal. For instance, the carrier can be turned on and off according to the international Morse code. In a sense, this is a form of amplitude modulation, since the amplitude of the carrier is caused to change between zero and a constant value as the carrier goes from off to on. Amplitude modulation is that form of modulation by which the amplitude of the carrier is caused to vary by the modulating signal.

If the carrier can be expressed by the voltage

$$e_c = E_c \sin \omega_c t \tag{12.17}$$

where ω_c is the frequency of the carrier, and if the modulating signal can be expressed by the voltage

$$e_m = E_m \sin \omega_m t \qquad (12.18)$$

then the amplitude-modulated (a-m) carrier can be expressed by

$$e_{am} = (1 + m \sin \omega_m t) E_c \sin \omega_c t \qquad (12.19)$$

where m is the fraction E_m/E_c and is less than unity. An example of an a-m carrier is shown in Fig. 12.9. The envelope of the modulated carrier is the modulating signal which is being transmitted and which must be extracted by the demodulator at the receiver.

The expansion of Eq. (12.19) by the appropriate trigonometric identity shows the frequencies present in Eq. (12.19). Using the identity

$$\sin x \sin y = \tfrac{1}{2}[\cos (x - y) - \cos (x + y)] \qquad (12.20)$$

Eq. (12.19) can be written

$$e_{am} = E_c \sin \omega_c t - \frac{mE_c}{2} \cos (\omega_c + \omega_m)t + \frac{mE_c}{2} \cos (\omega_c - \omega_m)t \qquad (12.21)$$

There are three sinusoids represented in Eq. (12.21), with frequencies ω_c, $\omega_c + \omega_m$, and $\omega_c - \omega_m$. Since ω_c is ordinarily very much greater than ω_m, the frequency spectrum of Eq. (12.21) is shown in Fig. 12.10. A bandwidth of at least $2\omega_m$, with ω_c at its

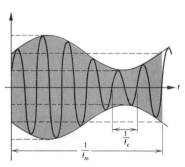

FIG. 12.9 *An a-m carrier with m* $= \tfrac{1}{2}, f_c \approx 7F_m$.

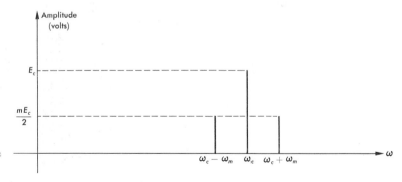

FIG. 12.10 *Frequency spectrum of a-m signal.*

center, is necessary for the transmission of the a-m signal represented by Eq. (12.21). The carrier frequency is present, and two other frequencies, known as "upper" and "lower" sidebands, are present. When $m = 1$, the condition for maximum modulation, the magnitude of the sideband is $E_c/2$. Since power is proportional to the square of the voltage and the maximum voltage each sideband possesses is $E_c/2$, each sideband has a maximum power of one-fourth that of the carrier.

A nonlinear device or circuit is required in order to accomplish amplitude modulation. The characteristic of a vacuum diode which follows Child's law can be expressed approximately for small values of e_b by the power series

$$i_b = a_0 + a_1 e_b + a_2 e_b^2 + \cdots \qquad (12.22)$$

where the cubic and all higher-order terms have been neglected. Figure 12.11 shows the modulating signal and the carrier added in series and impressed across the vacuum diode, whose characteristic is expressed approximately by Eq. (12.22). Then, if R_L is very much smaller than R_b or r_p for the diode,

$$e_b = E_m \sin \omega_m t + E_c \sin \omega_c t \qquad (12.23)$$

Substituting Eq. (12.23) into Eq. (12.22) gives

$$i_b = a_0 + a_1 E_m \sin \omega_m t + a_1 E_c \sin \omega_c t + a_2 E_m{}^2 \sin^2 \omega_m t$$
$$+ a_2 E_c{}^2 \sin^2 \omega_c t + 2 a_2 E_m E_c \sin \omega_m t \sin \omega_c t + \cdots$$

$$(12.24)$$

Using the identities

$$\sin^2 x = \tfrac{1}{2}(1 - \cos 2x)$$

$$\sin x \sin y = \tfrac{1}{2}[\cos (x - y) - \cos (x + y)] \qquad (12.25)$$

Eq. (12.24) can be written

$$i_b = a_0 + \frac{a_2 E_m{}^2}{2} + \frac{a_2 E_c{}^2}{2} + a_1 E_m \sin \omega_m t + a_1 E_c \sin \omega_c t$$

$$- \frac{a_2 E_m{}^2}{2} \cos 2\omega_m t - \frac{a_2 E_c{}^2}{2} \cos 2\omega_c t$$

$$- a_2 E_c E_m \cos (\omega_c + \omega_m)t$$

$$+ a_2 E_c E_m \cos (\omega_c - \omega_m)t + \cdots \qquad (12.26)$$

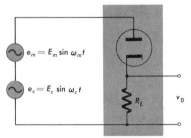

FIG. 12.11 *Diode square-law modulator.*

The various frequencies present in Eq. (12.26) are shown in the frequency spectrum of Fig. 12.12. At the low-frequency end of the spectrum, there is a d-c component, a component of the modulating frequency, and one of twice the modulating frequency. In the middle of the spectrum, the carrier frequency is shown, with its upper and lower sideband frequencies $\omega_c + \omega_m$ and $\omega_c - \omega_m$. There is also a component present of twice the carrier frequency.

It is obvious from Eq. (12.26) and Fig. 12.12 that the required frequency terms for amplitude modulation are present, consisting

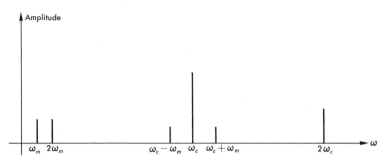

FIG. 12.12 *Frequency spectrum from nonlinear modulator.*

of ω_c, $\omega_c + \omega_m$, and $\omega_c - \omega_m$. If all the other frequency terms can be filtered out, an a-m signal remains. If the a-m signal must be a voltage v_0, it can be obtained across the small resistor R_L, as shown in Fig. 12.11. The unwanted frequency components can be filtered out by passing v_0 through a filter which discriminates against all frequencies except those between $\omega_c + \omega_m$ and $\omega_c - \omega_m$. After filtering, Eq. (12.26) coincides with Eq. (12.21) when $a_1 R_2 = 1$ and $a_2 = 1/2E_c$.

Square-law modulation, which relies upon the squared term in Eq. (12.22), can also be accomplished by taking advantage of the nonlinear characteristics of the vacuum triode. Several other circuits are possible for accomplishing amplitude modulation, usually by varying the gain of an amplifier as a linear function of the modulating signal. Furthermore, there are other ways to modulate the carrier besides amplitude modulation. For instance, the frequency or the phase of the carrier can be modulated by the modulating signal. The one example of square-law amplitude modulation presented in this section shows very briefly some of the principles of amplitude modulation; more extensive discussion of modulation is beyond the scope of this book.

Example 12.1

A modulating signal $e_m = 10 \sin 10^3 t$ and a carrier $e_c = 10 \sin 10^6 t$ are added together and impressed across a square-law electronic device whose characteristic can be expressed by

$$i = 0.000025e^2 \quad \text{amp}$$

Then

$$e = 10 \sin 10^6 t + 10 \sin 10^3 t$$

and

$$i = 0.000025 \,(10 \sin 10^6 t + 10 \sin 10^3 t)^2$$

$$= 0.0025 \sin^2 10^6 t + 0.0025 \sin^2 10^3 t + 0.005 \sin 10^6 t \sin 10^3 t$$

Using the identities

$$\sin^2 x = \tfrac{1}{2}(1 - \cos 2x)$$

and

$$\sin x \sin y = \tfrac{1}{2}[\cos (x - y) - \cos (x + y)]$$

$$i = 0.00125 - 0.00125 \cos 2 \times 10^6 t + 0.00125$$

$$- 0.00125 \cos 2 \times 10^3 t - 0.0025 \cos (10^6 + 10^3)t$$

$$+ 0.0025 \cos (10^6 - 10^3)t \tag{12.27}$$

Notice that there is no carrier-frequency term in i, only $2\omega_c$, $\omega_c + \omega_m$, $\omega_c - \omega_m$, and a constant term. Then the square-law device does not yield true amplitude modulation; a first-order term is needed in the i-versus-e characteristic.

12.6 AMPLITUDE DEMODULATION

The modulating signal, carrying the intelligence to be transmitted, is superimposed upon a carrier to simplify and make more economical the problem of transmission. At the receiver, the modulating signal must be extracted. This process, known as "demodulation" or "detection," can be accomplished by again using a nonlinear device such as a vacuum diode.

If the a-m signal expressed by Eq. (12.21) is impressed across a vacuum diode whose characteristic can be represented approximately by Eq. (12.22), the current i_b in the vacuum diode can be calculated. Substituting Eq. (12.21) as e_b into Eq. (12.22) gives

$$i_b = a_0 + a_1 E_c \sin \omega_c t + \frac{a_1 m E_c}{2} \cos (\omega_c + \omega_m)t$$

$$- \frac{a_1 m E_c}{2} \cos (\omega_c - \omega_m)t + a_2 E_c^2 \sin^2 \omega_c t$$

$$+ a_2 \left(\frac{m E_c}{2}\right)^2 \cos^2 (\omega_c + \omega_m)t$$

$$+ a_2 \left(\frac{m E_c}{2}\right)^2 \cos^2 (\omega_c - \omega_m)t$$

$$+ a_2 m E_c^2 \sin \omega_c t \cos (\omega_c + \omega_m)t$$

$$- a_2 m E_c^2 \sin \omega_c t \cos (\omega_c - \omega_m)t$$

$$- \left(\frac{m E_c}{2}\right)^2 \cos (\omega_c + \omega_m)t \cos (\omega_c - \omega_m)t \tag{12.28}$$

With the help of the identities of Eqs. (12.25) and (12.29), the frequency terms present in i_b can be determined.

$$\cos^2 x = \tfrac{1}{2}(1 + \cos 2x)$$

$$\cos x \cos y = \tfrac{1}{2}[\cos (x + y) + \cos (x - y)] \tag{12.29}$$

Notice that, when a sinusoid is squared, a d-c component and a double-frequency component result. When two sinusoids of different frequencies are multiplied together, sum and difference frequencies result. The frequency terms present in Eq. (12.28) are shown in Table 12.1. Notice that the modulating signal ω_m is present, in addition to the carrier and its side bands, and a group of frequencies clustered around $2\omega_c$. It is easy to filter out the high-frequency terms above ω_m and extract ω_m by itself. If it were not for the $e_b{}^2$ term in Eq. 12.22, ω_m would not have appeared by itself in the frequencies present in Eq. (12.28). Thus square-law detection takes advantage of the curvature of the i_b-versus-e_b characteristic of the diode. Square-law detection can also be accomplished by the nonlinear characteristic of a vacuum triode.

It is possible to extract the modulating signal from the modulated carrier by using the diode as an on-off device. A circuit for doing this is shown in Fig. 12.14a, where e_{in} is the modulated carrier. If the capacitor C were not present across the output terminal, e_o would appear as shown in Fig. 12.14b, where the modulating signal is the envelope of the peak values of the rectified carrier. Without C, the circuit appears to be a half-wave rectifier.

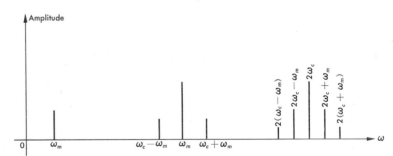

FIG. 12.13 *Frequency spectrum, square-law demodulator.*

TABLE 12.1 *Frequencies Present in Eq. (12.28) and Fig. 12.13*

0	$2\omega_c + \omega_m$	$2(\omega_c + \omega_m)$
ω_c	$2\omega_c - \omega_m$	$2(\omega_c - \omega_m)$
$\omega_c + \omega_m$	ω_m	$2\omega_c$
$\omega_c - \omega_m$		

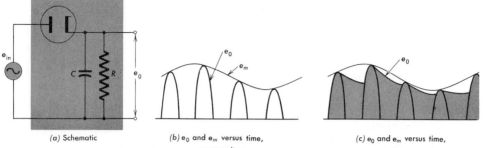

(a) Schematic

(b) e_0 and e_m versus time, no capacitor

(c) e_0 and e_m versus time, capacitor present

FIG. 12.14 *A diode linear detector.*

When C is added in parallel with R, the capacitor charges to the peak of the rectified modulated wave and discharges through R during the times when the diode is not conducting. Thus, with C in parallel with R, e_o appears as in Fig. 12.14c; e_o is not a perfect reproduction of e_{in} because it contains a d-c component and some high-frequency components. The d-c component of e_o can be eliminated by a blocking capacitor, and the high-frequency components can be eliminated by a filter. Thus the modulating signal is extracted from the modulated carrier in this linear detector.

Example 12.2

A particular electronic device has a current-versus-voltage characteristic of

$$i = 0.000025e^2 \qquad \text{amp}$$

It is used as an amplitude demodulator. An a-m signal of

$$v_{am} = 100 \sin 10^6 t + 25 \cos (10^6 + 10^3)t - 25 \cos (10^6 - 10^3)t$$

is applied across the square-law demodulator. Then

$$i = 0.000025\,[100 \sin 10^6 t + 25 \cos (10^6 + 10^3)t$$

$$- 25 \cos (10^6 - 10^3)t]^2$$

$$= 0.25 \sin^2 10^6 t + 0.0156 \cos^2 (10^6 + 10^3)t$$

$$+ 0.0156 \cos^2 (10^6 - 10^3)t$$

$$+ 0.125 \sin 10^6 t \cos (10^6 + 10^3)t$$

$$- 0.125 \sin 10^6 t \cos (10^6 - 10^3)t$$

$$- 0.0312 \cos (10^6 + 10^3)t \cos (10^6 - 10^3)t$$

Using the identities

$$\sin^2 x = \tfrac{1}{2}(1 - \cos 2x)$$

$$\cos^2 x = \tfrac{1}{2}(1 + \cos 2x)$$

$$\sin x \cos y = \tfrac{1}{2}[\sin (x + y) + \sin (x - y)]$$

$$\cos x \cos y = \tfrac{1}{2}[\cos (x + y) + \cos (x - y)]$$

Then

$$i = 0.141 - 0.141 \cos (2 \times 10^6)t$$

$$+ \ 0.0078 \cos (2 \times 10^6 + 2 \times 10^3)t$$

$$+ \ 0.0078 \cos (2 \times 10^6 - 2 \times 10^3)t$$

$$+ \ 0.062 \sin (2 \times 10^6 + 10^3)t - 0.12 \sin 10^3 t$$

$$- \ 0.062 \sin (2 \times 10^6 - 10^3)t - 0.0156 \cos 2 \times 10^3 t$$

The modulating frequency $\omega_m = 10^3$ radians/sec is present with an amplitude of 0.12 amp peak.

12.7 THE BISTABLE MULTIVIBRATOR

An important timing and counting circuit is the multivibrator, one variation of which is shown in Fig. 12.15a. A free-running, or astable, multivibrator is an oscillator whose fundamental frequency is a function of the RC time constant of the coupling-circuit elements and whose output is rich in harmonics of the fundamental frequency. A bistable multivibrator, such as the one shown in Fig. 12.15a, is not an oscillator but must be driven from one con-

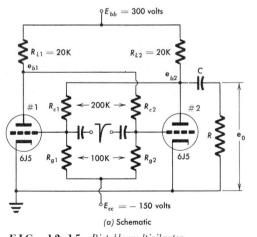

(a) Schematic

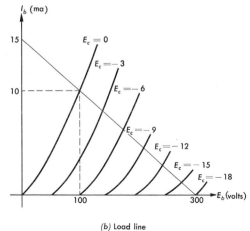

(b) Load line

FIG. 12.15 *Bistable multivibrator.*

ducting state to another conducting state. A bistable multivibrator is the basic counting and arithmetic circuit for the digital computer discussed in Chap. 15.

To visualize the operation of the bistable multivibrator of Fig. 12.15a, assume that each of the stages is identical; $R_{g1} = R_{g2}$, $R_{L1} = R_{L2}$, $R_{c1} = R_{c2}$, and the two triodes are also identical. The control grid of each triode is coupled to the anode of the other triode by a voltage divider consisting of R_c and R_g. The values of R_c, R_g, and E_{cc} have been chosen such that, when one triode is conducting with its grid at zero volts, the voltage coupled by R_c and R_g to the grid of the other triode cuts off that triode. Thus, although the two stages are identical, when one stage is conducting, the other is off, and vice versa. But if the two stages are identical, when the circuit is first energized by turning on E_{bb} and E_{cc}, how does one triode conduct and the other cut off? The answer is that the two stages are *not* identical even though the resistors of each stage have the same nominal values and the triodes are the same kind. Manufacturing processes permit reasonable tolerances, and it is very unlikely that all the corresponding circuit elements of the two stages would be identical. So assume that, when the circuit is first energized, triode 1 conducts slightly more than triode 2. Then the voltage drop across R_{L1} is slightly greater than that across R_{L2}, and the voltage coupled to grid 2 is slightly less than that coupled from triode 2 to grid 1. Then the anode current of triode 2 decreases, and the voltage drop across R_{L2} decreases. The voltage coupled from anode 2 to grid 1 increases, causing triode 1 to conduct more. The voltage drop across R_{L1} increases more, further decreasing the grid voltage on triode 2, and the process builds up until triode 2 is cut off and triode 1 is conducting a maximum amount, with E_{c1} only slightly above cathode potential.

In Fig. 12.15b, the plate characteristics of the 6J5 are represented, together with the load line. When triode 1 is conducting and $E_{c1} = 0$, $E_{b1} = 100$ volts approximately. The coupling circuit R_{c1} and R_{g2} couple -25 volts to the grid of triode 2, assuring that triode 2 is cut off; therefore E_{b2} is nearly 300 volts and the grid voltage coupled to triode 1 from anode 2 would be about $+75$ volts were it not for the diode action of grid 1 and cathode 1. As explained in Sec. 12.4, when a large resistance is in series with the grid, the grid cannot be made positive because it becomes an anode and virtually clamps its voltage to the cathode. A switch between cathode and control grid is an approximate equivalent circuit for the grid-to-cathode diode action; when the grid is negative, the switch is open, and when the grid tries to be positive, the switch closes, clamping the grid to the cathode voltage.

The bistable multivibrator can be triggered in a number of ways. Suppose that a negative voltage pulse is applied simultaneously to each grid. Triode 2 is already at cutoff, and when its grid goes more negative, the plate current is still at cutoff. But triode 1 is conducting, and the negative pulse applied to its grid tends to reduce I_{b1} and therefore increase E_{b1}. When E_{b1} is raised, the grid voltage of triode 2 is raised and triode 2 starts to conduct. Then E_{b2} drops, coupling a reduced grid voltage to triode 1. This cumulative process continues until triode 1 is cut off and triode 2 is conducting about 10 ma, with E_{c2} about zero. Another negative pulse of voltage applied to the two grids triggers the action again; the conducting tube cuts off, and the nonconducting tube conducts. Thus each negative pulse applied to the two grids changes the state of operation.

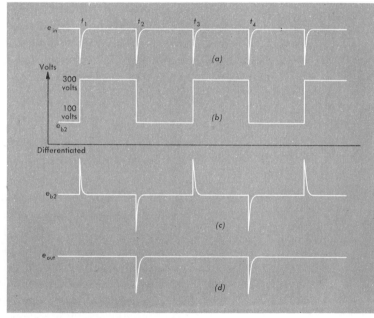

FIG. 12.16 *Bistable multivibrator used as a pulse counter or divider.*

The bistable multivibrator used as a counter is triggered either by a negative pulse or by a positive pulse applied to the grids of the triodes. In Fig. 12.16a is shown a series of negative pulses applied to the two grids. Before time t_1, triode 1 is off, and triode 2 is conducting. At time t_1, a negative pulse is applied to the grids. Only the conducting triode is sensitive to a negative pulse, and since triode 2 is conducting before t_1, it is driven off by the negative pulse at t_1. This action triggers triode 1 on, and it remains on until the next negative pulse at time t_2 triggers triode 1 off again. Each negative pulse shown in Fig. 12.16a drives the circuit from one state to the other. Figure 12.16b shows the anode voltage of triode 2, e_{b2}, at 100 volts before t_1, then at $E_{bb} = 300$ volts while triode 2 is off, then back to $e_{b2} = 100$ volts again during the conducting period.

If the output voltage e_o is differentiated by the RC circuit, e_o is a series of voltage pulses across R which alternate in polarity as shown in Fig. 12.16c. If the positive output pulses are clipped by a diode clipping circuit (not shown), the output voltage is a series of negative pulses only. For each two negative input pulses, only one output pulse occurs. Thus the circuit divides the number of input pulses by two.

Several bistable multivibrator circuits, sometimes called "flip-flop" circuits, can be cascaded together so that the output pulses from one stage are the input pulses to the next. The cascade of flip-flop circuits is an adder; the number of pulses fed into the first stage can be ascertained from the on-off conditions of the several flip-flops after the pulses have been fed in. This is the manner in which addition is performed in the digital computer described in Chap. 15.

12.8 CLASS B AMPLIFIERS AND PUSH-PULL OPERATION

Linear operation of vacuum-tube amplifiers, sometimes called "class A" operation, was discussed in Chap. 11. Class A operation requires that the vacuum-tube grid be biased negatively, but not to cutoff, so that the grid signal never drives the grid into the positive region or beyond cutoff. In contrast, a class B amplifier is defined as one biased to cutoff so that only the positive portion of the grid signal drives the grid above the cutoff voltage. A single tube operating class B is a clipper; the negative portion of the grid signal is clipped off.

When a single tube is operated class B with a resistive load, its operation can be predicted from a load-line analysis with the Q point at cutoff, as shown in Fig. 12.17, where the characteristic curves have been approximated by straight lines. A sinusoidal signal voltage $e_g = 6 \sin \omega t$ is applied to the grid in this example. Projecting the grid voltage e_c onto the load line, we see that the

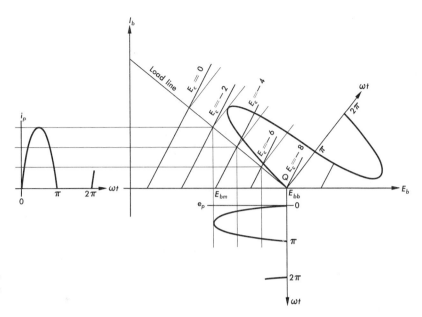

FIG. 12.17 *Class B operation of an amplifier with resistive load.*

operating point moves up the load line from the static Q point as the sinusoidal signal voltage e_g progresses through the first quarter cycle. From the load line, a projection onto the ordinate shows the plate current, and a projection onto the abscissa shows the plate voltage. Both plate current and plate voltage have been clipped; plate current is only the positive half of a sine wave, and plate voltage is correspondingly the bottom half of a sine wave. Thus a single tube operating class B distorts by clipping, adding an infinite series of harmonics to the fundamental frequency being amplified.

When there is no signal applied to the grid of a class B amplifier, plate current does not flow and there is no power being drawn from the plate-supply voltage source. This is in contrast to a linear amplifier, which draws power from the plate-voltage supply continuously. It is worthwhile to define a plate-circuit efficiency for an amplifier as the ratio of the a-c-power output to the d-c-power input, or

$$\text{Plate-circuit efficiency} = \frac{P_{\text{out}}}{P_{\text{in}}} \qquad (12.30)$$

where P_{in} is the input power supplied from the d-c supply. Ordinarily the efficiency for a class B amplifier is much higher than the efficiency of a class A, or linear, amplifier. The efficiency of the single tube operated class B is difficult to calculate, since so many harmonics must be considered in finding the a-c-power output.

12.8 *Class B Amplifiers and Push-pull Operation* **327**

To eliminate nonlinear distortion in the class B amplifier, two tubes are operated together in a push-pull circuit, as shown in Fig. 12.18a. Notice the symmetry of the circuit. A sinusoidal signal

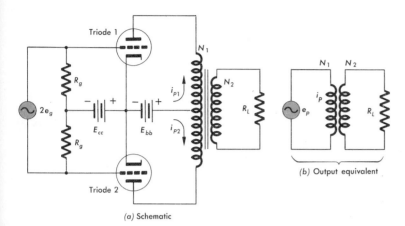

(a) Schematic

(b) Output equivalent

FIG. 12.18 *Push-pull class B amplifier.*

$2e_g$ is applied as the input across the two identical series grid resistors marked R_g. Then e_g is the signal voltage of the grid of each triode. When the grid of triode 1 is driven above cutoff by e_g, triode 1 conducts and the anode current i_{p1} flows through the top half of the transformer winding. During the time when triode 1 is conducting, triode 2 is cut off. Then, when e_g reverses its polarity so that triode 2 conducts, i_{p2} flows in the bottom half of the transformer winding and triode 1 is at cutoff, with $i_{p1} = 0$.

The transformer is a highly efficient device with few losses, and to a good approximation it can be treated as having 100 per cent efficiency. Then the power input to the two input windings each with N_1 turns must equal the power output delivered to R_L. The two input windings each conducts only one-half the time, equivalent to one winding conducting during the full cycle, as shown in Fig. 12.18b. Power output to a resistive load is $P_{out} = I_p E_p$, where I_p is the rms value of the sinusoidal plate current and E_p is the rms value of the sinusoidal plate voltage. Power input is $E_{bb} I_{pa}$, where E_{bb} is the plate-supply voltage and I_{pa} is the average plate current during the conducting half cycle. Plate-circuit efficiency is

$$\eta = \frac{I_p E_p}{2 E_{bb} I_{pa}} \tag{12.31}$$

The class B push-pull amplifier is an ideal amplifier for supplying large amounts of distortion-free a-c power to a resistive load with high efficiency. Maximum plate-circuit efficiency of a class B power amplifier is usually in the range between 50 and 75 per cent. This is in contrast to the plate-circuit efficiency of a class A power amplifier discussed in Chap. 11, which may be about 10 per cent. But class A amplifiers are ordinarily used as voltage amplifiers supplying a voltage output, and the power lost in the load resistor is so small that efficiency is unimportant. Class B amplifiers are ordinarily used to deliver relatively large amounts of power to a resistive load, and in this application high efficiency is desirable.

SUMMARY

In this chapter we have explored the nonlinear nature of electronic devices. Several nonlinear applications have been discussed, by no means exhausting the possibilities.

Diodes can be used as rectifiers to convert alternating current to unidirectional current; filters must be added to smooth out the rectified current if a constant-voltage and direct-current source is needed. A diode rectifier takes advantage of the on-off nature of its current-versus-voltage characteristic curve to allow current to flow in one direction but not in the other. The diode can be considered as a switching device; it conducts readily in one direction, and to turn it off the voltage across it need only be reversed. The diode as a switching device can be used for wave-shaping and clipping, applications being found in radar, television, telemetering, etc.

Modulation is the process by which one signal, known as the "carrier," is caused to vary by another signal, known as the "modulating signal." Modulation is used to change the necessary frequency components being transmitted, to make transmission easier and more economical. Amplitude modulation, one form of modulation, causes the amplitude of a sinusoidal carrier to vary according to the modulation signal, so that the modulated carrier can be expressed by Eq. (12.19),

$$e_{am} = (1 + m \sin \omega_m t) E_c \sin \omega_c t$$

Amplitude demodulation can be accomplished by a square-law device whose current-versus-voltage characteristic can be expressed for small values of e_b by Eq. (12.22),

$$i_b = a_0 + a_1 e_b + a_2 e_b{}^2 + \cdots$$

where a_2 is nonzero. If the carrier and the modulating signal are added as two sinusoidal voltages, substitution of the resulting voltage into Eq. (12.22) for e_b gives the frequency terms present in i_b. Evaluation of Eq. (12.19) shows that only three frequency components, ω_c, $\omega_c + \omega_m$, and $\omega_c - \omega_m$, are present in the a-m signal.

Demodulation of an a-m signal can also be accomplished by a square-law device. If the modulated carrier is substituted into Eq. (12.22) as the voltage term, the frequencies present in the current include the modulating frequency by itself, as well as higher-frequency terms, which can be filtered out.

The bistable multivibrator is an example of a circuit in which the triode is allowed to have only two stable states, on and off. Two triodes are used in this circuit, and when one tube is conducting, the other is off, and vice versa. The "on" tube is triggered off by a negative pulse; each pulse causes the "on" tube to cut off and the "off" tube to conduct. Applications of this circuit are mainly in computing and counting.

The class B push-pull power amplifier consists of two tubes which conduct alternately and which are biased exactly to cutoff. A center-tapped transformer is required in the plate circuit to put the two halves of the anode voltage and current together from each tube to make an undistorted sinusoidal voltage and current in R_L. Class B power amplifiers are more efficient than class A linear amplifiers, although efficiency is not always important in amplifier circuits.

FURTHER READING

An excellent reference on rectifiers and power supplies is Jacob Millman, *Vacuum-tube and Semiconductor Electronics* (McGraw-Hill Book Company, Inc., New York, 1958), chaps. 14 and 19, respectively; and Samuel Seely, *Electron-tube Circuits*, 2d ed. (McGraw-Hill Book Company, Inc., New York, 1958), chaps. 6 and 7, respectively. *Electron-tube Circuits* also has good chapters on "Amplitude Modulation" (chap. 17) and "Demodulation" (chap. 18). Joseph M. Pettit, *Electronic Switching, Timing, and Pulse Circuits* (McGraw-Hill Book Company, Inc., New York, 1959), is exceptionally readable and a good reference for switching circuits and multivibrators. Paul D. Ankrum, *Principles and Applications of Electron Devices* (International Textbook Company, Scranton, Pa., 1959), has a good chapter on "Rectifiers" (chap. 7) and one on "Large-signal Amplifiers" (chap. 14).

PROBLEMS

12.1 Verify Eq. (12.4) from Eq. (12.3).

12.2 From Eq. (12.5), evaluate the integrals, and verify Eq. (12.6).

12.3 The rectangular voltage wave shown in the illustration excites a diode rectifier with resistive load. Assume an ideal diode with zero resistance in the forward direction and infinite resistance in the reverse direction. (a) Find the average current in the load resistor; (b) find the rms current in R_L; (c) find the instantaneous current in R_L.

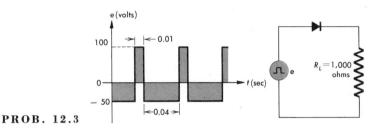

PROB. 12.3

12.4 Repeat Prob. 12.3, assuming that the diode has 1,000 ohms resistance in the forward direction and 5,000 ohms resistance in the reverse direction.

12.5 A half-wave rectifier with capacitive filter is shown in Fig. 12.3a, where $e = 400 \sin 377t$, $R_L = 20,000$ ohms, and $C = 10$ μf. Assume an ideal diode with zero forward resistance and infinite resistance in the reverse direction. Find the average, or direct, current in R_L.

12.6 The rectangular voltage source of Prob. 12.3 excites the circuit shown in the figure. Assume ideal diodes. Find and sketch v_o versus time and i versus t.

12.7 A sinusoidal voltage source of $e = 150 \sin \omega t$ is applied to the circuit of Prob. 12.6. Find and sketch v_o versus t and i versus t.

12.8 The triode clipper shown in Fig. 12.7 uses a 6J5 triode with $E_{cc} = 300$ volts, $R_L = 30,000$ ohms, and $E_{cc} = -4$ volts. A sinusoidal voltage $e_{in} = 50 \sin \omega t$ is applied at the input. Find and plot v_o as a function of time. Assume that $R_g = 1$ megohm.

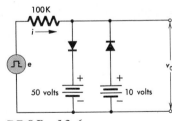

PROB. 12.6

12.9 An a-m signal is applied to the input of a filter, but only the upper sideband passes through the filter and appears in the filter output as a voltage across a square-law device whose characteristic is $i = 10^{-2}e^2$ amp. The upper sideband can be expressed as $e = 10 \cos (10^6 + 2 \times 10^3)t$

volts. Find the magnitude and amplitude of all frequency components in the current of the square-law device.

12.10 The filter characteristics of the filter of Prob. 12.9 are altered so that both the carrier and the upper sideband are passed by the filter and appear across the square-law device. Then $e = 20 \sin 10^6 t + 10 \cos (10^6 + 2 \times 10^3)t$. Find the magnitude and amplitude of all frequency components in the current of the square-law device.

12.11 The characteristics of the filter of Prob. 12.9 are again changed so that the upper and lower sidebands are passed by the filter but the carrier is stopped. Then the voltage across the square-law device is $e = 10 \cos (10^6 + 2 \times 10^3)t - 10 \cos (10^6 - 2 \times 10^3)t$. Find the amplitude of all frequency components of current in the square-law device.

12.12 Two voltages $e_1 = 2 \sin \omega_1 t$ and $e_2 = 5 \sin \omega_2 t$ are multiplied together and then impressed across the nonlinear device whose current-versus-voltage characteristic is $i = 0.1e + 0.04e^2$. Find the frequency terms present in i.

12.13 A triode operating class A is shown in Fig. 11.2a, where $Z_L = 10,000$ ohms resistance and the triode parameters are $\mu = 30$ and $r_p = 8,000$ ohms. A grid signal 1 volt peak-to-peak is applied. Find the a-c power delivered to Z_L.

12.14 A 6J5 triode is used in the circuit of Fig. 11.2a, where $Z_L = 30,000$ ohms resistance and $E_{bb} = 300$ volts. The grid bias is -6 volts. A grid signal $e_g = 6 \sin \omega t$ is applied to the grid. Find the a-c power delivered to Z_L and the plate-circuit efficiency.

FEEDBACK CIRCUITS

13.1 WHAT IS FEEDBACK?

Feedback is said to occur when part of the output quantity of a transmission or input-output system is returned to the input of the system and added to the input quantity. Feedback can be unintentional, such as occurs when part of the signal in the plate circuit of a vacuum triode is fed back to the grid circuit by the plate-to-grid interelectrode capacitance inherent in triodes. Feedback is often intentional, however, and is used when it improves the response characteristics of the transmission system.

The use of feedback is not restricted to electric circuits. Feedback occurs in many dynamic systems and is a necessary ingredient in the operation of automatic control systems, regulators, and instrumentation systems discussed in Chap. 20. Feedback need not be electrical; such mechanical quantities as position (rotational or translational), velocity, acceleration, and temperature are often used in control systems and regulators. In this chapter our aim is twofold: first, to study the effect of feedback when employed in electric circuits and electronic amplifiers, and, second, to gain a background for studying the effect of feedback in dynamic systems discussed in Chap. 20. In this chapter we use the frequency-response method of feedback analysis, generally assuming that the input signal is a sinusoid. The study of dynamic systems in Chap. 20 utilizes natural response as the design criterion.

A simple feedback system can be represented by the block diagram in Fig. 13.1, where X_1 is the sinusoidal input quantity, X_4 is the output quantity, G_{23} is the amplification, or gain, between X_2 and X_3, and G_{34} is the amplification, or gain, in the feedback path between X_3 and X_4. The gain quantities G_{23} and G_{34} are functions of frequency. The complex gain equations developed in Chap. 11, such as Eqs. (11.17) and (11.24) for the RC coupled triode amplifier, are examples of gain functions of the nature of G_{23} and G_{34}.

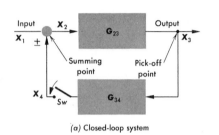

(a) Closed-loop system

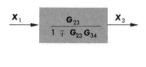

(b) Equivalent open-loop system

FIG. 13.1 *Block diagram of a feedback system.*

In the block diagram of Fig. 13.1a the summing point adds or subtracts X_4 to X_1, depending upon the sign shown at the input to the summing point for X_4. Thus the output of the summing point is given by

$$X_2 = X_1 \pm X_4 \tag{13.1}$$

If the positive sign is shown for X_4 at the summing point, X_1 and X_4 are added together; if the negative sign is used, X_4 changes its sign in passing through the summing point and is thus subtracted from X_1. If the switch in the feedback path of Fig. 13.1a is open, X_4 is zero and $X_2 = X_1$; when the switch is open, there is no feedback and the system is an open-loop system. For the open-loop system, the over-all gain is $G_{23} = X_3/X_1$. Thus, for example, if G_{23} is the complex gain for an RC coupled amplifier, then X_3 is the output voltage of the amplifier and $X_3 = X_1G_{23}$.

When the switch in Fig. 13.1a is closed, the system is said to be a "closed-loop" system and the over-all gain is no longer G_{23}. We define the over-all gain as the ratio of X_3/X_1. Since X_1 is the input quantity, the three variables X_2, X_3, and X_4 are all functions of X_1. Three equations in the three unknowns can be written [Eq. (13.1)]

$$X_2 = X_1 \pm X_4$$

$$X_3 = G_{23}X_2 \tag{13.2}$$

$$X_4 = G_{34}X_3 \tag{13.3}$$

Rearranging Eqs. (13.1), (13.2), and (13.3) gives

$$X_2 \mp X_4 = X_1$$

$$G_{23}X_2 - X_3 = 0 \tag{13.4}$$

$$G_{34}X_3 - X_4 = 0$$

a linear system of equations which can be solved for the output variable X_3 by Cramer's rule as follows:

$$X_3 = \frac{\begin{vmatrix} 1 & X_1 & \mp 1 \\ G_{23} & 0 & 0 \\ 0 & 0 & -1 \end{vmatrix}}{\begin{vmatrix} 1 & 0 & \mp 1 \\ G_{23} & -1 & 0 \\ 0 & G_{34} & -1 \end{vmatrix}} = \frac{G_{23}X_1}{1 \mp G_{23}G_{34}} \tag{13.5}$$

Or the over-all gain can be written

$$G_{13} = \frac{X_3}{X_1} = \frac{G_{23}}{1 \mp G_{23}G_{34}} \tag{13.6}$$

where G_{13} is a function of G_{23} and G_{34}. Thus we have shown that the closed-loop system of Fig. 13.1a is equivalent to the open-loop system of Fig. 13.1b.

The gain functions G_{23}, G_{34}, and G_{13} are often called "transfer functions." They are characterized by their output quantities being equal to the sinusoidal or exponential input quantity multiplied by the complex gain function, as shown in Eqs. (13.2) and (13.3). The transfer-function and block-diagram nomenclature of Fig. 13.1 is recommended by the Institute of Radio Engineers. In electric circuits the variables X_1, X_2, X_3, and X_4 are commonly voltages or currents. If Fig. 13.1a represents a feedback amplifier, X_3 may be the output voltage and X_1 the input voltage.

13.2 BLOCK-DIAGRAM ALGEBRA

The block diagram of a physical system containing feedback is often much more complex than shown in Fig. 13.1a. The block diagram is a method of representing the algebra of the physical system just as Fig. 13.1a represents the algebraic equations given by Eqs. (13.4). The solution of the system of equations in Eqs. (13.4) is given by Eq. (13.6), which represents a single block shown in Fig. 13.1b. Thus whenever a feedback system represented by a block diagram of Fig. 13.1a is given, the single block represented in Fig. 13.1b can be immediately substituted as its equivalent; it is not necessary to repeat the solution of the system of equations.

It is possible to develop a number of rules for manipulating complex block diagrams to simplify them; this corresponds to algebraic manipulation of the system of equations. The one rule previously mentioned permits us to write the single open-loop transfer function of Fig. 13.1b as equivalent to the closed-loop system of Fig. 13.1a.

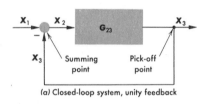

(a) Closed-loop system, unity feedback

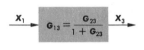

(b) Open-loop equivalent

FIG. 13.2 *Reduction of a closed-loop system with unity feedback gain to a single open-loop transfer function.*

A special case of unity feedback is shown in Fig. 13.2a, where the feedback quantity X_3 has its sign changed at the summing point. Figure 13.2b shows the open-loop equivalent of the closed-loop system, from which we can write

$$X_3 = \frac{G_{23}}{1 + G_{23}} X_1 \tag{13.7}$$

where $G_{34} = 1$ in Eq. (13.6).

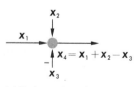

(a) Single summing point

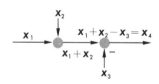

(b) Two-summing-point equivalent

FIG. 13.3 *A summing point with three input variables.*

The summing point of a system accomplishes the addition or subtraction of two or more variables. In Fig. 13.3a, the summing point combines X_1, X_2, and X_3 according to Eq. (13.8).

$$X_4 = X_1 + X_2 - X_3 \tag{13.8}$$

In Fig. 13.3b is shown an equivalent means of combining X_1, X_2, and X_3 by using two summing points. Thus a summing point with three or more input quantities can be represented by two or more summing points, each of which has only two input quantities.

A pickoff point is a point in the circuit at which a variable is obtained to be fed back (or forward) to another part of the diagram. In Figs. 13.1a and 13.2a a pickoff point is shown for feeding X_3 back to the summing point. In the manipulation of block diagrams, it is sometimes convenient to shift the pickoff point and obtain an equivalent block diagram with the pickoff point

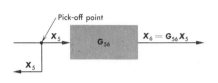

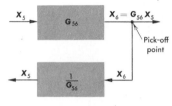

FIG. 13.4 *Shifting of the pickoff point.*

(a) A pick-off point to left of G_{56}

(b) An equivalent pick-off point to right of G_{56}

in a different position. In Fig. 13.4a, the variable X_5 is picked off to be fed back to another part of the system. In Fig. 13.4b, the pickoff point has been moved to the right of block G_{56}, multiplying X_5 by G_{56}. In order to feed back X_5 from the new pickoff point, X_6 must be multiplied by $1/G_{56}$, as shown. Thus (a) and (b) of Fig. 13.4 are equivalent.

It is sometimes convenient to be able to move summing points to different parts of the diagram or from one side of a block to another. This can be done in the same way in which pickoff points are moved. In Fig. 13.5a is shown a summing point to the

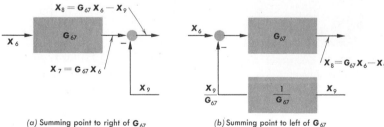

FIG. 13.5 *Shifting the summing point, equivalent circuits.*

(a) Summing point to right of G_{67}

(b) Summing point to left of G_{67}

right of the block G_{67}; the output X_8 is given by

$$X_8 = G_{67}X_6 - X_9 \tag{13.9}$$

Shifting the summing point to the left of G_{67} multiplies the contribution to X_8 from X_9 by G_{67}; therefore the block $1/G_{67}$ must be included in the path of $\mathbf{X}_9$ as shown in Fig. 13.5b. Thus (a) and (b) of Fig. 13.5 are equivalent.

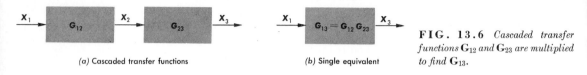

(a) Cascaded transfer functions

(b) Single equivalent

FIG. 13.6 *Cascaded transfer functions* $\mathbf{G}_{12}$ *and* $\mathbf{G}_{23}$ *are multiplied to find* $\mathbf{G}_{13}$.

Transfer functions appearing in cascade can be reduced to a single transfer function which is the product of the cascaded transfer functions. Figure 13.6 shows two transfer functions $\mathbf{G}_{12}$ and $\mathbf{G}_{23}$ in cascade. Since

$$\mathbf{X}_2 = \mathbf{G}_{12}\mathbf{X}_1 \quad \text{and} \quad \mathbf{X}_3 = \mathbf{G}_{23}\mathbf{X}_2 \tag{13.10}$$

then eliminating $\mathbf{X}_2$ in Eqs. (13.10) gives

$$\mathbf{X}_3 = \mathbf{G}_{12}\mathbf{G}_{23}\mathbf{X}_1 \tag{13.11}$$

This is shown in Fig. 13.6, where $\mathbf{G}_{13} = \mathbf{G}_{12}\mathbf{G}_{23}$.

Having defined our terms for block diagrams and their manipulations, we follow through an example of an electric circuit in the sinusoidal steady state.

Example 13.1

An impedance network is shown in Fig. 13.7 with $\mathbf{E}_1$ as the sinusoidal input voltage and $\mathbf{E}_2$ as the output voltage. We seek to express this circuit in a block diagram of the form of Fig. 13.1. First, we write the loop equations of the circuit as

$$(\mathbf{Z}_1 + \mathbf{Z}_2)\mathbf{I}_1 - \mathbf{Z}_2\mathbf{I}_2 = \mathbf{E}_1 \tag{13.12}$$

$$-\mathbf{Z}_2\mathbf{I}_1 + (\mathbf{Z}_2 + \mathbf{Z}_3 + \mathbf{Z}_4)\mathbf{I}_2 = 0 \tag{13.13}$$

$$\mathbf{Z}_4\mathbf{I}_2 = \mathbf{E}_2 \tag{13.14}$$

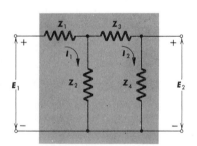

FIG. 13.7 *The circuit of imped-ances, Example 13.1.*

Solving Eq. (13.12) for $\mathbf{I}_1$ gives

$$\mathbf{I}_1 = \frac{\mathbf{E}_1}{\mathbf{Z}_1 + \mathbf{Z}_2} + \frac{\mathbf{Z}_2\mathbf{I}_2}{\mathbf{Z}_1 + \mathbf{Z}_2} \tag{13.15}$$

Equation (13.15) can be represented by the summing point and blocks shown in Fig. 13.8a.

Solving Eq. (13.13) for $\mathbf{I}_2$ gives

$$\mathbf{I}_2 = \frac{\mathbf{Z}_2}{\mathbf{Z}_2 + \mathbf{Z}_3 + \mathbf{Z}_4}\mathbf{I}_1 \tag{13.16}$$

which is represented.by the block in Fig. 13.8b. Equation (13.14) is represented diagrammatically in Fig. 13.8c. When the diagrams of

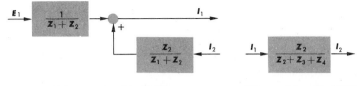

(a) Representation of Eq. (13.12)   (b) Representation of Eq. (13.13)

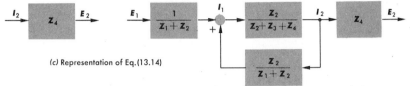

(c) Representation of Eq.(13.14)

(d) A complete block diagram representing
the circuit of Fig. 13.7

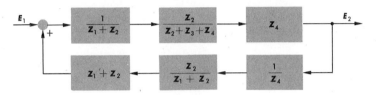

(e) Block diagram reduction of (d)

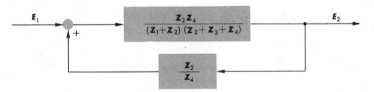

(f) Reduction of (e) to a single loop of the form of Fig. 13.1a

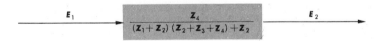

FIG. 13.8 *Synthesis of a block diagram and its simplification.*

(g) Reduction to an open-loop block of the form of Fig. 13.1b

Fig. 13.8a, b, and c are all interconnected, the complete block diagram is as shown in Fig. 13.8d.

The pickoff point in Fig. 13.8d can be moved to the right of the block marked Z_4, utilizing the equivalent diagram shown in Fig. 13.4. Likewise, the summing point can be moved to the left of the block marked $1/(Z_1 + Z_2)$, using the concepts illustrated in Fig. 13.5. A resulting block diagram is shown in Fig. 13.8e.

Further simplification of the block diagram can be obtained by recognizing that transfer functions in cascade can be multiplied to find a single equivalent transfer function. Thus Fig. 13.8e can be reduced to Fig. 13.8f, which is of the same form as Fig. 13.1a. Further simplification is obtained by reducing the closed-loop system to the equivalent open-loop system of Fig. 13.1b; this is accomplished in Fig. 13.8g.

In this example we have shown that the equations of a dynamic physical system such as an electric circuit can be represented by a block diagram which contains a feedback path. Simplification of the block diagram corresponds to the solution of the equations of the system. The open-loop block of Fig. 13.8g corresponds exactly to the algebraic solution of Eqs. (13.12) to (13.14).

13.3 THE CRITERION FOR OSCILLATION

In the block diagram representing the closed-loop system of Fig. 13.1a, $\mathbf{G}_{23}$ and $\mathbf{G}_{34}$ have been treated as functions of frequency; therefore $\mathbf{G}_{13}$ is also a function of frequency. Sinusoidal steady-state frequency analysis is the method being used in this chapter for studying feedback systems of the form represented in Fig. 13.1a. If, for example, $\mathbf{X}_1$ in Fig. 13.1 is a sinusoidal input quantity and $\mathbf{G}_{23}$ and $\mathbf{G}_{34}$ are linear transfer functions, the output quantity $\mathbf{X}_3$ is a sinusoid of the frequency of $\mathbf{X}_1$ whose amplitude and phase are functions of the amplitude and frequency of $\mathbf{X}_1$.

Consider a feedback system in which the feedback variable $\mathbf{X}_4$ is combined with the input variable at the summing point. Then the output of the feedback system is represented by

$$\mathbf{X}_3 = \frac{\mathbf{G}_{23}\mathbf{X}_1}{1 \mp \mathbf{G}_{23}\mathbf{G}_{34}} \tag{13.17}$$

Since $\mathbf{G}_{23}$ and $\mathbf{G}_{34}$ are frequency-dependent, it is conceivable that a frequency exists at which

$$1 \mp \mathbf{G}_{23}\mathbf{G}_{34} = 0 \tag{13.18}$$

At the frequency at which Eq. (13.18) is satisfied, the over-all gain $\mathbf{G}_{13}$ is infinite, and an output signal $\mathbf{X}_3$ can be produced when there is no input signal. When this occurs, the circuit is an oscillator, generating a sinusoidal output when no input signal is applied.

To illustrate how Eq. (13.18) can be used to study an oscillator, suppose that $\mathbf{G}_{23}$ consists of the transfer function of three identical stages of an RC coupled amplifier in cascade. Consider the high-frequency gain equation derived in Eq. (11.24),

$$\mathbf{A}_v = \frac{-g_m R'}{1 + j\omega C_{sh} R'}$$

Then for three stages $\mathbf{G}_{23}$ is given by

$$\mathbf{G}_{23} = \left(\frac{-g_m R'}{1 + j\omega C_{sh} R'}\right)^3 \tag{13.19}$$

Connecting the output voltage of the third stage directly to the input of the first stage makes $\mathbf{G}_{34} = 1$. Then $\mathbf{G}_{13}$ is given by

$$\mathbf{G}_{13} = \frac{\mathbf{G}_{23}}{1 - \mathbf{G}_{23}} = \frac{-g_m^3 R'^3}{(1 + j\omega C_{sh} R')^3 + g_m^3 R'^3} \tag{13.20}$$

Equating the denominator of Eq. (13.20) to zero gives

$$(1 + j\omega C_{sh} R')^3 + g_m^3 R'^3 = 0 \tag{13.21}$$

Multiplying the cubic term in Eq. (13.21) out and arranging terms gives

$$1 - 3\omega^2 C_{sh}^2 R'^2 + g_m^3 R'^3 + j\omega C_{sh} R'(3 - \omega^2 C_{sh}^2 R'^2) = 0 \tag{13.22}$$

For Eq. (13.22) to be satisfied, the real part of the equation must equal zero and the imaginary part must equal zero also. Equating the imaginary part to zero and solving for ω gives

$$\omega = \frac{\sqrt{3}}{C_{sh} R'} \tag{13.23}$$

which is the output frequency of the circuit as an oscillator. Equating the real part of Eq. (13.22) to zero and substituting in Eq. (13.23) gives

$$g_m R' = 2 \tag{13.24}$$

which must be satisfied if the system is to oscillate.

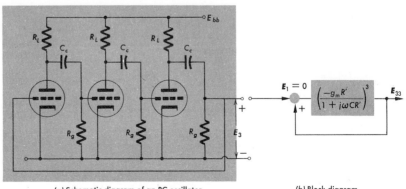

FIG. 13.9 *An RC oscillator.*

(a) Schematic diagram of an RC oscillator (b) Block diagram

The circuit diagram of the amplifier is shown in Fig. 13.9a, and the feedback block diagram is shown in Fig. 13.9b. The output voltage E_3 is sinusoidal provided that Eqs. (13.22) and (13.23) are satisfied. This is one example of an oscillator whose output is sustained by feedback.

13.4 FEEDBACK IN AMPLIFIERS

The use of feedback in amplifiers is justified only when the characteristics of the amplifier are improved by feedback. In amplifiers, feedback is generally employed in such a way as to maintain the denominator of Eq. (13.6) following with a magnitude greater than unity,

$$G_{13} = \frac{G_{23}}{1 \mp G_{23}G_{34}}$$

This is in contrast to the application of feedback in oscillators, where the denominator of Eq. (13.6) was required to be zero. From Eq. (13.6) it can be seen that the over-all gain G_{13} is less than the open-loop gain G_{23} when the magnitude of the denominator is maintained greater than unity.

Feedback paths or loops are not always apparent in amplifiers but appear when the equation of the circuit is written and the block diagram is drawn. For example, consider the triode amplifier shown in Fig. 13.10a and its equivalent circuit shown in (b). Qualitatively it can be seen that the plate current flowing through the cathode resistor R_K produces a voltage drop across R_K which must be added to E_1 to produce the grid-to-cathode voltage E_g.

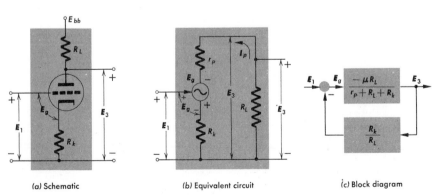

(a) Schematic   (b) Equivalent circuit   (c) Block diagram

FIG. 13.10 *A single-stage triode amplifier with feedback.*

Thus the alternating signal voltage across R_K is the feedback voltage of the amplifier.

Analyzing the amplifier circuit of Fig. 13.10 reveals three equations in four variables, given by

$$\mathbf{E}_g - R_K\mathbf{I}_p = \mathbf{E}_1$$
$$- R_L\mathbf{I}_p + \mathbf{E}_3 = 0 \qquad (13.25)$$
$$\mu\mathbf{E}_g + (r_p + R_L + R_K)\mathbf{I}_p = 0$$

Equations (13.25) can be solved for the output voltage $\mathbf{E}_3$ as a function of the input $\mathbf{E}_1$. Using Cramer's rule and determinants results in the solution

$$\mathbf{E}_3 = \frac{-\mu R_L\mathbf{E}_1}{r_p + R_L + (1 + \mu)R_K} \qquad (13.26)$$

from which the over-all gain is given by

$$\mathbf{G}_{13} = \frac{\mathbf{E}_3}{\mathbf{E}_1} = \frac{-\mu R_L}{r_p + R_L + (1 + \mu)R_K} \qquad (13.27)$$

As is to be expected, when R_K is reduced to zero, $\mathbf{G}_{13}$ becomes

$$\mathbf{G}_{13} = \frac{-\mu R_L}{r_p + R_L} \qquad (13.28)$$

which is the gain equation for the elementary vacuum-triode amplifier similar to Eq. (11.7). Thus by adding R_K in the cathode circuit we have added the term $(1 + \mu)R_K$ in the denominator of Eq. (13.28) to give Eq. (13.27), and the gain has been reduced by the addition of the feedback to the circuit.

In order to correlate Eq. (13.27) with the general feedback equation (13.6),

$$\mathbf{G}_{13} = \frac{\mathbf{G}_{23}}{1 \mp \mathbf{G}_{23}\mathbf{G}_{34}}$$

we can adopt techniques developed in Sec. 13.2. In the system of equations (13.25), the block diagram can be drawn to satisfy each of the equations. The resulting block is shown in Fig. 13.10c, where it can be recognized that

$$\mathbf{G}_{23} = \frac{-\mu R_L}{r_p + R_L + R_K} \qquad (13.29)$$

and

$$\mathbf{G}_{34} = \frac{R_K}{R_L} \qquad (13.30)$$

The student can verify that, when Eqs. (13.29) and (13.30) are substituted into Eq. (13.6), Eq. (13.27) results.

The elementary common-emitter transistor amplifier discussed in Sec. 11.6 is inherently a feedback amplifier, as are all transistor-amplifier circuits. The feedback path can be visualized from the loop equations of the circuit of Fig. 13.11, reproduced from Fig. 11.10. The loop equations (11.30) from which the equivalent circuit for the common-emitter transistor amplifier was derived are

$$(r_b + r_e)\mathbf{I}_1 - r_e\mathbf{I}_2 = \mathbf{V}_{in}$$

$$-(r_e - r_m)\mathbf{I}_1 + (r_e + r_c + R_L - r_m)\mathbf{I}_2 = 0$$

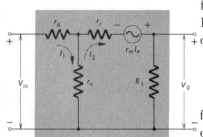

FIG. 13.11 *Equivalent circuit for the common-emitter amplifier.*

from which the block diagram can be drawn. Equations (11.30) can be written in the form

$$I_1 = \frac{V_{in}}{r_b + r_e} + \frac{r_e}{r_b + r_e} I_2 \tag{13.31}$$

$$I_2 = \frac{r_e - r_m}{r_e + r_c + R_L - r_m} I_1 \tag{13.32}$$

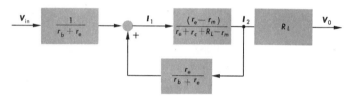

FIG. 13.12 *Block diagram representing the common-emitter amplifier of Fig. 13.11.*

The block diagram of Fig. 13.12 is divided to show those parts of the diagram for which each of the equations is responsible. The output voltage is given by

$$V_o = I_2 R_L \tag{13.33}$$

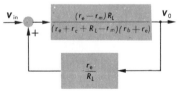

FIG. 13.13 *The block diagram of Fig. 13.12 reduces to this.*

which is also represented in Fig. 13.12. Simplification of the block diagram of Fig. 13.12 gives the diagram of Fig. 13.13, identical in form to the block diagram of Fig. 13.1a. It is apparent from Fig. 13.13 that

$$G_{23} = \frac{(r_e - r_m)R_L}{(r_e + r_c + R_L - r_m)(r_b + r_e)} \tag{13.34}$$

$$G_{34} = \frac{r_e}{R_L} \tag{13.35}$$

and

$$G_{13} = \frac{(r_e - r_m)R_L}{r_b(r_e + r_c + R_L - r_m) + r_e(r_c + R_L)} \tag{13.36}$$

Notice that G_{34} [Eq. (13.35)] for the transistor amplifier above is similar to G_{34} [Eq. (13.30)] for the triode amplifier with an unbypassed cathode resistor R_K. Thus the feedback element for the common-emitter transistor amplifier is r_e, and the feedback element for the triode amplifier is R_K. There are many other possible feedback circuits for amplifiers, but before analyzing any more we must determine what good comes from feedback.

13.5 WHAT FEEDBACK ACCOMPLISHES

Feedback invariably has an effect on the over-all gain of an amplifier. Only when G_{34} in Eq. (13.6) is zero (no feedback) does the over-all gain G_{13} equal the open-loop gain G_{23}. Suppose that G_{34} is not zero and that the magnitude of the denominator of Eq. (13.6) following is greater than unity,

$$G_{13} = \frac{G_{23}}{1 \mp G_{23}G_{34}}$$

$$|1 \mp G_{23}G_{34}| > 1 \qquad (13.37)$$

Then $|G_{13}|$ is less than $|G_{23}|$; the amplifier with feedback has less gain magnitude than the amplifier without feedback. In order to justify a loss in gain, improvements in amplifier characteristics must occur.

It was pointed out in Sec. 13.2 how the denominator of Eq. (13.6) can be made zero, in which case the feedback system becomes an oscillator. Now we consider the situation where $|G_{23}|$ is very large and the $G_{23}G_{34}$ product in Eq. (13.37) has a magnitude very much greater than unity. Then Eq. (13.6) reduces to

$$G_{13} \approx \frac{1}{\mp G_{34}} \qquad (13.38)$$

where $|G_{34}|$ must be less than unity for $|G_{13}|$ to be greater than unity, and thus the over-all gain G_{13} is independent of the open-loop gain G_{23}. The open-loop gain of the amplifier is a function of the tube or transistor parameters, which tend to drift with changes in temperature and with aging. But the block representing G_{34} can be made only of resistive elements or of resistive and reactive circuit elements which are relatively insensitive to temperature and aging. Then the gain of the amplifier with feedback, given by Eq. (13.38), is constant and does not tend to drift. For instrumentation and automatic controls, stable, drift-free amplifiers are often needed, and feedback in the amplifier is required. This is one of the main characteristics of feedback systems: the system gain is stable, and drift has been virtually eliminated. Thus we have traded amplifier gain for relative freedom from drift.

Besides the stability of amplification which the feedback amplifier possesses, other advantages to feedback also accrue. Distortion within the amplifier can be reduced by the use of feedback. Nonlinear distortion, caused by the nonlinearity of the characteristic curves, introduces harmonics as new frequencies in the amplifier output. Nonlinear distortion ordinarily occurs only in the last stage of an amplifier, because only at the last stage is the tube or transistor driven over a wide range on its characteristic curves. A feedback amplifier is represented in Fig. 13.14 with the

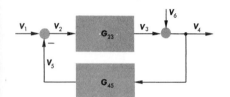

FIG. 13.14 *Block diagram of a feedback amplifier in which is generated a nonlinear distortion voltage* V_6.

distortion, consisting mainly of second-harmonic voltages represented by V_6, being introduced into the circuit at the output of G_{23}. Hence

$$V_4 = V_3 + V_6 \tag{13.39}$$

The output voltage V_4 consists of not only the desired frequencies contained in V_1 (and therefore V_3) but also the distortion frequencies contained in V_6. In addition to Eq. (13.39), the other algebraic equations required for the solution of a system shown in Fig. 13.14 are

$$V_1 - V_5 = V_2$$
$$G_{23}V_2 = V_3 \tag{13.40}$$
$$G_{45}V_4 = V_5$$

Equations (13.39) and (13.40) can be solved simultaneously for V_4 as a function of V_1 and V_6, giving

$$V_4 = \frac{V_1 G_{23} + V_6}{1 + G_{23}G_{34}} \tag{13.41}$$

The consequence of Eq. (13.41) is this: the addition of the feedback path with the feedback transfer function G_{34} reduces the over-all gain of the amplifier by the fraction $1/(1 + G_{23}G_{34})$, and it reduces the distortion signal from V_6 appearing in the output by the same fraction. Nothing has been gained when both the signal and the distortion have been reduced by the same fraction, unless some distortion-free amplification can be added at low signal levels. This is exactly what must be done to take advantage of feedback to reduce nonlinear distortion. Relatively distortion-free amplification can be obtained at low signal levels; only when an amplifier is driven by an input voltage covering a wide range on the characteristic curve does the nonlinear distortion occur. When several stages of amplification are cascaded together, nonlinear distortion occurs mainly in the last stage. By adding more distortion-free gain in the earlier low-level stages to make up for the loss of gain due to feedback, the over-all distortion as a fraction of the output signal can be greatly reduced. Figure 13.15 shows a distortionless

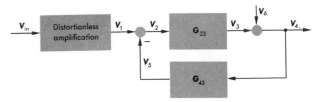

FIG. 13.15 *Adding distortionless gain at a low signal level to reduce nonlinear distortion.*

low-level amplifier preceding the feedback stages, building up the over-all gain, and reducing the effect of distortion caused by V_6. The fraction of distortion in the output can also be reduced if the distortionless amplifier is included within the feedback loop; this would be accomplished if the summing point producing V_2 were moved to the left of the distortionless amplifier in Fig. 13.15.

Frequency and phase distortion can also be greatly improved by the addition of feedback in an amplifier. Frequency distortion results from gain being a function of frequency, causing some frequencies to be amplified more than others. Reference to Eq. (13.38) shows that, when G_{34} is made frequency-insensitive, the over-all gain G_{13} is also frequency-insensitive. The feedback circuit can be designed by using only a resistive network in G_{34}, and therefore the frequency dependence of G_{13} results only from the effect of stray capacitance in the circuit. Thus G_{13} is made relatively frequency-insensitive, resulting in the upper and lower cutoff frequencies of the amplifier with feedback being extended to add greatly to the frequency range of the amplifier. Phase distortion (phase shift between the amplifier input and the amplifier output) is also minimized by the addition of feedback in the amplifier. This is also verified by examining Eq. (13.38) and observing that, if G_{34} is a resistive network, the phase shift between V_1 and V_3 does not change with frequency.

13.6 THE CATHODE FOLLOWER

A cathode follower is a vacuum-tube amplifier with a high input impedance and a low output impedance. It is used to couple a high-impedance voltage source to a low-impedance load to obtain maximum power transfer to the load. Thus it serves as an impedance transformer; it has no other use because its gain is less than unity.

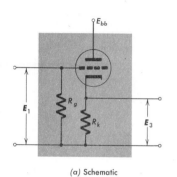

(a) Schematic

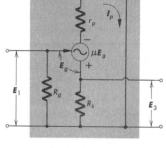

(b) Equivalent circuit

FIG. 13.16 *The cathode-follower amplifier.*

The schematic circuit of the cathode follower is shown in Fig. 13.16a, and the equivalent circuit is shown in Fig. 13.16b. The system of equations describing the equivalent circuit can be written

$$\mathbf{E}_g - R_K\mathbf{I}_p = \mathbf{E}_1$$

$$\mu\mathbf{E}_g + (r_p + R_K)\mathbf{I}_p = 0 \tag{13.42}$$

$$R_K\mathbf{I}_p + \mathbf{E}_3 = 0$$

where $\mathbf{E}_3$ is the output voltage and $\mathbf{E}_1$ is the input voltage. Using Cramer's rule to solve for $\mathbf{E}_3$ gives

$$\mathbf{E}_3 = \frac{\begin{vmatrix} 1 & -R_K & \mathbf{E}_1 \\ \mu & r_p + R_K & 0 \\ 0 & R_K & 0 \end{vmatrix}}{\begin{vmatrix} 1 & -R_K & 0 \\ \mu & r_p + R_K & 0 \\ 0 & R_K & 1 \end{vmatrix}} = \frac{\mu R_K\mathbf{E}_1}{(1 + \mu)R_K + r_p} \tag{13.43}$$

where the over-all voltage gain can be written

$$G_{13} = \frac{E_3}{E_1} = \frac{\mu R_K}{(1 + \mu)R_K + r_p} \tag{13.44}$$

Equation (13.44) shows that for positive values of μ, R_K, and r_p the gain is less than unity. But, for R_K very much greater than r_p and μ very much greater than 1, the gain approaches unity. Furthermore, there is no phase shift between the output voltage and the input voltage.

The system of equations given by Eqs. (13.42) can be represented by a block diagram as shown in Fig. 13.17. Notice that, when the feedback loop is open, the open-loop transfer function is the gain of the amplifier when the input signal is applied directly to the grid of the triode. From Fig. 13.17 it is apparent that

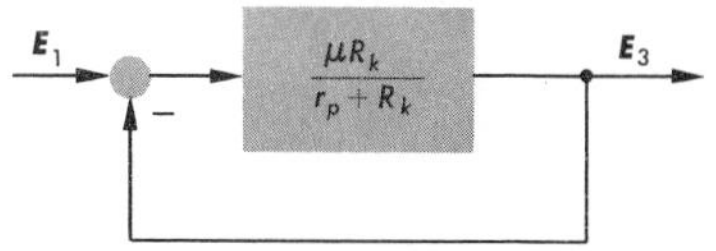

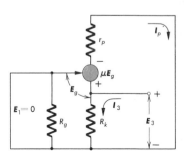

FIG. 13.17   *Block diagram of the cathode follower.*

$$G_{23} = \frac{\mu R_K}{r_p + R_K} \qquad G_{34} = 1 \tag{13.45}$$

An amplifier with a gain of less than unity can be accomplished by means of passive circuit elements such as resistors. A voltage divider has a gain of less than unity. To justify an amplifier with a gain of unity, the cathode follower must possess the advantage of impedance transformation with high input impedance and low output impedance. In order to find the output impedance of the cathode follower, the signal at the input terminals must be maintained zero, the output terminals must be driven by a voltage generator, and the output impedance obtained from the ratio of the output voltage to the output current. This procedure is shown in Fig. 13.18, where $E_1 = 0$ and the voltage generator E_3 has been connected to the output terminals. The output impedance as seen at the output terminals is E_3/I_3. The equations describing the circuit of Fig. 13.18 can be written

$$-R_K I_p + R_K I_3 = E_3$$

$$\mu E_g + (r_p + R_K)I_p - R_K I_3 = 0 \tag{13.46}$$

$$E_g - R_K I_p + R_K I_3 = 0$$

Solving the above equations for I_3 as a function of E_3 and then taking the ratio of E_3 to I_3 gives

$$Z_o = \frac{R_K r_p}{r_p + R_K(1 + \mu)} \tag{13.47}$$

which is the output impedance of the cathode follower. Equation (13.47) shows that the output impedance is less than R_K and r_p in

FIG. 13.18   *Equivalent circuit for finding output impedance of a cathode follower.*

parallel. The open-loop gain of the cathode follower is obtained by injecting the input signal directly between the control grid and the cathode. Output impedance for the cathode follower without feedback is obtained by constraining $\mathbf{E}_g$ to zero and obtaining the ratio of output voltage applied to the output terminals to the output current. This gives the output impedance without feedback as

$$\mathbf{Z}'_o = \frac{R_K r_p}{r_p + R_K} \tag{13.48}$$

where $\mathbf{Z}'_o$ is the symbol used for output impedance without feedback. It follows from Eqs. (13.47), (13.48), and (13.45) that

$$\mathbf{Z}_o = \frac{\mathbf{Z}'_o}{1 + \mathbf{G}_{23}\mathbf{G}_{34}} \tag{13.49}$$

Equation (13.49) shows that, when the feedback loop is closed, the output impedance decreases by the same factor that the gain decreases. This can be shown to be generally true for feedback amplifiers; when the feedback loop is closed, the voltage gain decreases by a factor of $1/(1 + \mathbf{G}_{23}\mathbf{G}_{34})$ and the output impedance decreases by the same factor.

Example 13.2

For a particular cathode follower it is required that $\mathbf{Z}_o = 100$ ohms. The triode being used has the constants $r_p = 10{,}000$ ohms and $\mu = 20$. To find the value of R_K required to furnish the output impedance of 100 ohms, solve Eq. (13.47) for R_K as a function of $\mathbf{Z}_o$. This gives

$$R_K = \frac{r_p \mathbf{Z}_o}{r_p - \mathbf{Z}_o(1 + \mu)} \tag{13.50}$$

Substituting $\mathbf{Z}_o$, r_p, and μ into Eq. (13.50) gives

$$R_K = 126.7 \text{ ohms}$$

The gain of the cathode follower for $R_K = 126.7$ ohms, $r_p = 10{,}000$ ohms, and $\mu = 20$ is obtained from Eq. (13.44),

$$\mathbf{G}_{13} = 0.2$$

13.7 FREQUENCY RESPONSE

Transfer function has been defined as the ratio of the output variable to the input variable when the input variable is a sinusoid. Complex impedance is an example of a transfer function if current

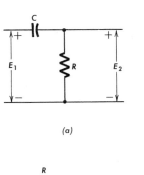

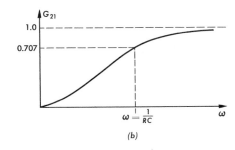

(a)

(b)

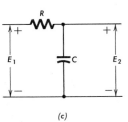

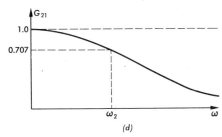

FIG. 13.19 *RC circuits and their gain-versus-frequency curves.*

(c)

(d)

is considered the input variable, a sinusoid, and the voltage is considered the output variable. The RC circuit shown in Fig. 13.19a is another example of a transfer circuit; if $\mathbf{E}_2$ is defined as the output voltage and $\mathbf{E}_1$ is the input voltage, then

$$\mathbf{G}_{12} = \frac{\mathbf{E}_2}{\mathbf{E}_1} = \frac{R}{R - j/\omega C} = \frac{1}{1 - j/\omega CR} \qquad (13.51)$$

Notice that the magnitude of Eq. (13.51) is maximum when ω is very large; as ω approaches infinity, $\mathbf{G}_{21}$ approaches unity. But for low frequencies, as ω approaches zero, $\mathbf{G}_{21}$ also approaches zero, as shown in Fig. 13.19b. The lower cutoff frequency occurs when $\mathbf{G}_{21} = 0.707$, or when $\omega CR = 1$, or

$$\omega_1 = \frac{1}{RC} \qquad (13.52)$$

The RC transfer circuit shown in Fig. 13.19c has the transfer function

$$\mathbf{G}_{12} = \frac{-j/\omega C}{R - j/\omega C} = \frac{1}{1 + j\omega CR} \qquad (13.53)$$

The magnitude of the transfer function represented by Eq. (13.53) is maximum at zero frequency, where $\mathbf{G}_{21} = 1$. As ω becomes large and approaches infinity, the magnitude of the transfer function approaches zero, as shown in Fig. 13.19d. The cutoff frequency occurs when $\omega CR = 1$, or $\omega_2 = 1/CR$.

13.7 Frequency Response **351**

The frequency response of an open-loop amplifier affects the over-all gain of the amplifier when feedback is added. Suppose that a single-stage RC amplifier is operating in a frequency range where the high-frequency equivalent circuit applies. The voltage-gain equation in this frequency range is Eq. (11.24),

$$\mathbf{A}_v = \frac{-g_m R'}{1 + j\omega C_{sh} R'}$$

If part of the output voltage is fed back to the input without loading the amplifier, the over-all gain of the amplifier with feedback has frequency characteristics different from the open-loop frequency characteristics. This is illustrated in the following example.

Example 13.3

Assume that the open-loop gain of an amplifier can be expressed by

$$\mathbf{G}_{23} = \frac{-10}{1 + j10^{-5}\omega} \tag{13.54}$$

and a resistive network picks off one-tenth of the output voltage to be fed back to the input. Then

$$\mathbf{G}_{34} = 0.1$$

Assume also that the feedback voltage is added to the input voltage. Then [Eq. (13.6)]

$$\mathbf{G}_{13} = \frac{\mathbf{G}_{23}}{1 - \mathbf{G}_{23}\mathbf{G}_{34}}$$

or

$$\mathbf{G}_{13} = \frac{-10}{2 + j10^{-5}\omega}$$

Compare the open-loop gain G_{23} with the closed-loop gain G_{13}, we first observe that the feedback reduced the gain magnitude at low frequencies from 10, the open-loop gain, to 5, the closed-loop gain. Furthermore, we observe that the upper cutoff frequency of the amplifier without feedback occurs when $10^{-5}\omega = 1$, or $\omega = 10^5$ radians/sec. With feedback the upper cutoff frequency occurs when $10^{-5}\omega = 2$, or $\omega = 2 \times 10^5$ radians/sec. Thus we see that by adding feedback to the amplifier the gain magnitude has been reduced one-half but the upper cutoff frequency has been extended by a factor of 2. We have traded gain magnitude for bandwidth by adding feedback.

SUMMARY

Feedback can best be explained with the help of the block diagram or signal-flow diagram of Fig. 13.1a, where X_1 is defined as the input variable and X_3 is defined as the output variable. Then feedback occurs when part of the output variable X_3 is returned to the input and added to or subtracted from the input variable X_1. The over-all gain of the system with feedback represented by Fig. 13.1a is

$$G_{13} = \frac{G_{23}}{1 \mp G_{23}G_{34}}$$

where [Eq. (13.1)]

$$X_2 = X_1 \pm X_4$$

G_{23} is the open-loop gain, and G_{34} is the gain in the feedback path.

A physical system with a sinusoidal input variable can be represented by a system of algebraic equations, which, in turn, can be represented by a block diagram. The solution of the system of equations corresponds to the reduction of the block diagram to a single open-loop block relating the output variable to the input variable.

A linear sinusoidal oscillator or sine-wave voltage generator can be described by Eq. (13.6) for the special case of Eq. (13.18),

$$1 + G_{23}G_{34} = 0$$

When Eq. (13.18) is satisfied, the output variable X_3 can be sustained when the input variable X_1 is zero; under the condition of Eq. (13.18), the denominator of Eq. (13.6) is zero and the closed-loop gain G_{13} is infinite. Thus an oscillator is a feedback amplifier which requires no input voltage.

By adding feedback to a linear electronic circuit, stability of gain can be greatly improved even though the over-all gain is reduced. The gain of an amplifier is a function of the tube or transistor parameters, which tend to change with changes of temperature and with aging. If the open-loop gain G_{23} is made large and G_{34} is the transfer function of the feedback loop containing only passive elements, then the closed-loop gain is [Eq. (13.38)]

$$\mathbf{G}_{13} \approx \frac{1}{\mp \mathbf{G}_{34}}$$

Then $\mathbf{G}_{13}$ is independent of $\mathbf{G}_{23}$ and the tube or transistor parameters. If $\mathbf{G}_{13}$ is to be greater than unity, $\mathbf{G}_{34}$ must have a magnitude less than unity.

Nonlinear distortion can be reduced in an amplifier by adding feedback, but additional stages of distortionless gain at the low signal levels are necessary to compensate for the reduced gain caused by the feedback. Frequency and phase distortion are also improved by feedback, as shown by reference to Eq. (13.38); since $\mathbf{G}_{34}$ can be made relatively insensitive to frequency, $\mathbf{G}_{13}$ is also relatively frequency-independent.

FURTHER READING

The literature of feedback systems is very extensive, and many useful reference books have been published since about 1947. Block-diagram analysis is discussed in David K. Cheng, *Analysis of Linear Systems* (Addison-Wesley Publishing Company, Reading, Mass., 1959), chap. 9, and in M. E. Van Valkenburg, *Network Analysis* (Prentice-Hall, Inc., Englewood Cliffs, N.J., 1955), chap. 15. Feedback-amplifier literature usually uses the nomenclature A for the forward gain G_{23} and β for the feedback gain G_{34}. Jacob Millman, *Vacuum-tube and Semiconductor Electronics* (McGraw-Hill Book Company, Inc., New York, 1958), chap. 17, and Samuel Seely, *Electron-tube Circuits*, 2d ed. (McGraw-Hill Book Company, Inc., New York, 1958), chap. 5, are conventional references on feedback amplifiers. L. Dale Harris, *Introduction to Feedback Systems* (John Wiley & Sons, Inc., New York, 1961), chap. 6, discusses feedback amplifiers using root-locus techniques mentioned in Chap. 20 of this text.

PROBLEMS

13.1 A certain voltage amplifier has a voltage gain of 10^4, with the output voltage exactly in phase with the input voltage. Feedback is added, and the voltage gain drops to 10^3, with the output voltage still in phase with the input. *Find* $\mathbf{G}_{34}$, and show a circuit of passive circuit elements which has the required transfer function.

13.2 The block diagram shown in the illustration in (*a*) can be reduced to the single open-loop block shown in (*b*). *Find* $\mathbf{G}_{16}$.

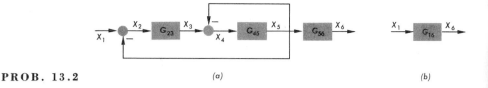

(a)

(b)

13.3 Given the system of equations

$$X_2 + X_5 = X_1$$

$$AX_2 - X_3 = 0$$

$$BX_3 - X_4 = 0$$

$$CX_4 - X_5 = 0$$

$$DX_4 - X_6 = 0$$

(a) Draw a block diagram, labeling all transfer functions and all variables. X_1 is the input variable, and X_6 is the output variable.

(b) Reduce the closed-loop transfer function to an open-loop transfer function with only one block.

13.4 For the circuit shown in the figure, write the system of equations, and represent the system of equations in a block diagram. Then reduce the block diagram to a single open-loop block. Use E_{in} as the input variable and E_o as the output variable.

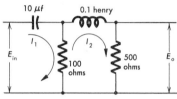

PROB. 13.4

13.5 Reduce the block diagram shown in the illustration in (a) to that shown in (b), and show the values of G_{23} and G_{34}.

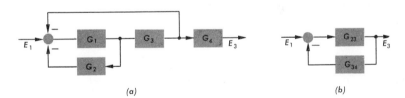

PROB. 13.5

(a)

(b)

13.6 Repeat Prob. 13.5 for the block diagram shown in the figure.

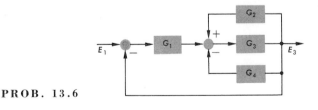

PROB. 13.6

13.7 A triode amplifier with an unbypassed cathode resistor is shown in the illustration. For the triode, $\mu = 80$, and $g_m = 0.0015$ mho; $R_L =$

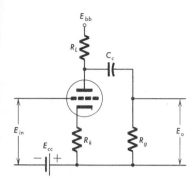

PROB. 13.7

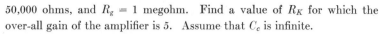

50,000 ohms, and $R_g = 1$ megohm. Find a value of R_K for which the over-all gain of the amplifier is 5. Assume that C_c is infinite.

13.8 In the circuit shown in the figure, consider E_1 as the input variable and E_2 as the output variable. Draw a block diagram with one block for each circuit element.

13.9 The single-stage amplifier circuit shown in the illustration uses cathode bias. Derive an equation for the mid-frequency gain of the circuit.

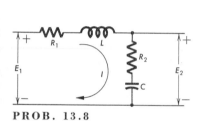

PROB. 13.8

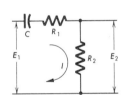

PROB. 13.9

13.10 Find transfer functions as functions of ω for the circuits shown in the figure. In each case assume that the input variable is E_1 and the output variable is E_2.

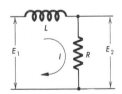
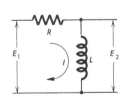

PROB. 13.10

13.11 Repeat Prob. 13.10, using I as the input variable and E_2 as the output variable.

13.12 The transfer function of the RC circuit of Fig. 13.19c is given by Eq. (13.53). Show the effect of loading on the circuit by connecting a load resistor R_L in parallel with the capacitor and deriving the new transfer function.

ELECTRONIC ANALOG COMPUTERS

14

14.1 NETWORK ANALYZERS

In the preceding chapters we have seen numerous examples in which electric circuits were described by differential equations of exactly the same form as the differential equations of mechanical systems. The solutions of the differential equations are independent of the nature of the system but depend rather on the form of the differential equation, the magnitude of the coefficients, the nature of the exciting function, and the initial conditions.

If a physical system can be described by a system of differential equations, it is often possible to find an electric network which has a system of identical differential equations. For example, the general form of the homogeneous second-order differential equation expressed in Eq. (3.56) describes a mechanical system of a spring, a dashpot, and mass shown in Fig. 14.1a, as well as an electric series *RLC* circuit shown in Fig. 14.1b.

$$\frac{d^2x}{dt^2} + 2\omega_n \zeta \frac{dx}{dt} + \omega_n{}^2 x = 0$$

Equation (14.1) shows that the sum of the forces acting on the mass equals zero, and the forces are expressed in terms of the dependent variable, velocity v.

$$M \frac{dv}{dt} + Bv + K \int v \, dt = 0 \qquad (14.1)$$

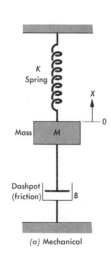

(a) Mechanical

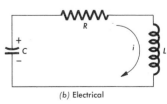

(b) Electrical

FIG. 14.1 *Two analogous physical systems.*

Equation (14.2) equates the voltages around the loop to zero, and each of these voltages is expressed as a function of the loop current i.

$$L\frac{di}{dt} + Ri + \frac{1}{C}\int i\, dt = 0 \qquad (14.2)$$

If we recognize that $v = dx/dt$ and $i = dq/dt$, then we can write Eqs. (14.1) and (14.2) as

$$M\frac{d^2x}{dt^2} + B\frac{dx}{dt} + Kx = 0 \qquad (14.3)$$

$$L\frac{d^2q}{dt^2} + R\frac{dq}{dt} + \frac{1}{C}q = 0 \qquad (14.4)$$

Comparison of Eqs. (14.1) and (14.2) or Eqs. (14.3) and (14.4) reveals the analogies shown in Table 14.1. In particular notice that displacement x is now analogous to electric charge q.

Comparison of the two pairs of equations, Eqs. (14.1) and (14.2) and Eqs. (14.3) and (14.4), shows that, if a correspondence between M and L, B and R, and K and $1/C$ exists, then the solution of one corresponds exactly to the solution of the other if the initial conditions are equivalent. This is the principle of the network analyzer.

By means of an analogous electric network, various physical systems can be studied. Electric currents and voltages can be recorded conveniently as functions of time even though they may be changing very rapidly with time. Often the electric quantities can be recorded more accurately than mechanical quantities. Furthermore, it may be easier to assemble a network of resistors, inductors, and capacitors than to assemble a complex system of springs, masses, and dashpots or equivalent thermal or hydraulic components. Convenience of recording electric quantities and

TABLE 14.1 *Mechanical-Electrical Analogies Shown by Eqs. (14.1) and (14.2)*

			Friction	Spring
Mechanical	Velocity v	Mass m	constant B	constant K
Electrical	Current i	Inductance L	Resistance R	Reciprocal capacitance $\frac{1}{C}$

ease of assembling networks of resistance, inductance, and capacitance have made the network analyzer an important tool of research and design.

The network analyzer, or differential analyzer, is a form of analog computer. The network analyzer, however, has two major weaknesses. One is that inductors always contain resistance, and if only a very small amount of resistance is allowed in the electric analog, the analog cannot be made. Another weakness is that it is not always easy or even possible to find an electric circuit analogous to the system under study. These disadvantages are not present in the electronic analog computer, to be studied later in this chapter.

Example 14.1

A thermometer is in equilibrium in a liquid at a temperature of $T_0°$ abs. At time $t = 0$, the thermometer is suddenly immersed in another liquid that is maintained at temperature T_1. Find an electric-circuit analog to find thermometer temperature T as a function of time.

First, the differential equation is obtained.

The rate of heat flow, proportional to the temperature difference, is $K(T_1 - T)$, where K is the heat-transfer constant. Then the rate of change of temperature T is

$$\frac{dT}{dt} = \frac{K(T_1 - T)}{MS}$$

where M is the mass of the mercury and S is its specific heat. Then

$$\frac{MS}{K}\frac{dT}{dt} + T = T_1$$

or

$$MS\frac{dT}{dt} + KT = KT_1$$

where at $t = 0+$, $T = T_0$ and the differential equation looks like the equation of an RL circuit,

$$L\frac{di}{dt} + Ri = E_1$$

At $t = 0+$, $i = I_0 = E_0/R$, where i corresponds to T. The electric-circuit analog might then be as shown in Fig. 14.2, where E_1 corresponds to KT_1, E_0 corresponds to KT_0, L corresponds to MS, R to K, and the time constant L/R corresponds to the thermal time constant MS/K. The switching must be accomplished instantaneously.

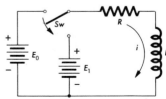

FIG. 14.2 *Electric-circuit analog to thermometer problem.*

14.2 INTEGRATING AND DIFFERENTIATING CIRCUITS

An electric circuit which performs the operation of integration or differentiation can be synthesized from a capacitance or an inductance or from combinations of resistance and capacitance or resistance and inductance. For instance, a characteristic of capacitance is that the voltage across the capacitor is equal to a constant $1/C$ times the integral of the current with respect to time, as shown in Eq. (1.35).

$$ v = \frac{1}{C} \int_0^t i\, dt + V_o $$

However, the capacitor also can be treated as a differentiator by recognizing that the current through the capacitor is proportional to the rate of change of voltage across the capacitance as shown in Eq. (1.36).

$$ i = C \frac{dv}{dt} $$

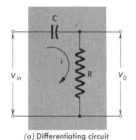

(a) Differentiating circuit

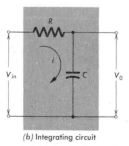

(b) Integrating circuit

FIG. 14.3 *RC circuits for differentiating and integrating.*

Thus a capacitor may be thought of either as an integrating device or as a differentiating device. This is also true of an inductor. In order to solve differential equations by means of integrators or differentiators, it is desirable to have only one dependent variable in each circuit. Either voltage or current can be used as the dependent variable, but not both. An ideal integrator is one in which the output voltage is proportional to the integral of the input voltage with respect to time, or the output current is proportional to the integral of the input current with respect to time. Likewise, a differentiator should produce an output voltage that is proportional to the derivative of the input voltage, or an output current that is proportional to the derivative of the input current.

Only approximate integrating and differentiating circuits can be achieved by RL and RC combinations with voltage as the dependent variable and time as the independent variable. Figure 14.3 shows an example of integrating and differentiating circuits using RC combinations. Consider the differentiating circuit of Fig. 14.3a. By Kirchhoff's voltage law, we can write Eq. (14.5), where iR is the output voltage v_o and $V_o = 0$.

$$v_{\text{in}} = \frac{1}{C}\int_0^t i\,dt + iR \qquad (14.5)$$

If the value of R is kept very small so that the iR term is very much less than the integral term on the right side of Eq. (14.5), by differentiating both sides with respect to time we can show that, to a good approximation,

$$v_o \approx RC\frac{dv_{\text{in}}}{dt} \qquad (14.6)$$

An integrating circuit is shown in Fig. 14.3b. Kirchhoff's voltage law allows us to write

$$v_{\text{in}} = Ri + \frac{1}{C}\int_0^t i\,dt \qquad (14.7)$$

where $V_o = 0$. If R is large so that Ri is very much larger than the integral term in Eq. (14.7), then the current i is a function of R and v_{in} only, as shown in Eq. (14.8).

$$i \approx \frac{v_{\text{in}}}{R} \qquad (14.8)$$

Since

$$v_o = \frac{1}{C}\int_0^t i\,dt \qquad (14.9)$$

then

$$v_o = \frac{1}{RC}\int_0^t v_{\text{in}}\,dt \qquad (14.10)$$

Thus we see that an RC circuit can accomplish approximate integration or differentiation with respect to time, as seen by Eqs. (14.6) and (14.10).

14.3 THE OPERATIONAL AMPLIFIER

An operational amplifier is a high-gain direct-coupled voltage amplifier. It is used in an electronic analog computer to synthesize integrators, differentiators, adders, sign changers, and constant multipliers. As a d-c amplifier, it has a flat gain-versus-frequency curve from zero frequency to several thousand cycles per second. The gain of an operational amplifier must be very high to satisfy the requirements of an integrator or differentiator. Ordinarily, the gain of the operational amplifier is at least 10^5. Several stages of amplification are necessary to achieve the required gain. Operational amplifiers always have an odd number of stages so that, if positive feedback from the output to the input develops to the slightest degree, oscillation will not take place. The gain, then, is negative since an incremental increase in the input voltage to the amplifier produces an incremental decrease in the output voltage.

An operational amplifier is characterized by a very high input impedance of the order of 10^9 or 10^{10} ohms. This is necessary in order to prevent the input of the amplifier from loading down the voltage source at the input of the amplifier. As a voltage amplifier, the operational amplifier has an output that is limited to about ± 100 volts. If we assume that ± 100 volts is the maximum possible output voltage and the gain of the amplifier is 100,000, then the maximum permissible voltage applied to the input of the amplifier is ± 0.001 volt. The reasons for these operational amplifier characteristics will become apparent in the next sections.

14.4 THE OPERATIONAL AMPLIFIER AS AN INTEGRATOR

The operational amplifier mentioned in the last section has several applications in electronic analog computers, one of which is its use as an integrator. Consider the circuit of Fig. 14.4a, where the triangle marked $-A$ is the operational amplifier. Since the output v_o of the amplifier cannot exceed ± 100 volts and the amplifier gain is greater than 10^5, the input v_a to the amplifier must be less than 1 mv. Thus, v_a is very much smaller than either v_{in} or v_o, and v_a can be considered to be very nearly equal to zero. Furthermore, the input impedance to ground of the amplifier is extremely high, which means that the current shown as i_{in} cannot flow to ground through the input impedance of the amplifier and must flow on through the capacitor C. In other words, $i_{in} \approx i_o$, and $v_a \approx 0$, which is justification for the equivalent circuit shown in Fig. 14.4b.

Equating i_{in} to i_o by Kirchhoff's current law, we have

$$i_{in} = \frac{v_{in}}{R} \tag{14.11}$$

$$i_o = -C \frac{dv_o}{dt} \tag{14.12}$$

from which

$$v_o = -\frac{1}{RC} \int v_{in}\, dt \tag{14.13}$$

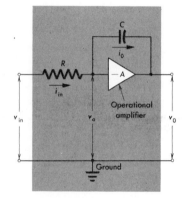

(a) Schematic

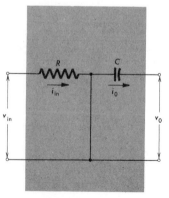

(b) Equivalent circuit

FIG. 14.4 *Operational amplifier as an integrator.*

Notice the sign change between v_o and the integral. Equation (14.13) shows that the output voltage v_o is proportional to the integral of the input voltage v_{in} to the circuit. If $R = 1$ megohm and $C = 1$ μf, then the coefficient of the integral is -1. The sign change still exists. Notice that gain A of the amplifier does not appear in Eq. (14.13). As long as the voltage gain is large, it may vary without significantly affecting the accuracy of the integrator.

14.5 THE OPERATIONAL AMPLIFIER AS A DIFFERENTIATOR

Interchanging the resistor and the capacitor used with the operational amplifier as an integrator results in the circuit of Fig. 14.5a. This circuit is a differentiator. Since v_a is very small, the circuit of Fig. 14.5b is an approximate equivalent to that in Fig. 14.5a. Equating i_{in} to i_o, we have

$$C\frac{dv_{in}}{dt} = -\frac{v_o}{R} \qquad (14.14)$$

or

$$v_o = -RC\frac{dv_{in}}{dt} \qquad (14.15)$$

Notice again the negative sign in Eq. (14.15), and keep in mind that the gain of the amplifier must be very high in order that the input voltage to the amplifier v_a be nearly zero.

14.6 THE OPERATIONAL AMPLIFIER AS A CONSTANT MULTIPLIER AND ADDER

The use of RC circuits with operational amplifiers can produce integration and differentiation. Now suppose that we use resistors both as the input impedance R_i and the feedback impedance R_f, as shown in Fig. 14.6. With the same assumptions and approximations as in the preceding analysis, we can equate i_{in} to i_o, from which

$$\frac{v_{in}}{R_i} = -\frac{v_o}{R_f} \qquad \text{or} \qquad v_o = -\frac{R_f}{R_i}v_{in} \qquad (14.16)$$

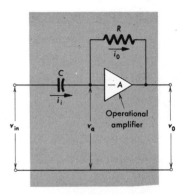

(a) Schematic

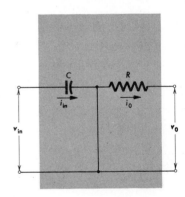

(b) Equivalent circuit

FIG. 14.5 *Operational amplifier as a differentiator.*

14.6 **The Operational Amplifier as a Constant Multiplier and Adder** **363**

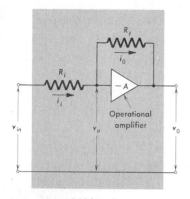

(a) Schematic

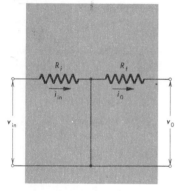

(b) Equivalent circuit

FIG. 14.6 *Operational amplifier as a constant multiplier.*

Equation (14.16) shows two applications of this circuit in computer work. First, the circuit can be used to multiply by a constant represented by $-R_f/R_i$. Second, if $R_f = R_i$, this circuit is merely a sign changer, multiplying the input voltage by -1. Notice again the negative sign in Eq. (14.16) caused by the negative gain of the amplifier.

Next, we seek to verify the multiple-input circuit of Fig. 14.7 as an adder. The operational amplifier has the usual characteristics. Equating the input current i_{in} to i_o, we have

$$\frac{v_1}{R_{i1}} + \frac{v_2}{R_{i2}} + \cdots + \frac{v_n}{R_{\text{in}}} = -\frac{v_o}{R_f}$$

or

$$v_o = -\left(\frac{R_f}{R_{i1}}v_1 + \frac{R_f}{R_{i2}}v_2 + \cdots + \frac{R_f}{R_{\text{in}}}v_n\right) \tag{14.17}$$

Notice that, if $R_f = R_{i1} = R_{i2} = \cdots = R_{\text{in}}$, the output voltage v_o is the sum of the input voltages, with a change in sign. Thus the circuit of Fig. 14.7 is an adder capable of adding several voltages together. However, it is even more flexible than that. In addition to adding each voltage, it can multiply each voltage by a constant before performing the process of addition. Thus, several voltages can be multiplied by constants and added together by means of this circuit.

14.7 A SOLUTION OF DIFFERENTIAL EQUATIONS BY SUCCESSIVE INTEGRATION

Up to this point we have considered several possible computer operations using operational amplifiers. In this section we shall show how these circuits can be used to solve complete differential equations or systems of differential equations in which time is the independent variable. The solution of dynamic equations is the most useful area for using electronic analog computers.

Consider a mechanical system which can be described by the second-order differential equation

$$\frac{d^2x}{dt^2} + 10\frac{dx}{dt} + 35x = 2\sin \omega t \tag{14.18}$$

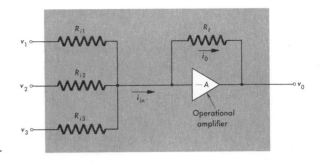

FIG. 14.7 *Operational amplifier as an adder.*

where x is displacement and t is time. In order to solve this equation by successive integration on the analog computer, we must first relate the displacement x from the problem to the voltage v as it appears on the computer. Then we solve Eq. (14.18) for the highest-order derivative, which is

$$\frac{d^2x}{dt^2} = 2 \sin \omega t - 10 \frac{dx}{dt} - 35x \qquad (14.19)$$

Thus we can generate the second derivative term by adding the terms on the right-hand side of Eq. (14.19), provided that the appropriate inputs to the adder are available. This process is shown in Fig. 14.8a, where voltage v corresponds to x. The number 1 placed near the resistors indicates that they are all equal and have a value of 1 megohm. In Fig. 14.8b, the negative of the second derivative is applied to an integrator, and the output of the in-

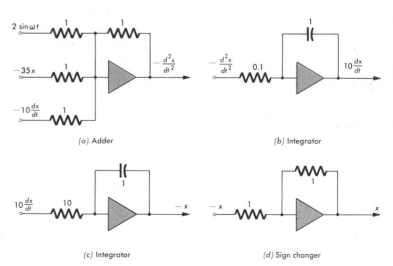

(a) Adder

(b) Integrator

(c) Integrator

(d) Sign changer

FIG. 14.8 *Circuits for an electronic analog of Eq. (14.18).*

14.7   A Solution of Differential Equations by Successive Integration   365

tegrator is the first derivative multiplied by 10. Notice the values of R and C, of 0.1 megohm and 1 μf, respectively, which produce multiplication by the constant 10 during the integration process. Notice further that the output of the integrator can be fed back as one of the inputs to the adder in Fig. 14.8a after changing its sign. In Fig. 14.8c the first derivative term is integrated again and multiplied by 0.1 to give $-x$ as the output. In Fig. 14.8d a sign changer is shown which changes $-x$ to $+x$, the dependent variable. The voltage corresponding to displacement x is recorded as a function of time and is the output of the computer and the solution to the problem.

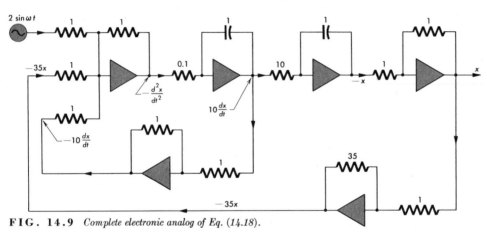

FIG. 14.9 *Complete electronic analog of Eq. (14.18).*

Figure 14.9 shows a complete electronic analog to Eq. (14.18). This is not the only electronic analog that can be used to solve Eq. (14.18) but is one of several. Values of resistance and capacitance are again shown in megohms and microfarads. The input is 2 sin ωt, and x is the output. In Fig. 14.10 the same equation has

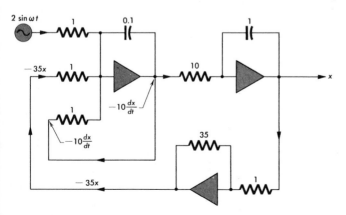

FIG. 14.10 *An electronic analog to Eq. (14.18) using three operational amplifiers.*

been solved with half as many amplifiers. Notice that the first amplifier simultaneously performs the addition of three variables, integration, and multiplication by 10. Also, a separate sign changer is not required in this configuration to generate $-10\,dx/dt$. This is an example of how, by careful programming, the number of amplifiers needed can be kept to a minimum.

The input to the electronic analog of Figs. 14.9 and 14.10 is the exciting function $2\sin\omega t$, which must come from a sinusoidal-voltage generator. In addition to the exciting function, the initial conditions of the problem must be set into the analog. There are two arbitrary constants in the solution of a second-order differential equation such as that of Eq. (14.18). It is necessary to know the initial value of x at $t = 0+$ and the derivative of x with respect to time at $t = 0+$ and set this information into the computer in order to find a unique solution. When these two initial values are known and fed into the computer, a single unique solution of x as a function of time can be obtained in the output of the computer. The initial conditions are not shown in Figs. 14.9 and 14.10 but can be taken care of in the following manner.

Let us first set in the initial value of x at $t = 0$ for the circuit of Fig. 14.9. Notice that x is the output of the analog and $-x$ is the output of the last integrator. Suppose that we set an initial charge on the capacitor of the last integrator so that the voltage on this capacitor is equal to the initial value of x as shown in Fig. 14.11a. The battery voltage V_o is analogous to the value of x at $t = 0+$, also in Fig. 14.11a. A mechanical system represented by Eq. (14.18) goes into operation at $t = 0+$. Assume that the switch in Fig. 14.11a is initially closed and that it opens at $t = 0$. Before the switch is opened, the capacitor C is charged to a potential equal to the battery voltage V_o. Since the potential at the input of the operational amplifier is approximately zero, the output of the operational amplifier $(-x)$ is initially $-V_o$. The output of the amplifier cannot change as long as the switch is in the closed position. To put the electronic analog into operation, the switch is opened. A similar switch on the first integrator of Fig. 14.9 sets in the value of the first derivative of x at $t = 0+$. In addition, constant multipliers, sign changers, and adders have switches as shown in Fig. 14.11b. All these switches are magnetic relays which can be controlled by a single switch and made to open at the same time. These switches, all opening simultaneously, set the electronic analog into operation. The next example will show how initial conditions are set into the analog computer.

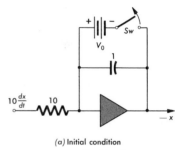

(a) Initial condition
$-x = -V_0$ at $t = 0$

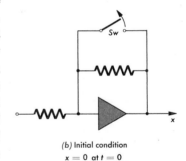

(b) Initial condition
$x = 0$ at $t = 0$

FIG. 14.11 *Establishing initial conditions with V_o and SW.*

14.7 A Solution of Differential Equations by Successive Integration 367

Consider the system of equations shown with their initial conditions as Eqs. (14.20)

$$\frac{d^2v_1}{dt^2} + 10v_2{}^2 = 5 \qquad\qquad (14.20a)$$

$$\frac{dv_2}{dt} + 2v_2 = v_1 \qquad\qquad (14.20b)$$

with initial conditions at $t = 0+$, $v_1 = 10$, $dv_1/dt = 0$, and $v_2 = 5$. These are simultaneous differential equations, and the first one is nonlinear. In these equations, v_1 and v_2 are the dependent variables, and t, of course, is the independent variable. These equations can be solved in a manner similar to the preceding single equation, but they must be solved simultaneously. Equation (14.21) shows the highest derivative in each equation, in preparation for setting up the electronic analog.

$$\frac{d^2v_1}{dt^2} = 5 - 10v_2{}^2$$

$$\qquad\qquad (14.21)$$

$$\frac{dv_2}{dt} = v_1 - 2v_2$$

Figure 14.12 shows one form of the electronic analog. No attempt has been made in this example to reduce the electronic analog to the one with the least number of operational amplifiers. Figure 14.12 also shows the switches and voltage sources with each operational amplifier that set in the initial conditions and put the system into operation when the switches are opened.

Some of the operational amplifiers of Fig. 14.12 can be eliminated. For instance, the process of addition and integration can be accomplished simultaneously by only one operational amplifier. This would combine the first two operational amplifiers of Fig. 14.12, but a change of sign results as shown in Fig. 14.13. Notice that two amplifiers in Fig. 14.13 accomplish what four amplifiers accomplished in Fig. 14.12.

The rectangular block marked M in Fig. 14.12 represents a multiplier of two variables. In this particular problem, the two variables happen to be v_2, so that the output of the M is proportional to $v_2{}^2$. At the same time v_2 is multiplied by itself, it is multiplied by the constant -10, so that the output of M is $-10v_2{}^2$. For the time being, we shall consider multipliers of two variables only as an element or block in the analog-computer diagram, and we shall not look inside the box until Sec. 14.9.

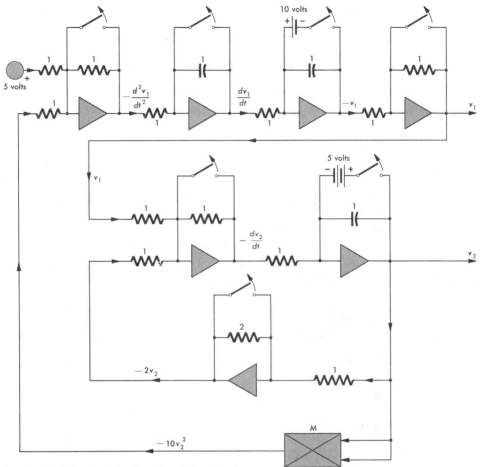

FIG. 14.12 *An electronic analog of Eqs. (14.20).*

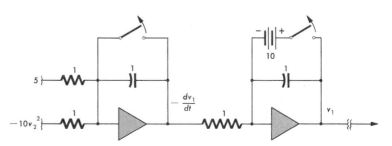

FIG. 14.13 *Method of eliminating two amplifiers of Fig. 14.12.*

14.8 SOLUTION BY DIFFERENTIATION

A differential equation or a system of differential equations can be solved by successive differentiation as well as by integration. As an example, consider Eq. (14.18), and rewrite it as

$$x = \frac{2}{35} \sin \omega t - \frac{10}{35} \frac{dx}{dt} - \frac{1}{35} \frac{d^2 x}{dt^2} \tag{14.22}$$

By using adders, constant multipliers, differentiators, and a function generator to produce the input voltage $\frac{2}{35} \sin \omega t$, one possible analog is shown in Fig. 14.14. Notice that the same

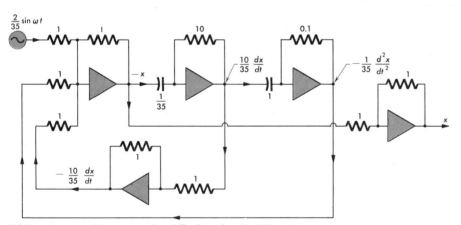

FIG. 14.14 *Electronic analog of Eq. (14.18) using differentiators.*

general procedure has been followed by using successive differentiation as was followed in the solution by successive integration, except that only differentiators are used.

Solution by differentiation has one weakness that solution by integration does not have. This weakness is the noise that is produced in the operational amplifiers that appears at the output when differentiators are used. The term "noise" does not signify audible noise or sound waves, but rather small random voltage and current fluctuations that occur at the input to the amplifier which are amplified along with the signal. The noise develops primarily from two sources. One source is resistance in the circuit. Noise associated with resistors is called "thermal" noise. Another source of noise is the electron stream from cathode to anode in a vacuum tube; this source of noise is called "shot" noise.

Thermal noise results from the random motion of the free electrons in a conductor. The free electrons possess kinetic energy associated with the temperature of the conductor. At absolute zero, the free electrons have no thermal energy; they are essentially stationary at this temperature. However, if the conductor is heated above absolute zero, the free electrons move in random directions and at random velocities that increase with the temperature. The random motion of the free electrons in the conductor produces a random current, and therefore a random voltage across the resistance. Ordinarily the voltage is small, of the order of microvolts. But since the voltage is random, it may vary rapidly with time and therefore the derivative of the noise voltage may be very large. On the other hand, the integral of the noise voltage over a long period of time is zero. This indicates that solution by differentiation may have considerable error due to the differentiated noise voltage, but solution by integration will have negligible error due to the integrated noise voltage.

Shot noise in vacuum tubes results from the current through the tube consisting of discrete electrons flowing from the cathode to the anode. Actually, the electrons are emitted at random from the cathode, and therefore the electron flow may vary slightly from instant to instant. This slight variation of current, caused by the random nature of the electron emission, is shot noise. Shot noise has essentially the same effect on the error in an electronic analog computer that thermal noise has.

A rule of thumb that is sometimes followed in programming the electronic analog computer is to program by integration if the differential equation is of second or higher order but to use either integration or differentiation if only first derivatives are present. Yet noise is sometimes troublesome even when differentiation is accomplished only once, and solution by integration is always preferred.

14.9 SERVO MULTIPLIERS

Multiplication by a constant can be performed by an integrator, differentiator, adder, or sign changer. Multiplication of two variables can be accomplished by a servo multiplier shown in Fig. 14.15, where v_1 and v_2 are the two variable inputs. The two resistors R_1

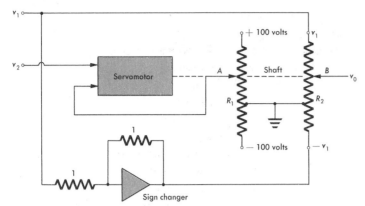

FIG. 14.15 *Servo multiplier where v_o is proportional to $v_1 v_2$.*

and R_2 are precision potentiometers with wiper contacts A and B, positioned by the shaft of the servomotor. The two inputs to the servomotor are v_2 and v_a, the voltage picked off potentiometer R_1 by wiper A. The difference between v_2 and v_a drives the servomotor until wiper A is at the same potential as v_2, at which time $v_2 - v_a = 0$, the motor input is 0 volts under this condition, and the motor torque is zero. Wiper B on potentiometer R_2 is also positioned by the motor shaft (shown as a dashed line). Notice that the position of wiper B is proportional to both v_2 and the voltage at the end of R_2, which is v_1. Therefore the output voltage v_o is proportional to the product $v_1 v_2$.

Notice that v_1 and v_2 can each be either $+$ or $-$ and v_o also can be either $+$ or $-$. The servo multiplier, as with operational amplifiers, operates equally well on either side of zero voltage to preserve the algebraic sign of the product.

The speed of response of the servo multiplier is obviously limited by the inertia in the servomotor, shaft, and potentiometer wipers. Accurate operation of the servo multiplier requires that rates of change of v_2 be kept fairly low. Of the two voltages v_1 and v_2 to be multiplied, the input to the servomotor v_2 is usually chosen as the voltage with the least rate of change with respect to time.

14.10   TIME-SCALE FACTORS

The output of an electronic analog computer is the solution to the problem programmed on the computer, with voltage analogous to the dependent variable and time always the independent variable. The output voltage of the computer is often used to drive an electromagnetic recording device, such as a pen recorder or a galvanometer, which plots the output voltage as a function of time. The moving parts of the mechanical recording device possess inertia, which limits the rate at which the moving parts can accelerate. For instance, if the recorder must plot sinusoidal quantities, an upper frequency limit exists above which its accuracy as a recorder is impaired; if it must plot exponential quantities, a minimum time constant exists below which its accuracy is also impaired by the inertia of the moving parts. Other electromechanical components, such as servo multipliers, also have this inertia restriction.

While mechanical elements in the computer limit its rate of response, errors in integrating amplifiers are accentuated by long computer runs. Thus, computer solutions which are too fast or too slow tend to be inaccurate. This limits the range to those problems which have solutions expressible as sinusoids whose frequencies are neither too high nor too low and as exponential functions whose time constants are neither too short nor too long.

Any practical problem can be scaled so that its solution lies within the range of frequencies and time constants amenable to accurate recording by the computer. Once the frequency and time-constant limitations of the computer have been established, the time scale of the solution can be adjusted so that the solution lies within the range of accurate computer response. Fast solutions can be slowed down, and slow solutions speeded up, making the time scale of the actual problem differ by a constant factor from the time scale of the computer.

The first step in time scaling is to determine approximately the frequencies and time constants present in the solutions. Some procedures for estimating these will now be mentioned. A first-order homogeneous differential equation [Eq. (3.20)]

$$a_1 \frac{di}{dt} + a_0 i = 0$$

has a solution, as shown in Eq. (3.25), of

$$i = I_0 \epsilon^{-(a_0/a_1)t}$$

with a time constant

$$\tau = \frac{a_1}{a_0}$$

A second-order homogeneous equation [Eq. (3.56)] of the form

$$\frac{d^2x}{dt^2} + 2\zeta\omega_n \frac{dx}{dt} + \omega_n{}^2 x = 0$$

has an undamped natural frequency ω_n. The frequency with damping is $\omega = \omega_n\sqrt{1 - \zeta^2}$ and is always less than ω_n. Thus it is possible to guess approximately the time constants or frequencies in the solution of first- and second-order systems to see whether the solution must be speeded up or slowed down to be within the range for accurate computing.

To change the speed of the solution by a factor of a, it is necessary only to change the independent variable t by a factor of a. Let

$$t = \frac{t'}{a} \tag{14.23}$$

where t' is the new computer time and a is a constant. Then

$$\frac{dx}{dt} = \frac{dx}{d(t'/a)}$$

$$= a\frac{dx}{dt'} \tag{14.24}$$

and

$$\frac{d^2x}{dt^2} = a\frac{d}{dt'}\left[\frac{dx}{d(t'/a)}\right]$$

$$= a^2 \frac{d^2x}{dt'^2} \tag{14.25}$$

Higher order derivatives can obviously be written

$$\frac{d^n x}{dt'^n} = a^n \frac{d^n x}{dt'^n} \tag{14.26}$$

First substitute Eq. (14.23) into Eq. (3.20). Then

$$a_1 a\frac{di}{dt'} + a_0 i = 0 \tag{14.27}$$

the new time constant of which is $a_1 a/a_0$. Notice that, if a is greater than unity, we have slowed down the solution or increased the time constant by a factor of a. If a is less than unity, we have speeded up the solution, decreasing the time constant by a factor of a. The computer time unit t' is now at sec.

Example 14.2

An electric circuit can be represented by the differential equation

$$\frac{d^2v}{dt^2} + 2\frac{dv}{dt} + 2{,}500v = 10 \sin 5t$$

Notice that the undamped natural frequency of the system is

$$\omega_n = \sqrt{2{,}500} = 50 \text{ radians/sec}$$

which we assume is too fast for the computer pen recorder. We choose to slow down the solution by letting $t = t'/10$. Then

$$100\frac{d^2v}{dt'^2} + 20\frac{dv}{dt'} + 2{,}500v = 10 \sin 0.5t'$$

or

$$\frac{d^2v}{dt'^2} + 0.2\frac{dv}{dt'} + 25v = 0.1 \sin 0.5t'$$

where ω_n is now 5 radians/sec of computer time. Thus, by making the change in variable $t = t'/10$, we have slowed down the solution by a factor of $\frac{1}{10}$. The time scale on the computer recording of the solution must be interpreted, then, as 10 actual, or computer, sec equals 1 problem sec or 1 radian/computer sec equals 10 radians/problem sec.

14.11 AMPLITUDE-SCALE FACTORS

The maximum output of each operational amplifier in the analog computer is limited to about ± 100 volts for the electron tubes to operate within the linear portion of their characteristic curves. Therefore it is important to choose an amplitude-scale factor such that the output of no amplifier exceeds ± 100 volts. It is also important to keep the output of the amplifiers as large as possible so that errors from noise can be minimized. The amplitude-scale factor, then, is used to adjust the magnitude of the output voltages of the various operational amplifiers so that the various output voltages never exceed ± 100 volts but are always as large as possible.

To visualize the necessity of amplitude scaling, suppose that the differential equation

$$\frac{d^2v}{dt^2} + 10\frac{dv}{dt} + 24v = 0 \tag{14.28}$$

with initial conditions at $t = 0$, $v = 0$, and $dv/dt = 20$ has the solution

$$v = 10\epsilon^{-4t} - 10\epsilon^{-6t} \tag{14.29}$$

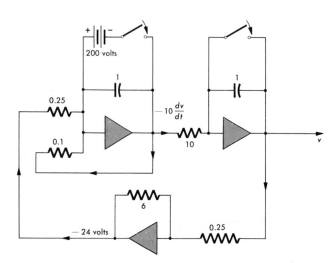

FIG. 14.16 *An electronic analog of Eq. (14.28).*

Equation (14.28) can be solved by the electronic analog shown in Fig. 14.16, where v is the solution, the output of the second integrator. The output of the first integrator is $-10\,dv/dt$, where

$$\frac{dv}{dt} = -40\epsilon^{-4t} + 60\epsilon^{-6t} \tag{14.30}$$

At $t = 0+$, $dv/dt = -40 + 60 = 20$, and $-10\,dv/dt = -200$ volts, too large a voltage for the output of the amplifier. Therefore the amplitude of all the voltages in the analog must be scaled down so that the output of the first amplifier does not exceed ± 100 volts and saturate.

To scale down the amplitude of the solution, and also the amplitude of the output voltages of all the amplifiers, the differential equation and its initial conditions must be divided through by the amplitude-scale factor. Suppose that the differential equation (14.28) and its initial conditions are divided through by the scale factor 4. Then we have

$$0.25\frac{d^2v}{dt^2} + 2.5\frac{dv}{dt} + 6v = 0 \tag{14.31}$$

with initial conditions at $t = 0$, $v = 0$, $dv/dt = 5$, which has the solution

$$v = 2.5\epsilon^{-4t} - 2.5\epsilon^{-6t} \tag{14.32}$$

The initial conditions set into the electronic analog of Fig. 14.16 are now reduced by $\frac{1}{4}$, reducing the voltage at the output of each amplifier accordingly. At $t = 0+$, the output voltage of the first integrator is now -50 volts, well within the range of linear operation for that amplifier. All that is really necessary is to reduce the initial-condition voltage level and the exciting voltage level by the scale factor. Likewise, to raise the voltage level at the outputs of the amplifiers, the initial-condition voltages and exciting voltages must be raised. No other change is actually made in the electronic analog.

Example 14.3

The equation

$$5\frac{d^2v}{dt^2} + 10\frac{dv}{dt} + 25v = 10\sin t$$

with initial conditions at $t = 0+$, $v = 10$ volts, $dv/dt = 50$ volts/sec, might be programmed as shown in Fig. 14.17. Notice that at $t = 0+$, when the greatest value of the derivative term dv/dt would

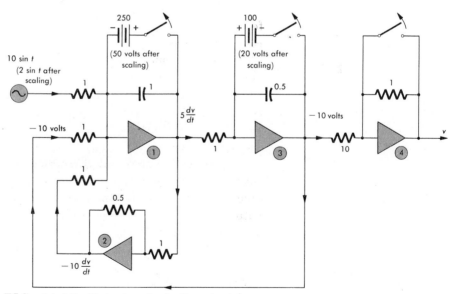

FIG. 14.17 *Electronic analog for Example 14.3.*

be expected, the output of the first amplifier is $5\,dv/dt = 250$ volts, exceeding the usable output of the amplifier. However, suppose that the differential equation and initial conditions are divided through by 5 and then programmed. The same program as above can be used, but with initial-condition batteries and exciting voltage 10 sin t reduced by $\frac{1}{5}$ so that now the maximum output of the first amplifier is 50 volts and the second amplifier is 20 volts. All voltages in the analog have been reduced by $\frac{1}{5}$, and the output voltage 0.2 volt must be multiplied by 5 on the recording scale to find the actual problem voltage.

Notice that time scaling changes the amplitude of the voltages at the amplifier outputs, too. Thus it is necessary to perform the change in time-scale factor before changing the amplitude scale if both must be changed.

SUMMARY

The electronic analog computer is an electronic model used to simulate a given physical system. The computer consists of operational amplifiers capable of simulating each term of the differential equation which describes the physical system. These operational amplifiers can be interconnected so that the computer is governed by the same differential equation that governs the system to be analyzed. Operational amplifiers can be used as integrators, differentiators, adders, constant multipliers, and sign changers. The computer, therefore, is capable of all the operations required to solve ordinary differential equations. The dependent variables are simulated by voltages with time as the independent variable.

The key element of the computer, the operational amplifier, is a high-gain direct-coupled voltage amplifier. The gain is at least 10^5. The input impedance of the operational amplifier is of the order of 10^9 or 10^{10} ohms.

In preparing a problem for an analog computer, one must consider the time-scale factor and the amplitude-scale factor for an accurate solution. Since time scaling changes the amplitude of the output voltage, it is necessary to perform the change in the time scale first before changing the amplitude scale. The capabilities of the physical devices used with an electronic analog computer are limited to a certain range of frequencies for accurate solutions, and the time scale may have to be modified so that the solution of the problem is within this range. Since the output of each operational amplifier is limited to about ±100 volts, the amplitude scale may have to be modified so that the solution of the problem is within this range.

FURTHER READING

For two excellent reference books covering electronic analog computers, refer to George W. Smith and Roger C. Wood, *Principles of Analog Computation* (McGraw-Hill Book Company, Inc., New York, 1959), and to Clarence L. Johnson, *Analog Computer Techniques* (McGraw-Hill Book Company, Inc., New York, 1956). For additional material relating to the derivation and explanation of analogous systems, refer to Walter W. Soroka, *Analog Methods in Computation and Simulation* (McGraw-Hill Book Company, Inc., New York, 1954). For additional material relating to analog computers, refer to Granino A. Korn and T. M. Korn, *Electronic Analog Computers*, 2d ed. (McGraw-Hill Book Company, Inc., New York, 1956). Albert S. Jackson, *Analog Computation* (McGraw-Hill Book Company, Inc., New York, 1960), is an excellent treatment of analog computation for readers with limited background in electronics.

PROBLEMS

14.1 Assume that the inductors shown in the figure are ideal inductors, and show that the circuits can approximate differentiation and integration.

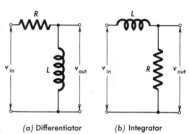

(a) Differentiator   (b) Integrator

PROB. 14.1

14.2 Verify that, if L is an ideal inductor, the circuit shown in the illustration is (a) an integrator; (b) a differentiator.

PROB. 14.2   (a) Integrator   (b) Differentiator

14.3 Set up an electronic analog to solve each of the equations or systems of equations below. Simplify each analog until it uses the least possible number of amplifiers.

(a) $\dfrac{d^2v}{dt^2} + 2v = 2 \sin \omega t$

at $t = 0$, $v = 0$, $dv/dt = 10$.

(b) $3\dfrac{d^3v}{dt^3} + 2\dfrac{d^2v}{dt^2} + \dfrac{dv}{dt} + 4v = 0$

at $t = 0$, $v = 0$, $dv/dt = 2$, $d^2v/dt^2 = 5$.

Problems   **379**

$$(c) \quad \frac{dv_1}{dt} + 10v_2 = 5$$

$$\frac{d^2v_2}{dt^2} + 5\frac{dv_1}{dt} + \frac{dv_2}{dt} + v_2 = 0$$

at $t = 0$, $v_1 = 0$, $v_2 = 5$, $d^2v_2/dt^2 = 0$.

14.4 The time scale of the equations below must be speeded up (time constants reduced) by a factor of 4. Find the time constants in the solution with the new fast speed.

$$(a) \quad \frac{d^2v}{dt^2} + 4\frac{dv}{dt} + 2v = 0$$

$$(b) \quad 2\frac{d^2v}{dt^2} + 10\frac{dv}{dt} + 12.5v = 0$$

14.5 A precision potentiometer can be used as a constant multiplier if the constant is less than unity. Often the circuit connected to the potentiometer loads it to the extent that one cannot predict the potentiometer output directly from the scale reading.

The 10-kilohm potentiometer shown in the figure is loaded with a 100-kilohm resistor. The potentiometer is set at its ½ scale marking of 5 kilohms. Find the output voltage v_o.

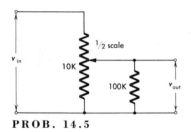

PROB. 14.5

14.6 The output of the electronic analog computer is the solution of the differential equation programmed on the computer. To make a function generator of the computer, it is necessary to find and program the differential equation whose solution is the desired function. Suppose that it is desired to generate the function $v = 10\epsilon^{-25t}$ on the computer. (a) Find the differential equation with its initial conditions whose solution is the above exponential function. (b) Draw the electronic analog of the differential equation, showing the above exponential function as the output.

14.7 Repeat Prob. 14.6 for the function $v = 5\sin(100t + \pi/4)$.

14.8 A mechanical vibration problem has a differential equation $5\,d^2x/dt^2 + 5\,dx/dt + 20x = 10$, where the initial conditions are $x(0) = 0$ and $dx/dt = 0$. Let the voltage in volts on the computer correspond to $5x$ in the problem, and find the electronic analog for this problem.

14.9 Check the natural frequency of Prob. 14.8, and make sure that it is approximately in the range $10 < \omega < 100$. If it is not, adjust the time scale so that ω lies in this range.

14.10 Adjust the amplitude scale of Prob. 14.9 so that, at $t = 0+$, the output voltage of no amplifier exceeds 50 volts.

14.11 Find the differential equation whose electronic analog is shown in the figure.

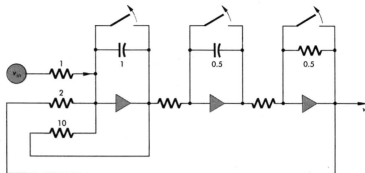

PROB. 14.11

14.12 The initial conditions of the circuit of Prob. 14.11 are zero. Assume that at $t = 0$, when the switches open, a step of voltage 10 volts in magnitude is applied at the input. Find the output voltage of each of the three amplifiers at $t = 0+$.

14.13 Refer to the circuit of Prob. 14.11. The initial conditions are changed so that, at $t = 0+$, $v = 10$ and $dv/dt = 50$. The input voltage $v_{\text{in}} = 0$. Find the output of each of the three amplifiers at $t = 0+$. Is amplitude scaling necessary? Explain.

15

D I G I T A L   C O M P U T E R S

15.1 INTRODUCTION

A modern digital computer is a device which performs arithmetic
operations and makes simple decisions according to the instructions
it receives. It is able to add, subtract, multiply, divide, and compare the size of numbers, and it performs these operations at a
tremendous rate of speed. Unlike the analog computer, which
solves ordinary differential equations with great facility, the digital
computer solves problems in arithmetic and comparison only.
Differential equations, both ordinary and partial, can often be
resolved into a form which can be solved approximately by a large
number of arithmetic processes. The digital computer is able to
perform the arithmetic operation very rapidly and solve the differential equations by a numerical method. Trigonometric functions can be found on a digital computer by adding up the terms
of a power series, a process which the digital computer performs
very rapidly. The digital computer is capable of storing large
numbers of data on which it must perform its operations. It is also
capable of storing instructions which tell it what to do and which
it can modify according to prearranged plan. But high-speed
arithmetic is its principal talent.

In this chapter we are concerned with what computers can
do and how to make them do it. There are many kinds of scientific

and engineering problems which can be solved on a digital computer but which require too much labor when ordinary slide rules or desk calculators are used. We are concerned in this chapter with the computer as an engineering tool, and in order to use the computer we must learn to communicate with it. The computer does only what it is told to do. In order to solve a problem on a digital computer, a complete set of instructions to the computer must be obtained. These instructions must be in the language of the computer so that the data and instructions can be understood by the computer and the computer results can be understood by us.

There are a few basic electronic circuits which perform the arithmetic operations in the computer and which are duplicated many times in the computer. Internal circuitry ties the electronic circuits together in such a way that the computer functions as a unit to perform the solutions requested. In this chapter we shall not be concerned particularly with the individual circuits, but rather with what the computers can do and how they are instructed to do it.

15.2 BASIC COMPUTER COMPONENTS

The digital computer consists of devices which perform five major operations: input, memory, control, arithmetic, and output. While these five operations are distinct, they may or may not be separated physically within the computer. A block diagram showing these operations and their interconnections is given in Fig. 15.1. Information-flow channels are shown in this diagram, as well as control channels or instruction channels which join the control unit with the input, memory, arithmetic, and output units.

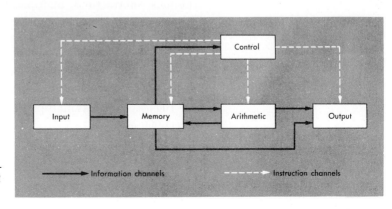

FIG. 15.1 *Information-flow channels and instruction channels in a digital computer.*

The input unit is a device through which data and instructions enter the computer. The data and instructions must be in a form that can be understood by the computer. The input information may be punched on cards or paper tape or recorded on magnetic tape. The input unit reads the information from the card or tape and transfers it to the memory in the computer. The input device may also be an interpreter; it must see the information in one form, such as holes punched in cards or tapes, and read the information into the memory in a form which the memory can store.

The memory must combine the ability to store large amounts of information with the ability to read out of storage a particular piece of information when it is desired. Access time to the stored information is important, since it may delay further operations of the computer. The memory unit must store not only the data on which the computer operates but also the step-by-step instructions which tell the computer exactly what to do. According to the block diagram of Fig. 15.1, the information stored in the memory comes either from the input unit or from the arithmetic unit. One form of memory unit is the magnetic drum revolving at high speeds. On the surface of the drum is a magnetic recording of the numbers which constitute the information in storage. Magnetic heads capable of recording or reading off information recorded on the drum are distributed along the surface of the drum as the drum revolves under them. Thus the access time to the information stored on the surface of the drum is never more than the time required for a single revolution of the drum.

The arithmetic unit, as the name implies, performs the arithmetic operations on the data or information stored in the memory. The arithmetic unit, often called the "accumulator," operates according to instructions also stored in the memory. It performs additions, subtractions, multiplication, and division. It can also compare two numbers to see which is the larger; this procedure is usually the basis for decision making in the computer. The arithmetic unit operates at a very fast rate, with addition and subtraction taking place even faster than multiplication and division. For example, the addition of two numbers of 10 decimal digits may take 100 μsec, whereas multiplication of the same numbers may require 1,000 μsec.

The purpose of the output unit is to make available outside the computer the results of the computer operations. There are several possible forms which the output unit can take. Ordinarily the data to be read out are in the form of decimal numbers which can be read out of the computer by an electric typewriter, a mechanical or photoelectric printer, a punched or magnetic tape, or a punched card. The output device does not ordinarily operate at as high a rate of speed as the arithmetic unit, and the results of the arithmetic unit must be stored in the memory before they are read out of the computer by the output unit.

The control operation within the computer directs the operation of the entire computer from the instructions stored in the memory. Generally the control operation is distributed throughout the various units of the computer and cannot be separated and collected into one chassis or cabinet; nevertheless it is present throughout the computer, and it must be shown on the block diagram of Fig. 15.1. The control unit receives its instructions from the memory unit, interprets these instructions, and then sends signals to other units to tell them what to do. Thus the entire operation of the computer is under the direct control of the control unit.

15.3 COMPUTER PROGRAMS

The list of instructions to the computer for the solution of a particular problem is known as the "program." The preparation of an extensive program for a difficult problem is a time-consuming operation. First, the problem to be solved must be expressed in a form amenable to computer solution. This requires a step-by-step list of instructions which the computer must follow to solve the problem. Each instruction is a simple one, and often thousands of instructions are needed to solve a problem on the computer. For simple engineering problems, the preparation time of the program may be longer than the time required to solve the problems with slide rule and pencil; obviously under these conditions computer solutions are impractical. But when problems are repetitive and identical problems must be solved over and over again with different numerical data, then one program serves the many solutions. Repetitive problems are usually solved on a computer with considerable saving of time.

The digital computer ordinarily performs only a small number of basic operations. By selecting various sequences of these operations, the computer can perform the arithmetic operation required of it. These operations are each directed by the program of instructions, and each instruction in the program directs one of the basic operations.

The location of a particular instruction or piece of data in the memory is called its "address," or "memory location." The instructions, each stored at a separate address in the memory, must contain not only the command which the computer follows but also the address at which the data being operated upon are located. For instance, suppose that it is required that two numbers be added together. The first instruction, consisting of a command and an address, comes from the memory into the control unit. The control unit executes the command, which is to fetch a number from a particular address in the memory and place it in the arithmetic unit. Then a second instruction appears at the control unit and commands it to take another number from another address in the memory and add it to the first number already in the arithmetic unit. A third instruction transfers the sum of the two numbers from the arithmetic unit to a designated address in the memory. In this example, three different instructions are required to perform the operation of addition of two numbers stored in the memory.

The preparation of an engineering problem for solution on a digital computer requires first that the problem be in a form which the computer can solve. One area of applied mathematics, sometimes known as "numerical methods," treats the solution of algebraic equations, transcendental equations, and differential equations by successive approximations, using arithmetic operations adaptable to computer use. Once the problem has been stated in a mathematical form adaptable to computer solution, the step-by-step program must be written. In many computer installations, trained programmers are available to assist an engineer in programming his problem for the computer. However, it is always helpful for an engineer to know the basic steps in programming. Since the computer follows the instructions of the program exactly, an error in the program results in an error in the solution. The engineer should be able to determine whether his computer solution is accurate or whether the solution contains errors.

15.4 COMPUTER CODES

The code under which the digital computer operates is the language of the computer. The digital computer can perform only a few basic operations, each of which is called forth by a separate instruction identifiable by a numerical or alphabetical code. A person wishing to instruct the computer on how to solve a problem must prepare a program of instructions, each of which is written in a code language which the computer understands. Computer codes are not standard, although they are generally similar. Once a person has become familiar with the code used in one make of digital computer, it is relatively easy for him to learn the code of another make of digital computer which uses a different code. Each command or instruction, represented by a particular code symbol, has associated with it the memory location in which are stored the data upon which the computer must operate. An example of computer instructions or commands for a hypothetical computer, together with the alphabetic symbol and numeric code, is listed in Table 15.1, along with a brief description of the operation performed by the particular command. Examine Table 15.1, and observe that some of the instructions perform arithmetic upon numbers stored in the memory. The test-for-minus command is the basis for decision making within the computer; it instructs the computer to check the algebraic sign of the number in the accumulator; if the sign is negative, the computer looks for its next instruction in a particular memory location, and if the sign is positive, the computer proceeds with the next step in the program. The unconditional-transfer instruction tells the computer unconditionally to go to the particular memory location for its next instruction. Both the TE command and the UT command add greatly to the flexibility of computer programming, as will be seen in the examples to follow.

15.5 AN EXAMPLE OF A PROBLEM PROGRAMMED FOR THE COMPUTER

Although the basic operations which a computer can perform are very elementary, the digital computer is able to solve many types of complex problems, depending upon the ingenuity of those persons involved in preparing the computer program. The example which follows is a simple problem which has been programmed for the hypothetical digital computer which follows the code defined in Table 15.1. It is an elementary problem which can be solved quickly even by longhand and is therefore obviously not a typical example of a problem to be solved by a digital computer. But the following example does illustrate how the various commands or instructions can be assembled in such an order that the computer

TABLE 15.1 *Table of Instructions*

Command	Alphabetic symbol	Numeric code	Operation performed
Clear, add	CAD	01	The accumulator or arithmetic unit is cleared and the number in specified memory location is entered into the accumulator
Add	AD	02	The number in the specified memory location is added to the number in the accumulator, and the sum is retained in the accumulator
Subtract	SU	03	The number in the specified memory location is subtracted from the number in the accumulator, and the difference is retained in the accumulator
Multiply	MU	04	The number in the specified memory location is multiplied by the number in the accumulator, and the product is retained in the accumulator
Divide	DI	05	The number in the accumulator is divided by the number in the specified memory location, and the quotient is retained in the accumulator
Store	ST	06	The number in the accumulator is stored in the specified memory location and also retained in the accumulator
Test for minus	TE	07	If the number in the accumulator is negative, control of the computer is transferred to the command in the memory location specified; otherwise the computer proceeds with the next step in the program
Print	PR	08	The number in the memory location specified is printed out
Unconditional transfer	UT	09	Transfer control unconditionally to the memory location specified
Stop	STOP	10	The operation of the machine is stopped

can proceed to solve the problem. In addition to the table of commands and codes, assume that the computer memory has 4,000 memory locations, designated 0000 to 3999, in which 10-digit numbers can be stored.

In this example, we seek to find a set of instructions or program which will solve the equation

$$y = ax + b \tag{15.1}$$

for three different values of x. In Eq. (15.1), a and b are constants. We designate the three values of x as x_1, x_2, and x_3 and the three corresponding values of y as y_1, y_2, and y_3. Actually, since we intend to solve Eq. (15.1) three times for the three different values of x, three similar equations can be solved.

$$y_1 = ax_1 + b \tag{15.2}$$

$$y_2 = ax_2 + b \tag{15.3}$$

$$y_3 = ax_3 + b \tag{15.4}$$

Once the program of instructions for the solution of y_1 has been written, it can be used again to find y_2 merely by substituting x_2 for x_1 and to find y_3 by substituting x_3 for x_1. The program of instructions for finding y_1 can be modified by the computer so that the same program results in a solution of y_2 and modified again to solve for y_3. Then, when y_1, y_2, and y_3 have been found, the computer must be directed to print out the solution and then turn itself off.

In this computer, assume that the 4,000 memory locations can be identified by the numbers 0000 to 3999 inclusive. Only a few of the memory locations are used in this example, and the choice of which ones to use is arbitrary. Suppose that we decide to store the constants a and b in memory locations 3000 and 3001, respectively, and x_1, x_2, and x_3 in memory locations 2000, 2001, and 2002, respectively. The anticipated results y_1, y_2, and y_3 can then be stored in memory locations 1000, 1001, and 1002, respectively. Some additional numbers are needed to alter the initial program for finding y_1 when the program must be changed to find y_2 and for changing the program for finding y_2 to the program for finding y_3. Suppose that we store the numbers 0001, 0001, and 0004 in memory locations 3002, 3003, and 3004, respectively. Now we have all the memory locations prearranged, and we can proceed with the programming.

Now that the storage locations have been assigned, the coded program of instructions for the solution of the problem can be completed. The specified storage locations are shown in Table 15.2, along with the program. The computer seeks its first instruc-

T A B L E 1 5 . 2 *Example Program*

Memory location	Alphabetic code	Numeric code	Address
0000	CAD	01	3000
0001	MU	04	2000
0002	AD	02	3001
0003	ST	06	1000
0004	CAD	01	3002
0005	AD	02	3003
0006	ST	06	3002
0007	SU	03	3004
0008	TE	07	0013
0009	PR	08	1000
0010	PR	08	1001
0011	PR	08	1002
0012	STOP	10	0000
0013	CAD	01	0001
0014	AD	02	3003
0015	ST	06	0001
0016	CAD	01	0003
0017	AD	02	3003
0018	ST	06	0003
0019	UT	09	0000

tion in memory location 0000, and then it seeks its second instruction in memory location 0001, and then 0002, and so on, unless specifically instructed to do otherwise. The program shown in Tables 15.2 and 15.3 is fed into the computer and stored in the indicated memory locations. Now assume that the computer is set

T A B L E 1 5 . 3 *Other Memory Locations Used*

Memory locations	Stored quantity	
1000	y_1	
1001	y_2	
1002	y_3	
2000	x_1	
2001	x_2	
2002	x_3	
3000	a	
3001	b	
3002	00	0001
3003	00	0001
3004	00	0004

into operation. We consider now the computing operation step by step to see how the computer solves the problem according to the program stored in the computer.

The first four commands cause the computer to calculate y_1 as follows:

01 3000   Brings a from memory location 3000 to the accumulator, clears the accumulator of any number remaining from previous operations, and adds a to the accumulator.

04 2000   Brings the contents of memory location 2000, which is x_1, to the accumulator and multiplies it with the contents of the accumulator, a, retaining the product ax_1 in the accumulator.

02 3001   Adds the contents of memory location 3001, which is the constant b, to the contents of the accumulator, ax_1, retaining the sum $ax_1 + b$ in the accumulator.

06 1000   Stores the contents of the accumulator in memory location 1000. Thus $y_1 = ax_1 + b$ is now stored in location 1000.

The four commands above, stored in the first four memory locations, have directed the computer to calculate y_1 and store it in the specified memory location for future reference. The next group of commands illustrate the decision-making ability of the computer as it checks to see whether or not all values of y have been calculated.

01 3002   Brings the number from memory location 3002, clears the accumulator, and adds it to the accumulator. Thus the number 00   0001 is now in the accumulator.

02 3003   Brings the number from memory location 3003 and adds it to the number in the accumulator. The number in the accumulator is now 00   0002.

06 3002   The contents of the accumulator is now stored in memory location 3002 and also retained in the accumulator. The contents of memory location 3002 has now been changed from 00   0001 to 00   0002, and 00   0002 is still held in the accumulator.

03 3004 Subtracts the number in memory location 3004 (00 0004) from the contents of the accumulator (00 0002); the difference is negative.

07 0013 Tests for the presence of a negative number in the accumulator. Since the negative number is present, control is transferred to memory location 0013.

The computer has computed y_1, stored it, and then tested to see whether or not it must go on to find another value of y. Each time the above procedure is followed, the contents of memory location 3002 is modified, increasing by 1. When three values of y have been calculated, the contents of memory location 3002 has been modified to become 00 0004, and when the above negative test has been performed, the computer then knows that all values of y have been computed.

Since the decision of the computer is to continue to calculate another value of y, it shifts control to memory locations 0013, where instructions for modifying the first four steps of the program begin and continue in sequence.

01 0001 Brings the number from memory location 0001, clears the accumulator, and adds it to the accumulator. The number in memory location 0001 is 04 2000, which is one of the instructions for calculating y.

02 3003 Brings the number from memory location 3003 (00 0001) and adds it to the number in the accumulator. The number in the accumulator is now 04 2001.

06 0001 Stores the number in the accumulator in memory location 0001. Thus the contents of memory location 0001 is now 04 2001.

The instructions have now been changed so that, when y is calculated, x is obtained from memory location 2001, where x_2 is located. If the computer proceeds to calculate y_2, the program must be changed again in such a way that when y_2 is obtained it will be stored in the appropriate memory location for y_2. The four commands below show how this is accomplished.

01 0003 Clears the accumulator and enters the number from memory location 0003 (06 1000) into the accumulator. The number in the accumulator includes the storage location for y, which is 1000.

02 3003 Adds the number in memory location 3003 (00 0001) to the number in the accumulator. The accumulator now reads 06 1001, which instructs the storage of y in location 1001.

06 0003 Stores the number in the accumulator in memory location 0003.

09 0000 Control is unconditionally transferred back to memory location 0000, and the computing cycle starts over.

The computer is now ready to compute another value of y by executing the first four commands of the program again. On the second cycle y_2 is calculated according to the modified program, and its value is stored in memory location 1001. Then the test is made again to see whether or not three values of y have been found. Since only two have been found, the program is again modified and y_3 is calculated and stored in memory location 1002. The test is made again to see whether or not three values of y have been found. The test for negative is made from the commands stored in memory locations 0004 to 0008, inclusive. After two previous tests, the number stored in memory location 3002 is 00 0003, and, for the third test for negative, the number in location 3002 is increased by 0001 again so that it becomes 00 0004. Now when 00 0004 in memory location 3004 is subtracted from 00 0004 in the accumulator (and location 3004), the difference is not negative but zero. The computer interprets zero as a positive number and is directed to continue in sequence to the instruction in memory location 0009.

The only remaining operations are to print out the results and then to stop.

08 1000 Prints out the contents of memory location 1000, which is y_1.

08 1001 Prints out the contents of memory location 1001, which is y_2.

08 1002 Prints out the contents of memory location 1002, which is y_3.

10 0000 Stops the computer.

The computer has completed its work according to the instructions it received, including the command to turn itself off. Each instruction was one that the computer was capable of executing, and the instruction was issued in the form of a prearranged number code which the computer understands.

It should be obvious by now that the program could have directed the computer to find the three values of y in a different manner. For example, the instructions for finding y_1 could have been written, after which the specific steps for finding y_2 and y_3 could also have been written. In this manner the original instructions would not have had to be modified, as they were in the program of Table 15.2. The above example was chosen to illustrate the ability of the computer to decide between two alternatives. In most computers this is accomplished by testing for a negative number, as it is in this example. The example also shows how the computer can store its instructions and modify them when instructed to do so. This attribute is particularly useful when a basic program must be repeated hundreds of times; it can be modified each time by the computer itself.

15.6 BINARY NUMBERS

The decimal number system in use today is probably based on the accident that we have 10 fingers and 10 toes. We have been taught how perfect the decimal number system is because of the ease with which we can multiply by 10 or divide by 10. But the number 10 is no more sacred as a base for a number system than is the number 6 or 8 or 12, and number systems built upon bases other than 10 are possible, practical, and often more useful than the decimal system.

Because our thinking is so conditioned by the decimal number system, the numbers at the input and output of a digital computer must be in the decimal form. But the arithmetic performed by the computer and the storage of the numbers within the computer are operations more conveniently performed in the binary number system. The rest of this chapter is devoted to the binary number system and the arithmetic operation used in the binary system. A computer using binary numbers for storage and arithmetic must perform the conversion from decimal numbers to binary numbers when the numbers are read into the computer and reconvert from binary to decimal when numbers are read out.

The decimal number system employs the digits 0, 1, 2, . . . , 9. The octal number system using 8 as a base uses the digits 0, 1, 2, . . . , 7. The binary number system, with 2 as a base, uses only the digits 0 and 1. Since the names for all numbers above 9 are based on the decimal number system, a certain amount of confusion results when numbers above 9 are expressed in other number systems. The decimal system accomplishes multiplications by 10, its base, by adding a zero to the right of the number or by moving the decimal point one place to the right. For example, $8 \times 10 = 80$. The octal number system accomplishes multiplication by its base 8 by adding a 0, such as $6 \times 8 = 60$. But 60 in the octal number system must be interpreted as equivalent to 48 in the decimal number system. In the binary system, adding a 0 after a number corresponds to multiplication by the number 2, the base of the binary system. Thus 1×2 is written 10, where 10 in the binary system corresponds to 2 in the decimal system.

Table 15.4 shows numbers in the decimal system and the same numbers written in the octal and binary systems. We have chosen the octal number system and the binary number system merely as examples of number systems using bases other than 10. Keep in mind that decimal digits 8 and 9 have no significance in the octal system and decimal digits 2 through 9 have no significance in the binary system. A decimal number such as 1,347 means

$$1347_{10} = 7 \times 10^0 + 4 \times 10^1 + 3 \times 10^2 + 1 \times 10^3$$

$$= 7 + 40 + 300 + 1{,}000 \tag{15.5}$$

where the subscript 10 signifies that the number is written to the base 10. Numbers to bases other than 10 can be written in the same fashion as Eq. (15.5). For instance, if 1347 is an octal number, it can be converted to a decimal number by writing it as

$$1347_8 = 7 \times 8^0 + 4 \times 8^1 + 3 \times 8^2 + 1 \times 8^3$$

$$= 7 + 32 + 192 + 512 = 743_{10} \tag{15.6}$$

Binary numbers, using only the digits 0 and 1, are easily converted to decimal numbers by the procedure mentioned in the preceding paragraph. The binary number 10111 can be converted to a decimal number as follows,

$$10111_2 = 1 \times 2^0 + 1 \times 2^1 + 1 \times 2^2 + 0 \times 2^3 + 1 \times 2^4$$

$$= 1 + 2 + 4 + 0 + 16 = 23_{10} \tag{15.7}$$

coinciding with the same binary number listed in Table 15.4. Conversion of decimal numbers to binary numbers is performed by successive division by 2. For example, to convert the decimal number

TABLE 15.4 *Corresponding Numbers in the Decimal, Octal, and Binary Systems*

Decimal	Octal	Binary
0	0	0
1	1	1
2	2	10
3	3	11
4	4	100
5	5	101
6	6	110
7	7	111
8	10	1000
9	11	1001
10	12	1010
11	13	1011
12	14	1100
13	15	1101
14	16	1110
15	17	1111
16	20	10000
17	21	10001
18	22	10010
19	23	10011
20	24	10100
21	25	10101
22	26	10110
23	27	10111
24	30	11000
25	31	11001

174 to a binary number, we divide the decimal number successively by 2, keeping track of the remainder. Then

$$
\begin{array}{r|l}
 & \textit{Remainder} \\
2 \mid 174 & \\
2 \mid 87 & 0 \\
2 \mid 43 & 1 \\
2 \mid 21 & 1 \\
2 \mid 10 & 1 \qquad (15.8) \\
2 \mid 5 & 0 \\
2 \mid 2 & 1 \\
2 \mid 1 & 0 \\
0 & 1 \\
\end{array}
$$

Then the binary equivalent to the decimal number 174 is obtained from the remainder.

$$174_{10} = 10101110_2 \qquad (15.9)$$

The same procedure can be followed for finding octal numbers from decimal numbers. For instance, suppose that the decimal number 743 must be converted to an octal number. Successive division by 8 yields

$$\text{Remainder}$$

$$
\begin{array}{r|l}
8 & 743 \\
8 & 92 \\
8 & 11 \\
8 & 1 \\
& 0 \\
\end{array}
\qquad
\begin{array}{c}
\\
7 \\
4 \\
3 \\
1 \\
\end{array}
\qquad (15.10)
$$

and the octal equivalent to the decimal number 743, obtained from the remainder, is

$$743_{10} = 1347_8 \qquad (15.11)$$

Example 15.1

1. To convert the octal number 61304 to a decimal number,

6 1 3 0 4

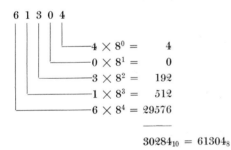

$$
\begin{aligned}
4 \times 8^0 &= & 4 \\
0 \times 8^1 &= & 0 \\
3 \times 8^2 &= & 192 \\
1 \times 8^3 &= & 512 \\
6 \times 8^4 &= & 29576 \\
\hline
\end{aligned}
$$

$$30284_{10} = 61304_8$$

2. To convert the binary number 1101101 to a decimal number,

1 1 0 1 1 0 1

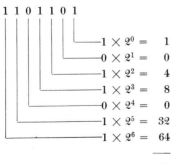

$$
\begin{aligned}
1 \times 2^0 &= & 1 \\
0 \times 2^1 &= & 0 \\
1 \times 2^2 &= & 4 \\
1 \times 2^3 &= & 8 \\
0 \times 2^4 &= & 0 \\
1 \times 2^5 &= & 32 \\
1 \times 2^6 &= & 64 \\
\hline
\end{aligned}
$$

$$109_{10} = 1101101_2$$

3. To convert the decimal number 387 to a number of the base 5,

Remainder

$$
\begin{array}{r|l}
5 & 387 \\ \hline
5 & 77 \\ \hline
5 & 15 \\ \hline
5 & 3 \\ \hline
 & 0
\end{array}
\qquad
\begin{array}{l}
\\
2 \\
2 \\
0 \\
3
\end{array}
$$

Then $387_{10} = 3022_5$.

4. To convert the decimal number 387 to a binary number,

Remainder

$$
\begin{array}{r|l}
2 & 387 \\ \hline
2 & 193 \\ \hline
2 & 96 \\ \hline
2 & 48 \\ \hline
2 & 24 \\ \hline
2 & 12 \\ \hline
2 & 6 \\ \hline
2 & 3 \\ \hline
2 & 1 \\ \hline
 & 0
\end{array}
\qquad
\begin{array}{l}
\\
1 \\
1 \\
0 \\
0 \\
0 \\
0 \\
0 \\
1 \\
1
\end{array}
$$

Then $387_{10} = 110000011_2$.

Most digital computers work only in the binary number system, converting to binary numbers the decimal digits fed into the computer, and converting from binary numbers to decimal digits at the read out.

15.7 BINARY ARITHMETIC

Arithmetic in the binary number system can be performed in exactly the same way as in the decimal number system. Addition in the binary system corresponds exactly to addition in the decimal system. In the decimal system, when a column adds to more than ten, a carry must be added to the next column on the left. Similarly, in the binary system when a column adds to more than two, a carry must be added in the next column to the left. An example is shown on the next page.

Example 15.2

In the decimal system, if we add 374 and 178, we write

```
  1 1
  374
  178
  ───
  552
```

Adding the units column, $4 + 8 = 12$; we write 2 in the units column of the sum and carry 1 to the tens column. Adding the tens column, $1 + 7 + 7 = 15$; we write 5 in the tens column of the sum and carry 1 to the hundreds column. Adding the hundreds column, $1 + 3 + 1 = 5$; we write 5 in the hundreds column for the sum. The sum is 552. Using the same procedure for the binary number, we add 1100101 and 1001111.

```
   1111
  1100101
  1001111
  ────────
  10110100
```

Adding the units column on the right, $1 + 1 = 10$; we write 0 in the units column for the sum and carry 1 to the twos column. Adding the twos column, $1 + 0 + 1 = 10$; 0 is recorded in the twos place in the sum, and 1 is carried. Adding the fours column, $1 + 1 + 1 = 11$; 1 is recorded in the fours place of the sum, and 1 is carried. Adding the eights column, $1 + 0 + 1 = 10$; 0 is recorded in the eights place of the sum, and 1 is carried. Adding the sixteens column, $1 + 0 + 0 = 1$; 1 is recorded in the sixteens place of the sum, and nothing is carried. For the thirty-twos column, $1 + 0 = 1$, and, for the sixty-fours, $1 + 1 = 10$.

Arithmetic operations of addition and multiplication are sometimes defined by a table showing the sum or product of the various numbers. The binary-addition table is shown in Table 15.5. The

TABLE 15.5
Binary-addition Table

	0	1
0	0	1
1	1	10

table can be entered either from the left or from the top. Possible sums shown are $0 + 0 = 0$, $0 + 1 = 1$, $1 + 0 = 1$, and $1 + 1 = 10$.

Subtraction of binary numbers follows the same procedure as with decimal numbers. For example, to subtract the number 1010 from 1101, we write

$$
\begin{array}{r}
1101 \\
1010 \\
\hline
0011
\end{array}
$$

Starting with the units column, we first subtract 0 from 1, leaving 1. Then in the twos column, we must borrow from the fours column and subtract 1 from 10, leaving 1. In the fours column we have borrowed 1; so we subtract 0 from 0, leaving 0. In the eights column we subtract 1 from 1, leaving 0.

Multiplication of binary numbers can be accomplished in much the same way as with decimal numbers once the multiplication table is defined. Table 15.6 shows the binary-multiplication

TABLE 15.6
Binary-multiplication Table

	0	1
0	0	0
1	0	1

table, which reads $0 \times 0 = 0$, $0 \times 1 = 0$, $1 \times 0 = 0$, and $1 \times 1 = 1$. Binary multiplication is much simpler than decimal multiplication because there is never any carry to keep track of during the multiplication process. For example, to multiply 1010 and 1101, we write

$$
\begin{array}{r}
1010 \\
1101 \\
\hline
1010 \\
0000 \\
1010 \\
1010 \\
\hline
10000010
\end{array}
$$

A carry develops only when we perform the addition part of the process.

Division is a difficult procedure to mechanize for a computer, but it can be done in the same way we perform decimal division. Suppose that we divide 1100 into 1111000 as follows:

```
            1010
      ┌─────────
 1100 │ 1111000
        1100
      ─────────
        001100
          1100
      ─────────
          00000
```

The divisor is divided into the first four terms of the dividend with a quotient of 1 and a remainder of 11. Bringing down the next binary digit, 0, we see that the divisor 1100 is greater than 110; so we add a 0 to the right of the 1 in the quotient and bring down the next binary digit, also 0. Now the divisor divides into 1100 once, with 0 remainder. We add 1 to the right in the quotient and bring down the last 0 of the dividend. The divisor is divided into 0, which gives 0 at the last place in the quotient, with 0 remainder. Other methods exist for accomplishing long division, and some of these are easier for a computer to follow.

SUMMARY

A digital computer performs according to instructions written step by step in a program of operations. Each instruction must give the memory location of the data on which the operation is to be performed or the location to which the results are sent and stored. The stored program computer seeks its instructions in successive memory locations until directed to seek instructions out of sequence by a decision of the computer. The decisions are ordinarily reached by subtracting two numbers; if a negative difference results, the computer seeks the next instruction from a specified location, and if the difference is positive, the computer continues to execute its instructions or commands in sequence. The computing ordinarily consists of basic arithmetic, such as addition, multiplication, subtraction, and division.

Most computers perform their arithmetic in binary numbers, and the results are stored in the memory as binary numbers. Only the read-in and read-out operations are performed in decimal numbers. Binary numbers utilize only the digits 0 and 1. A table of binary addition such as Table 15.5 indicates that $0 + 0 = 0$, $0 + 1 = 1$, $1 + 0 = 1$, and $1 + 1 = 10$. Binary multiplication by 2 is performed by moving the binary point one place to the right, or adding a zero on the right. Multiplication is defined by the binary-multiplication table (Table 15.6), as $0 \times 0 = 0$, $0 \times 1 = 0$, $1 \times 0 = 0$, and $1 \times 1 = 1$. Computers use binary numbers to perform the arithmetic operations because it is easier to make electronic circuits perform the necessary operations in the binary number system than in the decimal system.

FURTHER READING

D. D. McCracken, *Digital Computer Programming* (John Wiley & Sons, Inc., New York, 1957), is an excellent introduction to programming, as well as binary and octal number systems, decimal-point location, floating-decimal methods, input-output methods, etc. Samuel B. Williams, *Digital Computing Systems* (McGraw-Hill Book Company, Inc., New York, 1959), reviews basic types of computing machinery available, as well as elementary computer programming. Marshal H. Wrubel, *A Primer of Programming for Digital Computers* (McGraw-Hill Book Company, Inc., New York, 1959), is an elementary introduction to programming, and Robert E. Stephenson, *Introduction to Analog and Digital Computers* (John Wiley & Sons, Inc., New York, 1961), discusses programming, number systems, switching theory, and computer logic.

PROBLEMS

Use Table 15.1 for the commands in preparing programs for Probs. 15.1 to 15.6.

15.1 The example in Sec. 15.5 requires decision making and program modification by the computer. Prepare a program for finding y_1, y_2, and y_3 without the decision-making and program-modification feature.

15.2 Prepare a program for solving the quadratic equation $y = a_2 x^2 + a_1 x + a_0$, where a_2, a_1, and a_0 are constants and x is known.

15.3 Prepare a program for evaluating $\sin \theta$ from the power-series expansion $\sin \theta = \theta - \dfrac{\theta^3}{3!} + \dfrac{\theta^5}{5!} - \dfrac{\theta^7}{7!} + \cdots$.

15.4 Prepare a program for evaluating ϵ^x from the power-series expansion $\epsilon^x = 1 + x + \dfrac{x^2}{2!} + \dfrac{x^3}{3!} + \cdots$.

15.5 Integration on a digital computer can be done numerically by Simpson's rule, a method of finding the area under a curve. If $y = 2 + 2x - 0.1x^2$ and it is desired to integrate y between the limits $x = 0$ and $x = 6$, by Simpson's rule, $\displaystyle\int_{x=0}^{x=6} y \, dx = \tfrac{1}{3}(y_0 + 4y_1 + 2y_2 + 4y_3 + 2y_4 + 4y_5 + y_6)$, where y_0 is y at $x = 0$, y_1 is y at $x = 1$, etc. (a) Prepare a program to find $y_0, y_1, y_2, \ldots, y_6$. (b) Then prepare a program to find $\displaystyle\int_{x=0}^{x=6} y \, dx$.

15.6 Find the integral of the polynomial in Prob. 15.5, using Simpson's rule. Then check your results by integrating the polynomial and substituting in the limits $x = 0$ and $x = 6$.

15.7 Convert the following decimal numbers to octal numbers: (a) 23; (b) 384; (c) 8,743; (d) 37,829.

15.8 Convert the following decimal numbers to binary numbers: (a) 31; (b) 78; (c) 321; (d) 783.

15.9 Convert the following binary numbers to decimal numbers: (a) 11001; (b) 101100; (c) 1110001; (d) 1011110001.

15.10 Perform the addition of the following binary numbers: (a) 1001 + 1001; (b) 11100 + 11011; (c) 101 + 1111110; (d) 111111 + 10101.

15.11 Perform the binary subtraction as indicated: (a) 1010 − 1001; (b) 11100 − 11001; (c) 1111110 − 10101; (d) 1000000 − 1001.

15.12 Perform the binary multiplication as indicated: (a) 1011 × 110; (b) 1110111 × 10011; (c) 101100111 × 111001101.

15.13 Perform the following binary multiplication. Check your results by converting the numbers to decimal numbers and multiplying the decimal numbers. (a) 100111010 × 111011; (b) $(111111001)^2$.

15.14 Perform the following binary division, checking results by decimal division: (a) 100111010 ÷ 111011; (b) 111111001 ÷ 101.

16

MAGNETIC FIELDS AND CIRCUITS

16.1 ELECTROMAGNETIC ENERGY CONVERSION

For the engineer, electric energy is, in a sense, an intermediate form of energy. It does not exist in a usable form in nature to any considerable extent. Furthermore, the most useful forms of energy as an end result are heat (for industrial processes and personal comfort), light, sound (for communication), mechanical energy (for work and for communication), and chemical energy (for chemical processes). Yet electric energy has several advantages which make its use in industry and communications very extensive. For example, electric energy can be transmitted from one point to another almost instantaneously. Furthermore, the conversion of electric energy into mechanical energy, heat, light, sound, etc., is relatively efficient, and the control over the conversion process is relatively simple. Economic transmission and conversion of electric energy are the principal reasons for the wide use of electric energy.

Energy conversion must occur at both ends of the transmission line. At one end of the line electric energy must be produced from other forms of energy, and at the other end of the line the electric energy must be converted into the form required. Consider an electric-power plant which converts the chemical energy in coal first to heat, then to mechanical energy, and finally to electric energy. An atomic plant converts atomic energy to heat, then mechanical energy, and finally to electric energy. The electric energy is transmitted over power lines to energy consumers who may need heat, light, mechanical energy, or chemical energy. After transmission the energy must be converted into the final form required. The devices used to accomplish energy conversion are many. We have seen that a resistor converts electric energy to heat. An electric motor converts electric energy to mechanical energy. A loudspeaker converts electric energy to acoustic energy. A light globe converts electric energy to light and heat. In order to produce electric energy, a device is required which yields electric energy in its output. An electric generator converts mechanical energy to electric energy. Electric energy can be produced from chemical energy by means of a battery, from acoustic energy by means of a microphone, from light by means of a phototube, and from heat by a thermocouple.

Some forms of energy converters require the presence of a magnetic field surrounding conductors carrying electric current. Rotating electric machines, whether motors or generators, fall in this category, as do loudspeakers and some kinds of microphones. Magnetic fields are the consequence of moving electric charges, or current. In this chapter we shall discuss the production of magnetic fields by electric current in conductors. We shall define some terms necessary to describe magnetic fields, their units, and their significance. We shall observe that a magnetic field can be largely confined to a particular region by the use of iron or steel. Once the fields are established, we shall see in later chapters how we can incorporate them with current-carrying conductors to produce energy transformation or conversion. The study of energy converters, often called "transducers," is a major part of engineering. Electromagnetic transducers—electric motors and generators —and the circuits in which they are used occupy the major part of the remaining chapters.

16.2 MAGNETIC-FORCE EXPERIMENTS

Magnetic fields are produced by moving electric charges and by currents in conductors. In order to visualize some of the characteristics of magnetic fields, let us first perform some hypothetical experiments on some current-carrying conductors. Assume that one conductor, which we call conductor A, is very long and straight and carrying a current I_1. Conductor A is shown in Figs. 16.1 to 16.4. In order to investigate the magnetic field about conductor A, we use a probe consisting of a very short current element which we can move about in the region near conductor A. The short current element, which we call conductor B, has an incremental length dl and a current I_2. We are not concerned with how the circuit for conductor B and current I_2 is completed (the short current element may be a part of a longer conductor), but we are concerned with the force acting on the short current element carrying I_2. A magnetic field is produced by current I_1 and conductor A, and the short current element, conductor B, carrying current I_2, is used as a probe to determine the nature of the magnetic field.

As a first experiment, we align the short current element parallel to conductor A at a distance r, with I_1 and I_2 in the same

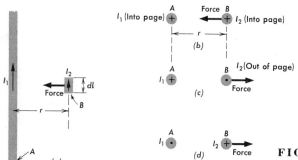

FIG. 16.1 *Magnetic-force experiments—parallel conductors.* ⊕ *current into plane of page,* ⊙ *current out of plane of page.*

direction. This is shown in Fig. 16.1a, and in (b) the two conductors are shown carrying current into the page. In this configuration, a force is observed on the short current element B, and the direction of the force is toward conductor A, as shown in Fig. 16.1a and b. The magnitude of the force is found to be proportional to I_1, I_2, and length dl, and inversely proportional to r, the spacing between the conductors. If the direction of either current I_1 or I_2 is reversed, the direction of the force on the short current element B is found to reverse, as shown in Fig. 16.1c and d. If I_1 and I_2 are in the same direction, conductor B is attracted to A; if the currents are in opposite directions, the force on B is away from conductor A.

Now, as a second experiment, let us change the orientation of the short current element B with respect to the long conductor A. Suppose that B is turned 90° so that it still lies in the plane of the paper and that a line parallel to B intersects conductor A at

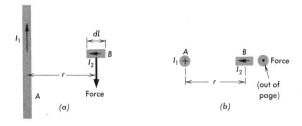

FIG. 16.2 *Magnetic-force experiment—conductors perpendicular.*

right angles to A, as shown in Fig. 16.2a and b. In this configuration a force is observed on the short current element B which is downward in Fig. 16.2a and out of the plane of the paper in Fig. 16.2b. The magnitude of this force is found to be proportional to I_1, I_2, and dl, and inversely proportional to the distance r, just as in the first experiment. Furthermore, we find that, if either I_1 or I_2 is reversed, the direction of the force on conductor B is reversed also. If the directions of *both* I_1 and I_2 are reversed from the directions shown in Fig. 16.2a, the force will be in the same direction as shown in (a).

As a third experiment, suppose that the short current element B is turned so that its direction is into, or perpendicular to, the plane of the paper, as shown in Fig. 16.3a. A line joining con-

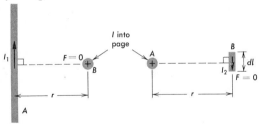

FIG. 16.3 *Magnetic-force experiments—conductor B perpendicular to plane of page.*

ductors A and B is perpendicular to each conductor. The observed force on the short current element B is zero regardless of the direction of either current. Notice in this case that the direction of conductor B is perpendicular to the plane containing conductor A and the line joining conductors A and B.

For the fourth experiment the two conductors are in the same plane, but they are not parallel or perpendicular to each other. Let the angle α be the angle between the direction of the current in the short current element B and the direction parallel to conductor A, as shown in Fig. 16.4. The force observed on the short current element B is perpendicular to the direction of conductor B and is proportional to I_1, I_2, and dl, and inversely proportional to distance r, as shown in Fig. 16.4. We observe that, if the two

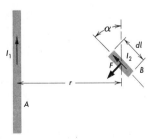

FIG. 16.4 *Magnetic-force experiments—conductors neither parallel nor perpendicular.*

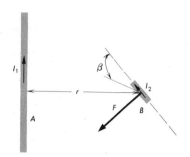

FIG. 16.5 *General magnetic-force experiment.*

conductors A and B lie in the same plane, the magnitude of the force on conductor B is independent of the angle α.

As a final experiment, suppose that we orient the short current element B in such a way that it is at angle β with respect to the plane containing conductor A and the line joining conductor A and B. This is shown in Fig. 16.5. Now we observe the force on the short current element B and find that the direction of the force lies in the plane of conductor A and the line joining the two conductors A and B and is at right angles to the projection of the short current element onto that plane. Furthermore, we find that the magnitude of the force is proportional to I_1 and I_2, inversely proportional to the distance r, and directly proportional to the projection of the length dl of current element B into the plane containing conductor A and the line joining the two conductors A and B. In other words, the magnitude of the force is proportional to $dl \cos \beta$. Our experiments have established that the direction of the force is always in the plane containing conductor A and the line joining the two conductors A and B and that the magnitude of the force is proportional to the length of the projection of conductor B into that plane.

16.3 PERMEABILITY

The magnitude of the force experienced by the short current element B can be written

$$F = \frac{\mu}{2\pi} \frac{I_1 I_2}{r} dl \cos \beta \qquad \text{newtons} \qquad (16.1)$$

where I_1 is the current in conductor A in amperes, I_2 is the current in conductor B in amperes, r is the distance between conductors A and B in meters, $dl \cos \beta$ is the projection of dl on the plane containing conductor A and the line joining conductors A and B, F is the force on the short current element B in newtons, and $\mu/2\pi$ is the constant of proportionality. Equation (16.1) was obtained by experiment. From this experimental relationship, we shall define or derive the quantities useful in describing magnetic fields.

The constant of proportionality $\mu/2\pi$ in Eq. (16.1) depends upon the nature of the material in the space between and surrounding the two conductors in the experiment. If the experiment is performed in air or a vacuum, the value of μ is known as the "permeability" of free space, written μ_0, and

$$\mu_0 = 4\pi \times 10^{-7} \tag{16.2}$$

The units of μ_0 will be discussed in a later paragraph. Substituting Eq. (16.2) into Eq. (16.1) yields

$$F = 2 \times 10^{-7} \frac{I_1 I_2}{r} dl \cos \beta \qquad \text{newtons} \tag{16.3}$$

which is the magnitude of the force on the short current element B when the experiment is performed in free space or air.

If the experiment is repeated with the space between the conductors A and B and surrounding them occupied by any other homogeneous material such as water, hydrogen, glass, etc., it would be found that the permeability is the same for these materials as that of free space. But iron, cobalt, and nickel possess very different and higher values of permeability. This will be discussed in a later section.

We have used the short current element B as a probe, and we have moved it about in a magnetic field produced by current I_1 in conductor A, observing the force on B. Equation (16.3) shows that, if the current I_1 in conductor A is zero, there is no force on the short current element B. Current I_1 in conductor A is necessary to produce the force on the short current element B at a distance r from A, and the force diminishes as r increases. This is true even if the experiment is performed in a perfect vacuum and there is nothing of a material nature joining the two conductors. This is an example of the so-called "action at a distance" principle. A gravitational field is another example of this principle. In a gravitational field, the force between two masses is independent of the material between them and exists even if a vacuum separates them. The only way we know that a gravitational field exists about the earth is from the force we observe, which we call weight, that is experienced by a mass placed in the earth's gravitational field. Conductor A must produce a magnetic field, which in turn produces a force on the short current element B when B is carrying a current I_2.

16.4 MAGNETIC QUANTITIES AND UNITS

Let us investigate further the field which surrounds the current-carrying conductor and which produces a force on another nearby current-carrying conductor. Suppose that we examine Eq. (16.1) and factor from it the terms which apply to the short current element B. The remaining terms are defined as the magnetic-flux density B,

$$B = \frac{\mu I_1}{2\pi r} \tag{16.4}$$

which is a measure of the strength of the magnetic field around conductor A.

Since μ is a function of the material between and enclosing the two conductors, it is convenient to define the term for magnetic-field strength that is independent of the nature of the material in the magnetic field. From Eq. (16.4) we can define the magnetic-field intensity H as

$$H = \frac{I_1}{2\pi r} \qquad \text{amp/m} \tag{16.5}$$

where H is independent of μ. Notice from Eq. (16.5) that H has units of amperes per meter. From Eqs. (16.4) and (16.5) we have the relationship

$$B = \mu H \tag{16.6}$$

Keep in mind that Eqs. (16.4) and (16.5) apply only to the magnetic field about a very long, straight conductor carrying current I_1.

From Eq. (16.1) it is obvious that μ has units of newtons per square ampere. But since a newton-meter is a joule, or a volt-ampere-second, then μ has units of volt-seconds per ampere-meter. But the units of inductance, obtainable from Eq. (1.30), can be expressed in volt-seconds per ampere, or henrys. Then μ has units of henrys per meter, and B has units of ampere-henrys per meter, or volt-seconds per square meter. Suppose that we call the product of ampere-henrys, or volt-seconds, webers. Then B has units of webers per square meter, which we call magnetic-flux density. The product of magnetic-flux density and area is magnetic flux, represented by ϕ, which is shown as

$$\phi = \int_a B \, da \qquad \text{webers} \tag{16.7}$$

and the integration is made over the area a through which the flux passes.

The magnetic units discussed above are all mks units and are summarized in Table 16.1.

TABLE 16.1

Magnetic quantity	Magnetic units (mks)	Other mks units	
Magnetic-field intensity H	$\dfrac{\text{amperes}}{\text{meter}}$		
Magnetic-flux density B	$\dfrac{\text{webers}}{\text{meter}^2}$	$\dfrac{\text{ampere-henrys}}{\text{meter}^2}$	$\dfrac{\text{volt-seconds}}{\text{meter}^2}$
Magnetic flux ϕ	webers	ampere-henrys	volt-seconds
Permeability μ	$\dfrac{\text{henrys}}{\text{meter}}$	$\dfrac{\text{newtons}}{\text{ampere}^2}$	

The experiments discussed in Sec. 16.2 determine the force on a short current element attributed to the magnetic field produced by a long current-carrying conductor. But the experiments could have been done the other way; the force on a *long* conductor could have been measured and a magnetic field about the *short* current element described by that force. This implies that a magnetic field is produced about each conductor by the current flowing through the conductor. The only way we know that one conductor has a magnetic field around it is by observing the force on another conductor carrying current. If each conductor produces a magnetic field around itself, they are each carrying currents and therefore a force exists on each conductor. The mechanism producing the force is unknown; that the force exists is an experimental fact.

16.5 VECTOR MAGNETIC FIELD

So far we have said little concerning the directions associated with the magnetic quantities. We were able to find experimentally the direction of the force on the exploring current element as a function of the direction of the other two currents in the conductors of the experiment. In the preceding experiments, if the current I_1 in the long conductor A produces a magnetic field which encloses the short current element B, there must be something of a directional nature in the magnetic field which determines the direction of force on the short current element B. In Fig. 16.1b, we see the current in both the long conductor A and in the short current element B directed into the plane of the page, and the force on B is to the left toward A. In Fig. 16.1d, the direction of the current in conductor A has been reversed, and the direction of force on the short current element B is to the right away from A. So, in order that the magnetic field can have the required direction to produce a force on the short current element in the direction corresponding to the experimental facts, we adopt this concept: the magnetic field is at right angles to the direction of force and also perpendicular to the plane of conductor A and the line joining conductors A and B, as shown in Fig. 16.6. The short arcs concentric

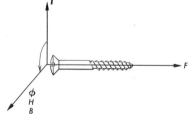

FIG. 16.6 *Flux around conductor A and force on B.*

with conductor A represent the direction of the magnetic flux ϕ. The density of these flux lines as they pass through the plane containing conductors A and B represents the flux density B. And magnetic-flux density B is related to magnetic-field intensity H by the constant μ. Then ϕ, B, and H are all in the same direction.

Notice in Fig. 16.6 that, when the flux is downward and current I_2 is into the plane of the paper, then the force F is to the left. Flux, I_2, and force F are mutually at right angles to each other in this example. This right-angle relationship can be kept in mind by any of several ways. One is to keep in mind the principle of the right-hand screw, as shown in Fig. 16.7. If the vector marked I is rotated into the direction of the magnetic-field quantities ϕ, H, or B, the screw progresses in the direction of force F. This is consistent with Fig. 16.6, where I_2 is directed into the paper, and if rotated downward until it is in the direction of the magnetic flux ϕ, the right-hand-screw principle tells us that the screw would progress in the direction of the force F when rotated in this manner.

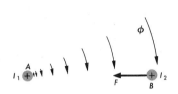

FIG. 16.7 *The right-hand screw for determining directions of I, φ, and F.*

A useful method for determining the direction of the magnetic flux about a conductor carrying current is to use the well-known right-hand rule. If the conductor is grasped with the right hand so that the thumb points along the conductor in the direction of the current, then the magnetic flux encircles the conductor in the direction of the fingers. In Fig. 16.6 the direction of the magnetic flux is consistent with this thinking, because, when the thumb is aligned with the direction of the current into the plane of the paper and the fingers closed, they point clockwise about the conductor.

Another right-hand rule for determining the directions of currents, magnetic flux ϕ, and force F uses the thumb, index finger, and third finger of the right hand. If these three fingers are aligned so that they are mutually at right angles with each other, and the index finger is in the direction of the current, and the third finger is in the direction of the magnetic flux, then the thumb will be in the direction of the force. It is necessary that the *right* hand be used and not the left hand in determining these mutual directions.

16.6 AMPÈRE'S LAW

That a magnetic field exists about a long, straight current-carrying conductor has been established in preceding sections. But a long, straight conductor is a special case, and we now consider the more general case of a short section of conductor, of length dl, and the field produced by it. If this can be determined, then the field produced by many short segments can be determined by superposition and we have a means of finding the field produced by a conductor of any shape.

In an ingenious series of experiments (similar to those mentioned in Sec. 16.2) by the French mathematician Ampère between 1820 and 1825, the magnetic-force and magnetic-flux relationships were determined for an incremental length of conductor. Ampère's law can be stated in several ways, and here we choose to state it in terms of the magnetic-flux density B at some point attributed to a current I in an incremental length dl of a conductor. Figure 16.8 shows a conductor of arbitrary shape carrying current I. A differential length dl is identified along the conductor. Point A is the point at which the magnetic-flux density caused by current I in the differential length dl is to be determined. Ampère found that the increment of magnetic-flux density dB at point A caused by the differential length dl carrying current I was inversely proportional to the square of the distance r between dl and A, directly proportional to current I, and a function of the property of the material in which the system is immersed, which we call "permeability." The magnetizing effect of element dl was found to be proportional to the cosine of the angle α between the perpendicular to dl and the line joining point A with dl. These concepts of Ampère's can be expressed in mks units as

$$dB = \frac{\mu I \cos \alpha \, dl}{4\pi r^2} \tag{16.8}$$

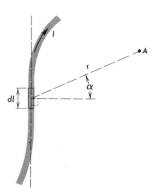

FIG. 16.8 *To illustrate Ampère's law.*

where α is the angle shown in Fig. 16.8 between the line perpendicular to dl and the line joining dl and A, μ is the permeability, I is the current in amperes, dl is the differential length of the conductor in meters, r is the distance from dl to point A in meters, and dB is the increment of flux density at point A in webers per square meter. The above equation tells the magnitude of magnetic-flux density at A. The direction is perpendicular to the plane of dl and A, and the sense, determined by one of the methods described in Sec. 16.5, is into the plane of the page.

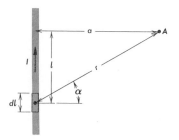

FIG. 16.9 *Deriving flux density at A by Ampère's law.*

If we now consider a long, straight conductor and apply Ampère's law to each increment of it, we should be able to derive, and thus verify, Eq. (16.4). Figure 16.9 shows point A at a distance a from the long, straight conductor. Using Eq. (16.8) and integrating along the entire length of the conductor from $-\infty$ to $+\infty$, the magnetic-flux density at A is

$$B = \frac{\mu I}{4\pi} \int_{-\infty}^{+\infty} \frac{\cos \alpha \, dl}{r^2}$$ (16.9)

But

$$r^2 = l^2 + a^2$$

and

$$\cos \alpha = \frac{a}{r} = \frac{a}{\sqrt{l^2 + a^2}}$$

Then Eq. (16.9) can be written

$$B = \frac{\mu I}{4\pi} \int_{-\infty}^{\infty} \frac{a \, dl}{(l^2 + a^2)^{3/2}}$$

where a is a constant. Integration yields

$$B = \frac{\mu I a}{4\pi} \left[\frac{l}{a^2 \sqrt{l^2 + a^2}} \right]_{l=-\infty}^{l=+\infty}$$

or

$$B = \frac{\mu I}{2\pi a} \qquad \text{webers/m}^2$$ (16.10)

Notice that in the formulation of the problem in Fig. 16.9 we defined a as the distance of point A from the conductor. In Sec. 16.2 we used r as that distance. Therefore, Eqs. (16.10) and (16.4) are identical.

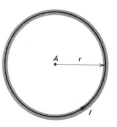

FIG. 16.10 *Deriving flux density at center of circular conduction loop.*

Another example of simple geometry is a circular conducting loop of radius r, as shown in Fig. 16.10. The magnetic-flux density at the center A is

$$B = \int_0^{2\pi} \frac{\mu I}{4\pi r^2} r \, d\theta$$

where $dl = r \, d\theta$. Integration yields

$$B = \frac{\mu I}{2r} \qquad\qquad\qquad\qquad (16.11)$$

Now suppose that there are N turns, each carrying current I, in the circular loop of radius r instead of the one shown in Fig. 16.10. Then

$$B = \frac{\mu}{2r} NI \qquad \text{webers/m}^2 \qquad\qquad (16.12)$$

and NI has units of amperes, though "ampere-turns" is the term more commonly used. Then magnetic-flux density in the center of the loop is directly proportional to the number of ampere-turns. The direction of the flux is out of the paper in Fig. 16.10, according to the right-hand rule.

16.7 THE MAGNETIC CIRCUIT

The concept of the magnetic circuit can be developed by considering a toroid of circular cross section composed of a nonmagnetic material, as shown in Fig. 16.11. The cross section of the toroid has a radius r, and the radius from the center of the doughnut's hole to the center of the cross section is a. The toroid is wound uniformly with N turns closely spaced. The current I is supplied by the battery. Magnetic flux produced within the toroid is in the clockwise direction as shown, determined by the right-hand rule. Ampère's law could be used to determine the flux density at any point within the toroid. However, the geometry of the problem is such as to make its solution very difficult. Instead, we can make some generalizations and from them fabricate a fairly good picture of the magnetic circuit.

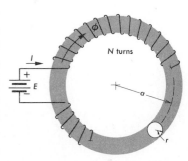

FIG. 16.11 *Toroid with N turns distributed around it.*

We found in the preceding section how the magnetic-flux density in the center of a circular coil of N turns is proportional to NI, or [Eq. (16.12)]

$$B = \frac{\mu}{2r} NI \qquad \text{webers/m}^2$$

It seems logical to expect, then, that the flux density in the toroid is proportional to NI, the product of current times the number of turns of wire. The product NI is known as "magnetomotive force," abbreviated mmf. Magnetomotive force for the magnetic circuit is analogous to emf or voltage in the electric circuit. If we think of the flux ϕ as resulting from the mmf, just as current in the resistive circuit is caused by the emf, a magnetic Ohm's law can be defined as

$$NI = \phi\mathcal{R} \tag{16.13}$$

analogous to Ohm's law for the resistive circuit

$$E = IR$$

The term $\mathcal{R}$ in Eq. (16.13) is known as "reluctance" and is analogous to resistance R in the electric circuit. Just as resistance can be expressed in terms of the dimensions of the conductor of uniform cross-sectional area as [Eq. (1.25)]

$$R = \rho\,\frac{L}{A}$$

so reluctance can be defined in terms of the dimensions of the magnetic-circuit or -flux path as

$$\mathcal{R} = \frac{L}{\mu A} \tag{16.14}$$

where L is the mean length of the flux path. Table 16.2 shows the analogies between resistive electric circuits and the magnetic circuit.

TABLE 16.2 *Electric and Magnetic Analogies*

	Electric circuit	Magnetic circuit
Ohm's law	$E = IR$	$NI = \phi\mathcal{R}$
Exciting force	E	NI
"Through" variable	I	ϕ
By dimensions	$R = \rho\dfrac{L}{A}$	$\mathcal{R} = \dfrac{1}{\mu}\dfrac{L}{A}$
Proportionality constant	ρ	$\dfrac{1}{\mu}$

16.8 THE MAGNETIZATION CURVE

Now assume that the material of the toroid is iron, one of the magnetic elements. The reluctance of the iron circuit as defined by Eq. (16.14) is not constant but is dependent on several factors which contribute to changes in the permeability of the iron. These factors are: (a) magnetic history of the iron; (b) kind of iron alloy composing the core; (c) amount of mmf applied. By choosing an iron core of a particular composition and eliminating the effect of previous magnetic history by an averaging process, we can study the relationship between mmf and magnetic-flux density in the iron. We find that the flux density is not directly proportional to the mmf as predicted by Eq. (16.13) for constant μ. The plot of B versus NI is shown in Fig. 16.12. Notice that, for small

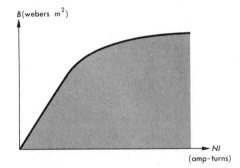

FIG. 16.12 *Flux density versus ampere-turns for iron core.*

values of NI, B is approximately proportional to NI but that, for large values of NI, the slope of the curve decreases and saturation is said to be present. The unsaturated region is the region of greatest slope.

Substituting Eq. (16.14) into (16.13) and solving for ϕ/A results in

$$\frac{\phi}{A} = \mu \frac{NI}{L} \tag{16.15}$$

where an average flux density can be defined as $B = \phi/A$, or

$$B = \mu \frac{NI}{L} \tag{16.16}$$

Substituting $B = \mu H$ [Eq. (16.6)] into Eq. (16.16) results in

$$H = \frac{NI}{L} \qquad (16.17)$$

Since L, the mean length of the flux path around the toroid, is a constant, magnetic-field intensity is proportional to the ampere-turns. Since NI is the mmf, NI/L is a magnetic-potential gradient, or mmf gradient. Magnetomotive force per unit length, or NI/L = H, could have been used for the abscissa in Fig. 16.12 if we had so chosen. In fact, the magnetization curve in Fig. 16.12 is often known as a BH curve and plotted as B versus H, as in Fig. 16.13.

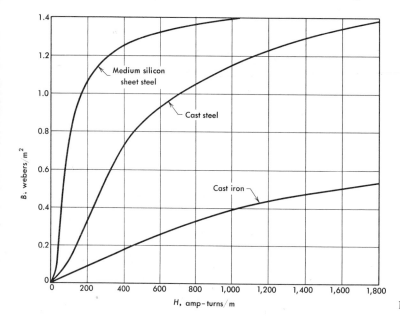

FIG. 16.13 *BH curves.*

The flux density in an iron circuit or core is independent of the cross-sectional area, since it is found approximately by dividing the total flux by the area. Likewise, the magnetic-field intensity NI/L is independent of the length of core. A BH curve therefore is a function of the characteristics of the iron itself, and not of the shape of the core. BH curves for several different iron alloys are shown in Fig. 16.13.

Since permeability is the ratio of B to H, the curves in Fig. 16.13 demonstrate that the permeability for any kind of iron is several hundred to several thousand times the permeability of free space. Furthermore, permeability is not a constant for iron but is a function of the mmf gradient.

16.9 SERIES MAGNETIC CIRCUITS

The magnetic circuit discussed in Sec. 16.8 consists of a toroidal core of homogeneous magnetic material of uniform cross-sectional area. If the core material is iron, the flux produced in the core is "conducted" by the iron and confined almost entirely to the iron core. Flux density in the iron can be obtained graphically from the magnetization curve for the particular kind of iron. The magnetic circuit is analogous to a resistive circuit with a nonlinear resistor and a battery in series, as shown in Fig. 16.14. The

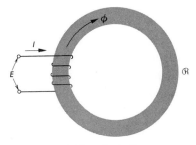

(a) Magnetic circuit

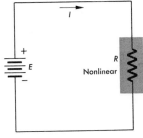

(b) Analogous electric circuit

FIG. 16.14 *Analogous magnetic and electric circuits.*

analogy shows NI corresponding to E, ϕ corresponding to I, and $\mathcal{R}$ corresponding to R. The nonlinear-resistive-electric-circuit problem was discussed in Chap. 8. Similar methods can be used to solve magnetic circuits.

Example 16.1

A toroid of cast steel with a circular cross section has the dimensions given in Fig. 16.15. It is magnetized by 5 amp in the winding of 100 turns. To find the flux density in the steel core, we first find the mean length $L = 2\pi a$.

$$L = 2\pi(0.160) = 1.005 \text{ m}$$

Then

$$H = \frac{NI}{L} = \frac{100(5)}{1.005} = 497 \text{ amp-turns/m}$$

From the curve for cast steel in Fig. 16.13, if $H = 497$ amp-turns/m, $B = 0.844$ weber/m².

The total flux $\phi = BA$, where $A = \pi r^2 = \pi(0.0130)^2 = 0.000531$ m². Then $\phi = 0.844(0.000531) = 0.000448$ weber.

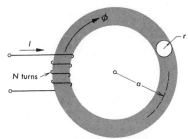

FIG. 16.15 *Magnetic circuit of Example 16.1. a = 0.160 m, r = 0.0130 m, N = 100 turns, I = 5 amp.*

Often magnetic circuits are not uniform or homogeneous over the entire length of the flux path. Such magnetic circuits can be considered in a manner similar to the series electric circuit with nonlinear elements described in Chap. 8. Kirchhoff's laws apply to magnetic circuits as well as electric circuits. For a series magnetic circuit the sum of the mmf around the circuit must be zero, or the sum of the mmf drops must equal the ampere-turns exciting the circuit. In Example 16.1, Kirchhoff's law is the basis for equating NI to the mmf drop in the iron.

When the cross-sectional area of the iron flux path is not uniform, or when the magnetic properties around the flux path are not uniform, then Kirchhoff's law expresses the fact that

$$NI = (\text{mmf})_1 + (\text{mmf})_2 + \cdots \tag{16.18}$$

where NI is the exciting force in ampere-turns and $(\text{mmf})_1$, $(\text{mmf})_2$, etc., are the mmf drops across the series branches of the flux path. An analogous electric circuit consists of a constant-voltage source E (analogous to NI) and several resistors in series. Then

$$E = IR_1 + IR_2 + \cdots$$

where the voltage across each resistor is analogous to the mmf drop across each branch of the magnetic circuit.

An air gap often is inserted in practical magnetic circuits and must be treated as a linear part of the circuit. Since the permeability of air is constant ($\mu_0 = 4\pi \times 10^{-7} h/m$), flux density in the air is always proportional to the mmf drop across the air gap. The following example illustrates the solution of a series magnetic circuit consisting of an iron flux path and an air gap.

Example 16.2

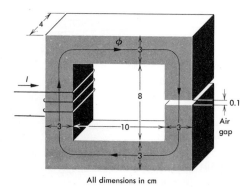

All dimensions in cm

FIG. 16.16 *Magnetic circuit of Example 16.2.*

A rectangular core of laminated sheet steel has the dimensions shown in Fig. 16.16. A winding of 240 turns carrying 5.5 amp is placed on the core. To find the air-gap flux, we first calculate a mean length of the flux path and the cross-sectional area. The mean length of the flux path in the iron, L_i, is approximately

$$L_i \approx 2(10 + \tfrac{3}{2} + \tfrac{3}{2}) + 2(8 + \tfrac{3}{2} + \tfrac{3}{2}) - 0.1$$

$$\approx 48 \text{ cm}$$

or

$$L_i \approx 0.48 \text{ m}$$

The length of the flux path in air, L_a, is given as

$$L_a = 0.001 \text{ m}$$

The cross-sectional area is

$$A = 4(3) = 12 \text{ cm}^2$$

or

$$A = 0.0012 \text{ m}^2$$

The total mmf is

$$NI = 240(5.5) = 1,320 \text{ amp-turns}$$

Since the relationship between B and H in air is linear, the magnetization curve for air can be drawn as a straight line through the origin. For another point on the B-versus-NI curve for the air gap, let $NI = 1,320$; then

$$H = \frac{NI}{L} = \frac{1,320}{0.001} = 1.320 \times 10^6 \text{ amp-turns/m}$$

and

$$B = \mu_0 H$$

$$= 4\pi \times 10^{-7} \times 1.320 \times 10^6 = 1.657 \text{ webers/m}^2$$

The B-versus-NI curve for air is drawn as shown in Fig. 16.17. Subtracting the mmf for the air gap from the total number of ampere-turns available, 1,320, gives the B-versus-NI characteristic for the 1,320 amp-turns minus the mmf drop in the air gap. The intersection of the B-versus-NI curve for the iron core and the NI-minus-mmf$_{air}$ characteristic is the solution to the problem. At the intersection, $B = 1.33$ webers/m^2, the mmf drop in the iron is $NI_i = 255$ amp-turns, and the mmf drop in the air gap is $NI_a = 1,065$ amp-turns.

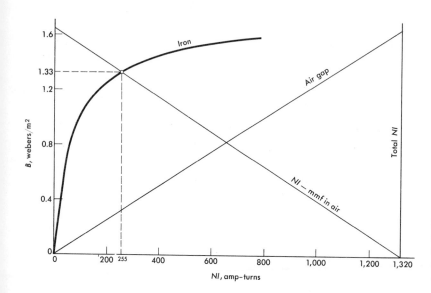

FIG. 16.17 *Graphical solution of Example 16.2 showing B versus NI for the iron core, for the air gap, and total mmf available.* $NI_{\text{total}} = mmf_{\text{iron}} + mmf_{\text{air}}$.

The solution of magnetic circuits containing parallel branches can be obtained with the help of Kirchhoff's current law in its analogous magnetic form. Since magnetic flux is analogous to current, the flux entering a node must equal the flux leaving the node. Furthermore, the mmf drop across two parallel paths is identical for each.

Successive approximation is a useful way to solve magnetic circuits, just as it is useful for solving nonlinear electric resistive circuits (Chap. 8). In Example 16.3, a parallel circuit is solved by successive approximation. A value of flux density in one branch is assumed, and the exciting mmf for the entire circuit is determined. If the determined value of exciting mmf is lower than the known exciting ampere-turns, then the problem is worked again by using a higher assumed value of flux density than the initial assumed value. This process is continued until a value of B is assumed which requires an exciting mmf that is equal to the known exciting mmf. When parallel magnetic branches are present, Kirchhoff's flux law can be written

$$\Sigma\phi = 0 \qquad\qquad (16.19)$$

or the magnetic flux in a direction toward the junction equals the magnetic flux in a direction away from the junction. This is also illustrated in Example 16.3.

Example 16.3

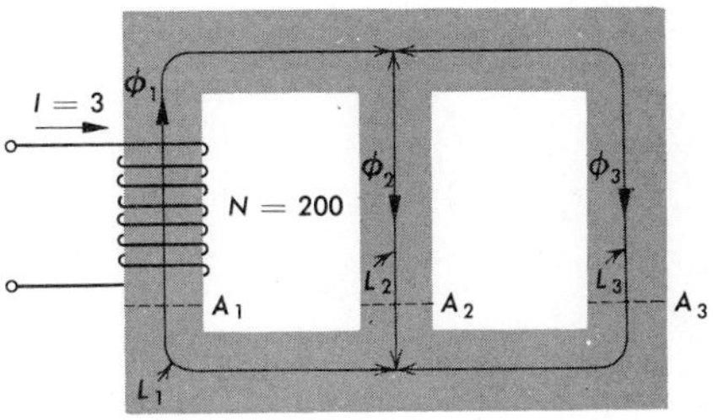

FIG. 16.18 *Parallel magnetic circuit of Example 16.3.* $L_1 =$
0.320 m, L_2 = 0.120 m, L_3 = 0.220 m; A_1 = 0.000685 m^2, A_2 =
0.000250 m^2, A_3 = 0.000275 m^2.

The cast-iron core shown in Fig. 16.18 has average flux path of
lengths given in the figure and cross-sectional areas in each of these
paths also given in the figure. A winding of 200 turns, carrying 3
amp, provides the magnetizing force or exciting mmf. To find the
flux density in the various branches, first assume a flux density in
one of them. Assume that $B_3 = 0.4$ weber/m^2. Then $\phi_3 = B_3 A_3$
or $\phi_3 = 0.4(0.000275) = 0.000110$ weber.

From the magnetization for cast iron (Fig. 16.13), for $B_3 =$
0.4 webers/m^2,

$$H_3 = 1{,}020 \text{ amp-turns/m}$$

and

$$\text{mmf}_3 = H_3 L_3 = 1{,}020(0.220) = 224.5 \text{ amp-turns}$$

But mmf_3 is the same as the mmf for the second path of length L_2.

$$H_2 = \frac{\text{mmf}_2}{L_2} = \frac{224.5}{0.120} = 1{,}870 \text{ amp-turns/m}$$

From the magnetization curve, for $H = 1{,}870$ amp-turns/m, after
extrapolating,

$$B_2 = 0.53 \text{ weber/m}^2$$

$$\phi_2 = B_2 A_2 = 0.53 \ (0.00025) = 0.0001325 \text{ weber}$$

Since

$$\phi_1 = \phi_2 + \phi_3$$

$$\phi_1 = 0.0001325 + 0.000110 = 0.000242 \text{ weber}$$

$$B_1 = \frac{\phi_1}{A_1} = \frac{0.000242}{0.000685} = 0.354 \text{ weber/m}^2$$

From the magnetization curve, for $B = 0.354$ weber/m^2,

$$H_1 = 880 \frac{\text{amp-turns}}{\text{m}}$$

$$\text{mmf}_1 = H_1 L_1 = 880(0.320)$$

$$= 281 \text{ amp-turns}$$

Then $\mathrm{mmf}_1 + \mathrm{mmf}_2 = 281 + 224.5 = 505.5$ amp-turns. This is less than the 600 amp-turns of magnetizing force present; so the original guess for the value of B_3 is too low. The process can be repeated again and again until the assumed value of B_3 finally shows an exciting mmf of 600 amp-turns.

SUMMARY

Two conductors carrying current exert forces on each other. The magnitude of the force on a short current-carrying element of length dl in the presence of a very long, straight conductor is [Eq. (16.1)]

$$F = \frac{\mu}{2\pi} \frac{I_1 I_2}{r} \, dl \cos \beta \qquad \text{newtons}$$

where I_1 is the current in the long conductor, I_2 is the current in the short element of length dl, r is the distance between the two conductors, and β is the angle between the short element and its projection on the plane which passes through the long conductor and the line perpendicular to the long conductor drawn through the short one.

The magnetic field existing around the long conductor is defined in terms of magnetic-flux density B, which consists of that part of Eq. (16.1) not directly related to the short current element, or [Eq. (16.4)]

$$B = \frac{\mu I_1}{2\pi r} \qquad \text{webers/m}^2$$

The magnetic intensity H is independent of permeability μ of the surrounding material, or [Eq. (16.5)]

$$H = \frac{I_1}{2\pi r} \qquad \text{henrys/m}$$

and [Eq. (16.6)]

$$B = \mu H$$

and if B is uniform, the magnetic flux ϕ is

$$\phi = BA$$

where A is the area perpendicular to the direction of B and ϕ.

When the conductor establishing a magnetic field is not long and straight, Ampère's law can be useful to determine flux density contributed by a short current element of that conductor. Ampère's law can be written [Eq. (16.8)]

$$dB = \frac{\mu I \cos \alpha \, dl}{4 \pi r^2}$$

where dB is the contribution to the flux density of the current element of length dl carrying current I. α and r are defined in Fig. 16.8.

When the flux path is confined to a magnetic circuit, flux densities in the iron core tend to be many times what they would be for a nonmagnetic core of the same dimensions. The magnetic circuit is analogous to a nonlinear electric circuit, mmf NI corresponding to voltage in the electric circuit. Then Kirchhoff's mmf law can be written [Eq. (16.18)]

$$NI = (\text{mmf})_1 + (\text{mmf})_2 + \cdots$$

where each of the mmfs can be expressed as

$$(\text{mmf})_1 = (HL)_1 \qquad (\text{mmf})_2 = (HL)_2, \text{ etc.}$$

where L is the length of a branch of the magnetic circuit and H is the magnetic-field intensity of that branch.

The magnetic flux in the direction into a junction of a magnetic circuit must equal the magnetic flux in the direction out of the junction, or [Eq. (16.19)]

$$\Sigma \phi = 0$$

The solution of nonlinear magnetic circuits follows the same patterns as the solution of nonlinear electric circuits discussed in Chap. 8.

FURTHER READING

Magnetic-field and -circuit concepts are developed in a logical way in Bruce O. Watkins, *Electrical Engineering Fundamentals* (International Textbook Company, Scranton, Pa., 1958), chaps. 7 and 8, and in R. Galbraith and D. W. Spence, *Fundamentals of Electrical Engineering* (The Ronald Press Company, New York, 1955), chaps. 6 to 9.

PROBLEMS

16.1 Plot μ versus H for sheet steel, whose BH curve is shown in Fig. 16.13.

 Note: Use the BH curve for medium silicon sheet steel for the problems below.

16.2 A core of the dimensions (all in centimeters) shown in (*a*) of the figure must have a magnetic-flux density in the iron of 1.200 webers/m². If the number of turns is 100, what current is required in winding?

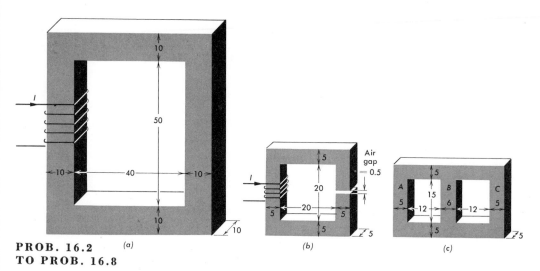

PROB. 16.2   (a)   (b)   (c)
TO PROB. 16.8

16.3 There are 600 amp-turns of mmf on the core shown in (*a*) of the figure. What is the flux in webers in the core?

16.4 Assume an air-gap flux of 0.0028 weber in (*b*) of the figure. Find the total number of ampere-turns necessary to produce this flux in the iron and air gap.

16.5 There are 1,600 amp-turns of mmf applied to the magnetic circuit of (*b*) of the figure. Using the graphical method, find the flux density in the iron and in the air gap.

16.6 Repeat Prob. 16.5, using successive approximation instead of the graphical method.

16.7 Assume that it is necessary to establish a flux density of 0.45

weber/m² in leg C of the core in (c) of the figure and that the winding to produce this flux is on leg B. How many ampere-turns are necessary on leg B?

16.8 Repeat Prob. 16.7, assuming that the winding is placed on leg A instead of leg B.

16.9 The iron core shown in the illustration has an effective length L of 0.500 m, an effective cross-sectional area of 0.00080 m², and an air-gap length of 0.0005 m. The mmf is 1,800 amp-turns. Find the magnetic flux ϕ.

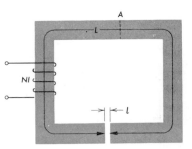

PROB. 16.9

16.10 It is required that the core in Prob. 16.9 have a flux density of 0.75 weber/m². Find the mmf that will establish the required flux density.

16.11 The air gap in the core of Prob. 16.9 is adjusted until the mmf drop in the air gap is equal to the mmf drop in the iron. NI is 1,800 amp-turns. Find the flux in the air gap.

16.12 The magnet for a cyclotron is shown in the figure with dimensions in meters. The air gap has a length of 3 in., and the windings on the two legs produce flux in the center leg that is downward. The mmfs of the two windings are equal. A flux density of 1.00 weber/m² must be maintained in the air gap. How many ampere-turns must each winding have?

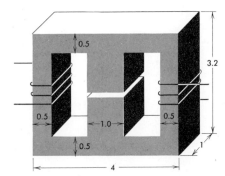

PROB. 16.12

16.13 One of the windings is removed from the core in Prob. 16.12, and the other is made to be 5,200 amp-turns. Find the flux density in each of the three legs.

16.14 An iron core such as the one in Prob. 16.12 has a single winding on the center leg producing 3,200 amp-turns of mmf. Find the air-gap flux.

16.15 The magnetic-flux density at the center of a circular conducting loop carrying current I is given by Eq. (16.11) as $B = \dfrac{\mu I}{2r}$. A point p is located a distance x along the axis from the plane of the loop as shown.

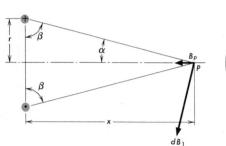

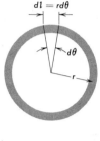

$$dl = rd\theta$$

PROB. 16.15

The increment of flux density dB_1 is established by the short incremental length of conductor dl. Prove that the total flux density B_p at point p is along the axis of the loop as shown, with a magnitude of

$$B_p = \frac{\mu I r^2}{2(r^2 + x^2)^{3/2}}$$

Notice that, when $x = 0$, the flux density B_p corresponds to the flux density given by Eq. (16.11).

16.16 A long solenoid consists of N turns distributed uniformly along the distance L, as shown in the figure, with point C the geometric center

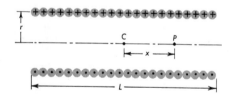

PROB. 16.16

of the solenoid. A point P is located on the axis of the solenoid a distance x from C. The number of turns in an incremental length dx is $N \, dx/L$. Prove that the flux density B_p at point P on the axis of the solenoid is

$$B_p = \frac{\mu N I}{2L} \left\{ \frac{L/2 + x}{[r^2 + (L/2 + x)^2]^{1/2}} + \frac{L/2 - x}{[r^2 + (L/2 - x)^2]^{1/2}} \right\}$$

16.17 From the results of Prob. 16.16, verify that, when L is large compared with $2r$, the flux density at C is given by $B_c = \dfrac{\mu N I}{L}$ and the flux density at P is given by $B_p = \dfrac{\mu N I}{2L}$. Then show that, if $L \gg r$ and the solenoid is bent into a toroid, B_p equals B_c and at any point on the axis of the toroid $H_p = \dfrac{N I}{L} = \dfrac{N I}{2\pi r}$.

GENERATION OF VOLTAGES

17.1 FARADAY'S LAW

It is an experimental fact that an emf is induced in a closed circuit when the net magnetic flux enclosed by the circuit changes with respect to time. This discovery was first announced by the English physicist Michael Faraday in 1831 after a brilliant series of experiments. Now known as "Faraday's law," it can easily be interpreted by considering a closed conducting ring as shown in

FIG. 17.1 *Faraday's law applies to voltage induced in a closed path.*

(a) Conducting loop enclosing magnetic flux ϕ

(b) Equivalent circuit for loop

Fig. 17.1a. Magnetic flux is shown passing through the plane of the conducting ring. Faraday's law tells us that the magnitude of the voltage induced in the ring is proportional to the rate of change of magnetic flux with respect to time, or

$$e = \frac{d\phi}{dt} \quad \text{volts} \tag{17.1}$$

where ϕ is in webers and t is in seconds. If the flux passing through the conducting ring is increasing with time, the emf induced in the ring is distributed along the ring as represented by the batteries shown in Fig. 17.1b. Since the ring is a closed circuit, each very short length along the ring's circumference has resistance represented by the distributed resistance shown in Fig. 17.1b. The sum of all the battery voltages shown in Fig. 17.1b adds up to the induced voltage e given by Eq. (17.1). The sum of all the resistance around the ring shown in (b) adds up to the total resistance around the ring. We are assuming that the inductance is negligible compared with the resistance of the ring. A current i flows in a clockwise direction, and its magnitude is determined by Ohm's law, where the applied voltage is expressed by Eq. (17.1) and the resistance is the total resistance around the ring.

Faraday's law, as expressed by Eq. (17.1), shows the *magnitude* of the induced voltage. If the flux in the ring is increasing in the direction upward in Fig. 17.1a, the induced voltage is in a direction that causes current i to flow clockwise, as shown. This is also an experimental fact. If the flux is decreasing so that $d\phi/dt$ directed upward is negative, then the induced voltage is in the opposite direction. In order to determine the actual direction of the induced voltage, several different experiments are summarized in Fig. 17.2. The relationship between changing flux and the direction of the induced voltage can be stated as Lenz's law: any change in the magnetic flux enclosed by a closed circuit induces a voltage in the circuit that tends to produce a current in

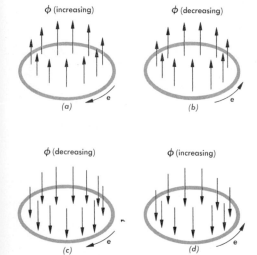

FIG. 17.2 *Illustrating Lenz's law relating the direction of e and $d\phi/dt$.*

the circuit in such a direction as to oppose the changing flux. Thus, in Fig. 17.2a, the induced voltage e is clockwise in direction, tending to produce a current in the same direction. This current, according to the right-hand rule, produces a flux which opposes the increasing flux, and is thus downward in the direction opposite to the field flux. Notice in Fig. 17.2b that the induced voltage e is counterclockwise for a flux that is upward but decreasing in magnitude. A counterclockwise current in (b) tends to produce a flux which, by the right-hand rule, is upward inside the ring, tending to cause the net flux through the ring to remain constant.

Faraday's law applies to many different configurations of conductors and flux besides those illustrated in Fig. 17.2. The examples in Fig. 17.2 assume that the conducting ring is stationary and the flux through the ring varies with time. Another possible situation is one in which the flux is fixed and constant in time but the conductor moves in such a way that the net flux through the ring varies with time. Another possibility is when the flux changes with time and the conductor moves, the motion adding to the changing flux through the ring. Some of these concepts will be developed further in this chapter.

17.2 FLUX LINKAGES

In the preceding section we considered some magnetic flux surrounded by a conducting ring which we can think of as a coil of one turn. But suppose that we wind the coil through two or more turns before we close the coil on itself. In Fig. 17.3 we have shown N turns (in Fig. 17.3 $N = 3$), each turn completely enclosing the flux ϕ. Faraday's law tells us that this is equivalent to a single turn enclosing a flux of $N\phi$ webers. Then, if each turn encloses the same flux, Faraday's law can be written

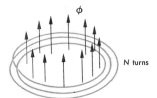

FIG. 17.3 *Flux ϕ enclosed by N turns is equivalent to flux $N\phi$ through one turn.*

$$e = N\frac{d\phi}{dt} \quad \text{volts} \tag{17.2}$$

where N is a dimensionless quantity. The quantity $N\phi$ can be defined as λ, or flux linkages. A further modification of Faraday's law yields

$$e = \frac{d\lambda}{dt} \quad \text{volts} \tag{17.3}$$

where

$$\lambda = N\phi \quad \text{flux linkages} \tag{17.4}$$

Equation (17.4) applies only when each winding is linked by flux ϕ. If the coil is not wound on an iron core and is not tightly packed as in Fig. 17.3, each turn links a different amount of flux and Eq. (17.4) does not apply.

17.3 TRANSFORMER ACTION

Faraday's law applies to many different configurations of conductors and flux besides those shown in Fig. 17.2. One important example is the transformer, shown in Fig. 17.4. One winding of

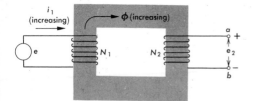

FIG. 17.4 *Transformer action: changing i_1 causes induced e_2.*

the transformer, known as the "primary," is excited by a source of electric energy which causes the current i_1 to flow through N_1 turns on the iron core. In Chap. 16 we determined a method for finding the flux ϕ produced by $N_1 i_1$ amp-turns of mmf. In this example we are assuming that there is no leakage flux, so that the entire flux is confined to the path of the iron core. Notice that ϕ is encircled N_2 times by the second, or secondary, winding, which means there are ϕN_2 flux linkages in the secondary winding. If i_1 is increasing with time, ϕ also increases in the direction shown. The emf induced in the second winding is, by Faraday's law,

$$e_2 = N_2 \frac{d\phi}{dt} \tag{17.5}$$

By Lenz's law, the direction of the induced voltage e_2 is such as to tend to cause a current to flow that will oppose the changing flux. It matters not that the circuit is open; the emf is still induced. A voltmeter connected across the terminals a–b would measure an induced voltage of the magnitude given by Eq. (17.5) in the direction determined by Lenz's law, shown in Fig. 17.4. If i_1 decreases, causing $d\phi/dt$ to change sign, then the induced voltage e_2 would change sign also.

Now suppose that i_1 is a sinusoid, the iron core does not saturate, and the flux is proportional to the current i_1. Let

$$i_1 = I_m \sin \omega t \tag{17.6}$$

Then, by means of Eqs. (16.13) and (16.14), we can write

$$\phi = \frac{N_1 i_1}{\mathcal{R}} = N_1 i_1 \frac{\mu A}{l} \tag{17.7}$$

By Faraday's law [Eq. (17.5)],

$$e_2 = N_2 \frac{d\phi}{dt}$$

from which

$$e_2 = \frac{N_1 N_2 \mu A I_m \omega}{l} \cos \omega t \tag{17.8}$$

Notice the phase relationship between Eqs. (17.8) and (17.6); the magnetic flux ϕ and the primary current i_1 are in phase, but the induced voltage e_2 is $90°$ ahead of i_1.

17.4 INDUCED VOLTAGES CAUSED BY CONDUCTOR MOTION

Faraday's law makes no restriction concerning the method by which the changing flux linkages through the closed electric circuit are produced. In this section we shall investigate possible systems in which the magnetic flux is constant with time and fixed in space and the electric circuit moves relative to the fixed flux.

As a first example, consider a constant and uniform magnetic-flux density, the flux directed into the plane of the paper as shown in Fig. 17.5. A rectangular conducting circuit is shown in the plane of the paper, constrained always to remain in a plane perpendicular to the flux. Now assume that the loop moves with a velocity v to the right. Since the magnetic-flux density is constant and uniform, always the same amount of flux passes through the conducting rectangle. Therefore the induced voltage in the circuit is zero. Another possible mode of motion for the loop in Fig. 17.5 is to have it move with velocity v in a direction perpendicular to the plane of the paper and parallel to the lines of magnetic flux. In this configuration the loop always encloses the same flux lines since it is moving parallel to them. Therefore the induced voltage is still zero. From these examples we can see that, under the conditions of constant uniform flux density, a loop constrained always to be in a plane perpendicular to the flux has no induced voltage regardless of the direction of motion.

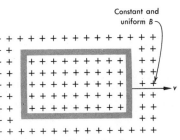

FIG. 17.5 *Conducting loop perpendicular to magnetic flux. Crosses indicate flux directed into the page.*

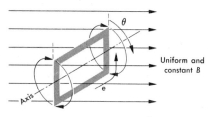

Uniform and
constant B

θ

e

Axis

FIG. 17.6 *Rotating rectangular loop in magnetic field.*

As a second example, suppose that a uniform and constant magnetic-flux density is directed to the right, as shown in Fig. 17.6. The conducting loop is placed in the magnetic field in a plane that is initially perpendicular to the flux. An axis in the plane of the loop bisects the loop and is perpendicular to the magnetic flux; this is the axis of a revolution for the loop. Now assume that the conducting loop is in a position where it links a flux equal to $B \times A$, where A is the area of the loop. After the loop has rotated 90° from its initial position, it is parallel to the flux and does not link any flux. Notice that the net flux through the loop is equal to $BA \cos \theta$, where θ is the angle through which the loop has turned from its initial position. If $\theta = \omega t$, where ω is the angular velocity of the rotating loop, the maximum rate of change of flux linkages with respect to time occurs when ωt is 90°, 270°, 450°, etc. Flux linkages and induced voltage in the loop, both functions of ωt, are shown in Fig. 17.7. Notice that the flux linkages are proportional to $\cos \omega t$, while the voltage is proportional to $\sin \omega t$. Here is one way to generate a sinusoidal voltage.

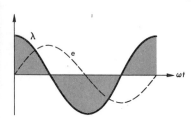

λ

e

ωt

FIG. 17.7 *Flux linkages and induced voltage versus ωt for loop in Fig. 17.6.*

Another configuration is represented in Fig. 17.8 in which a uniform and constant flux density is directed into the plane of the paper. Three sides of a conducting loop are fixed in space, and the fourth moves to the right at an instantaneous velocity v, maintaining sliding contact with the fixed sides. The net flux enclosed by the conducting loop increases in a direction into the paper, because the area of the loop increases as the sliding conductor moves to the right. The induced voltage, by Lenz's law, is counterclockwise around the loop as shown. The rate at which the flux linkages are increasing is equal to the rate at which flux density times the area of the loop is increasing. Then

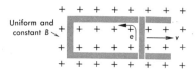

Uniform and
constant B

e

v

FIG. 17.8 *Sliding-bar generator, constant and uniform flux density.*

$$e = Blv \qquad (17.9)$$

where lv is the rate at which the area of the loop is increasing with time, since v is the instantaneous velocity. If v is constant, the induced voltage is also constant. If the velocity of the sliding conductor is sinusoidal, the induced voltage is also a sinusoid.

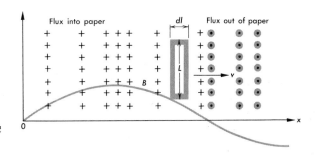

Flux into paper

dl

Flux out of paper

FIG. 17.9 *Flux varies in the x direction but is constant in time.*

Now consider an example where the flux density B is constant with time but varies in the x direction. This is represented in Fig. 17.9, where

$$B = B_m \sin ax \tag{17.10}$$

and B_m and a are constants. The net flux passing through the rectangular loop is a function of the position of the loop along the x axis, or

$$\lambda = BL \, dl \tag{17.11}$$

Now assume that the rectangular loop is moving in the x direction at a constant velocity v. Then

$$x = vt \tag{17.12}$$

and substituting Eqs. (17.10) and (17.12) into Eqs. (17.11) gives

$$\lambda = B_m L \, dl \sin avt \tag{17.13}$$

By Faraday's law the induced voltage around the loop is

$$e = B_m L \, dl \, av \cos avt \tag{17.14}$$

Notice that the induced voltage as well as the frequency is directly proportional to the velocity of the loop. It is assumed in this example that dl is so small that the flux density B does not vary in the x direction within the area of the loop.

If the flux in Fig. 17.9 is constant and uniform along the x direction, there is no induced voltage around the loop; this problem is identical to that illustrated by Fig. 17.5. If, however, the flux varies as

$$B = Kx \tag{17.15}$$

where K is constant, then

$$\lambda = KL \, dl \, x \tag{17.16}$$

and if v is constant, the induced voltage is

$$e = KLv \, dl \tag{17.17}$$

In this example also, the induced voltage is proportional to the constant velocity v.

17.5 SELF-INDUCTANCE

In Chap. 1 we defined self-inductance as the proportionality constant between the rate of change of current with respect to time in a coil and the voltage across the coil, or [Eq. (1.30)]

$$v = L\frac{di}{dt}$$

It is obvious now that this voltage is induced by the changing magnetic-flux linkages established by the current through the inductor.

In the inductor shown in Fig. 17.10, a magnetic core is used to constrain essentially all the flux to a path passing through the N turns of the coil. Assume that the iron is always in the unsaturated region, where its permeability is essentially constant and its flux is proportional to the current in the winding. The voltage induced in the winding can be found from Faraday's law. Equating the induced voltage to the voltage defined in Eq. (1.30), we have

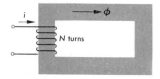

FIG. 17.10 *Iron-core inductor.*

$$N\frac{d\phi}{dt} = L\frac{di}{dt} \tag{17.18}$$

from which

$$L = N\frac{d\phi}{di} \qquad \text{henry} \tag{17.19}$$

or

$$L = \frac{d\lambda}{di} \qquad \text{henry} \tag{17.20}$$

Equation (17.20) is another definition of self-inductance; self-inductance is the rate of change of flux linkages with respect to current.

Since we have assumed that the iron in the core shown in Fig. 17.10 is not saturated and that flux is proportional to current, Eq. (17.20) can be written

$$L = \frac{\lambda}{i} \qquad \text{henry} \tag{17.21}$$

Equation (17.21) shows us that a linear self-inductance can be defined as the number of flux linkages per ampere. Whenever flux is proportional to current, Eqs. (17.20) and (17.21) are equivalent.

If saturation develops in the iron, flux is no longer proportional to current. The self-inductance defined by Eq. (17.20) can be called the "incremental" self-inductance, which applies for small changes in current. Incremental self-inductance is a function of the amount of current magnetizing the iron core. Incremental self-inductance is proportional to the slope of the magnetization curve. For a high degree of saturation, the incremental self-inductance is small; when the current is small and saturation does not occur, the incremental self-inductance is larger. Inductors with iron cores that saturate are not linear inductors, since their inductance depends upon the magnitude of the current flowing through the winding.

If an iron core is not used in the inductor, the flux is not confined to a well-determined path. In Fig. 17.11 we see an inductor of N turns wound on a nonmagnetic cylindrical form. Flux lines are shown, not all of which link all the turns. Since there are no magnetic materials in the vicinity of this inductor, the flux is always proportional to the current and Eq. (17.21) defines the inductance of the coil. The number of flux linkages is equal to the flux passing through each turn summed over the number of turns, or

$$\lambda = \phi_1 + \phi_2 + \phi_3 + \cdots + \phi_N$$

$$= \sum_{n=1}^{N} \phi_n \qquad \text{flux linkages} \qquad (17.22)$$

where ϕ_1 is the flux through the first turn, ϕ_2 is the flux through the second turn, etc., and ϕ_N is the flux through the Nth, or last, turn. Equation (17.19) has little significance here because all the flux does not link all the turns.

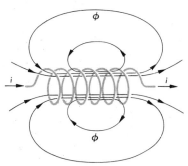

FIG. 17.11 *Air-wound inductor with leakage flux.*

17.6 MUTUAL INDUCTANCE

We have previously defined mutual inductance from circuit concepts as the proportionality constant between the time rate of change of current in one part of a circuit and the voltage at another part of the circuit [Eq. (1.31)]. Then we saw in Sec. 17.3 how a changing current i_1 in one winding of a transformer (Fig. 17.5) caused a changing flux ϕ which induced a voltage e_2 in another

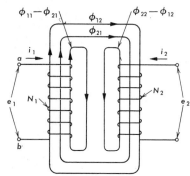

$\phi_{11} - \phi_{21}$ ϕ_{12} $\phi_{22} - \phi_{12}$

ϕ_{21}

FIG. 17.12 *Two windings with mutual flux and leakage flux.*

winding. Thus the voltage caused by mutual inductance is magnetically induced, just as it is for self-inductance.

Mutual inductance and self-inductance often occur simultaneously in a magnetically coupled circuit such as is shown in Fig. 17.12. If a voltage e_1 is connected to the input terminals a–b, the resulting current i_1 establishes flux ϕ_{11}. Part of flux ϕ_{11} links the second coil; this part we call ϕ_{21}. Flux ϕ_{11} is responsible for λ_{11} flux linkages of the first winding with itself. Flux ϕ_{21} establishes λ_{21} flux linkages in the secondary winding caused by i_1 flowing in the primary winding. If a current i_2 flows in the secondary winding, the resulting magnetic flux ϕ_{22} establishes λ_{22} flux linkages in the secondary winding. Part of ϕ_{22} also links the primary winding, providing λ_{12} flux linkages to the primary. Then the voltage induced in the primary winding is, by Faraday's law and the superposition principle, the sum of the voltages induced by $d\lambda_{11}/dt$ and $d\lambda_{12}/dt$, or

$$e_1 = \frac{d\lambda_{11}}{dt} + \frac{d\lambda_{12}}{dt} \qquad \text{volts} \qquad (17.23)$$

From circuit concepts, the voltage induced in the primary is

$$e_1 = L_1 \frac{di_1}{dt} \pm M_{12} \frac{di_2}{dt} \qquad \text{volts} \qquad (17.24)$$

Then

$$L_1 = \frac{d\lambda_{11}}{di_1} \qquad \text{henry} \qquad (17.25)$$

and

$$M_{12} = \pm \frac{d\lambda_{12}}{di_2} \qquad \text{henry} \qquad (17.26)$$

By the same logic, the induced voltage in the secondary winding is

$$e_2 = \frac{d\lambda_{22}}{dt} + \frac{d\lambda_{21}}{dt} \qquad \text{volts} \qquad (17.27)$$

which, by circuit concepts, can be written

$$e_2 = L_2 \frac{di_2}{dt} \pm M_{21} \frac{di_1}{dt} \qquad \text{volts} \qquad (17.28)$$

and

$$L_2 = \frac{d\lambda_{22}}{di_2} \qquad \text{henry} \qquad (17.29)$$

$$M_{21} = \pm \frac{d\lambda_{21}}{di_1} \qquad \text{henry} \qquad (17.30)$$

Mutual inductance as defined by Eqs. (17.26) and (17.30) is a consequence of the linking of one circuit with another by means of a magnetic field. Since magnetic fields are produced by electric currents, mutual- and self-inductance can be studied entirely from the point of view of circuit quantities relating changing currents to induced voltages, as shown in Chap. 1.

17.7 THE ELEMENTARY GENERATOR

In Fig. 17.6 a conducting rectangular loop had induced in it a sinusoidal voltage as a result of being rotated in a magnetic field.

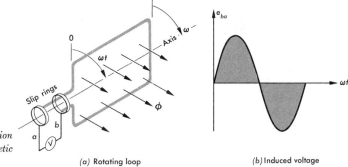

FIG. 17.13 *Alternating-voltage generation by rotating conducting loop in uniform magnetic field.*

(a) Rotating loop

(b) Induced voltage

In Fig. 17.13a, the rotating loop is seen connected to slip rings, which are mounted on, but insulated from, the shaft or axis on which the loop turns. Carbon brushes, fixed in space, maintain sliding contact with the slip rings as they rotate. A sinusoidal emf generated by the loop is now seen by the voltmeter connected to the brushes and is shown in Fig. 17.13b. It is assumed that the flux density is constant and uniform and that the angular velocity of the rotating loop is constant. If the area of the loop is A, then the flux enclosed by the loop is $BA \cos \omega t$, where ωt is the angle made by the plane of the loop and the reference position shown in Fig. 17.13a. Then,

$$e = -BA\omega \sin \omega t$$

and the radian frequency of the induced voltage in the loop is equal to the angular velocity of the loop. Notice that, by Lenz's law, the brush marked a is positive with respect to the one marked b during the first one-half cycle, as shown in Fig. 17.13b.

The elementary generator illustrated in Fig. 17.13 is capable of producing only a sinusoidal alternating voltage and current. Slip rings and brushes permit the rotating loop to rotate and at the same time to be part of the circuit which does not rotate and which absorbs electric energy from the generator. In order to produce a unidirectional voltage in the stationary part of the circuit, switching must occur each one-half cycle, reversing the connection of the stationary circuit to the rotating circuit. Conversion of an alternating voltage to a unidirectional voltage is known as "rectification." When rectification is done by mechanical means, it is called "commutation."

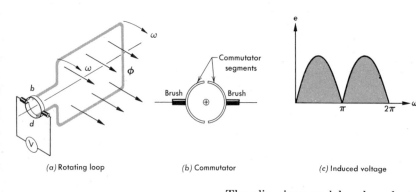

(a) Rotating loop   (b) Commutator   (c) Induced voltage

FIG. 17.14   *Unidirectional voltage generation utilizes brushes and commutator.*

The slip rings and brushes shown in Fig. 17.13a have been replaced with a commutator and brushes in Fig. 17.14a. The commutator is fastened to but insulated from the rotor. The brushes are fixed in space and maintain sliding contact with the commutator. The commutator in Fig. 17.14 is composed of two segments, each one of which is connected to one end of the rotating loop. Notice in the position shown in Fig. 17.14a that the brushes short-circuit both halves of the commutator. The induced voltage in the loop is zero at this instant, however. As the loop rotates, the commutator segments rotate under the brushes, which are fixed in space, and a single circuit is formed consisting of the rotating loop and the electric circuit connected to the brushes. When the loop has rotated 90° from the position shown in Fig. 17.14a, the induced voltage is maximum and the brushes contact the two sides of the commutator separately as shown in Fig. 17.14b; in this position the full induced voltage in the loop is seen by the voltmeter connected to the brushes. When the induced voltage has reduced to zero at π radians, the brushes again short-circuit the commutator, which rotates and exchanges the respective commutator segments under the brushes. This pre-

vents the voltage seen by the brushes from reversing in polarity
and produces the rectified sine wave of potential seen in Fig.
17.14c. By inspection of Fig. 17.14c we can express the induced
voltage seen by the brushes as

$$e = BA\omega \sin \omega t \qquad 0 \le \omega t \le \pi$$

$$= -BA\omega \sin \omega t \qquad \pi \le \omega t \le 2\pi$$

The elementary alternator (alternating-voltage generator)
represented in Fig. 17.13a and the elementary d-c generator represented in Fig. 17.14a illustrate how such generators produce induced voltages from moving conductors in a constant magnetic
field. Yet to produce a magnetic field of desired strength, an iron
path is necessary with air gaps to allow for rotation of the conductors of the loop. Furthermore, to maximize the amount of
electric-power output per unit weight or unit volume of the
generator, more turns than the one shown in the figures are required. In the sections that follow, more practical alternators and
d-c generators are discussed.

17.8 THE ALTERNATOR

A practical form of alternator is shown in Fig. 17.15. In this configuration, the magnetic field is not uniform and fixed in space but
rotates past the conducting loops. The rotor, or rotating part of
the machine, produces the magnetic field. A constant field current
I_f entering the rotor through the brushes and slip rings produces a
constant mmf NI_f, where N is the number of turns on the rotor
core. The path of the flux produced by the mmf passes through
the rotor, air gap, frame, or yoke of the stator, through another
air gap, and back to the rotor. This kind of magnetic circuit can
be solved by methods illustrated in Chap. 16.

The conductors shown embedded in slots in the frame are
part of the stator and are fixed in space. Conductor A is connected
across the back of the stator to A' and forms one loop. Notice
that, in the rotor position shown in Fig. 17.15a, the net flux linking
the conducting loop consisting of conductors $A–A'$ is zero. If
the rotor is turning clockwise at a constant angular velocity ω,
the maximum rate of change of flux linkages for loop $A–A'$ occurs
at the instant of time represented by the position shown in Fig.
17.15a. The loop formed by conductors $B–B'$ is situated $120°$ in a
clockwise direction around the stator from $A–A'$. Consequently,

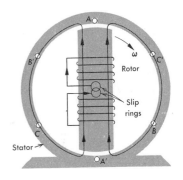

(a) Three-phase alternator with
two magnetic poles

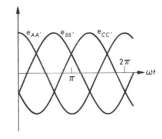

(b) Voltages induced in windings AA',
BB', and CC' as functions of time

FIG. 17.15 *A three-phase alternator and its generated voltages.*

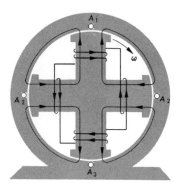

(a) Four-pole alternator

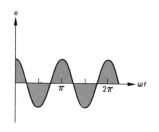

(b) Induced voltage in winding $A_1A_2A_3A_4$

FIG. 17.16 *Four-pole alternator.*

the induced voltage in loop $B–B'$ is 120° of rotor rotation behind $e_{A–A'}$. Likewise, the voltage induced in loop $C–C'$ reaches a maximum 240° of rotor rotation from the position of the rotor shown. The three loops, with induced voltages 120° apart from each other, can be connected together either Y or delta to form a three-phase voltage source as discussed in Chap. 6.

In order to ensure that sinusoidal voltages are induced in each of the three loops, the time rate of change of flux linkages through each loop must be sinusoidal. This can be accomplished by maintaining sinusoidal flux distribution around the inside periphery of the stator, which requires that the air gap between the field poles must be longer at the edge of the poles than at the center and that the pole faces be very broad to cover most of the inside of the stator.

A two-pole machine such as the one shown in Fig. 17.15a generates 1 cycle of emf for each revolution. Therefore, to generate the common power frequency of 60 cycles/sec requires a speed of 60 rps, or 3,600 rpm. If the machine has four poles as shown in Fig. 17.16a, the magnetic flux sweeping past one loop composed of conductors $A_1–A_2$ passes through 1 complete cycle for each 180° of rotor rotation. In 1 complete revolution of the rotor, the induced voltage in any loop in the stator has passed through 2 complete cycles. Therefore, to generate 60 electric cycles/sec, the rotor must turn at the rate of 30 rps, or 1,800 rpm. Likewise, a six-pole machine, to generate 1 electric cycle or 360 electrical degrees of voltage, must turn through 120 mechanical degrees. For an n-pole machine, the speed of the machine is related to the frequency of the induced voltage by

$$f = \frac{p}{2}\frac{s}{60} \qquad (17.31)$$

where s is the speed in rpm, p is the number of poles (always even), and f is the frequency in cycles per second. Notice in Fig. 17.16, if the angular velocity to the rotor is constant at ω radians/sec, the frequency of the induced voltage is 2ω radians/sec. Conductor A_1 is connected to A_2 across the back of the stator, A_2 is connected to A_3 across the front of the stator, and A_3 to A_4 across the back of the stator. In addition to winding A shown in Fig. 17.16a, windings B and C, not shown, are located 60 and 120 mechanical degrees in a clockwise direction from A, respectively. Thus there are three single-phase windings on the stator of the alternator. As with the two-pole alternator previously discussed, they may be connected together **Y** or delta to form a three-phase voltage source.

The alternator can be thought of as an input-output device, as shown in Fig. 17.17. Both the field current i_f and the speed s can be thought of as the input quantities, with the generated voltage e_g as the output quantity. If the magnetic circuit is not saturated and the magnetic flux is proportional to i_f, the induced voltage is also proportional to i_f. By Faraday's law and Eq. (17.31) it can be shown that, when speed is constant,

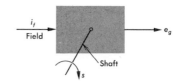

FIG. 17.17 *Alternator as an input-output device.*

$$e_g = Ksi_f \sin(\omega t + \alpha)$$

where

$$\omega = 2\pi \frac{s}{60} \frac{p}{2}$$

where K is a constant, s is the speed in rpm, i_f is field current, ω is the radian frequency of the generator voltage, and $p/2$ is the number of pairs of poles possessed by the rotor. The angle α is an arbitrary phase angle. The prime mover of the generator furnishes the mechanical energy, which the alternator converts to electric energy. The speed of the prime mover determines the frequency of the sinusoidal voltage, and in most power systems frequency is maintained constant. Therefore the alternator must be driven at a constant speed by the prime mover, and e_g can be written

$$e_g = K_g i_f \sin(\omega t + \alpha) \tag{17.32}$$

where $K_g = Ks$. At constant speed, Eq. (17.32) shows that the generated voltage is proportional to the field current.

The generated voltage is not the terminal voltage of the alternator; on the basis of constant speed and constant frequency, the impedance of the stator windings causes **IZ** voltages within the stator that must be subtracted from the generated voltage of the stator to obtain the terminal voltage. Figure 17.18a shows the circuit representing the stator winding of one phase of the alternator, with $\mathbf{E}_g$ the generated voltage. The terminal voltage $\mathbf{V}_T$ appears across the load impedance $\mathbf{Z}_L$, and $\mathbf{V}_T$ equals $\mathbf{I}_L\mathbf{Z}_L$, where $\mathbf{I}_L$ is the current in the load impedance and also in the stator winding. In the phasor diagram of Fig. 17.18b, terminal voltage $\mathbf{V}_T$ is shown as the reference phasor, with load current $\mathbf{I}_L$ lagging $\mathbf{V}_T$ by an angle θ. The stator impedance, known as "synchronous" impedance, is represented by R_S and L_S. The voltage drop in R_S is $\mathbf{I}_L R_S$, in phase with $\mathbf{I}_L$. The voltage across L_S is $j\mathbf{I}_L X_L$, leading $\mathbf{I}_L$ by 90°. Then the generated voltage $\mathbf{E}_g$ is the phasor sum of

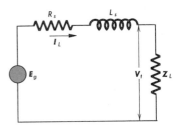

(a) Equivalent circuit of one phase

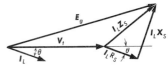

(b) Phasor diagram

FIG. 17.18 *The effect of synchronous impedance on alternator terminal voltage.*

$\mathbf{I}_L\mathbf{Z}_L$, $\mathbf{I}_L R_S$, and $j\mathbf{I}_L X_L$. Notice that, if $\mathbf{Z}_L$ is made larger and larger so that $\mathbf{I}_L$ approaches zero, $\mathbf{V}_T$ approaches $\mathbf{E}_g$. In the example shown in Fig. 17.18, the terminal voltage is different from the generated voltage by the synchronous-impedance voltage $\mathbf{I}_L\mathbf{Z}_S$.

If the alternator is required to maintain relatively constant terminal voltage independent of the load current, the magnitude of the synchronous impedance must be kept to a minimum. Voltage regulation is a measure of the change in terminal voltage from no load to full load. Voltage regulation is defined as the fraction

$$\mathrm{VR} = \frac{V_{NL} - V_{FL}}{V_{FL}} \tag{17.33}$$

where V_{FL} is the terminal voltage at full load, corresponding to $\mathbf{V}_T$ in Fig. 17.18, and V_{NL} is the terminal voltage at no load, corresponding to $\mathbf{E}_g$. Voltage regulation of an alternator is a function of the power factor angle θ of the load impedance. A phasor diagram such as Fig. 17.18b is needed to obtain voltage regulation by calculation.

The efficiency of a device is defined as the ratio of the average useful power output to the average power input. Efficiency is a figure of merit for any large machine, since power lost in the machine is money lost. The difference between the power input to the machine and the useful power output is the power lost due to heating effects in the machine. Efficiency can be expressed as the fraction

$$\eta = \frac{P_{\mathrm{out}}}{P_{\mathrm{in}}} = \frac{P_{\mathrm{out}}}{P_{\mathrm{out}} + \mathrm{losses}} = \frac{P_{\mathrm{in}} - \mathrm{losses}}{P_{\mathrm{in}}} \tag{17.34}$$

Power lost in the alternator includes i^2R losses in the stator and field windings, windage and friction losses, and iron or core losses caused by hysteresis and eddy currents in the iron of the rotor. An efficient alternator is one which keeps the losses to a minimum. The efficiency of practical alternators is generally in the range between 0.8 and 0.9.

17.9 THE D-C GENERATOR

The practical d-c generator is shown in Fig. 17.19a where a strong, uniform magnetic field is established across short air gaps between the drum-shaped iron rotor and the poles of the stator. The copper armature conductors are contained in slots in the periphery of the

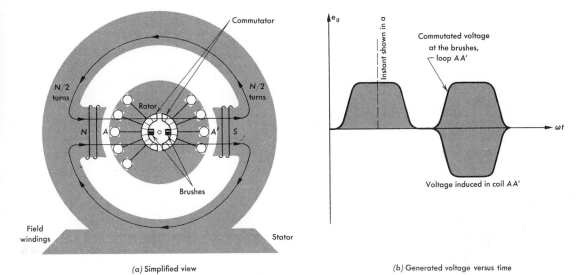

(a) Simplified view

(b) Generated voltage versus time

FIG. 17.19 *Direct-current generator showing rotor, stator, field windings, armature windings, brushes, etc.*

rotor. One coil, consisting of conductors A–A', has the induced-voltage waveform as shown in Fig. 17.19b. The induced voltage is maximum while the conductors are directly under the pole faces; the induced voltage passes through zero when the flux linkage for the coil is maximum and the rate of change of flux linkage is zero. The commutator contains as many segments as there are coils, and each coil is shown connected to two commutator segments, each commutator segment having two coils connected to it. Adjacent coils are connected in series at the commutator so that the voltage at the brushes consists of the sum of the induced voltages in the several coils in series. For the rotor winding shown in Fig. 17.19a, if there are n conductors distributed around the periphery of the rotor, there are two parallel paths of $n/2$ conductors in series between the two brushes. In each path, the induced voltage of those conductors not under the pole faces is zero. The fraction of the conductors having voltage induced in them is the fraction of the rotor periphery that is under the pole faces.

Faraday's law indicates that the generated voltage in the path of conductors between the brushes is equal to $d\lambda/dt$. Since λ is proportional to the field flux in the air gap, the generated voltage seen at the brushes is proportional to the field flux and the speed of the rotor, or

$$e_g = K\phi s \qquad (17.35)$$

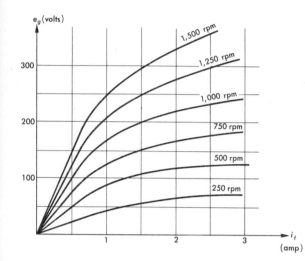

FIG. 17.20 *Generated voltage e_g versus field current i_f with speed as a parameter.*

where ϕ is the net field flux, s is the rotor speed in rpm, and K is the constant of proportionality between e_g and ϕs. The net field flux is a function of field current. The magnetization curves of Fig. 17.20 are plots of the generated voltage e_g as a function of field current i_f with speed as a parameter; the curves are non-linear because the field flux ϕ is not proportional to the field current i_f because of saturation in the iron circuit. The family of curves shown in Fig. 17.20 are somewhat similar to the family of curves representing the i_b-versus-e_b characteristics of a vacuum triode, with e_c as the parameter; each family of curves is a representation of three variables, where one variable is held constant while the other two variables are plotted.

The generated-voltage curves of Fig. 17.20 resemble magnetization curves in which magnetic flux or flux density is plotted as the function of field current or magnetic-field intensity. Indeed, from Eq. (17.35) for constant speed, e_g is proportional to field flux ϕ. Thus the curve has the same shape as the ϕ-versus-NI curve for the magnetic circuit consisting of the iron path and the air gap. For small values of field current, the generated voltage is proportional to the field current; this is the region of linear operation. For large values of field current, corresponding to large values of magnetic-field intensity, the iron saturates, and the induced voltage is no longer proportional to field current.

The total differential can be applied to Eq. (17.35) just as it was applied to the vacuum triode to find its equivalent circuit. Recognizing that ϕ is a function of i_f, we write Eq. (17.35) as

$$e_g = f(i_f, s) \tag{17.36}$$

Taking the total differential of Eq. (17.36) gives

$$\Delta e_g = \frac{\partial e_g}{\partial i_f} \Delta i_f + \frac{\partial e_g}{\partial s} \Delta s \qquad (17.37)$$

The derivative terms in Eq. (17.37) can be found from the curves of Fig. 17.20 just as they were found for the vacuum triode and for the transistor; $\partial e_g/\partial i_f$ is the slope of the e_g-versus-i_f curve at the operating point, and $\partial e_g/\partial s$ is found approximately by taking $\Delta e_g/\Delta s$ while holding i_f constant. Once the derivative terms of Eq. (17.37) have been evaluated, Eq. (17.37) can be used to relate small changes in e_g, s, and i_f in a linear fashion. In particular, for low values of i_f where there is no saturation, the derivative terms are constant, and Eq. (17.37) can be applied for large changes in e_g, i_f, and s; then Eq. (17.37) can be written for this special condition as

$$\Delta e_g = K_1 \Delta i_f + K_2 \Delta s \qquad \text{volts} \qquad (17.38)$$

where $K_1 = \partial e_g/\partial i_f$ and $K_2 = \partial e_g/\partial s$ in the linear region of the curves just to the right of the origin. But since the curves are linear and pass through the origin in this region, the e_g–i_f–s relationship can be expressed

$$e_g = K_3 s i_f \qquad \text{volts} \qquad (17.39)$$

where K_3 can be found by reading e_g, s, and i_f at some point in the linear region and then solving Eq. (17.39) for K_3. Notice that Eq. (17.39) gives the magnitude of e_g, whereas Eq. (17.38) gives only the changes in magnitude.

The field windings of a d-c generator can be excited from an external-voltage source or from the generated voltage of the armature. Figure 17.21 represents a d-c generator with a sepa-

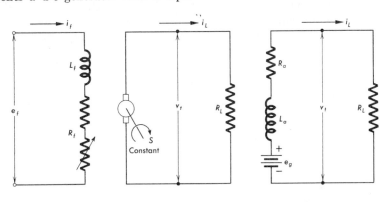

FIG. 17.21   *Direct-current generator with separately excited field.*

(a) Circuit diagram

(b) Equivalent armature circuit

rately excited field which can be represented in the circuit as a series combination of resistance R_f and inductance L_f. The inductance is not linear above the knee of the magnetization curve, but in the linear region below the knee, where L_f is constant,

$$L_f \frac{di_f}{dt} + R_f i_f = e_f \tag{17.40}$$

where e_f is the exciting voltage. The solution of Eq. (17.40) for i_f gives the field current which produces the field flux. If e_f is a constant E_f volts and the circuit has reached the steady state, then $i_f = E_f/R_f$.

The differential equations describing the armature circuit of Fig. 17.21 can be written

$$e_g = K_g i_f$$
$$L_a \frac{di_L}{dt} + R_a i_L + R_L i_L = e_g \tag{17.41}$$
$$v_t = R_L i_L$$

where L_a and R_a are the inductance and resistance of the armature circuit and K_g is the constant relating e_g to i_f. The simultaneous solution of Eqs. (17.40) and (17.41) for v_t as a function of e_f assumes that the generator operates in the linear region on its magnetization curves. If e_f is a step input of magnitude E_f, the solution of Eq. (17.40) gives

$$i_f = \frac{E_f}{R_f}(1 - \epsilon^{-(R_f/L_f)t}) \qquad \text{amp} \tag{17.42}$$

Substituting Eq. (17.42) into Eq. (17.41) and solving for terminal voltage v_t results in a solution of the form

$$v_t = A_1 + A_2 \epsilon^{-[(R_a + R_L)/L_a]t} + A_3 \epsilon^{-(R_f/L_f)t} \tag{17.43}$$

where the constants A_1, A_2, and A_3 can be evaluated from the initial conditions. In the final steady state, the exponential terms approach zero, and the steady-state terminal voltage is

$$v_{ts} = A_1 = \frac{K_g E_f R_L}{R_f(R_a + R_L)} \tag{17.44}$$

where v_{ts} is directly proportional to E_f and inversely proportional to R_f. If a variable resistor is added in series with the shunt field, making the resistance R_f adjustable, the terminal voltage can be varied or adjusted by means of the variable resistor. This is a common method of voltage control for a d-c generator, either separately excited or self-excited. The variable resistor in the shunt-field circuit is known as the "field rheostat."

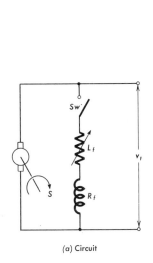

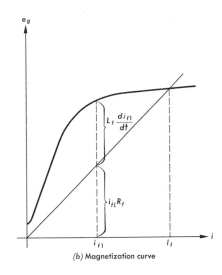

FIG. 17.22 *Self-excited d-c shunt generator.*

(a) Circuit

(b) Magnetization curve

Direct-current generators are often operated self-excited (Fig. 17.22a) to provide the current for its own field. When the generator is brought up to rated speed by the prime mover, residual magnetic flux in the poles causes a slight induced voltage in the rotor windings. When the field switch is closed, the differential equation of the field circuit can be written

$$L_f \frac{di_f}{dt} + R_f i_f = e_g \tag{17.45}$$

where L_f is not constant but is a function of i_f and $e_g = v_t$ at no load. The instant after the switch Sw is closed, $i_f = 0$ and $e_g = L_f \, di_f/dt$. Thus $L_f \, di_f/dt$ is the voltage available for building up the current in the field windings, and the rate of change of i_f with respect to time at $t = 0+$ is e_{g0}/L_f. When i_f has built up to i_{f1}, as shown in Fig. 17.22b, $i_{f1}R_f$ is the voltage across the field resistance and $L_f \, di_{f1}/dt$ is the voltage available to increase the current through the field winding. Thus the field current builds up until it reaches I_f, when $L_f \, di_f/dt = 0$. Notice that, if the R_f characteristic is too steep, the generator does not build up. The critical value of R_f is the slope of the magnetization curve over its linear portion. For stable operation of a self-excited shunt generator, I_f should be well into the saturated region of the magnetization curve. An unstable situation occurs when the R_f characteristic falls along the linear portion of the magnetization curve; in this region, the generated voltage is not uniquely determined, and it may drift from one value to another along the linear portion of the magnetization curve.

Both regulation and efficiency are important characteristics of d-c generators. Regulation has been defined in Eq. (17.33), and efficiency has been defined in Eq. (17.34). These characteristics can be determined for a given machine from a test of the machine, or they can be calculated from data obtained under no-load conditions.

The external characteristic curve of the d-c generator is a plot of the steady-state terminal voltage as a function of steady-state load current. The field flux of a separately excited shunt generator is essentially constant and independent of armature current. The external characteristic of the separately excited

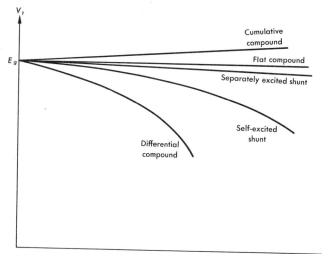

FIG. 17.23   *External steady-state characteristic curves, d-c shunt and compound generators.*

shunt generator is essentially linear, as shown in Fig. 17.23. Its terminal voltage can be expressed as

$$V_T = \frac{E_g R_L}{R_a + R_L} = E_g - I_a R_a \tag{17.46}$$

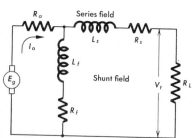

FIG. 17.24 *Circuit of a compound generator with both series and shunt fields.*

where E_g is constant, independent of the value of load current. The shunt-field winding of the self-excited shunt generator is connected across V_T; as V_T decreases owing to the $I_L R_a$ drop in the armature, the field current, and therefore the field flux, also decreases. Thus the self-excited shunt generator has an external characteristic which is concave downward, as shown in Fig. 17.23.

By adding a second field winding, known as the "series" field, the external characteristic curve can be changed considerably. In the circuit of the compound generator shown in Fig. 17.24, the series-field winding carries the load current. Ordinarily the load current is very much greater than the shunt-field current, and few turns are required in the series field to produce considerable field flux. If the series field is connected in such a direction that the series-field flux reinforces the shunt-field flux, the machine is said to be a "cumulative-compound" generator; if the series-field flux opposes the shunt-field flux, the generator is said to be a "differential-compound" generator. The external characteristic curves for both cumulative-compound and differential-compound generators are shown in Fig. 17.23. If the series-field winding is a strong one, the terminal voltage of a cumulative-compound generator can have a positive slope, increasing with load current. One curve shown in Fig. 17.23 represents a generator whose series field is just strong enough to cause the full-load voltage to equal the no-load voltage; this is known as "flat compounding."

17.10 THE IRON-CORE TRANSFORMER

Transformer action was described in Sec. 17.3. In this section we seek to describe further characteristics of iron-core transformers.

First, consider an ideal transformer similar to the one shown in Fig. 17.4, in which all the flux links both windings and each winding has zero resistance. If a sinusoidal voltage $v_1 = V_1 \sin \omega t$ is applied to one winding, by Kirchhoff's voltage law the induced voltage in that winding must be equal to the applied voltage. Then, by Faraday's law,

$$v_1 = N_1 \frac{d\phi}{dt} \qquad \text{volts} \tag{17.47}$$

The core flux also induces voltage v_2 in the secondary winding. Then

$$v_2 = N_2 \frac{d\phi}{dt} \qquad \text{volts} \tag{17.48}$$

where the $d\phi/dt$ in Eqs. (17.47) and (17.48) are equal. Dividing Eq. (17.47) by Eq. (17.48) gives

$$\frac{v_1}{v_2} = \frac{N_1}{N_2} = \frac{V_1}{V_2} \tag{17.49}$$

where v_1 and v_2 are both sinusoidal voltages whose ratio is identical to the ratio of the peak voltages V_1 to V_2 or the rms voltages. Thus, in an ideal transformer excited by a sinusoidal voltage, the turns ratio is equal to the ratio of the induced rms voltages in the windings.

Consider now the ideal transformer with resistive load excited by the sinusoidal voltage V_1 as shown in Fig. 17.25. There are no

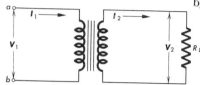

FIG. 17.25 *Ideal transformer with resistive load.*

losses in the ideal transformer, and, by conservation of energy, the input power to the ideal transformer must equal the output power delivered to R_L. Then

$$V_1 I_1 = V_2 I_2 \quad \text{or} \quad \frac{I_1}{I_2} = \frac{V_2}{V_1} \tag{17.50}$$

where V_1, V_2, I_1, and I_2 are either peak or rms values. Substituting Eq. (17.50) into Eq. (17.49) gives

$$\frac{I_2}{I_1} = \frac{N_1}{N_2} \tag{17.51}$$

In order to find the impedance seen looking in at terminals a and b in Fig. 17.25, we take the ratio

$$\mathbf{Z}_{\text{in}} = \frac{\mathbf{V}_1}{\mathbf{I}_1} \tag{17.52}$$

Using Eqs. (17.49) and (17.51) to express V_1 and I_1 of Eq. (17.52) in terms of V_2 and I_2, we find that $\mathbf{Z}_{\text{in}}$ can be written

$$\mathbf{Z}_{\text{in}} = \left(\frac{N_1}{N_2}\right)^2 R_L \tag{17.53}$$

According to Eq. (17.53), a transformer is an impedance-transforming device, transforming the load impedance R_L by the square of the turns ratio N_1/N_2.

A practical iron-core transformer can often be approximated by the ideal-transformer concept just discussed. A more accurate model of an iron-core transformer, however, must take into account such factors as winding resistance, leakage reactance, iron losses, and exciting currents. An equivalent circuit for an iron-core transformer, more realistic than the ideal transformer, is shown in Fig. 17.26. In this equivalent circuit, R_1 is the resistance of the primary winding of the transformer, and R_2 is the resistance of the transformer secondary winding. The reactance X_1 is the in-

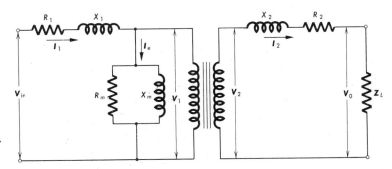

FIG. 17.26 *Iron-core-transformer equivalent circuit.*

ductive reactance of the primary winding resulting from that part of the total core flux linking only winding 1 and not linking winding 2; this is $\phi_{11}-\phi_{21}$ of Fig. 17.12. Thus X_1 is caused by leakage flux in the primary. X_2 is the secondary reactance caused by secondary leakage flux, shown as $\phi_{22}-\phi_{12}$ in Fig. 17.12. The ideal transformer accounts for the ratio of the induced voltage in primary and secondary windings resulting from the common flux which links both windings. An exciting current in the primary winding produces the core flux. Part of the exciting current can be considered to be 90° out of phase with the voltage $\mathbf{V}_1$ across the ideal transformer; this is the current through the reactance marked X_m. The current through the resistance marked R_m accounts for the core loss in the iron of the transformer. The sum of the current through R_m and X_m is called the "exciting" current $\mathbf{I}_e$; it remains essentially constant and independent of the load current I_2. The exciting current is very much smaller than the current I_1 in the primary winding at full load. The transformer equivalent circuit of Fig. 17.26 has been simplified in Fig. 17.27. First, the parallel

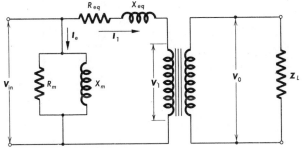

FIG. 17.27 *Simplified transformer equivalent circuit.*

combination of R_m and X_m has been moved to the input terminals of the transformer; this move is justified because the voltage drop across R_1 and L_1 is very small, and therefore the exciting current $\mathbf{I}_e$ has not been changed appreciably by this move. The second change has been to use Eq. (17.53) to reflect R_2 across the ideal transformer into the primary circuit and also reflect X_2 across the ideal transformer to the primary. Then

$$R_{eq} = R_1 + \left(\frac{N_1}{N_2}\right)^2 R_2 \qquad \text{ohms}$$

$$X_{eq} = X_1 + \left(\frac{N_1}{N_2}\right)^2 X_2 \qquad \text{ohms}$$

(17.54)

From the simplified equivalent circuit of Fig. 17.27, voltage regulation and efficiency of the transformer can be calculated.

The circuit parameters of the simplified transformer equivalent circuit of Fig. 17.27 can be obtained from laboratory tests of the transformer. These tests, known as the "open-circuit" test and the "short-circuit" test, are described in the following example.

Example 17.1

A transformer is rated at 2,300:230 volts, 60 cycles/sec, 50 kva. This rating means that the high-voltage winding is rated at 2,300 volts, the low-voltage winding is rated at 230 volts, 60 cycles/sec, and the product of input voltage and maximum input current (or the product of output voltage and maximum output current) is 50 kva, or 50,000 va. Maximum current is determined by the ability of the transformer to dissipate heat produced in its conductors.

The open-circuit test is performed first. The rated voltage of 2,300 volts is connected to the high-voltage winding as shown in Fig. 17.28a, and the low-voltage winding is left open-circuited. In-

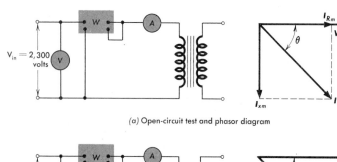

(a) Open-circuit test and phasor diagram

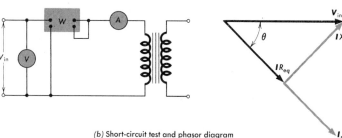

(b) Short-circuit test and phasor diagram

FIG. 17.28 *Transformer tests, Example 17.1*

put voltage, current, and power are measured by means of the voltmeter, ammeter, and wattmeter shown in Fig. 17.28a. From the equivalent circuit of Fig. 17.27 it is apparent that the input current observed is the exciting current I_e. Measured input voltage is $V_{in} = 2,300$ volts, measured input current is $I_e = 0.341$ amp, and input power measured by the wattmeter is $P = 378$ watts. Then R_m is found from $P = V_{in}^2/R_m$, or

$$R_m = \frac{2,300^2}{378} = 14,000 \text{ ohms}$$

The power factor under the open-circuit condition is obtained from $P = V_{in}I_e \cos \theta$, or

$$\cos \theta = \frac{378}{2,300(0.341)} = 0.482$$

Then $\theta = \cos^{-1} 0.482 = 61.2°$.

From the phasor diagram of Fig. 17.28c, X_m is obtained from $V_{in} = (I_e \sin \theta)X_m$, or

$$X_m = \frac{2,300}{0.341(0.877)} = 7,600 \text{ ohms}$$

Thus both R_m and X_m are obtained from the open-circuit-test data.

The short-circuit test is performed by reducing the input voltage, short-circuiting the secondary terminals, and adjusting the input voltage until rated current flows in the primary (or secondary) winding. The circuit diagram is shown in Fig. 17.28b; under the short-circuit conditions the ammeter reads $I_1 = 21.7$ amp, the voltmeter reads $V_{in} = 37.5$ volts, and the wattmeter reads $P = 335$ watts. Neglecting the small exciting current and recognizing that $V_1 = 0$ in Fig. 17.27, we see that

$$R_{eq} = \frac{335}{21.7^2} = 0.71 \text{ ohm}$$

From the phasor diagram of Fig. 17.28d,

$$I_1 X_{eq} = \sqrt{37.5^2 - (21.7 \times 0.71)^2}$$

and

$$X_{eq} = \frac{\sqrt{37.5^2 - 15.4^2}}{21.7} = 1.57 \text{ ohms}$$

Thus we see that the parameters R_{eq} and X_{eq} can be obtained from the short-circuit test.

Once the circuit parameters have been found for the transformer equivalent circuit, they may be used to calculate voltage regulation and efficiency, as shown in the following example.

Example 17.2

A transformer, identical to the one tested in Example 17.1, is rated at 2,300:230 volts, 60 cycles/sec, 50 kva. R_{eq} referred to the primary high side is 0.71 ohm (determined by test), and X_{eq} is 1.57 ohms. $R_m = 14,000$ ohms, and $X_m = 7,600$ ohms. The transformer load impedance Z_L has a power factor of 0.707.

To find the voltage regulation, first draw the phasor diagram showing Z_L reflected across the ideal transformer to the input side, where the voltage across $(N_1/N_2)^2 Z_L$ is $\mathbf{V}_1'$ and the current is $\mathbf{I}_1$. The power-factor angle $\theta = \cos^{-1} 0.707 = 45°$. Let $V_1 = 2,300$ volts. At full load,

$$I_1 = \frac{50,000}{2,300} = 21.7 \text{ amp}$$

$$I_1 R_{eq} = 21.7(0.71) = 15.4 \text{ volts}$$

$$I_1 X_{eq} = 21.7(1.57) = 34.1 \text{ volts}$$

$\mathbf{V}_{in}$ is the phasor sum of $\mathbf{V}_1$, $\mathbf{I}_1 R_{eq}$, and $j\mathbf{I}_1 X_{eq}$, as shown in Fig. 17.29.

$$\mathbf{V}_{in} = 2,300 + 0.707(15.4 + 34.1) + j0.707(34.1 - 15.4)$$

$$= 2,335 + j13.2 \text{ volts}$$

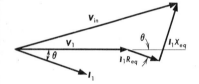

FIG. 17.29 *Phasor diagram of simplified transformer equivalent circuit.*

$$V_{in} = \sqrt{2,335^2 + 13.2^2} = 2,336 \text{ volts}$$

Then the voltage regulation is

$$\text{VR} = \frac{V_{NL} - V_{FL}}{V_{FL}} = \frac{2,336 - 2,300}{2,300} = 0.01564$$

Efficiency is found from

$$\eta = \frac{P_{out}}{P_{out} + \text{losses}}$$

$$P_{out} = 50,000 \cos \theta = 50,000(0.707) = 35,350 \text{ watts}$$

$$\text{Copper loss} = I_1^2 R_{eq} = 21.7^2(0.71) = 335 \text{ watts}$$

$$\text{Core loss} = \frac{V_{in}^2}{R_m} = \frac{2,336^2}{14,000} = 389 \text{ watts}$$

$$\eta = \frac{35.350}{35,350 + 335 + 389} = 0.980$$

SUMMARY

Faraday's law shows the relationship between the induced voltage in a closed path and the magnetic flux linking the closed path. Faraday's law can be written [Eq. (17.3)]

$$e = \frac{d\lambda}{dt} \quad \text{volts}$$

where e is the induced voltage and λ is the number of flux linkages with the closed path. If N turns of a coil all link the same flux ϕ, then Faraday's law can be written [Eq. (17.2)]

$$e = N\frac{d\phi}{dt} \quad \text{volts}$$

From the voltage-current relationship for inductance, and by using Faraday's law, it can be shown that [Eq. (17.19)]

$$L = N\frac{d\phi}{di} \quad \text{henry}$$

An alternator, or alternating-current generator, consists of a revolving field whose flux sweeps past the windings embedded in the inside periphery of the stator; this is shown in Fig. 17.15. The voltage induced in the stator winding is proportional to the speed of the stator and the flux of the field. If the flux is proportional to field current, then

$$e_g = Ksi_f \sin(\omega t + \phi)$$

where $\omega = 2\pi sp/120$. Voltage regulation is defined by Eq. (17.33),

$$\text{VR} = \frac{V_{NL} - V_{FL}}{V_{FL}}$$

In an alternator, E_g corresponds to the no-load terminal voltage, and V_T corresponds to full-load terminal voltage. Efficiency is always defined by Eq. (17.34),

$$\eta = \frac{P_{\text{out}}}{P_{\text{in}}} = \frac{P_{\text{out}}}{P_{\text{out}} + \text{losses}} = \frac{P_{\text{in}} - \text{losses}}{P_{\text{in}}}$$

The generated voltage in a d-c generator is given by Eq. (17.35)

$$e_g = K\phi s \qquad \text{volts}$$

where ϕ is the net field flux and s is the rotor speed in rpm. Since ϕ is a function of i_f, Eq. (17.35) can be written as Eq. (17.36),

$$e_g = f(i_f, s)$$

Generated voltage versus field current is shown in Fig. 17.20. In the linear region below saturation, the generated voltage can be expressed by Eq. (17.39),

$$e_g = K_3 s i_f$$

An ideal transformer satisfies the relationship [Eq. (17.49)]

$$\frac{V_1}{V_2} = \frac{N_1}{N_2}$$

If an impedance R_L is connected across the output of an ideal transformer, the impedance seen at the input terminal is [Eq. (17.53)]

$$Z_{\text{in}} = \left(\frac{N_1}{N_2}\right)^2 R_L$$

and the output impedance R_L is reflected across the ideal transformer with a factor equal to the square of the turns ratio.

FURTHER READING

Transformers, alternators, and d-c generators are topics extensively treated in Clifford C. Carr, *Electric Machinery* (John Wiley & Sons, Inc., New York, 1958), and in A. E. Fitzgerald and Charles Kingsley, Jr., *Electric Machinery* (McGraw-Hill Book Company, Inc., New York, 1952). Direct-current generators and motors are treated in Alexander S. Langsdorf, *Principles of Direct-current Machines*, 6th ed. (McGraw-Hill Book Company, Inc., New York, 1959). Alternating-current machines are discussed extensively in Puchstein, Lloyd, and Conrad, *Alternating Current Machines* (John Wiley & Sons, Inc., New York, 1954).

Energy-conversion concepts are developed in White and Woodson, *Electromechanical Energy Conversion* (John Wiley & Sons, Inc., New York, 1959) and Y. H. Ku, *Electric Energy Conversion* (The Ronald Press Company, New York, 1959).

PROBLEMS

17.1 In the figure a square conducting loop of 1 m on a side is in the plane of the page. A magnetic field, directed into the page, is constant in the y direction but varies as $B = 10\epsilon^{0.01x}$, $0 < x$, and $B = 10$, $x < 0$, in the x direction. The loop moves in the plane of the page at a velocity of 15 m/sec. Find the magnitude and direction of the emf induced in the loop.

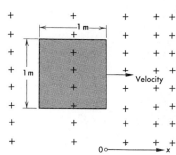

17.2 Repeat Prob. 17.1 above for a flux density of $B = 10 \sin 0.4x$, $0 < x$, and $B = 0$, $x < 0$. Velocity and dimensions remain the same.

PROB. 17.1

17.3 In the illustration a rectangular loop of dimensions 0.5 by 0.7 m is rotated about an axis which coincides with one of its 0.5-m sides. The constant angular velocity is 10 radians/sec. The flux is in the x direction.

(a) If $B = 0.08$ weber/m^2, derive an expression for the emf induced in the loop as a function of time.

(b) If $B = 0.2\epsilon^{-2y}$ weber/m^2, derive an expression for the emf induced as a function of time.

17.4 In the figure the flux density through a circular loop of radius $a = 0.75$ m is a function of time and also of the distance from the center of the loop. $B = 10\epsilon^{-r} \sin 100t$, where r is the distance from the center of the loop. Find the voltage induced in the loop as a function of time.

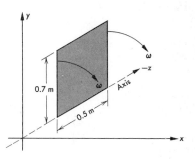

PROB. 17.3

17.5 A 5-henry and a 10-henry iron-core inductor are connected in series. They carry a constant current of 15 amp. Assume that they are linear (the iron has not saturated). Find the flux linkages of each.

17.6 A three-phase-Y-connected alternator, rated at 10 kva output at 440 volts, has a synchronous resistance R_s of 1.8 ohms and a synchronous reactance X_s of 7.6 ohms. Find the alternator voltage regulation if the power factor of the load is 0.5.

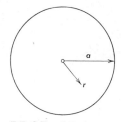

17.7 In electric machines, some of the losses are essentially constant, independent of the load current, but the copper loss at i^2R is proportional to the square of the load current. In an arbitrary machine, let P_K be the constant losses and $I_L{}^2R$ be the copper loss. Output power is $V_T I_L$. Prove that the maximum efficiency occurs when $P_K = I_L{}^2R$.

PROB. 17.4

17.8 Derive Eq. (17.46) for the separately excited d-c shunt generator in the steady state.

17.9 A shunt generator is driven at a rated speed of 1,200 rpm at no load while data for an e_g-versus-i_f curve are obtained.

e_g	47	94	134	165	193	218	241	263
i_f	0.2	0.4	0.6	0.8	1.0	1.2	1.4	1.6

After the magnetization curve has been determined, the armature resistance is measured at $R_a = 0.247$ ohm.

(a) At rated speed with $I_a = 50$ amp and $I_f = 1.3$ amp, what is the terminal voltage?

(b) At rated speed with $I_f = 1.3$ amp and $V_T = 224$ volts, what is I_a?

(c) The speed is dropped to 1,000 rpm. If $I_f = 1.4$ amp and $I_a = 50$ amp, what is the terminal voltage V_T?

(d) At a speed of 1,000 rpm the terminal voltage is 200 volts, and I_a is 60 amp. Find I_f.

17.10 The d-c shunt generator of Prob. 17.9 is separately excited. The field current is fixed at 1.4 amp, and at $t = 0$ the prime mover begins to build up speed according to the equation $s = 1,200(1 - \epsilon^{0.35t})$ rpm. Find e_g as a function of time, evaluating all constants.

17.11 An ideal transformer with turns ratio $N_2/N_1 = 4$ is connected to an impedance $Z_L = 10 + j40$ at the N_2 side. What is the impedance seen at the terminals of the N_1 winding?

17.12 An ideal transformer has three separate windings of N_1, N_2, and N_3 turns, all wound on the same core. Resistors R_1 and R_2 are connected across the terminals of windings N_1 and N_2, respectively. What is the impedance seen at the terminals of N_3?

17.13 An alternator driven at 1,000 rpm is operating in the linear portion of its magnetization curve. At no load the rms terminal voltage is 240 volts, and the frequency is 50 cycles/sec. The speed is reduced to 800 rpm, and the field current remains the same.

(a) What are the frequency and the rms terminal voltage at no load?

(b) By what factor must the field current be increased to raise the no-load terminal voltage to 250 volts after the speed has dropped to 800 rpm?

17.14 A transformer is rated at 66,000:6,600 volts, 1,000 kva, 60 cycles/sec. The effective resistance of the high side is 17.5 ohms, and the effective resistance of the low side is 0.149 ohm. Leakage reactance of the high side is 127.0 ohms, and leakage reactance of the low-voltage side is 1.13 ohms. Core loss is 8,370 watts, and the exciting current is 0.470 amp.

(a) Draw a complete equivalent circuit of the transformer, showing all values of resistance and reactance.

(b) Refer all low-voltage resistances and reactances to the high side, and draw another equivalent circuit, showing all resistances and reactances.

(c) Calculate the voltage regulation for the transformer at 0.707 power factor lagging, full load.

(d) Calculate the efficiency of the transformer at 0.707 lagging power factor, full load.

(e) What impedance is seen across the high-side terminals when a 0.707 lagging power factor, full load, is on the low side?

17.15 The data for Prob. 17.14 are obtained from open-circuit and short-circuit tests.

(a) Find the open-circuit-test input voltage, current, and power measured at the high-voltage side of the transformer.

(b) Find the short-circuit input voltage, current, and power measured at the high-voltage winding of the transformer.

18
ELECTROMAGNETIC FORCES
AND TORQUE

18.1 FORCES ON MOVING CHARGES
IN A MAGNETIC FIELD

Several experiments were performed in Chap. 16 to ascertain the
nature of the electromagnetic force on a conductor carrying current
in a magnetic field. The strength of the magnetic field, or magnetic-flux density, was defined as the force on a conducting element
of unit length carrying unit current in a direction perpendicular to
the magnetic field. In this section we shall investigate the force
on moving electric charges in a magnetic field. A series of hypothetical experiments will be described to show the nature of the
force on the electric charge moving in the magnetic field.

As a first experiment, a particle of mass M and charge $+q$ is
accelerated to a velocity v in a vacuum and then allowed to enter
a region of uniform magnetic-flux density directed at right angles
to the path of particle motion. Observation of the particle path
in the magnetic field shows that the linear velocity of the particle
is not changed but that the path does change direction at a uniform
rate as it follows the arc of a circle of radius r, as shown in Fig.
18.1. The path of the particle while in the magnetic field is such
that it is always perpendicular to the direction of the magnetic
field. This is shown in Fig. 18.1, where the magnetic field is

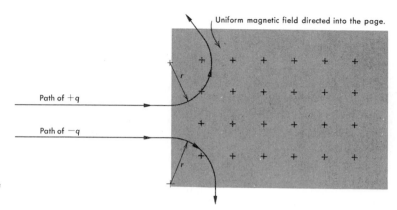

Path of $+q$

Path of $-q$

FIG. 18.1 *Charged particles move in a curved path in a magnetic field.*

directed into the page and the path of the particle is shown in the plane of the page. When the sign of the charge on the particle is changed, but not its magnitude, and the velocity of the particle remains unchanged, we observe that the path in the magnetic field bends in the opposite direction. Yet it remains always at right angles to the direction of the magnetic flux.

Since we have observed that the path is the arc of a circle of radius r, we know that the magnetic force must be directed toward the center of the circular path and must have a magnitude

$$F_c = \frac{Mv^2}{r} \qquad \text{newtons} \tag{18.1}$$

where M is the particle mass, v is its velocity, r is the radius of its circular path, and F_c is its centrifugal force. The magnetic force must equal the centrifugal force. For a particle with a given mass, it is of interest to observe the effect of charge, magnetic-field strength, and initial velocity on the particle's trajectory. First, if we let the magnitude of the charge q change and observe the magnetic force by measuring the radius of the path, we observe that r is inversely proportional to q. Thus, if we double the charge on the particle, the radius of the circular path in the magnetic field is reduced to one-half. Now assume that the charge is maintained constant, and let the uniform magnetic-flux density change. We observe that the radius r of the path is inversely proportional to magnetic-flux density B. Thus, as flux density is increased, the radius of the circular path decreases proportionally. Finally we let the particle velocity change and hold flux density and charge constant. Again we find that the radius of the path is inversely proportional to velocity. Therefore, we can write

$$F_m = Bqv \qquad \text{newtons} \tag{18.2}$$

18.1 Forces on Moving Charges in a Magnetic Field **463**

where F_m is the magnetic force, B is the uniform magnetic-flux density, q is the charge on the particle, and v is the velocity. Observe that Eq. (18.2) is dimensionally correct; it shows the magnitude of the *magnetic* force on the particle directed radially toward the center of the path, while Eq. (18.1) shows the *centrifugal* force on the particle.

In the experiments just described, the path of the particle was always perpendicular to the direction of magnetic flux. As another experiment, let a charged particle at constant velocity be directed into a uniform magnetic field in a direction parallel to the magnetic flux, as shown in Fig. 18.2. The path of the particle is observed in

Uniform magnetic
flux density

Path of charge q with velocity v

FIG. 18.2 *A moving charged particle is not affected by a parallel magnetic field.*

the magnetic field to continue in the same straight line with the same velocity it had when entering. This implies, of course, that there is no magnetic force on the particle, even though it is in a magnetic field. Charged particles moving in a magnetic field in the direction of the flux are not influenced by a magnetic force caused by the flux.

As a last experiment, suppose that the charged particle enters the magnetic field with velocity v at an angle α with respect to the direction of the magnetic flux. The particle has a component of velocity v_1 perpendicular to the flux and a component of velocity v_2 parallel to the direction of the flux, as shown in Fig. 18.3. In Fig. 18.3, the particle is moving in the plane of the paper before it enters the magnetic field. We observe that the particle continues in the magnetic field with the same linear velocity it had when it

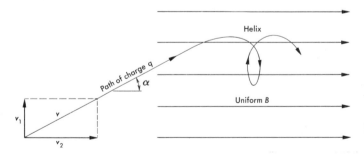

Helix

Path of charge q

α

Uniform B

v_1

v

v_2

FIG. 18.3 *Path of charged particle which enters magnetic field at angle α.*

entered the field. Furthermore, the component of velocity parallel to the magnetic field remains unchanged. But v_1, the component of velocity perpendicular to the field, remains unchanged in magnitude although its direction changes at a constant rate. The path of the particle is a helix. The radius of the helix can be predicted be equating Eqs. (18.1) and (18.2), where v_1 is the perpendicular component of the velocity v. Solving for r, we have

$$r = \frac{Mv_1}{Bq} \qquad (18.3)$$

Thus the charged particle progresses in the direction of the magnetic field with a velocity v_2, but it follows a circular path when seen looking in the direction of the magnetic field.

Example 18.1

A charged particle of mass M and charge $+q$, traveling at velocity v, enters a uniform magnetic field at time $t = 0$ at a vertical angle of $30°$ with respect to the direction of flux, as shown in Fig. 18.4. The

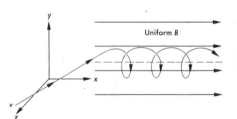

FIG. 18.4 *Helical path of charged mass in a magnetic field.*

component of velocity parallel to the flux is $v_2 = 0.866v$, and the component perpendicular to the flux is $v_1 = 0.5v$. The position of the particle in the x direction is always

$$x = v_2 t$$
$$= 0.866vt \qquad \text{meters} \qquad (18.4)$$

The circular path of the helix has a radius

$$r = \frac{Mv_1}{Bq} \qquad \text{meters}$$

where v_1 is the velocity around the circular path, or at right angles to B. The time required for one cycle of the helix is

$$T = \frac{2\pi r}{v_1} \qquad \text{sec}$$

Solving Eq. (18.3) for v_1 and substituting it into the above equation gives

$$T = \frac{2\pi M}{Bq} \quad \text{sec}$$

The frequency of the circular path in a magnetic field, known as the "cyclotron" frequency, is

$$f = \frac{1}{T} = \frac{Bq}{2\pi M} \quad \text{cycles/sec}$$

Since $y^2 + z^2 = r^2$ and by choosing the origin at the center of the circular path where $y = 0$ at $t = 0$, then

$$y = r \sin 2\pi \, ft \tag{18.5}$$

and

$$z = r \cos 2\pi \, ft \tag{18.6}$$

where $r = Mv_1/Bq$. Equations (18.4) to (18.6) are the solutions which show the position of the particle in the field in three coordinates as a function of time.

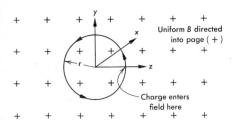

FIG. 18.5 *Path of charged mass looking in the direction of the field.*

18.2 FORCES ON CURRENT-CARRYING CONDUCTORS

The force on a current element in a magnetic field is useful in defining field strength. It is also the medium by which electromechanical energy conversion is accomplished.

The force on a current-carrying conductor and the force on a charged particle in motion are one and the same thing. In a conductor carrying a current of I amp, assume that the current is made up of positive charges distributed uniformly along the length of the conductor and moving at a constant velocity along the conductor. Let ρ be the uniform charge density along the conductor in coulombs per meter and v be the constant velocity of the charge as it moves along the conductor. Then, according to Eq. (1.1), the definition of electric current,

$$I = \rho v \qquad \text{or} \qquad v = \frac{I}{\rho} \qquad\qquad (18.7)$$

If the length of the conductor is l m, the amount of moving charge in the conductor is

$$q = \rho l \qquad \text{coulombs} \qquad\qquad (18.8)$$

Substituting Eqs. (18.7) and (18.8) into Eq. (18.2) gives

$$F_m = BlI \qquad \text{newtons} \qquad\qquad (18.9)$$

which is the force on a conductor of length l in a uniform magnetic field of flux density B carrying a current I at right angles to the direction of the flux. Equation (18.9) is also derivable from Eq. (16.1) by substituting Eq. (16.4) into Eq. (16.1) and recognizing that dl is now replaced by l and that the angle β is zero.

The force on a conductor in a magnetic field contributes to the transfer of energy when the force is allowed to move through a distance. A simple linear motor illustrates this principle. Assume that a conductor of length l maintains sliding contact with two parallel conductors shown in Fig. 18.6. A uniform magnetic field

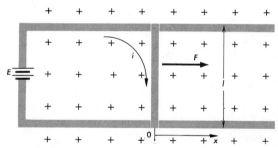

FIG. 18.6 *Linear motor with force F on the moving conductor.*

of flux density B is directed into the plane of the page. Assume that constant current I flows through the sliding conductor and that a force F is produced on the conductor in the direction to the right, as shown. If the mass of the conductor is M and the inertia force is the only force acting on the conductor besides the magnetic force, then by D'Alembert's principle

$$BlI = M \frac{dv}{dt} \qquad\qquad (18.10)$$

The solution of Eq. (18.10) gives the velocity as a function of time. Suppose that the initial conditions are $x = 0$ and $v = 0$ at $t = 0$.

Then

$$dv = \frac{BlI}{M}\, dt$$

and

$$v = \int \frac{BlI}{M}\, dt$$

or

$$v = \frac{BlI}{M}\, t + A_0 \qquad \text{m/sec} \qquad (18.11)$$

Since $v = 0$ at $t = 0$, the constant of integration A_0 must be zero also and the velocity is directly proportional to time. Distance traveled by the conductor is

$$x = \int v\, dt$$

$$= \int \frac{BlI}{M}\, t\, dt$$

Integrating, we have

$$x = \frac{BlI}{2M}\, t^2 + A_1 \qquad \text{meters} \qquad (18.12)$$

where $A_1 = 0$ because of the initial conditions. The acceleration is

$$a = \frac{dv}{dt}$$

or

$$a = \frac{BlI}{M} \qquad \text{m/sec}^2 \qquad (18.13)$$

Equations (18.11), (18.12), and (18.13) give the velocity, distance traveled, and acceleration of the sliding conductor as a function of time, on the assumption that the only forces acting on the conductor are the magnetic force and the inertia force on the conductor.

If an additional force such as viscous friction, which is assumed to be directly proportional to but opposite to the direction of the velocity, acts on the moving conductor of Fig. 18.6, the summation of the forces on the conductor is

$$M\frac{dv}{dt} + B_f v = BlI \qquad (18.14)$$

where B_f is the friction constant. This is a first-order linear differential equation with constant coefficients and with a constant driving force; its solution, from the methods explained in Chap. 5, is

$$v = \frac{BlI}{B_f}(1 - \epsilon^{-(B_f/M)t}) \qquad \text{m/sec} \tag{18.15}$$

for the initial conditions $v = 0$ at $t = 0$. Notice that the velocity of the conductor increases at a decreasing rate and approaches the steady-state velocity at which the friction force is equal to the magnetic force. Under this final steady-state condition, dv/dt is zero, and the velocity remains constant. The acceleration of the conductor can be found by differentiating Eq. (18.15) with respect to time; the distance traveled by the conductor is found by integrating Eq. (18.15) with respect to time.

18.3 CONSERVATION OF ENERGY

Whenever there is a flow of energy into a system, either the energy must be stored in the system or it must be dissipated by the system. In an electric circuit, for example, energy delivered to the circuit from the generator must either be stored in the energy-storage elements of inductance and capacitance or be dissipated as heat by the resistors. In a mechanical system, energy delivered to the system can be stored in the mass by inertia, or it can be stored in the spring, but friction dissipates the energy as heat.

In this section we are concerned with the energy relationships of the various mechanical and electric elements. From the energy relationships are developed the power relationships, which show the rate at which energy stored is changing with respect to time. A modification of the conservation-of-energy principle is the conservation-of-power principle, which requires that the instantaneous power input to a system must equal the rate at which energy is being stored plus the rate at which energy is dissipated. We shall see that the conservation-of-power principle leads to the same system differential equations that can be obtained by Kirchhoff's laws or by D'Alembert's principle.

In a mechanical system an increment of energy or work can be described as force times an increment of distance. The force must have a component in the same direction as the distance traveled. If the force moves along path s always in a direction corresponding to the direction of the path, as shown in Fig. 18.7, then

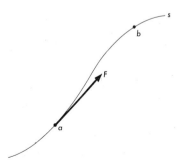

FIG. 18.7 *Force F moving along path s in the same direction as s.*

an increment of work is

$$dW = F\, ds \tag{18.16}$$

and

$$W = \int_a^b F\, ds \qquad \text{joules} \tag{18.17}$$

where W is the energy or work of the force moving from point a to point b on the path s.

In the mechanical system, kinetic energy of a mass M with linear velocity v is

$$W_M = \tfrac{1}{2}Mv^2 \qquad \text{joules}$$

Power, the rate of change of energy with respect to time, is obtained from the equation for kinetic energy. Then

$$p_M = \frac{d}{dt}(\tfrac{1}{2}Mv^2) = Mv\,\frac{dv}{dt} \tag{18.18}$$

Or, from the force-times-distance point of view, mechanical power can be expressed as

$$p = \frac{d}{dt}\int F\, ds = F\,\frac{ds}{dt} \tag{18.19}$$

where the force F is a function of distance along the path s. Notice the similarity between Eqs. (18.18) and (18.19). In Eq. (18.18), $M\, dv/dt$ is the inertia force, corresponding to F in Eqs. (18.19). The velocity v in Eq. (18.18) corresponds to ds/dt in Eq. (18.19).

If power is being consumed by viscous friction, where the friction force is proportional to the velocity, then from Eq. (18.19)

$$p_f = B_f vv = B_f v^2 \qquad \text{watts} \tag{18.20}$$

where B_f is the friction constant and $B_f v$ is the friction force. Power being delivered to a linear spring that is in the process of being compressed is, from Eq. (18.19), the product of force times velocity, or

$$p_s = \left(K\int_0^t v\, dt\right)v \tag{18.21}$$

where K is the spring constant. Replacing velocity under the integral sign in Eq. (18.18) with dx/dt, we have

$$p_s = \left(K\int_0^x \frac{dx}{dt}\, dt\right)v \tag{18.22}$$

or

$$p_s = Kxv \qquad \text{watts} \tag{18.23}$$

assuming zero displacement at $t = 0$.

In the electrical system we have already seen that the electric power delivered to a resistor is [Eq. (1.21)]

$$p_r = vi = i^2 R \quad \text{watts}$$

Energy stored in inductance is [Eq. (1.34)]

$$W_L = L \frac{i^2}{2} \quad \text{joules}$$

and the power delivered to an inductor is

$$p_L = \frac{dW_L}{dt}$$

or

$$p_L = Li \frac{di}{dt} \quad \text{watts} \tag{18.24}$$

Energy stored by capacitance is [Eq. (1.41)]

$$W_c = C \frac{v^2}{2} \quad \text{joules}$$

and the time rate of change of energy stored in the capacitor is

$$p_c = Cv \frac{dv}{dt} = \frac{qi}{C} \quad \text{watts} \tag{18.25}$$

where q is the charge on the capacitor. Equations (18.24) and (18.25) can also be developed from $p = vi$. Thus, for the inductance,

$$p_L = L \frac{di}{dt} i \quad \text{watts}$$

and, for the capacitance,

$$p_c = \left(\frac{1}{C} \int i \, dt \right) i$$

$$= \frac{i}{C} \int \frac{dq}{dt} dt$$

or

$$p_c = \frac{iq}{C} \quad \text{watts}$$

on the assumption that the charge on the capacitor is zero at $t = 0$.

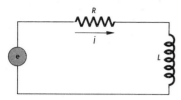

FIG. 18.8 *RL circuit excited by voltage source e.*

Conservation-of-energy principles apply to both electric systems and mechanical systems. In the RL circuit shown in Fig. 18.8, the electric energy delivered by the generator in a given interval of time is equal to the energy delivered to the resistance during that time plus the energy delivered to the inductance during that interval. Then,

$$\int_0^t ei \, dt = \int_0^t Ri^2 \, dt + L\frac{i^2}{2} \tag{18.26}$$

where the initial current in L is zero. Differentiating Eq. (18.26) with respect to time and rearranging the terms yields

$$Li\frac{di}{dt} + Ri^2 = ei \tag{18.27}$$

or, dividing out i from Eq. (18.27),

$$L\frac{di}{dt} + Ri = e \tag{18.28}$$

which we know to be the Kirchhoff's-voltage-law equation for Fig. 18.8. Thus, an energy-balance equation such as Eq. (18.26) can be used to find a system differential equation such as Eq. (18.28).

Consider next a spring-mass-dashpot system such as is shown in Fig. 18.9. The mass is displaced and then allowed to oscillate until it comes to rest. The sum of the forces is, by D'Alembert's principle,

$$M\frac{d^2x}{dt^2} + B_f\frac{dx}{dt} + Kx = 0 \tag{18.29}$$

where M is the mass, B is the friction constant, and K is the spring constant. Multiplying each of the forces in Eq. (18.29) by the instantaneous velocity of the mass results in

$$M\frac{d^2x}{dt^2}v + B_f\frac{dx}{dt}v + Kxv = 0$$

which can be written

$$Mv\frac{dv}{dt} + B_fv^2 + Kxv = 0 \tag{18.30}$$

Now we recognize that Eq. (18.30) is an expression of the conservation-of-energy principle written as the summation of the power equal to zero. The first term in Eq. (18.30) is the rate of

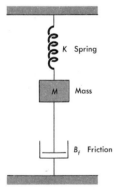

FIG. 18.9 *Spring-mass-dashpot mechanical system.*

change of kinetic energy of the mass and corresponds to Eq.
(18.18). The second term is the power dissipated by friction in the
dashpot, corresponding to Eq. (18.20). The third term is the
rate of change of energy stored in the spring, corresponding to
Eq. (18.23). Notice that the friction power is always positive,
being proportional to the square of the velocity. The power of the
mass and the power of the spring have signs which are functions of
the signs of v, dv/dt, and x. Thus, from the differential equation of
the system, we can arrive at the energy-balance equation for the
system, or from the differential equation we can arrive at the
conservation-of-energy equation.

18.4 ENERGY CONVERSION

Conservation of energy must apply not only for electric systems
and mechanical systems but also for systems in which electric and
mechanical energy are both present simultaneously. We now seek
to apply the conservation-of-energy principle to the linear motor
of Fig. 18.6. Since the magnetic flux remains constant during the
operation of the motor, the energy of the magnetic field is constant.
We are concerned only with the electric energy supplied by the
battery, the mechanical energy imparted to the moving conductor,
and the energy losses in between.

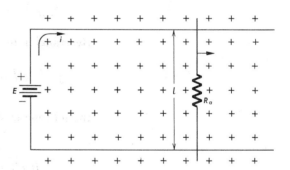

FIG. 18.10 *Linear motor with constant excitation E.*

Assume now that, instead of a constant current flowing in the
moving conductor, there is a constant applied voltage from the
battery and that all the resistance in the conducting loop occurs in
the sliding conductor. This resistance we define as R_a, as shown
in Fig. 18.10. At $t = 0$, a current $i = E/R_a$ is flowing around the
loop, and the conductor is released with a velocity of zero. As the
sliding conductor accelerates to the right, an emf is induced in the

loop which, by Lenz's law, is opposite to the battery voltage. Then

$$i = \frac{E - e_g}{R_a} \tag{18.31}$$

where e_g is the generated voltage in the loop, E is the battery voltage, and i is the current in the loop. Since [Eq. (17.9)]

$$e_g = Blv$$

where v is the velocity of the sliding conductor and l is the length of the conductor,

$$i = \frac{E - Blv}{R_a} \quad \text{amp} \tag{18.32}$$

Now equate the sum of the forces acting on the sliding conductor to zero, and assume that the magnetic force, the inertia force, and the friction force are the only forces present. The sum of these forces is

$$M \frac{dv}{dt} + B_f v = Bli \tag{18.33}$$

Substituting Eq. (18.32) into Eq. (18.33), we have

$$M \frac{dv}{dt} + B_f v = \left(\frac{E - Blv}{R_a} \right) Bl \tag{18.34}$$

Rearranging terms,

$$M \frac{dv}{dt} + \left(B_f + \frac{B^2 l^2}{R_a} \right) v = \frac{EBl}{R_a} \tag{18.35}$$

the solution of which is

$$v = \frac{EBl}{R_a(B_f + B^2 l^2 / R_a)} [1 - \epsilon^{-(B_f/M + B^2 l^2 / R_a M)t}] \quad \text{m/sec} \tag{18.36}$$

for the initial condition $v = 0$ at $t = 0$.

In order to satisfy the law of conservation of energy, the instantaneous-electric-power input must equal the sum of the instantaneous inertia power of the mass and the power being lost by friction. Thus,

$$p_e = p_M + p_f \tag{18.37}$$

where p_e is the electric-power input, p_M is the inertia power of the mass, and p_f is the friction power. Equation (18.37) can also be derived by multiplying Eq. (18.33) by velocity, resulting in

$$Mv \frac{dv}{dt} + B_f v^2 = Blvi \tag{18.38}$$

where

$$p_M = Mv \frac{dv}{dt}$$

$$p_f = B_f v^2 \tag{18.39}$$

$$p_e = Blvi$$

Substituting Eq. (18.32) into Eq. (18.39) results in

$$p_e = \frac{Blv}{R_a} (E - Blv) \tag{18.40}$$

which is an expression for electric power as a function of velocity. In Eq. (18.39), velocity v is a function of time as given by Eq. (18.36). We see from Eq. (18.40) that the electric power delivered to the linear motor is equal to the power delivered to the mass to cause it to increase its stored energy plus the power lost as heat by friction.

The magnetic energy stored in the field of an iron-core inductor can be derived in terms of the reluctance of the core and the square of the flux in the core. Consider the energy stored in the magnetic field of Fig. 18.11. There are N turns wound on the

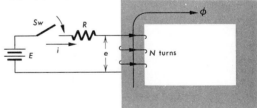

FIG. 18.11 *Magnetic-field energy stored in an iron-core inductor.*

core, and they are excited by a battery E connected in series with resistance R. At $t = 0$, the switch is closed, and the current builds up in the winding. Simultaneously, the magnetic flux builds up in the iron core. If e is the voltage induced in the winding by the inductance of the winding, then

$$e = N \frac{d\phi}{dt} \qquad \text{volts} \tag{18.41}$$

The electric energy delivered to the magnetic field is

$$W_m = \int_0^t ei\,dt \qquad \text{joules} \tag{18.42}$$

Substituting Eq. (18.41) into Eq. (18.42), we have

$$W_m = \int_0^\phi Ni\,d\phi \qquad \text{joules} \tag{18.43}$$

Taking the differential of both sides of Eq. (18.43) yields

$$dW_m = Ni\,d\phi \tag{18.44}$$

where Ni is the mmf of the winding.

A linear approximation can now be made. Since reluctance was defined in Eq. (16.13) as

$$Ni = \Re\phi$$

we substitute Eq. (16.13) into Eq. (18.44), yielding

$$dW_m = \Re\phi\,d\phi \qquad \text{joules} \tag{18.45}$$

If we assume that reluctance is constant and independent of flux and that the flux is therefore proportional to the mmf for this special case, Eq. (18.45) can be written

$$W_m = \Re\,\frac{\phi^2}{2} \qquad \text{joules} \tag{18.46}$$

Notice that Eq. (18.46) is identical in form to the equations for energy stored in a moving mass, in an inductance, or in a capacitance. But it must be emphasized that Eq. (18.46) applies only when reluctance is constant and independent of the amount of the flux in the circuit.

Now consider a situation where the reluctance is not constant and the flux is maintained constant. These are the conditions for the two pole pieces separated by an air gap as shown in Fig. 18.12.

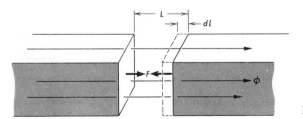

FIG. 18.12 *Force of attraction in a magnetic circuit.*

In this situation we seek to find the force of attraction between the two pole pieces. If we assume that flux is constant and independent of L for this example, Eq. (18.46) permits us to express the differential energy when one pole face moves a distance dl toward the other as

$$dW_m = \frac{\phi^2}{2} d\mathcal{R} \tag{18.47}$$

But this change in energy can also be represented by a force F times the distance dl. Then

$$dW_m = F \, dl \tag{18.48}$$

where F is the force on the pole face. Solving for F, we have

$$F = \frac{\phi^2}{2} \frac{d\mathcal{R}}{dl} \qquad \text{newtons} \tag{18.49}$$

Thus, from Eq. (18.49), the force on the pole faces is proportional to the rate of change of reluctance with respect to distance as the air gap is changed. The direction of the force is that of attraction between pole faces. This is seen by considering the pole faces initially to be adjacent to and then separated from each other. The process of separation increases the stored energy in the air gap, and the amount of the stored energy in the air gap must be the integral of the force with respect to distance as the pole faces are separated.

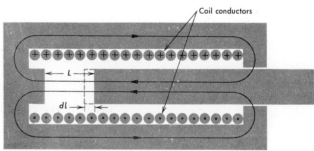

FIG. 18.13 *Magnetic solenoid or plunger.*

Another configuration for the study of magnetic forces is the iron plunger shown in Fig. 18.13. It is desired to find the force on the plunger when the coil is energized. An approximation can be made here to simplify our derivation: assume that the reluctance of the air gap is large compared with the reluctance of the iron path and that the reluctance in the iron path does not change appreciably when the plunger moves a distance dl inward. Let $\mathcal{R}_i$ be the reluctance of the iron path, which is assumed to be constant and independent of the amount of flux. Let $\mathcal{R}_a$ be the air-gap reluctance. Then define the total reluctance $\mathcal{R}$ by

$$\mathcal{R} = \mathcal{R}_i + \mathcal{R}_a \tag{18.50}$$

When the plunger is out a distance L, the air-gap reluctance, neglecting fringing, is

$$\mathcal{R}_a = \frac{L}{\mu_0 A} \tag{18.51}$$

where A is the cross-sectional area of the air gap. For a change in the air-gap length of dl,

$$dW_m = \mathcal{R}\phi \, d\phi \tag{18.52}$$

where $\mathcal{R}$ is defined by Eq. (18.50). Substituting Eq. (18.52) into Eq. (18.48), assuming F to be constant throughout the short distance dl, and solving for F, we have

$$F = \mathcal{R}\phi \frac{d\phi}{dl} \qquad \text{newtons} \tag{18.53}$$

where $\mathcal{R}$ and ϕ both are functions of the length of the air gap L. Let ϕ_1 be the flux for an air gap of length L and ϕ_2 be the flux for an air-gap length of $L - dl$. Then

$$\phi_1 - \phi_2 = d\phi \tag{18.54}$$

where

$$\phi_1 = \frac{Ni}{\mathcal{R}_i + \mathcal{R}_a} \tag{18.55}$$

and

$$\phi_2 = \frac{Ni}{\mathcal{R}_i + \mathcal{R}_a[(L - dl)/L]} \tag{18.56}$$

Substituting Eqs. (18.55) and (18.56) into Eq. (18.54) and simplifying, we have

$$d\phi = \frac{-Ni\mathcal{R}_a \, dl/L}{\mathcal{R}_i{}^2 + \mathcal{R}_a{}^2 + 2\mathcal{R}_i\mathcal{R}_a + (\mathcal{R}_i + \mathcal{R}_a)\mathcal{R}_a \, dl/L} \tag{18.57}$$

The last term in the denominator of Eq. (18.57) is negligible compared with other terms in the denominator, since dl/L is very nearly zero. Equation (18.57) then reduces to

$$d\phi = -\frac{Ni\Re_a}{L(\Re_i + \Re_a)^2}\, dl \tag{18.58}$$

Substituting Eq. (18.58) into Eq. (18.44) gives

$$dW_m = \frac{-(Ni)^2\Re_a}{L(\Re_i + \Re_a)^2}\, dl \tag{18.59}$$

where Ni is the mmf, assumed constant during the change dl. Solving Eq. (18.59) for force F results in

$$F = \frac{-(Ni)^2\Re_a}{L(\Re_i + \Re_a)^2} \tag{18.60}$$

which is the force on the plunger, directed inward. The magnetic force is always in a direction that tends to minimize the reluctance of the magnetic circuit.

18.5 ELECTROMAGNETIC TORQUE ON ROTATING MACHINES

Rotating machines can be classified into three major categories, depending upon the nature of the magnetic field and the relationship between the magnetic field and the current-carrying conductors. In one category are the machines in which the magnetic-field winding is stationary, producing a flux which is fixed in space. The rotor or armature contains the current-carrying conductors on which the magnetic flux from the stationary field reacts to produce an electromagnetic torque. These are the d-c motors. In the second category of rotating machines are those in which the magnetic field rotates, reacting with the magnetic field produced by a stationary winding carrying sinusoidal currents; this is the principle of the a-c synchronous motor. In a third category is the machine with no d-c field winding, but with alternating currents in the stationary winding producing, by transformer action in the rotor conductors, induced currents which react with the magnetic field resulting from the current in the stationary windings to produce forces on rotor conductors. Alternating-current induction motors fall in this third category.

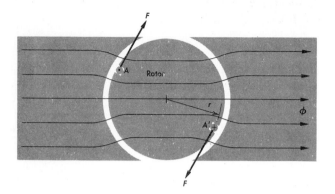

FIG. 18.14 *The basic d-c-motor configuration.*

Consider the stationary field and the rotor containing conducting loops shown in Fig. 18.14. The force F on conductor A is given by

$$F_A = Bli \qquad \text{newtons} \qquad (18.61)$$

where B is the uniform flux density surrounding the rotor conductor, l is the length of the conductor in the magnetic field, and i is the current it carries. The torque produced on conductor A is

$$T_A = Blir \qquad (18.62)$$

where r is the radius shown in Fig. 18.14. If there are n conductors on the rotor periphery, if the fraction a of the n conductors is in the flux under a pole face at any instant, and if each conductor carries current i, then the net magnetic torque developed by the rotor is

$$T_m = Bliran \qquad \text{newton-m} \qquad (18.63)$$

For a given machine, l, r, a, and n are fixed. If we let $K = lran$, then

$$T_m = KBi_a \qquad \text{newton-m} \qquad (18.64)$$

where K is a constant for any given machine and i_a is the total brush current to the rotor. Thus the electromagnetic torque is proportional to the air-gap flux density and the rotor current.

For rotating masses, D'Alembert's principle states that the sum of the torques, including the inertia torque, is zero. For the rotor of Fig. 18.14, if we assume a friction torque proportional to angular velocity, an inertia torque, and an electromagnetic torque, then

$$J \frac{d\omega}{dt} + B_f \omega = T_m \qquad (18.65)$$

where J is the moment of inertia of the rotor, ω is the angular velocity of the rotor, and B_f is the friction constant. If other torques are present, such as a load torque or a spring torque, they would also have to be included in Eq. (18.65). If the electromagnetic torque T_m in Eq. (18.65) is a step of magnitude T_{m1}, the solution of Eq. (18.65) is

$$\omega = \frac{T_m}{B_f}(1 - \epsilon^{-(B_f/J)t}) \qquad \text{radians/sec} \qquad (18.66)$$

If the rotor conductors are connected to a commutator with brushes in a manner similar to the rotor of the d-c generator of Fig. 17.19, the generated voltage at the brushes is given by Eq. (17.35),

$$e_g = K\phi s \qquad \text{volts}$$

where K is a constant of proportionality and s is the speed in rpm. Expressing the speed in radians per second allows us to write

$$e_g = DB\omega \qquad \text{volts} \qquad (18.67)$$

where D is a different constant of proportionality, B is the flux density under the pole faces, and ω is the speed in radians per second. If the rotor is connected to a direct-voltage source V_t as shown in Fig. 18.15, on the assumption that the flux produced by the armature current is negligible and B is uniform and constant in the air gap, then

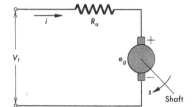

$$i = \frac{V_t - e_g}{R_a} = \frac{V_t - DB\omega}{R_a} \qquad (18.68)$$

FIG. 18.15 *Direct-current-motor armature circuit.*

where R_a is the resistance of the rotor conductors. Substituting Eqs. (18.68) and (18.64) into Eq. (18.65) results in

$$J\frac{d\omega}{dt} + B_f\omega = KB\frac{V_t - DB\omega}{R_a} \qquad (18.69)$$

or

$$J\frac{d\omega}{dt} + \left(B_f + \frac{KDB^2}{R_a}\right)\omega = \frac{KBV_t}{R_a} \qquad (18.70)$$

The solution of Eq. (18.70) for a constant voltage V_t applied at $t = 0$ is

$$\omega = \omega_s (1 - \epsilon^{-(B_f/J + KDB^2/JR_a)t}) \qquad \text{radians/sec} \qquad (18.71)$$

which is identical in form to Eq. (18.36), the solution for the linear motor. The steady-state solution is

$$\omega_s = \frac{KBV_t}{R_a(B_f + KDB^2/R_a)} \qquad \text{radians/sec} \qquad (18.72)$$

This equation was derived on the basis that the load torque is zero; it tells us that, when a step input of voltage is applied to the motor, the speed builds up from zero at a decreasing rate and finally reaches a steady-state speed shown in Eq. (18.72). Notice in Eq. (18.72) that the steady-state speed is proportional to the applied voltage V_t. If the friction constant B_f is small compared with KDB^2/R_a, the steady-state speed is inversely proportional to the air-gap flux density B in Eq. (18.72).

18.6 THE ELEMENTARY D-C MOTOR

Physically, the d-c shunt motor is identical to the d-c shunt generator; indeed, the same machine can be used interchangeably as a motor or as a generator. When the machine is used as a generator, magnetic torque is developed by the armature conductors, opposing the driving torque of the prime mover. When the machine is used as a motor, the developed magnetic torque is opposed by the torque of the mechanical load driven by the motor. As a motor, the machine takes advantage of the developed magnetic torque, and the output of the machine can be considered to be both torque and speed.

The d-c shunt motor is shown in Fig. 18.16, identical in form to the d-c shunt generator of Fig. 17.19. The drum-type rotor, containing the current-carrying conductors in slots, produces the

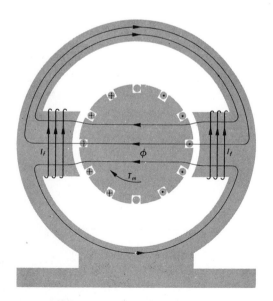

FIG. 18.16 *The d-c-motor field and armature configuration.*

electromagnetic torque and speed which is the output of the machine. The stator, consisting of an iron path for the field flux and the field windings, also serves as the structural frame of the machine. Two poles are shown in the field of Fig. 18.16; four poles, six poles, eight poles, and even more, are possible.

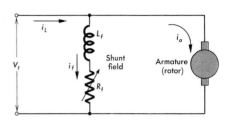

FIG. 18.17 *Direct-current shunt-motor circuit.*

The shunt-field winding is connected in parallel with the armature or rotor and receives power from the constant direct-voltage source, as shown in Fig. 18.17. The line current divides between the armature and the shunt field,

$$i_L = i_f + i_a \tag{18.73}$$

where i_L is the line current being supplied to the motor, i_f is the current to the field, and i_a is the armature current. The field current is adjustable by means of R_f, where an adjustable resistor has been added in series with the shunt field. If the armature current is in the direction shown in the armature conductor in Fig. 18.16 and the field current i_f produces flux in the direction shown in the same figure, the electromagnetic torque is clockwise. Reversal of either i_f or i_a reverses the direction of the electromagnetic torque in the rotor.

According to Faraday's law, the rotating conducting loops in the armature are subject to an induced emf which, according to Eq. (17.35), can be written

$$e_g = K\phi s$$

where K is a constant, s is the armature speed in rpm, and ϕ is the field flux in webers. The voltage e_g is induced in the conductors independent of the current flowing through them. The induced voltage is a function only of the factors in Eq. (17.35). Armature current i_a is found by Ohm's law to be

$$i_a = \frac{V_t - e_g}{R_a} \tag{18.74}$$

where V_t is the terminal or line voltage, R_a is the armature resistance measured between the brushes, and armature inductance is negligible. Solving Eq. (18.74) for induced voltage gives

$$e_g = V_t - i_a R_a \tag{18.75}$$

Now equating Eqs. (17.35) and (18.75) and solving for speed results in

$$s = \frac{V_t - i_a R_a}{K\phi} \qquad \text{rpm} \tag{18.76}$$

which is the well-known speed equation for d-c motors running at constant speed and constant armature current. Speed inversely proportional to the field flux is the important speed characteristic of the shunt motor. Since the field flux is a function of field current, which is easily adjusted by the field resistor or rheostat R_f in Fig. 18.17, speed can be controlled over a wide range by merely adjusting R_f. The numerator of Eq. (18.76) is fairly constant over a wide range of loading, since R_a is relatively small. If the field flux is held constant and armature current i_a is increased by applying an opposing torque to the armature, the speed decreases

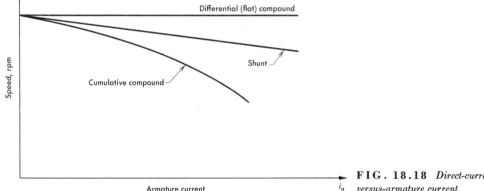

FIG. 18.18 *Direct-current motors, speed-versus-armature current.*

slightly as shown in Fig. 18.18. This curve is sometimes known as the "speed characteristic" of a d-c shunt motor. If the motor is operating on the linear portion of its magnetization curve, field flux ϕ is proportional to V_t. Then small changes in V_t have little effect on the speed of the motor.

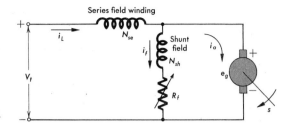

FIG. 18.19 *Compound d-c motor with series field.*

If the slope of the speed characteristic of the shunt motor shown in Fig. 18.18 is not as desired, a series-field winding can be added as shown in Fig. 18.19. The additional mmf produced by the new series winding is approximately proportional to the current through the armature since under load conditions $i_a \gg i_f$. The flux caused by N_{se} turns in the series field either aids or opposes the flux produced by the shunt-field mmf depending on the connection of the series field. The total mmf, then, is

$$\text{mmf} = N_{sh}i_f \pm N_{se}i_L \tag{18.77}$$

If the two components of flux oppose each other, the net flux decreases as i_L increases. If the denominator of Eq. (18.76) decreases at the same rate as the numerator, the speed characteristic becomes essentially constant and independent of the loading. A machine with this speed characteristic is said to be "flat-compounded," because the speed at full load is equal to the speed at no load. In other words, as i_aR_a increases, the denominator of Eq. (18.76) decreases at the same rate as the numerator. If the number of turns in the series winding N_{se} is large and the component of flux in a series field opposes the flux in the shunt field, the net flux may decrease very fast as i_a increases. This can result in a speed characteristic with the full-load speed much greater than the speed at no load. Another extreme occurs when the two field windings produce fluxes which aid each other. In this case, the net field flux increases as the load increases, and by Eq. (18.76) the speed decreases rapidly with load; this is shown in Fig. 18.18 for cumulative compounding.

Direct-current motors and generators have much in common. Besides being identical in physical form, each develops an electromagnetic torque in its rotor, and each generates an emf in its rotor conductors. Yet the motor converts electric energy to mechanical energy, and the generator converts mechanical energy to electric energy. The difference between the motor and generator can be explained with the help of Fig. 18.20, where the shunt machine is

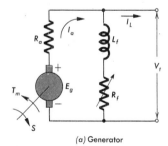

FIG. 18.20 *The d-c shunt machine as a generator and as a motor.*

connected to a constant-voltage line (where the constant-voltage feature is obtained by a large battery or generator in parallel with the load). The shunt machine of Fig. 18.20a is driven clockwise as a generator by the prime mover, which is constrained to turn at a constant speed S. The generator delivers current I_a to the constant-voltage line of voltage V_t, where, from Eq. (17.46),

$$V_t = E_g - I_a R_a$$

The developed torque in the rotor, T_m, opposes the driving torque of the prime mover; the driving torque is clockwise, and the electromagnetic torque T_m is counterclockwise. Now, keeping the speed S and the terminal voltage V_t constant, decrease the generated voltage E_g by increasing the field resistance R_f. From Eq. (17.46), with V_t constant, as E_g decreases, I_a must also decrease. Continue to reduce E_g until $E_g = V_t$ and $I_a = 0$. Now there is no developed torque, since I_a is zero. The machine is still generating a voltage E_g, but not supplying any current to the line. If E_g is reduced still further, I_a reverses, since V_t is now greater than E_g. Once I_a reverses, the developed torque also reverses; T_m is now in the direction of rotation. The machine is behaving like a motor, tending to drive the prime mover in the direction of rotation. The prime mover, constrained to constant speed, acts like a mechanical load and presents an opposing torque to the clockwise developed torque, as shown in Fig. 18.20b.

Example 18.2

A d-c shunt motor operating at a terminal voltage of 220 volts has 50 amp of armature current. The armature resistance R_a is 0.380 ohm, and the motor speed is 1,500 rpm.

An additional load torque is applied, increasing the armature current to 80 amp. Assume that the field flux remains unchanged. With this additional loading, what is the speed of the motor?

From the speed equation (18.76),

$$s = \frac{V_t - i_a R_a}{K\phi}$$

we solve for $K\phi$ for $s = 1{,}500$ rpm and $i_a = 50$ amp.

$$K\phi = \frac{V_t - i_a R_a}{s} = \frac{220 - 50(0.380)}{1{,}500} = 0.134$$

Then, for $i_a = 80$,

$$s = \frac{220 - 80(0.380)}{0.134} = 1{,}414 \text{ rpm}$$

When all external load is removed from the motor, $i_a = 3.5$ amp. The no-load speed is now

$$s = \frac{220 - 3.5(0.380)}{0.134} = 1,632 \text{ rpm}$$

18.7 ROTATING SYNCHRONOUS FLUX

Alternating-current motors (induction motors and synchronous motors) require for their operation a revolving magnetic flux produced by the current in the stator windings of the machine. In this section we shall show how the revolving flux is obtained.

Consider the stator winding identical to that of the alternator discussed in Chap. 17. The three-phase windings are distributed around the stator periphery 120° apart in space and are excited by three-phase currents that are 120° apart in time. The stator windings are shown in Fig. 18.21a, where conductors A–A' make up the winding of phase A, conductors B–B' make up the winding of phase B, and conductors C–C' make up the winding of phase C. The direction of positive current flow is defined by the dots and crosses on the conductors, and the three-phase currents are shown in Fig. 18.21b. A drum-type rotor is shown to complete the flux paths developed by the currents in the stator conductors.

The three stator currents can be expressed as functions of time by

$$i_a = I_m \sin (\omega t - 90°)$$

$$i_b = I_m \sin (\omega t + 150°) \qquad (18.78)$$

$$i_c = I_m \sin (\omega t + 30°)$$

By assuming that the flux produced by the stator currents is proportional to the stator currents, the three components of flux produced by the three windings can be expressed as

$$\phi_a = KI_m \sin (\omega t - 90°)\epsilon^{j180°}$$

$$\phi_b = KI_m \sin (\omega t + 150°)\epsilon^{j60°} \qquad (18.79)$$

$$\phi_c = KI_m \sin (\omega t + 30°)\epsilon^{-j60°}$$

where the sinusoidal terms show the flux as a function of time and the $\epsilon^{j\theta}$ term shows the space relationship of the fluxes. Thus, for winding A–A', when the current is positive, the flux is to the left, as indicated by $\epsilon^{j180°}$. At the origin in time, shown in Fig. 18.21b,

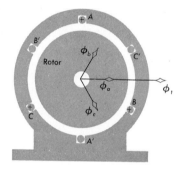

(a) Stator windings

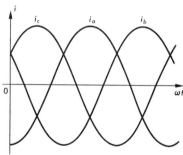

(b) Stator currents

FIG. 18.21 *Stator windings displaced 120° in space, excited by three-phase stator currents.*

the current in A–A' is negative, the sinusoidal term is negative in Eq. (18.79) for ϕ_a, and the direction of ϕ_a is to the right, as shown in Fig. 18.21a. The three components of flux, ϕ_a, ϕ_b, and ϕ_c, are all shown for $t = 0$ in Fig. 18.21a; at that instant their vector sum is ϕ_t, as shown.

The vector sum of ϕ_a, ϕ_b, and ϕ_c can be obtained by adding the real and the imaginary parts of each. Recalling from Eq. (2.33) that

$$\epsilon^{j\theta} = \cos \theta + j \sin \theta$$

then $\epsilon^{j180°} = -1$, $\epsilon^{j60°} = 0.5 + j0.866$, and $\epsilon^{-j60°} = 0.5 - j0.866$. The identity

$$\sin (x \pm y) = \sin x \cos y \pm \cos x \sin y$$

allows us to write, with the help of Eq. (2.42), Eqs. (18.78) in the form

$$\phi_a = KI_m \cos \omega t$$

$$\phi_b = 0.5\ KI_m(-0.866 \sin \omega t + 0.5 \cos \omega t) + j0.866KI_m$$

$$(-0.866 \sin \omega t + 0.5 \cos \omega t) \qquad (18.80)$$

$$\phi_c = 0.5KI_m(0.866 \sin \omega t + 0.5 \cos \omega t) - j0.866KI_m$$

$$(0.866 \sin \omega t + 0.5 \cos \omega t)$$

Adding ϕ_a, ϕ_b, and ϕ_c in Eqs. (18.80) gives ϕ_t, where

$$\phi_t = \phi_a + \phi_b + \phi_c = 1.5KI_m \cos \omega t - j1.5KI_m \sin \omega t$$

$$(18.81)$$

Equation (18.81) can be written, according to Eq. (2.42), as

$$\phi_t = 1.5KI_m\epsilon^{-j\omega t} \qquad (18.82)$$

Equation (18.82) shows that the sum of the flux from each stator winding is a constant of magnitude $1.5KI_m$ which rotates in space in a clockwise direction at an angular velocity of ω, the radian frequency of the sinusoidal currents in the windings.

In order to accomplish the constant, rotating flux expressed by Eq. (18.82), it is necessary that the stator windings be displaced in space by 120° and that the currents in the stator windings be displaced in time by 120°. The angular velocity of the revolving flux is determined by the frequency of the three-phase currents; if the currents are 60 cycles/sec, the flux rotates 60 rps, or 3,600 rpm. Now that the concept of the rotating flux has been developed, applications of this phenomenon are discussed in the following sections on the induction motor and the synchronous motor.

18.8 THE INDUCTION MOTOR

The a-c induction motor, used extensively in industrial applications, requires a stator of the form described in the preceding section. The drum-shaped cylindrical rotor of the squirrel-cage induction motor contains copper conductors embedded in slots on the periphery of the rotor, just as in the rotor of the d-c machine. The squirrel-cage induction motor, however, has no commutator and brushes, and the ends of the rotor conductors are connected together, as shown in Fig. 18.22. Thus, in effect, the rotor conductors form short-circuited loops. No direct electrical connection is made to the rotor. The only currents which flow in the rotor conductors are caused by voltages induced by the rotating flux and predictable from Faraday's law.

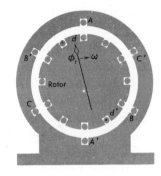

(a) Rotor and stator

The electromagnetic torque is developed in the rotor by the interaction of the induced current in the rotor conductor and the revolving magnetic flux established by the stator currents. In Fig. 18.22b is given the squirrel-cage configuration of the rotor conductors by themselves, showing the ends of the conductors connected together by conducting rings. The rotor appears to be made up of a number of closed conducting loops, of which the two rotor conductors $d-d'$ are an example. Suppose that the rotor is at rest and that the stator is excited by the three-phase voltage. The rotating magnetic flux established by the stator currents induces an emf in the loop of conductors $d-d'$. The induced voltage is maximum when the flux sweeps past the plane of $d-d'$; in this position the rate of change of flux linkages with respect to time in $d-d'$ is maximum. Since the loop is a closed one, current flows as a result of the induced voltage. The direction of the current is into the page at d and out of the page at d', as shown in Fig. 18.22a. The conductors $d-d'$ are carrying induced currents, and they are in a magnetic field; a magnetic force develops on these conductors, producing a torque on the rotor. The direction of the torque is clockwise, the same direction as the revolving flux of the stator. Each pair of conductors in the rotor produces torque in the same way that conductors $d-d'$ do, and each pair contributes to the total torque of the rotor.

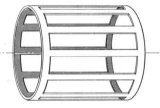

(b) Squirrel-cage rotor conductors

FIG. 18.22 *Squirrel-cage induction motor.*

Now consider what happens when the rotor is turning at synchronous speed, the speed of the revolving flux. There is no rate of change of flux linkages with respect to time in the loops of the rotor, since the flux is rotating at the same speed as the windings themselves; therefore, no torque develops. It appears, then, that the rotor must turn at a speed that is less than the synchronous speed of the stator flux for the developed torque to be in the direction of flux rotation. If the rotor is turning in the same direction as the revolving flux, but at a lower speed, the current induced in the rotor is still in the right direction to produce electromagnetic torque in the direction of the rotating flux.

The magnetic torque developed in each conductor can be expressed by Eq. (18.64), where B is the flux density surrounding the conductor, i is the current induced in the conductor, and K is a constant of proportionality. The net torque developed by the rotor is the summation of the torques developed in each conductor. In order to maximize the net rotor torque, the current in each conductor must reach a maximum value at the same time that the flux density surrounding the conductor is a maximum. The analysis of the induction-motor-torque problem can be simplified if the magnetic-flux density distributed around the rotor periphery is considered to be sinusoidal. Then the induced voltage in the rotor is, by Faraday's law, maximum at zero speed, reducing in a linear fashion to zero at synchronous speed. The frequency of the induced voltage in the rotor is also maximum at zero speed, decreasing in a linear fashion to zero at synchronous speed. Thus the frequency of the induced voltage in the rotor can be expressed by ω_r, where

$$\omega_r = \omega_s \left(1 - \frac{s_r}{S_s} \right) \tag{18.83}$$

where ω_s is the radian frequency of a current in the stator winding, s_r is the rotor speed, and S_s is the synchronous speed of the rotor. In a similar vein, the generated voltage in one loop of the rotor can be expressed as

$$E_g = E_{g0} \left(1 - \frac{s_r}{S_s} \right) \tag{18.84}$$

where E_{g0} is the generated voltage in one loop at zero speed.

The generated-voltage magnitude and frequency are important factors in the developed torque of the rotor. At zero speed, the voltage induced in the rotor and its frequency are both maximum, and the inductive reactance of the rotor is also maximum. If the inductive reactance is very much greater than the resistance of the rotor conductors, the magnitude of the rotor current does not change appreciably as the speed builds up from zero. The current lags the flux by nearly 90°, and the developed torque is not large. As the speed builds up, the generated voltage decreases and the reactance also decreases. Rotor current also decreases as speed increases, but the rotor current becomes more and more in space phase with the flux. A maximum torque is developed below synchronous speed, where the product of current and flux density for each conductor has been maximized. This is shown in Fig. 18.23, where developed torque in the rotor is plotted against rotor

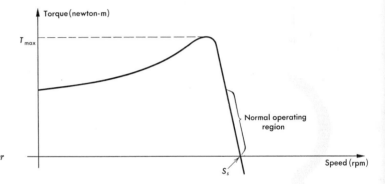

FIG. 18.23 *Rotor torque versus rotor speed, squirrel-cage induction motor.*

speed. Beyond the speed of highest torque, the rotor torque decreases in approximately a linear fashion; here the current and flux are very nearly in space phase with each other, and the current decreases in a linear fashion as the speed increases. In this region, the inductive reactance of the rotor conductor is very much less than the resistance, and for this reason the rotor current is in phase with and proportional to the induced voltage. At a speed greater than synchronous speed, the torque reverses. Thus, if the rotor is driven at a speed greater than synchronous speed, the magnetic torque developed in the rotor is in a direction tending to cause the rotor to return to synchronous speed.

The squirrel-cage induction motor is ordinarily operated in the linear region below the synchronous speed. It is never loaded beyond the maximum torque T_{max}. The induction motor has a starting torque at zero speed that is in the direction required to build up the speed of the motor. Often, a starting compensator must be used to limit the stator current while the rotor builds up speed. The starting compensator is ordinarily a three-phase autotransformer which reduces the applied line voltage of the stator windings to about half its rated value. After the rotor has built up speed, the compensator connects the stator winding directly to the power line.

The squirrel-cage induction motor is, for all practical purposes, a constant-speed motor. At a given load torque, the only way to change the speed of the rotor is to change the frequency of the voltage applied to the stator windings. This is not practical, and if a variable speed motor is required, a d-c shunt motor must ordinarily be used.

18.9 THE SYNCHRONOUS MOTOR

The synchronous motor operates on somewhat the same principle as the magnetic compass; a magnet tends to align itself with the direction of the magnetic field. If the magnetic field rotates, the magnet also rotates and thus becomes the rotor of an electric motor. This principle coincides with that expounded in Sec. 18.5, in which it was shown that magnetic forces are in directions which tend to minimize the reluctance of magnetic circuits.

Means for producing the rotating magnetic field were discussed in Sec. 18.7. A synchronous motor consists of such a rotating magnetic field and a rotor made up of an electromagnet or d-c magnetic-field structure identical to that of the alternator discussed in Chap. 17. The rotor field is excited by direct current delivered to the rotor through slip rings and brushes. Unlike the induction motor, which runs at a speed slightly less than synchronous speed, the synchronous motor runs at exactly synchronous speed.

Just as the d-c motor and generator are physically identical, so the a-c synchronous motor is physically identical to the a-c generator or alternator. Regardless of whether the machine is used as a motor or generator, voltages are induced in the stator and magnetic torques develop on the rotor.

Synchronous-motor operation can be visualized with the help of Figs. 18.24 and 18.25. The flux ϕ established by the currents in the stator windings is rotating clockwise at synchronous speed S_s as indicated in Figs. 18.24b and 18.25b. First we consider the operation of the motor when the external load is zero and the motor must produce only enough torque to overcome the windage and friction. The rotor is very nearly in phase with the flux ϕ, as shown in Fig. 18.24b; the rotor lags the flux by the very small angle α. The generated voltage E_g in the stator windings, caused by the flux of the rotor sweeping past the stator windings, is adjusted to

(a) Circuit diagram

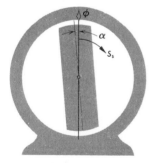

(b) Rotor and flux

(c) Phasor diagram

FIG. 18.24 *Synchronous motor at no load.*

the same magnitude as the terminal voltage V_t by adjusting the resistor in the rotating d-c field and thus controlling the field current. According to the circuit diagram of Fig. 18.24a, the phasor sum of the generated voltage $\mathbf{E}_g$ and the synchronous-impedance voltage $\mathbf{I}_a\mathbf{Z}_s$ must give the terminal voltage $\mathbf{V}_t$. (Synchronous impedance is the phase impedance of the stator winding, consisting of stator resistance and stator inductive reactance.) Then

$$\mathbf{E}_g + \mathbf{I}_a\mathbf{Z}_s = \mathbf{V}_t \qquad (18.85)$$

as shown in the phasor diagram of Fig. 18.24c. The small angle α shown on the phasor diagram corresponds to the angle α by which the rotor lags the rotating flux of the stator. The input power to the motor is $P_{\mathrm{in}} = \sqrt{3}V_tI_a \cos\theta$, where θ is the angle between $\mathbf{V}_t$ and $\mathbf{I}_a$; at no load the input power merely supplies the losses of the machine.

Now consider what happens when a load torque T_L is applied to the rotor in a direction opposite to the direction of rotation; this condition is described in Fig. 18.25a to c. The magnetic torque T_m of the motor is in the direction of rotation and opposite to the direction of T_L. The rotor shifts its position with respect to ϕ, increasing the angle α by which the rotor lags ϕ. The speed of the rotor is still the synchronous speed; only momentarily has the speed dropped to allow the rotor to lag the flux. But see what the larger angle α does to the phasor diagram in Fig. 18.25c; by causing $\mathbf{E}_g$ to lag $\mathbf{V}_t$ by a large angle α, $\mathbf{I}_a\mathbf{Z}_s$ must increase to satisfy Kirchhoff's law, and therefore $\mathbf{I}_a$ must increase. The power input to the motor has increased to account for the additional power delivered to the mechanical load; power input is $P_{\mathrm{in}} = \sqrt{3}V_tI_a \cos\theta$, where I_a is now large and the power-factor angle θ has not changed appreciably from the no-load condition. Thus we see that, by adding load torque to the motor, the rotor torque lags the stator flux by a larger angle, causing greater line current and therefore more power to be delivered to the motor than with no load.

Now consider what happens when an external torque is applied to the rotor in the same direction as the rotating flux; this condition is shown in Fig. 18.26. The rotor moves ahead of the rotating flux, leading the flux by the angle α. The voltage across the synchronous impedance is $\mathbf{I}_a\mathbf{Z}_s$, lagging $\mathbf{V}_t$ by a large angle. The current $\mathbf{I}_a$ must lag the voltage across the synchronous impedance, which is highly inductive; this makes $\mathbf{I}_a$ lag $\mathbf{V}_t$ by nearly 180°. Power flow is out of the machine toward the terminals; the machine is behaving as a generator supplying power to the trans-

(a) Circuit diagram

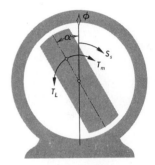

(b) Rotor and flux

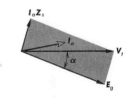

(c) Phasor diagram

FIG. 18.25 *Synchronous motor at full load.*

(a) Circuit diagram

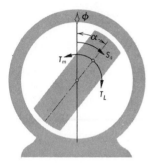

(b) Rotor and flux

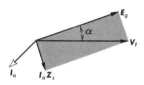

(c) Phasor diagram

FIG. 18.26 *The synchronous machine as an alternator.*

mission line. Thus the same machine serves either as a motor or as a generator, depending upon the direction of the load torque.

The synchronous motor is truly a constant-speed motor; it runs at exactly synchronous speed. If an excessive load torque is applied to the motor, it may pull out of synchronism and stop. Only at synchronous speed does the machine develop a constant torque in the direction of rotation. The synchronous motor develops no starting torque by itself unless some short-circuited rotor conductors are added to the rotor to make the machine behave like a squirrel-cage induction motor. The addition of these conductors to the rotor gives the motor the necessary starting torque, but when the machine is running at synchronous speed, the squirrel-cage windings add nothing to the average rotor torque.

18.10 THE PERMANENT-MAGNET MOVING-COIL AMMETER

Electric indicating instruments are devices for measuring voltage, current, and power. Indicating instruments rely upon magnetic torques produced by magnetic fields acting upon current-carrying conductors to cause a deflection of the pointer. The permanent-magnet moving-coil instrument, sometimes called the "D'Arsonval instrument," is the basic d-c instrument; it is shown in Fig. 18.27. A permanent magnet establishes a constant and uniform flux density across the air gaps shown. All iron parts of the magnetic circuit are fixed in space; only the coil and pointer are movable about the axis of the coil. Two springs, one above the coil and one underneath, provide the spring torques to the movement and also provide the current path through which the direct current enters and leaves the coil.

The instrument behavior can be described as follows: Assume that the coil is initially at rest in its neutral position with no current flowing. At $t = 0$, the current in the coil increases to I amp. A magnetic torque is developed by the coil, since the coil conductors are in a magnetic field. The magnetic torque T_m is proportional to the current I and the magnetic flux density B, or

$$T_m = K_m I B \tag{18.86}$$

where K_m is the constant of proportionality. As the coil starts to rotate under the influence of the magnetic torque, inertia torque, friction torque, and spring torque oppose T_m. Equating the sum

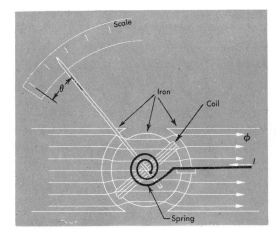

FIG. 18.27 *The permanent-magnet moving-coil d-c indicating instrument.*

of the torques to zero and using the angle θ as the dependent variable results in the second-order differential equation

$$J \frac{d^2\theta}{dt^2} + B_f \frac{d\theta}{dt} + K\theta = K_m I B \tag{18.87}$$

where J is the moment of inertia of the coil and pointer, B_f is the friction constant, and K is the spring constant. The characteristic equation of Eq. (18.87) can be written

$$Jp^2 + B_f p + K = 0 \tag{18.88}$$

the roots of which are

$$p_1 = -\frac{B}{2J} + \sqrt{\frac{B^2}{4J^2} - \frac{K}{J}}$$

and $\tag{18.89}$

$$p_2 = -\frac{B}{2J} - \sqrt{\frac{B^2}{4J^2} - \frac{K}{J}}$$

If p_1 and p_2 are complex, the solution of Eq. (18.87) is of the form

$$\theta = \epsilon^{-\alpha t}(A_1 \cos \omega t + A_2 \sin \omega t) + \frac{K_m B I}{K} \tag{18.90}$$

where $\alpha = B/2J$ and $\omega = \sqrt{K/J - B^2/4J^2}$. If p_1 and p_2 are real, the solution of Eq. (18.87) is of the form

18.10   The Permanent-magnet Moving-coil Ammeter   495

$$\theta = A_3 \epsilon^{p_1 t} + A_4 \epsilon^{p_2 t} + \frac{K_m B}{K} I \qquad (18.91)$$

In either case, the final steady-state angle of deflection θ is directly proportional to the current I, or

$$\theta_s = \frac{K_m B}{K} I \qquad (18.92)$$

A scale under the pointer can be calibrated linearly, showing current in amperes proportional to the angle of deflection θ. The steady-state value of θ is determined when the magnetic torque T_m is exactly equal to the spring torque $K\theta$ and the angular velocity is zero.

The characteristics of the permanent-magnet moving-coil instrument are described in Appendix 2.

SUMMARY

Electric charges moving in a magnetic field have forces exerted upon them by the magnetic field. The magnetic force is proportional to the magnetic-flux density B, the electric charge q, and the component of velocity perpendicular to the magnetic field, or [Eq. (18.2)]

$$F_m = Bqv \qquad \text{newtons}$$

In a conductor of length l carrying current I at right angles to the magnetic flux of density B, the force is given by Eq. (18.9),

$$F_m = BlI \qquad \text{newtons}$$

These forces are fundamental to all electromechanical energy-conversion devices.

Energy stored in an iron-core magnetic circuit is given by Eq. (18.46),

$$W_m = \mathfrak{R} \frac{\phi^2}{2} \qquad \text{joules}$$

where $\mathfrak{R}$ is the reluctance of the magnetic circuit and ϕ is the flux in the circuit. Whenever either $\mathfrak{R}$ or ϕ or both are changed, energy must either be added to or extracted from the stored energy. Changes in the physical dimensions of the magnetic circuit result in changes in the amount of stored energy, some of which can be extracted mechanically. If none of the change in stored energy is returned to the electric circuit, the mechanical energy can be expressed by Eq. (18.48),

$$dW_m = F\,dl$$

where F is the mechanical force and dl is the distance through which it moves.

The d-c shunt-motor steady-state speed equation [Eq. (18.76)] is

$$s = \frac{V_t - i_a R_a}{K\phi} \qquad \text{rpm}$$

where V_t is the applied terminal voltage, i_a is the armature or rotor current, R_a is the armature resistance, ϕ is the total field flux, and K is a constant. Rotor torque is proportional to i_a, so speed is a function of torque. The torque equation (18.64) is

$$T_m = KBi_a \qquad \text{newton-m}$$

where B is the flux density under the pole faces and K is another constant. Comparison of the speed and torque equations shows that, as the torque increases and B is constant, i_a also increases and the speed decreases slightly. Speed can be adjusted easily by a variable resistor in the field circuit which controls field flux.

The induction motor and the synchronous motor both require a rotating synchronous flux for the production of their rotor torques. The rotating flux is produced by stator windings separated in space and carrying currents which are sinusoidal but separated in time phase. The induction-motor rotor consists of an iron drum in which the conductors are embedded. The rotor conductors make short-circuited loops; currents induced in the conductors react with the rotating synchronous flux to produce a magnetic torque in the direction of the rotating flux. Induction motors operate at speeds slightly below synchronous speed; the starting torque is usually sufficient to build up the speed of the machine.

The synchronous motor runs at exactly synchronous speed. Its rotor consists of a d-c field structure which aligns itself with the synchronous flux and rotates with it. When a load torque is applied, the rotor lags behind the rotating synchronous flux but it continues to turn at the synchronous speed.

Inherently, a-c motors are constant-speed motors. Speed adjustment can easily be made with the d-c shunt motor.

FURTHER READING

The references listed at the end of Chap. 17 apply also to this chapter. Electric-motor control is concerned with starting electric motors and controlling their speed and torque. Two books discussing motor control are P. B. Harwood, *Control of Electric Motors*, 3d ed. (John Wiley & Sons, Inc., New York, 1952), and G. W. Heumann, *Magnetic Control of Industrial Motors*, 2d ed. (John Wiley & Sons, Inc., New York, 1954). The practicing engineer will find Charles C. Libby, *Motor Selection and Application* (McGraw-Hill Book Company, Inc., New York, 1960), a valuable reference.

PROBLEMS

18.1 In the figure a proton is accelerated to a velocity of 10^7 m/sec and then enters a region of uniform magnetic field of flux density 0.75 weber/m². (a) The path of the proton is at right angles to the boundary of the magnetic field and also at right angles to the direction of the magnetic flux. Find the distance A between the point at which the proton enters the field and the point at which it leaves the field. (b) The proton enters the field at right angles to the flux but at an angle of 30° with the field boundary. Find A.

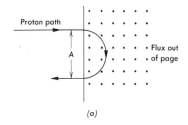

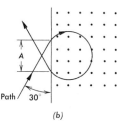

PROB. 18.1

18.2 A transformer of the dimensions shown in the illustration has an air gap of 0.0005 m cut into the iron. The magnetization curve for sheet steel in Fig. 16.13 applies. Current in the primary winding is $i_1 = 5 \sin 377t$. The secondary winding is open. $N_1 = 25$ turns. $N_2 = 250$ turns. Find the maximum force of attraction on the two sides of the air gap.

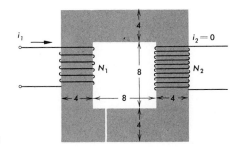

PROB. 18.2

18.3 Verify that Eq. (18.2) is dimensionally correct.

18.4 Derive Eq. (18.9) from Eq. (16.1).

18.5 Two parallel conductors are spaced 0.15 m apart and carry 100 amp in the same direction. Find the magnetic forces per unit length acting between these two conductors, and show the direction of the forces.

18.6 A linear motor is connected to a constant 110-volt source. The flux density between the parallel conductors is constant and uniform at 0.5 weber/m^2 directed into the plane of the page. Dimensions of the motor are shown in the figure. At time $t = 0$ the sliding conductor is at rest and is released. It moves to the right at such a velocity that its position is $x = 80t^2$, where t is in seconds. The mass of the sliding conductor is 0.350 kg, and the resistance in the conducting loop is constant at 10 ohms.

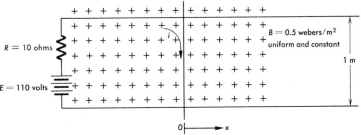

PROB. 18.6

(a) Over what range of x does the machine behave as a motor, and over what range as a generator?

(b) At $t = 2$ sec, what is the direction of the electromagnetic force?

(c) At $t = 0.25$ sec, how much power is being delivered by the battery?

(d) Find an expression for the inertia power as a function of time.

18.7 A rotating d-c shunt motor is constrained always to run at 5,000 radians/sec by the nature of its load. The field is separately excited, and field flux is constant. At a terminal voltage of 220 volts connected to the armature, the motor delivers 3,500 watts of mechanical power to its load. At the speed and excitation stated, the generated voltage is 204 volts.

(a) What power is being lost by the resistance of the armature? Windage, friction, and iron losses are 410 watts at this speed and excitation.

(b) If the terminal voltage drops to 210 volts, how much mechanical power is being delivered to the load?

(c) If the armature terminal voltage drops to 195 volts, what is the armature current and how much electric power is being delivered by the armature to the line?

(d) If the terminal voltage is 220 volts and the generated voltage is 204 volts and if the speed of the load drops to 4,600 radians/sec, how much electric power will the armature draw from the line?

18.8 In the figure the magnetic field along the periphery of the rotor of a squirrel-cage induction motor is distributed in space in a sinusoidal manner and rotates at constant angular velocity ω_1. The rotor turns at an angular velocity of ω_2 which is less than ω_1. There are 10 conductors distributed uniformly around the rotor, each with an effective resistance of R_1, and the resistance of the end connections is negligible. Assume that there is negligible rotor inductance at the speed ω_2. Derive an equation for the torque of the rotor.

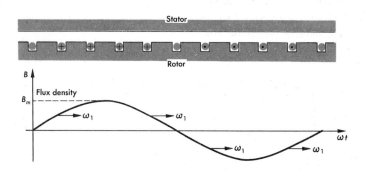

PROB. 18.8

18.9 The armature resistance of a d-c shunt motor is 0.40 ohm, and at rated load the armature draws 50 amp at 125 volts.

(a) If the armature is connected to the 125-volt line when it is at rest, how much steady-state current does it draw?

(b) A resistor is connected in series with the armature to limit the current during the starting period. If the current during the starting period cannot exceed 125 amp, how much resistance must the resistor have?

18.10 Verify, using Eqs. (18.79), that, when $\omega t = 0$, the net flux $\phi_t = 1.5KI_m$ and is directed to the right, when $\omega t = 45°$, $\phi_t = 1.5KI_m$ directed at an angle of $-45°$, and when $\omega t = 90°$, $\phi_t = 1.5KI_m$ directed at an angle of $-90°$ (downward).

18.11 A 5-hp (1 hp = 746 watts) induction motor delivers full power output at 1,700 rpm. It is 80 per cent efficient and is connected to a balanced three-phase 120-volt line. Its power factor is 0.70 lagging; what is the line current?

18.12 A conveyor belt in a plant moves at a velocity of 400 ft/min and requires a force of 1,450 lb at this speed. A 440-volt three-phase 60-cycles/sec supply is available. Assume that the induction motor chosen to drive the conveyor belt is 80 per cent efficient, 70 per cent power factor, and can be obtained in 5-hp, 10-hp, 15-hp, 20-hp, 25-hp, and 50-hp sizes.

(a) What size induction motor would you choose to do the job without overloading?

(b) Approximately what will be the line current of the induction motor?

18.13 A synchronous motor connected Y is rated at 10 kva, 220 volts, 60 cycles/sec, with synchronous speed of 3,600 rpm. The synchronous reactance per phase is $Z_s = 0.65 + j2.1$ ohms. The generated voltage E_g per phase has been adjusted to equal the terminal voltage per phase.

(a) Find the angle α for the rated input to the machine.

(b) The field excitation is increased so that $E_g = 1.25V_t$. What is the power factor of the motor at rated input?

(c) The field excitation is reduced until $E_g = 0.75V_t$. Find the power factor of the motor at rated input.

(d) For part c, find the line current.

18.14 A synchronous motor is operating at rated voltage and current. The field excitation is increased (I_f increased), causing a decrease in stator current. Was the motor operating with leading or lagging power factor? Explain.

18.15 In the figure a beam of electrons moving at a velocity of 2.5 × 10^7 meters/sec in the x direction enters a uniform magnetic field of flux density $B = 0.001$ weber/m^2, $x < 0$, which is directed in the $-z$ direction. If the beam enters the field at the origin, find the y and z coordinates of the beam when $x = 0.10$ m. $B = 0$ for $x < 0$.

18.16 A linear motor such as the one shown in Fig. 18.10 has $E = 100$ volts, $l = 1$ m, and the resistance around the conducting loop $R_a = 0.5$ ohm is driven in such a manner that the displacement of the sliding bar is constrained to $x = 0.254 \sin 210t$, where t is in seconds. Find the force on the sliding bar as a function of time.

18.17 A pendulum consists of a conductor directed into the paper, and suspended between the poles of a magnetic core, as shown in the illustration. Assume that the magnitude of the pendulum swing is always short compared with l, the length of the pendulum, so that the conductor is always

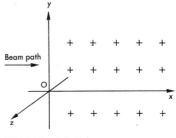

PROB. 18.15

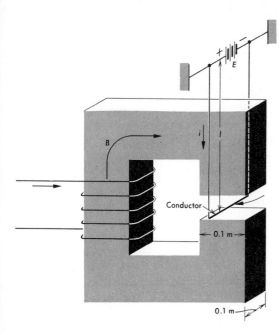

PROB. 18.17

in the magnetic field between the poles. The mass of the conductor is 2 g, and the mass of the suspending wires of length l is negligible. A current $i = I_m \cos \omega t$ flows in the conductor, and the magnetic-flux density in the air gap is $B = 0.75$ weber/m². Assume that only the inertia force and the electromagnetic force on the conductor are appreciable. Derive an equation for the displacement of the conductor as a function of time. Then find the velocity as a function of time.

LINEAR APPROXIMATIONS
TO MACHINE ANALYSIS

19.1 PIECEWISE LINEAR ANALYSIS

In Sec. 8.2 we saw how nonlinear current-versus-voltage characteristic curves could be approximated over limited regions of the curve by linear current-versus-voltage curves. Since the analysis of linear equations is inherently easier than the analysis of nonlinear equations, such approximations usually lead to simpler mathematics. Nonlinear analysis is often accomplished by graphical means; piecewise linear analysis can be accomplished analytically. In Chap. 12 piecewise linear analysis was used effectively in the analysis of some nonlinear electronic circuits.

As an example of piecewise linear analysis, consider the circuit in Fig. 19.1a, an RL circuit in which the resistance is linear but the inductance is not. Inductance can be defined according to Eq. (17.19) as

$$L = N \frac{d\phi}{di} \quad \text{henry}$$

Only when $d\phi/di$ is constant and independent of ϕ or i is the inductance constant and Eq. (17.19) linear. If the inductance is wound with N turns on an iron core, the magnetization curve can

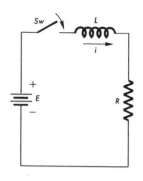

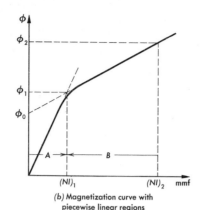

(a) Nonlinear RL circuit

(b) Magnetization curve with piecewise linear regions

FIG. 19.1 *Nonlinear magnetic circuit undergoes piecewise linear analysis.*

be plotted as flux versus mmf as in Fig. 19.1b. Since mmf is proportional to i, two regions on the magnetization curve can be seen to have nearly constant slope. The linear region A in Fig. 19.1b defines inductance L_a, and the linear region B defines the inductance L_b. Then

$$L_a = N^2 \frac{\phi_1}{(NI)_1} \tag{19.1}$$

and

$$L_b = N^2 \frac{\phi_2 - \phi_1}{(NI)_2 - (NI)_1} \tag{19.2}$$

The inductor and resistor are connected in series to a battery of constant potential E, as shown in Fig. 19.1a. At $t = 0$ the switch in the circuit is closed. If the inductance L were constant, the linear differential equation describing the circuit would be given by

$$L \frac{di}{dt} + Ri = E \tag{19.3}$$

where L is the constant inductance. The steady-state solution of Eq. (19.3) when $di/dt = 0$ is $i = E/R$. Even if L is allowed to vary in Eq. (19.3), the final steady-state solution will always be $i = E/R$.

If the steady-state current results in a mmf less than $(NI)_1$, then the value of inductance is defined by Eq. (19.1) for the piecewise linear region between mmf $= 0$ and mmf $= (NI)_1$. The usual linear solution of Eq. (19.3) is

$$i = \frac{E}{R} \left(1 - \epsilon^{-(R/L_a)t}\right) \tag{19.4}$$

where L_a is defined in Eq. (19.1). Thus for small values of i the RL circuit of Fig. 19.1b can be considered linear.

On the other hand, if the steady-state current $I = E/R$ results in a mmf greater than $(NI)_1$, then the solution of Eq. (19.3) is complicated by the fact that $L = L_a$ initially but changes to L_b as NI becomes greater than $(NI)_1$. The approximate solution can be found in two steps. In region A of Fig. 19.1a,

$$i = \frac{E}{R}(1 - \epsilon^{-(R/L_a)t}) \qquad 0 < t < t_1 \tag{19.5}$$

where t_1 is the time required for i to reach a value of I_1. To solve for t_1, we set $i = I_1$ in Eq. (19.4), where $I_1 = (NI)_1/N$, and solve for t.

$$I_1 = \frac{E}{R}(1 - \epsilon^{-(R/L_a)t_1}) \qquad \text{or} \qquad \epsilon^{-(R/L_a)t_1} = 1 - \frac{I_1 R}{E} \tag{19.6}$$

Taking the natural logarithm of both sides of Eq. (19.6) results in

$$-\frac{R}{L_a}t_1 = \ln\left(1 - \frac{I_1 R}{E}\right) \qquad \text{or} \qquad t_1 = -\frac{L_a}{R}\ln\left(1 - \frac{I_1 R}{E}\right) \tag{19.7}$$

where t_1 is the time required for the flux in the inductor to increase from zero to ϕ_1, or for the mmf to increase from zero to $(NI)_1$.

The second step in the piecewise linear solution is to find i for t greater than t_1. In this region let $i = I_1 + i_d$, where I_1 is the current which produces $(NI)_1$, ampere-turns of mmf. Then Eq. (19.3) can be written

$$L_b\frac{di}{dt} + R(I_1 + i_d) = E \tag{19.8}$$

where $di/dt = di_d/dt$. Equation (19.8) can be written

$$L_B\frac{di_d}{dt} + Ri_d = E - RI_1 \tag{19.9}$$

the solution of which is

$$i_d = \frac{E - RI_1}{R}(1 - \epsilon^{-(R/L_B)t'}) \tag{19.10}$$

where $t' = t - t_1$ and $i = I_1 + i_d$. Rewriting Eq. (19.10),

$$i = \left(I_1 - \frac{E}{R}\right)\epsilon^{-(R/L_B)(t-t_1)} + \frac{E}{R} \qquad t_1 < t \tag{19.11}$$

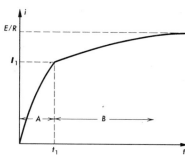

FIG. 19.2 *Current versus time for nonlinear RL circuit of Fig. 19.1b.*

Equations (19.5) and (19.11) are the two equations for current in the nonlinear RL circuit. For region A as defined by Fig. 19.1a, Eq. (19.5) applies; in region B, Eq. (19.11) applies. The time t_1, expressed in Eq. (19.7), is the dividing line between the two regions. Figure 19.2 shows current versus time for the nonlinear RL circuit. A discontinuity exists at t_1; this is the intersection of Eqs. (19.5) and (19.11). The discontinuity in Fig. 19.2 is produced by the discontinuity in the magnetization curve which results from the piecewise linear approximation to the magnetization curve.

19.2 SELF-EXCITED SHUNT GENERATOR IN THE STEADY STATE

Piecewise linear analysis not only is useful in dynamic problems, as shown in the preceding section, but also can be applied to systems in the steady state. Piecewise linear approximations to voltage-current and current-voltage characteristics of nonlinear devices were discussed in Sec. 8.2 and further elaborated on for the example of the diode, in Sec. 10.1. In this section, we again apply the piecewise linear approximation to the shunt generator.

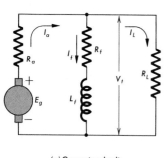

(a) Generator circuit

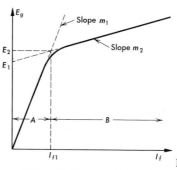

(b) Magnetization curve, rated speed

FIG. 19.3 *Self-excited shunt generator.*

The self-excited shunt generator represented in Fig. 19.3a has the magnetization curve shown in Fig. 19.3b. Straight-line segments have been drawn on the magnetization curve to approximate the curve in two regions, region A and region B. Assume that the excitation of the shunt generator is such that the no-load generated voltage is in region B, where

$$E_g = E_1 + m_2 I_f \tag{19.12}$$

and E_1 and m_2 are defined in Fig. 19.3b. The steady-state field current is given by

$$I_f = \frac{V_T}{R_f} \tag{19.13}$$

and the generated voltage E_g is related to the terminal voltage V_T by

$$V_T = E_g - I_a R_a \tag{19.14}$$

where

$$I_a = I_L + I_f \tag{19.15}$$

Substituting Eqs. (19.12), (19.13), and (19.15) into (19.14) and solving for the terminal voltage V_T, we have

$$V_T = \frac{E_1 - I_L R_a}{1 + R_a/R_f - m_2/R_f} = \frac{R_f(E_1 - I_L R_a)}{R_f + R_a - m_2} \tag{19.16}$$

which is a linear relationship between V_T and I_L. Keep in mind that Eq. (19.16) applies only in region B of the magnetization curve, where Eq. (19.12) applies. The maximum value of terminal voltage occurs when the load current I_L is zero; both terminal voltage V_T and generated voltage E_g decrease linearly as I_L increases. If I_L increases until E_g is less than E_2, the limit of the B region has been reached and any further increase in I_L requires analysis in region A.

Suppose now that the generated voltage E_g falls in region A, where the slope of the magnetization curve is m_1. Then

$$E_g = m_1 I_f = \frac{V_T}{R_f} m_1 \tag{19.17}$$

and the terminal voltage V_T is related to the generated voltage E_g by Eq. (19.14). Substituting Eq. (19.17) into (19.14) and solving for V_T as a function I_L results in

$$V_T = \frac{R_a R_f}{m_1 - R_a - R_f} I_L \tag{19.18}$$

which shows that, in region A, the terminal voltage is directly proportional to the load current in the steady state. Since the effect of the shunt-field inductance has been neglected in this steady-state analysis, Eq. (19.18) shows only that, once the load current has been established, a given terminal voltage can be expected. In Eq. (19.16) it is assumed that $R_f + R_a$ is greater than

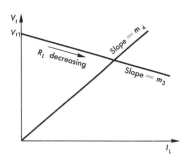

FIG. 19.4 *External characteristic of self-excited shunt generator, piecewise linear analysis.*

m_2, and in Eq. (19.18) it is assumed that m_1 is greater than $R_a + R_f$.

Equations (19.16) and (19.18) are plotted in Fig. 19.4. Equation (19.16) intersects the $I_L = 0$ axis at V_{t1}, where

$$V_{t1} = \frac{R_f E_1}{R_f + R_a - m_2} \tag{19.19}$$

and the slope of Eq. (19.16) is given by m_3, where

$$m_3 = -\frac{R_f R_a}{R_a + R_f - m_2} \tag{19.20}$$

Equation (19.18) passes through the origin with a slope of m_4, where m_4 is given by

$$m_4 = \frac{R_a R_f}{m_1 - R_a - R_f} \tag{19.21}$$

At the intersection of the two linear curves in Fig. 19.4, the transition between region A and region B of Fig. 19.3 occurs.

The above analysis applies only to the steady state. The significance of the above analysis can be seen by assuming that the generator of Fig. 19.3a operates at constant speed with its initial load resistance R_L infinite and $I_L = 0$, in which case the terminal voltage is V_{T1} as shown in Fig. 19.4. As I_L increases, the terminal voltage decreases following the curve of Eq. (19.16); the load resistance R_L is decreasing as I_L increases. As R_L decreases further, a value of I_L is reached at which the two curves of Fig. 19.4 intersect. Further reduction in R_L causes both V_T and I_L to decrease, until the limit is reached at which the terminal voltage is zero, R_L is zero, and I_L is zero. Thus, under short-circuit conditions, the self-excited shunt generator produces a steady-state short-circuit current of zero.

19.3 TORQUE-VERSUS-SPEED CHARACTERISTICS

In Chap. 18, the shunt-motor torque equation was derived, showing that the electromagnetic torque developed in the machine rotor is proportional to field flux density and armature current. The torque equation (18.64) was expressed as

$$T_m = KBi_a \qquad \text{newton-m}$$

where K is a constant of proportionality, B is the field flux density under the pole faces, and i_a is the total armature current between the brushes. The steady-state speed equation for the d-c shunt motor can be written from Eq. (18.76) as

$$s = \frac{V_T - I_a R_a}{K'B} \qquad \text{rpm} \qquad (19.22)$$

where $K'B = K\phi$ of Eq. (18.64), V_T is the d-c terminal voltage applied to the rotor or armature at the brushes, I_a is the rotor current seen at the brushes, R_a is the rotor or armature resistance, K' is another constant of proportionality, and B is the flux density under the pole faces. Solving Eq. (19.22) for I_a and substituting it into Eq. (18.64) gives

$$T_m = \frac{KB}{R_a} V_t - \frac{KK'B^2}{R_a} s \qquad (19.23)$$

Equation (19.23) shows the relationship between the electromagnetic torque T_m and the motor speed s. Since the terminal voltage V_t and the flux density B are ordinarily constant, Eq. (19.23) expresses T_m as the function of s in a linear fashion. If B is held constant and V_t is allowed to vary as a parameter, a family of torque-versus-speed curves can be drawn for the various constant

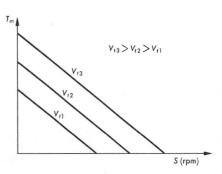

FIG. 19.5 *Torque-versus-speed curves of a separately excited shunt motor, with V_t as a parameter.*

values of V_t, as shown in Fig. 19.5. The slope of these curves is constant and given by

$$\text{Slope} = -\frac{KK'B^2}{R_a} \qquad (19.24)$$

and the torque axis intercept is proportional to V_T and given by

$$\text{Intercept} = \frac{KB}{R_a} V_T \qquad (19.25)$$

The torque-versus-speed curves of Fig. 19.5 show that for any constant terminal voltage the magnetic torque increases as the speed decreases. If for any reason the speed increases until the torque becomes negative, the machine behaves as a generator and the negative torque tends to slow the speed of the machine. Maximum mechanical-power output occurs when the product of T_m and s is a maximum. Multiplying Eq. (19.23) by s gives

$$sT_m = \frac{KBV_t}{R_a} s - \frac{KK'B^2}{R_a} s^2 \tag{19.26}$$

Differentiating Eq. (19.26) with respect to s, setting the derivative to zero, and solving for s gives

$$s = \frac{V_t}{2K'B} \qquad \text{rpm} \tag{19.27}$$

which is the speed of maximum-power output of the motor.

Another approach to the torque-versus-speed relationship is to recognize that the torque is a function of speed and terminal voltage, a consequence of Eq. (18.64), where i_a is a function of terminal voltage and speed. Writing

$$T_m = f(V_t, s) \tag{19.28}$$

and taking the total differential of Eq. (19.28), we have

$$\Delta T_m = \frac{\partial T_m}{\partial V_t} \Delta V_t + \frac{\partial T_m}{\partial s} \Delta s \tag{19.29}$$

If we assume a linear relationship between torque, terminal voltage, and speed, Eq. (19.29) can be written

$$T_m = \frac{\partial T_m}{\partial V_t} V_t + \frac{\partial T_m}{\partial s} s \tag{19.30}$$

where it can be recognized from Eq. (19.23) that

$$\frac{\partial T_m}{\partial V_t} = \frac{KB}{R_a} \qquad \text{and} \qquad \frac{\partial T_m}{\partial s} = -\frac{KK'B^2}{R_a} \tag{19.31}$$

Now suppose that a shunt motor with torque-versus-speed characteristics expressed by Eqs. (19.23) and (19.30) is initially at rest when a step input of voltage V_t is applied to the armature. Assuming that the inertia torque and the viscous-friction torque are the only torques opposing the magnetic torque, we can write

$$J \frac{d\omega}{dt} + B_f \omega = A_1 V_t + A_2 \omega \tag{19.32}$$

where J is the moment of inertia, B_f is the friction constant, and A_1 and A_2 are given by

$$A_1 = \frac{KB}{R_a} \quad \text{and} \quad A_2 = -\frac{KK'B^2}{R_a}\frac{2\pi}{60} \qquad (19.33)$$

If we write Eq. (19.32) as

$$J\frac{d\omega}{dt} + (B_f - A_2)\omega = A_1 V_t \qquad (19.34)$$

the solution of Eq. (19.34) is

$$\omega = \frac{A_1 V_t}{B_f - A_2}(1 - \epsilon^{-[(B_f - A_2)/J]\,t}) \qquad \text{radians/sec} \qquad (19.35)$$

Thus the speed increases at a decreasing rate until the magnetic torque is equal to the friction torque and the speed reaches the steady state.

When the motor is connected to a mechanical load, the speed-versus-torque characteristic of the mechanical load determines the steady-state speed and torque of the motor. The sum of all torques must equal zero, and in the steady state, the inertia torque is zero. Therefore, in the steady state, the magnetic torque must equal the friction torque plus the load torque. Suppose, for example, that the load torque is constant, independent of speed, and designated T_L. Then in the steady state

$$B_f \omega_s + T_L = A_1 V_t + A_2 \omega_s \qquad (19.36)$$

where $B_f \omega_s$ is the friction torque and the term on the right-hand side of the Eq. (19.36) is the electromagnetic torque. Solving Eq. (19.36) for steady-state speed gives

$$\omega_s = \frac{A_1 V_t - T_L}{B_f - A_2} \qquad \text{radians/sec} \qquad (19.37)$$

where, for constant V_t, the speed decreases as the load torque increases.

Graphical solutions of steady-state-speed-versus-torque problems are possible, just as graphical solutions for current-versus-voltage problems are possible. In particular, graphical solutions are advantageous when one or more of the torques is nonlinear (the torque is not a linear function of speed). Consider the example of a nonlinear load torque T_L shown in Fig. 19.6, connected to a d-c

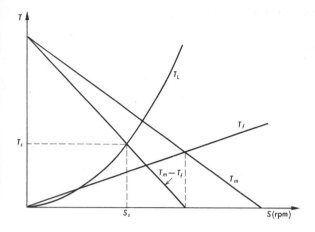

FIG. 19.6 *Graphical solution of torque-versus-speed problem when load torque T_L is nonlinear.*

shunt motor whose torque-versus-speed characteristic, designated T_m in Fig. 19.6, is linear just as in Fig. 19.5. The friction torque T_f is also linear, being proportional to speed. In order to find the torque available for driving the mechanical load T_L, the friction torque can be subtracted from the developed magnetic torque for various values of speed. This results in the curve marked $T_m - T_f$, which is the output torque of the motor. At the intersection of the load-torque curve T_L with $T_m - T_f$, the sum of the torques equals zero, and the steady-state speed S_s and steady-state torque T_s are found. This kind of graphical solution is useful for any nonlinearity as when coulomb friction, or friction torque proportional to the square of the speed, is present.

19.4 FIRST-ORDER DYNAMIC ANALYSIS

A first-order system is defined as a physical system describable by one or more first-order linear differential equations. One example was explained in Sec. 17.9, where a generator driven at constant speed was excited by a step voltage at the field windings. As another example of a first-order system, consider the d-c shunt motor with the armature current constrained always to be constant. From the circuit diagram in Fig. 19.7, the system of equations can be written

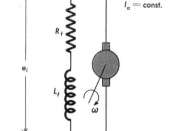

FIG. 19.7 *First-order system of a d-c shunt motor with I_a constant.*

$$L_f \frac{di_f}{dt} + R_f i_f = e_i \tag{19.38}$$

$$T_m = A i_f \tag{19.39}$$

$$J \frac{d\omega}{dt} + B_f \omega = T_m \tag{19.40}$$

Equation (19.38) is written by applying Kirchhoff's voltage law through the field windings; it is assumed that the inductance is constant. Equation (19.39) relates the field current to the magnetic torque developed by the rotor; A is a constant. Equation (19.40) sums the torques to zero; J is the moment of inertia of the rotor and mechanical load, and B_f is the friction constant. If the input voltage e_i is a step E, then, for $i_f = 0$ at $t = 0$,

$$i_f = \frac{E}{R_f} \left(1 - \epsilon^{-(R_f/L_f)t} \right) \tag{19.41}$$

Substituting Eqs. (19.39) and (19.41) into Eq. (19.40) results in

$$J \frac{d\omega}{dt} + B_f \omega = \frac{AE}{R_f} \left(1 - \epsilon^{-(R_f/L_f)t} \right) \tag{19.42}$$

the solution of which is

$$\omega = \frac{AE}{R_f B_f} + \frac{AEL_f}{R_f(B_f L_f - J)} \epsilon^{-(R_f/L_f)t}$$
$$- \frac{AE}{B_f R_f} \left(\frac{2B_f L_f - J}{B_f L_f - J} \right) \epsilon^{-(B_f/J)t} \tag{19.43}$$

All three of Eqs. (19.38), (19.39), and (19.40) are required to find the solution [Eq. (19.43)] by the classical methods of Chap. 5.

19.5 SECOND-ORDER DYNAMIC ANALYSIS

The natural response of a first-order system is an exponential function, and when two or more first-order linear differential equations are solved simultaneously as in Sec. 19.4, the solution may contain the sum of two or more exponential terms, as in Eq. (19.43). But sometimes the differential equations describing a linear system of machines is second-order, resulting in a natural response which can be a damped sinusoid or the sum of two exponential functions. It is not always possible to determine the order of the system without writing the differential equations. In this section we shall examine some examples of systems of machines that can be described by second-order differential equations.

Consider first two identical cumulative-compound d-c generators that are connected in parallel to deliver a load current i_L to resistance R_L, as shown schematically in Fig. 19.8. Machine 1 has a shunt field with inductance L_{f1} and field resistance R_{f1}.

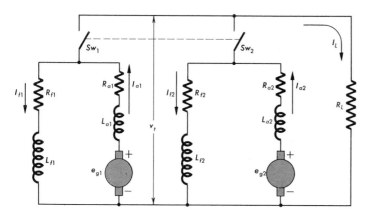

FIG. 19.8 *Two cumulative-compound d-c generators operating in parallel.*

The total inductance of the armature and series field is labeled L_{a1}, and the resistance of the armature and series field is R_{a1}. The generated voltage in the armature is e_{g1}. Machine 2 is a duplicate of machine 1; L_{f2} and R_{f2} are the inductance and resistance of the shunt field, and L_{a2} and R_{a2} are the inductance and resistance of the armature and series field in series. Likewise, the generated voltage in the armature of machine 2 is e_{g2}.

Two approximations can be made to simplify greatly our analytical process. First, assume that under load i_{f1} and i_{f2} are negligible compared with i_{a1} and i_{a2}, so that

$$i_L = i_{a1} + i_{a2} \tag{19.44}$$

As a second approximation, assume that the series-field flux is in the same direction as the shunt-field flux and that the induced voltage increases in a linear fashion as the armature current increases; this is one way of saying that the machine is operating on the linear portion of the magnetization curve. Then

$$e_g = E_g + K_a i_a \tag{19.45}$$

where E_g is the induced voltage when $i_a = 0$ and K_a is the slope of the e_g-versus-i_a curve. Now assume that both the switches are initially open, the machines are both running at rated speed, and at $t = 0$ the switches are both closed, connecting the two generators in parallel across R_L. Since the terminal voltage is common to both machines, two identical equations can be written, one for each machine. Then

$$v_t = e_{g1} - i_{a1} R_{a1} - L_{a1} \frac{di_{a1}}{dt} \tag{19.46}$$

$$v_t = e_{g2} - i_{a2} R_{a2} - L_{a2} \frac{di_{a2}}{dt} \tag{19.47}$$

and

$$v_t = R_L(i_{a1} + i_{a2}) \tag{19.48}$$

Substituting Eq. (19.45) and Eq. (19.48) into Eqs. (19.46) and (19.47) and rearranging the terms results in

$$L_a \frac{di_{a1}}{dt} + (R_a + R_L - K_a)i_{a1} + R_L i_{a2} = E_g \tag{19.49}$$

$$L_a \frac{di_{a2}}{dt} + (R_a + R_L - K_a)i_{a2} + R_L i_{a1} = E_g \tag{19.50}$$

where Eqs. (19.49) and (19.50) have been written recognizing that the two machines are identical and that $L_{a1} = L_{a2}$, $R_{a1} = R_{a2}$, $K_{a1} = K_{a2}$, and $e_{g1} = e_{g2}$. These two simultaneous differential equations [Eqs. (19.49) and (19.50)] with dependent variables i_{a1} and i_{a2} can be reduced to a single differential equation in i_{a1} or i_{a2} by solving Eq. (19.49) for i_{a2} and substituting i_{a2} into Eq. (19.50). Of course the alternative is to solve Eq. (19.50) for i_{a1} and substitute i_{a1} into Eq. (19.49). Performing the first indicated substitution, and letting $K_b = R_a + R_L - K_a$, we have

$$L_a^2 \frac{d^2 i_{a1}}{dt^2} + 2L_a K_b \frac{di_a}{dt} + (K_b^2 - R_L^2)i_a = E_g(K_b - R_L) \tag{19.51}$$

The solution of this second-order differential equation depends upon the roots of the characteristic equation

$$L_a^2 p^2 + 2L_a K_b p + (K_b^2 - R_L^2) = 0 \tag{19.52}$$

By using the quadratic equation, the two roots of Eq. (19.52) can be written

$$p = -\frac{K_b}{L_a} \pm \sqrt{\left(\frac{K_b}{L_a}\right)^2 - \frac{K_b^2 - R_L^2}{L_a^2}}$$

or

$$p_1 = -\frac{K_b}{L_a} - \frac{R_L}{L_a} \qquad p_2 = -\frac{K_b}{L_a} + \frac{R_L}{L_a} \tag{19.53}$$

Notice that p_1 and p_2, the roots of Eq. (19.52), are always real. If R_L is greater than K_b, p_2 is positive, and since $K_b = R_a + R_L - K_a$, if $R_a - K_a$ is greater than R_L, p_2 is positive. The general solution of Eq. (19.51) has the form

$$i_{a1} = A_1 \epsilon^{p_1 t} + A_2 \epsilon^{p_2 t} + A_3 \tag{19.54}$$

where A_1, A_2, and A_3 are constants. If either p_1 or p_2 is positive, as t increases without bound, i_{a1} increases also without bound.

This is an unstable situation which must be guarded against in the operation of cumulative-compound generators in parallel. The nature of p_1 and p_2, and not the coefficients A_1, A_2, and A_3, determines the instability of the generator. The constants A_1, A_2, and A_3 of Eq. (19.54) can be determined from the solution of Eq. (19.51). Assuming the initial conditions $i_{a1} = i_{a2} = I_0$ at $t = 0+$, then

$$A_1 = \frac{R_L + K_b}{2R_L}\left(I_0 - \frac{E_g}{R_L + K_b}\right)$$

$$A_2 = \frac{R_L - K_b}{2R_L}\left(I_0 - \frac{E_g}{R_L + K_b}\right) \qquad (19.55)$$

$$A_3 = \frac{E_g}{K_b + R_L}$$

where A_1 and A_2 are determined from the initial conditions. But when the switches are closed in Fig. 19.8, the current i_{a1} can increase without bound, not reaching a constant d-c value. If we solve for i_{a2}, we find that i_{a2} also takes the form of Eq. (19.54). From Eq. (19.48) it is obvious that the terminal voltage increases without bound when i_{a1} and i_{a2} both increase without bound. The circuit of Fig. 19.8 is not a practical one.

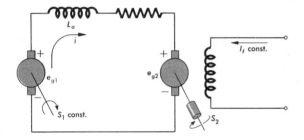

FIG. 19.9 *A constant-speed series generator drives a separately excited shunt motor.*

The series generator driving a separately excited shunt motor is another example of a second-order system of academic interest; it is shown in Fig. 19.9. The series generator is driven at constant speed by its prime mover. In Fig. 19.9, L_a represents the total inductance in the loop around which i flows, and includes the series-field inductance and the armature inductance of both machines. Similarly R_a represents the total series resistance in the same loop. The generator is excited only by its series field through which i flows; the shunt motor has constant field current I_f. The rotor of the shunt motor has a moment of inertia of J, and we assume that the friction is negligible. The system of equations describing the system can be written

$$L_a \frac{di}{dt} + R_a i = e_{g1} - e_{g2} \tag{19.56}$$

$$e_{g1} = K_1 i \tag{19.57}$$

$$e_{g2} = K_2 \omega_2 \tag{19.58}$$

and, neglecting friction,

$$J \frac{d\omega_2}{dt} = K_3 i \tag{19.59}$$

where K_1, K_2, and K_3 are constants. Notice that Eq. (19.57) assumes that the series generator is operating in the linear region on its magnetization curve. Solving Eq. (19.59) for i results in

$$i = \frac{J}{K_3} \frac{d\omega_2}{dt} \tag{19.60}$$

Substituting Eqs. (19.60), (19.57), and (19.58) into Eq. (19.56) gives

$$\frac{d^2\omega_2}{dt^2} + \frac{R_a - K_1}{L_a} \frac{d\omega_2}{dt} + \frac{K_2 K_3}{J L_a} \omega_2 = 0 \tag{19.61}$$

Comparing Eq. (19.61) with the standard form of the homogeneous second-order differential equation [Eq. (4.56)]

$$\frac{d^2x}{dt^2} + 2\zeta\omega_n \frac{dx}{dt} + \omega_n{}^2 x = 0$$

we recognize that if the damping ratio is zero, or $R_a - K_1/L_a = 0$, the speed of the shunt motor varies sinusoidally with a frequency of

$$\omega_n = \sqrt{\frac{K_2 K_3}{J L_a}} \tag{19.62}$$

For this special case, the solution of Eq. (19.61) is of the form

$$\omega_2 = A_1 \cos \omega_n t + A_2 \sin \omega_n t \tag{19.63}$$

where A_1 and A_2 are dependent upon initial conditions of the system and ω_n is given by Eq. (19.62).

If the damping ratio in Eq. (19.61) is made greater than zero, the speed as a function of time becomes a damped sinusoid or, for large damping ratios, the sum of two exponential terms with real exponents. In either case the speed approaches zero for large values of time. This example shows again that the system response is not always predictable from the system itself but can be found only from the differential equations of the system.

SUMMARY

Piecewise linear analysis permits the use of linear differential equations for the solution of dynamic problems in electric machines. Usually this means that the magnetic circuits are operated only on the linear portion of the magnetization curve below saturation, or that the magnetization curve is approximated by two or more straight lines.

As an example of using only the linear portion of the generator magnetization curve below saturation, the induced voltage in a shunt generator is given by Eq. (19.17),

$$E_g = m_1 I_f$$

and shown in Fig. 19.3. In the region above the knee of the saturation curve [Eq. (19.12)],

$$E_g = E_1 + m_2 I_f$$

where E_1 is the vertical-axis intercept (Fig. 19.3). Thus Eqs. (19.17) and (19.12) describe the magnetization curve in their appropriate regions.

Torque-versus-speed characteristics for a shunt motor are derived from the torque equation and the speed equation [Eqs. (18.64) and (18.76)]. The torque-versus-speed characteristics are linear if the flux density B is constant and are given by Eq. (19.23),

$$T_m = \frac{KB}{R_a} V_t - \frac{KK'B^2}{R_a} s$$

Then torque is a linear function of both V_t and s. Graphical solutions summing torques to zero are convenient for steady-state solutions just as Kirchhoff's voltage law can be applied to graphical solutions of resistive networks.

Systems of differential equations can be written for systems of machines. The order of the system is not always apparent until the equations are reduced to one dependent variable. First-order systems have solutions which are exponential; second-order solutions can be exponential or a sinusoid multiplied by an exponential. Whenever the exponential parts of the solutions increase with time, the system is said to be unstable.

PROBLEMS

19.1 The magnetization curve for an iron-core inductor of 100 turns can be plotted from the following data:

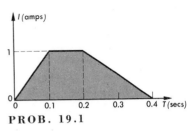

I, amp	0	0.2	0.4	0.6	0.8	1.0	1.2	1.4
ϕ, webers	0	0.0052	0.01	0.0117	0.0126	0.0133	0.014	0.0146

(*a*) A current is passed through the inductor winding of the shape shown in the figure. Using piecewise linear analysis, find the induced voltage across the inductor winding.

(*b*) A sinusoidal current of $1.5 \sin \omega t$ is applied to the inductor. Neglect the inductor resistance. Using piecewise linear analysis, find the induced voltage in the inductor as a function of time.

(*c*) A step voltage of 25 volts is applied to the inductor, whose internal resistance is 20 ohms. Using piecewise linear analysis, find the current in the inductor as a function of time.

19.2 The self-excited shunt generator of Fig. 19.3 is operating in the region B, where $E_1 = 100$ volts and $m_2 = 25$ volts/amp, and is driven at rated speed. Other machine constants are $R_a = 0.75$ ohm, $R_f = 110$ ohms, and $R_L = 5$ ohms.

(*a*) Find the steady-state terminal voltage at rated speed.

(*b*) If the speed is dropped to 0.8 rated value, what is the terminal voltage?

19.3 The torque equation of a certain d-c shunt motor when separately excited is represented approximately by $T = 1.15V_t - 0.130s$ newton-m, where V_t is terminal voltage in volts and s is speed in rpm. The motor is connected to a d-c source of 230 volts, and it drives a constant load torque (including its own windage and friction) of 22.5 newton-m. Find the power output of the motor in watts and in horsepower.

19.4 The motor of Prob. 19.3 drives a nonlinear torque (including its own windage and friction) which can be represented by $T_L = 0.5 \times 10^{-3}s^2$ newton-m, where s is in rpm. Find the power output of the motor in watts and in horsepower.

19.5 A tachometer generator is a d-c generator with constant flux whose generated voltage is directly proportional to speed. A certain tachometer generator is calibrated at 1,800 rpm; its generated voltage is 125 volts at that speed. The armature resistance is 100 ohms. A 15,000-ohm 150-volt d-c voltmeter measures 75 volts at a certain speed. What is the speed?

Problems **519**

19.6 The torque-versus-speed curve over the normal operating range of a certain three-phase a-c induction motor can be plotted from the following data:

Speed, rpm	1,100	1,120	1,140	1,160	1,180	1,200	1,220
Torque, newton-m	155	123	92	61	30	0	−30

(a) Find an approximate linear equation of torque as a function of speed over the normal operating range.

(b) Find an approximate linear equation of speed as a function of torque over the normal operating range.

(c) Approximately what horsepower rating does this motor have?

19.7 The load driven by the induction motor of Prob. 19.6 has a nonlinear torque-versus-speed characteristic curve which can be represented approximately by the piecewise linear expressions $T_L = 0.095s$ newton-m, for $0 \leq s \leq 1,150$, and $T_L = -633 + 0.55s$ newton-m, $1,150 < s$, where s is in rpm.

(a) Find the steady-state speed of the induction motor in rpm.

(b) Find the power output in watts and in horsepower.

19.8 The induction motor of Prob. 19.6 simultaneously drives three different mechanical loads whose steady-state torque-versus-speed characteristics are: (a) $T_{L1} = 24.0$ newton-m, (b) $T_{L2} = 17.5 + 0.045s$ newton-m, and (c) $T_{L3} = 2.5 \times 10^{-5}s^2$ newton-m, where s is in rpm. Graphically find the steady-state speed of the induction motor and calculate its power output.

19.9 A nonlinear spring is described by a displacement-versus-force relationship which can be plotted from the following data:

Displacement, m	0	0.045	0.089	0.132	0.172	0.192
Force, newtons	0	50	100	150	200	250

Displacement, m	0.210	0.227	0.243	0.258	0.273
Force, newtons	300	350	400	450	500

Find the displacement-versus-force equations, using piecewise linear approximations.

19.10 A force of $f = 38.5 + 73.5d + 1,340d^2$ newtons (d is displacement in meters) is applied to the spring of Prob. 19.9. Find the displacement of the spring.

19.11 In Sec. 19.5 two cumulative-compound d-c generators operating in parallel were analyzed, and it was found that under certain conditions their terminal voltage can increase without bound as t increases. Find the conditions for stable operation of these two parallel generators, and derive an equation for the steady-state terminal voltage.

19.12 At rated speed and no load the terminal-voltage-versus-field-current curve for a d-c shunt generator is obtained from the following data:

V_t, volts	2.0	40.2	80.0	118.0	154.2	174.2	192.0	208.0	223.0
I_f, amp	0	0.2	0.4	0.6	0.8	1.0	1.2	1.4	1.6

The armature resistance is 0.28 ohm, and the armature inductance is 0.068 henry. The generator is operating separately excited at rated speed and with no load (R_L is infinite). The field current is set at $I_f = 0.75$ amp. At $t = 0$ a load is suddenly applied; the load resistor is $R_L = 3.5$ ohms. Find the armature current i_a as a function of time.

19.13 Repeat Prob. 19.12, but assume that I_f is maintained at 1.5 amp.

19.14 Repeat Prob. 19.12, but assume that the generator is self-excited and that I_f is initially 1.25 amp.

20

AUTOMATIC CONTROL SYSTEMS

20.1 INTRODUCTION

Systems which automatically regulate or control themselves are common in modern technology. Historically, one of the first self-regulators was the flyball governor invented by James Watt to control the speed of his steam engines. When the engine speed increased above the desired speed, two heavy weights, or flyballs, rotating with the shaft of the engine were forced outward from the shaft by the centrifugal force, their radial movement being used to throttle the steam and slow the engine down. When the engine slowed down to a speed below the desired speed, the flyballs fell inward toward the shaft, opening the throttle and thus increasing the speed of the engine. Since the time of Watt's invention of the flyball governor in 1788, machines, devices, systems, and processes have been made to govern and control themselves more and more. The principles of automatic control are becoming better understood, and the application of these principles is constantly being extended. The automatic factory is being realized more extensively every day.

Automatic control relies upon feedback, discussed to some extent in Chap. 13. The controlled variable is the output of the feedback system shown in Fig. 13.1 and reproduced again in Fig. 20.1. The variable x_3, or some function of x_3, the feedback signal

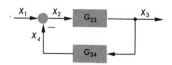

FIG. 20.1 *Block diagram of the feedback system.*

x_4, is fed back through the summing point and compared with the input variable of the system, x_1. The output of the summing point, x_2, sometimes referred to as the "error signal," tends to drive the output variable toward its desired value. If no error is present, the feedback variable x_4 corresponds exactly to the input variable x_1. Automatic control systems rely upon feedback to determine when the output variable corresponds to the input variable in the desired manner.

As an example of an automatic control system, consider the heating system of a room with thermostatic control. The desired temperature, the input variable x_1, is fed into the system by setting the thermostat dial to the desired temperature. The output variable x_3 is the actual temperature of the room as detected by the thermostat. When the room temperature drops appreciably below the temperature to which the thermostat is set, the error (the difference between x_1 and x_3) becomes sufficient to turn on the source of heat in order to raise the room temperature x_3. When the error x_1-x_3 becomes small again, the heat source is turned off; heat slowly dissipates from the room, and the room temperature drops until the error is large enough to turn the heat source on again. This is an example of an on-off control device. Continuous feedback or closed-loop automatic control is illustrated by the example of temperature control when the heat source is always on, supplying heat at a rate proportional to the error x_1-x_3. An open-loop heating system is one in which the heat source supplies heat at a preset rate irrespective of the temperature. In this case, the person often supplies the feedback path himself; he turns on more heat if the room becomes cold, and he turns the heat down when it becomes too hot.

A servomechanism is a feedback control system in which one or more of the variables is a mechanical quantity. Servomechanisms are usually characterized by high power gain, and often the output variable is either a mechanical position, velocity, or acceleration. An example of a servomechanism is the positional servo shown in Fig. 20.2, where the shaft position θ_1 of the potentiometer R_1 controls the shaft position θ_2 of the motor. Only a small torque is required to turn the shaft of R_1, but a large electromagnetic torque is developed by the motor to position the motor shaft through the angle θ_2. The operation of this servo can be followed qualitatively in a step-by-step fashion. A shaft position θ_1 is fed into the system, positioning the wiper arm of potentiometer R_1. The wiper arm of R_1 picks off the voltage e_1, which is

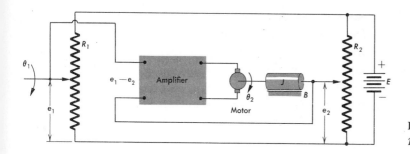

FIG. 20.2 *A servomechanism for positioning θ_2 by remote control.*

a linear function of θ_1. The shaft of potentiometer R_2 is connected to the motor shaft, and the voltage e_2, a linear function of θ_2, is picked off the potentiometer by its wiper arm. The amplifier input is e_1-e_2, and this difference voltage is amplified and used to drive the armature of the d-c motor whose field is constant and separately excited. The motor torque is in the direction which tends to move the wiper arm of potentiometer R_2 in the direction that makes e_2 approach e_1; thus e_1-e_2 approaches zero, and $\theta_1-\theta_2$ also approaches zero. The moment of inertia J and the viscous friction of friction constant B provide torques acting on the motor shaft in addition to the electromagnetic torque of the rotor. This kind of positioning system can be used to position the rudder of a ship by remote control from the wheelhouse, to position a control shaft in an atomic reactor from a remote-control console, or to transmit information in the form of dial readings from one position to another.

A regulator is a feedback system which tends to maintain one of the system variables constant. The temperature-control example previously discussed is an example of a temperature regulator whose task is to maintain the temperature of a room constant even though the rate of heat dissipation from the room may vary. A speed regulator, such as Watt's steam-engine governor, is a feedback device which tends to maintain constant shaft speed even though the load torque of the engine may vary. These are only a few examples of automatic regulation; it is possible to devise automatic regulators for many physical variables such as current, torque, power, velocity, acceleration, concentration of a solution, heat dissipation, etc.

A voltage regulator for a d-c shunt generator is shown in Fig. 20.3a as an example of automatic regulation. The amplifier shown in Fig. 20.3a need not be electronic; indeed it is sometimes possible to design the regulator without using an amplifier at all. But the one shown is excited by the difference voltage E_1-e_6, where E_1 is

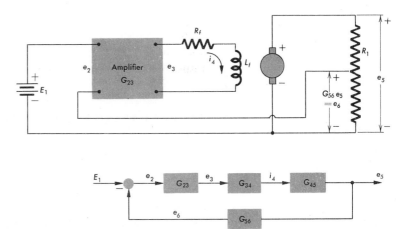

FIG. 20.3 *Voltage-regulator schematic and block diagram for a d-c shunt
generator.*

the constant input voltage used as a voltage standard and e_6 is
the feedback voltage, a function of the output voltage e_5. The
difference voltage e_2 undergoes a gain of G_{23} in the amplifier, and
therefore $e_3 = G_{23}e_2$. The voltage e_3 excites the shunt field of the
generator whose armature generator voltage is proportional to the
field current if the machine operates in the linear portion of the
magnetization curve. The output voltage e_5 is here assumed to
be equal to the generated voltage, and the generator is assumed
to be driven at a constant speed by its prime mover. The effect
of the armature resistance of the generator has been neglected.

A qualitative explanation of how the regulator operates can
be obtained by assuming that the output voltage e_5 suddenly
drops for some reason. The feedback voltage e_6, a fraction of e_5,
also drops. The difference voltage $e_2 = E_1 - e_6$ increases, and e_2
is amplified and then applied to the RL circuit of the shunt field,
tending to increase the field current. An increased generated
voltage results from the increased field current, tending to offset
the original drop in terminal voltage.

The study of feedback control systems is an extensive one,
and several methods of analysis and synthesis are thoroughly discussed in the literature. All these methods rely upon the differential equation analysis. The system of differential equations
describing the physical system is written in operational form by
using the Laplace transformation, and the number of variables is
reduced until the output variable and the input variable are the
only dependent variables in the resulting equation. The natural
response of the system is of major importance because it determines
the relative stability of the system; steady-state response to a step

input or to a sinusoidal input is ordinarily used to study steady-state response. Since sinusoidal response was discussed in Chap. 13, in this chapter the discussion is restricted to the natural response and to the steady-state response to a step input.

20.2 CLASSICAL SOLUTIONS

Formulation of the system equations is always an important step in system analysis and synthesis. As an example to show the formulation of the differential equations, consider the voltage regulator described in the preceding section. Taking into account the effect of armature resistance and considering also the armature current as one of the system variables, the system is shown again in Fig. 20.4. Assume that the gain of the amplifier is constant and

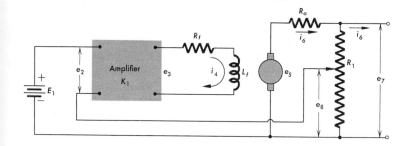

FIG. 20.4 *Voltage regulator for a d-c shunt generator. Armature resistance R_a is included.*

equal to K_1 and that the generated voltage of the rotor is proportional to the field current, with a constant of proportionality of K_2. Let K_3 be the fraction of the output voltage e_7 fed back to the summing point; then K_3 is determined by the setting of potentiometer R_1, and R_1 is assumed to be large so that it draws negligible current. The system of equations can be written

$$E_1 - e_8 = e_2$$

$$e_3 = K_1 e_2$$

$$e_3 = L_f \frac{di_4}{dt} + R_f i_4 \qquad (20.1)$$

$$e_5 = K_2 i_4$$

$$e_7 = e_5 - i_6 R_a$$

$$e_8 = K_3 e_7$$

If the input voltage E_1 is considered as a variable, there are eight dependent variables in Eq. (20.1). Systematically eliminating the variables of Eq. (20.1) until only E_1, i_6, and e_7 remain results in the equation

$$L_f \frac{de_7}{dt} + (R_f + K_1 K_2 K_3)e_7$$

$$= -L_f R_a \frac{di_6}{dt} + R_f R_a i_6 - K_1 K_2 E_1 \quad (20.2)$$

Since the function of the regulator is to maintain a constant output voltage e_7, independent of load current i_6, and directly proportional to the reference voltage E_1, both i_6 and E_1 can be considered input variables with e_7 the output variable. Equation (20.1) can be represented directly by a block diagram similar to Fig. 20.3, where E_1 and i_6 are inputs and e_7 is the output.

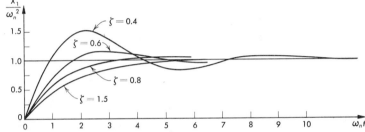

FIG. 20.5 *Response of a second-order system to a unit step, with damping ratio ζ as the parameter.*

The complete solution of Eq. (20.2) requires that the input quantities i_6 and E_1 be known functions of time. The reference voltage E_1 is usually set at a constant value, and i_6 varies at random according to the generator load. Much can be learned about the system response by finding the response of the system to a step of current i_6, with E_1 maintained constant, and by finding the response to a step of reference voltage E_1 with $i_6 = 0$. Letting $i_6 = 0$, Eq. (20.2) becomes

$$L_f \frac{de_7}{dt} + (R_f + K_1 K_2 K_3)e_7 = K_1 K_2 E_1 \qquad (20.3)$$

and if $e_7 = 0$ at $t \leq 0$, the solution of Eq. (20.3) is

$$e_7 = \frac{K_1 K_2 E_1}{R_f + K_1 K_2 K_3} (1 - \epsilon^{-(R_f + K_1 K_2 K_3)t/L_f}) \qquad (20.4)$$

Now K_1 and K_2 are numerically very much greater than unity, and $K_1 K_2 K_3 \gg R_f$. The output voltage can now be written approximately as

$$e_7 = \frac{E_1}{K_3} (1 - \epsilon^{-K_1 K_2 K_3 t/L_f}) \qquad (20.5)$$

Notice in Eq. (20.5) that K_3 appears both in the denominator and in the exponent. K_3 is the fraction of the output voltage that is fed back to the summing point; it is less than unity. If E_1 is the magnitude of the input-voltage step, a constant, then making K_3 approach unity makes the steady-state output voltage approach the minimum value of E_1, but the time constant is also kept short, being $L_f/K_1 K_2 K_3$. This is typical of feedback systems; by minimizing the time constant or response time, the magnitude of the steady-state response is also minimized.

Next, assume that E_1 is constant and that i_6 is a step of magnitude $-I_6$. Then Eq. (20.2) can be written

$$L_f \frac{de_7}{dt} + (R_f + K_1 K_2 K_3) e_7 = R_f R_a I_6 + K_1 K_2 E_1 \qquad (20.6)$$

In the steady state before $t = 0$ when the step of current i_6 occurs, e_7 is constant, and

$$e_7 = \frac{K_1 K_2 E_1}{R_f + K_1 K_2 K_3} \qquad t \leq 0 \qquad (20.7)$$

After $t = 0$ when the step of i_6 occurs, the natural response is of the form

$$e_{7n} = A \epsilon^{-(R_f + K_1 K_2 K_3) t / L_f} \qquad (20.8)$$

and when t is very much greater than zero, the final steady-state terminal voltage is

$$e_{7s} = \frac{R_f R_a I_6 + K_1 K_2 E_1}{R_f + K_1 K_2 K_3} \qquad (20.9)$$

Then the terminal voltage e_7 as a function of time after $t = 0$ can be written

$$e_7 = A \epsilon^{(R_f + K_1 K_2 K_3) t / L_f} + \frac{R_f R_a I_6 + K_1 K_2 E_1}{R_f + K_1 K_2 K_3} \qquad (20.10)$$

where A is the arbitrary constant.

In order to evaluate the arbitrary constant A in Eq. (20.10), consider the initial voltage expressed by Eq. (20.7). Substituting Eq. (20.7) and $t = 0$ into Eq. (20.10) and solving for A results in

$$A = - \frac{R_f R_a I_6}{R_f + K_1 K_2 K_3}$$

and the complete solution of Eq. (20.2) for the step of load current i_6 can be written

$$e_7 = \frac{R_f R_a I_6}{R_f + K_1 K_2 K_3} (1 - \epsilon^{-(R_f + K_1 K_2 K_3) t/L_f}) + \frac{K_1 K_2 E_1}{R_f + K_1 K_2 K_3}$$

$$(20.11)$$

Notice again that, if the $K_1 K_2$ product is very large so that $K_1 K_2 E_1 \gg R_f R_a I_6$, the regulation is good and the step change of load current i_6 has little effect on the controlled variable e_7. Thus the regulator tends to hold a terminal voltage that is a function of the voltage reference E_1 but is independent of changes in load current.

The exponential term in Eq. (20.5) and Eq. (20.11) also tells about the stability of the circuit. If the product $K_1 K_2 K_3$ is positive, the exponential term decreases with time, approaching zero as an asymptote. (L_f and R_f are inherently positive.) But if the product $K_1 K_2 K_3$ is negative, which occurs when either K_1 or K_2 is negative, the exponential term increases in magnitude as time increases, approaching infinity, and never reaching a steady-state value. When this occurs, the system is said to be unstable. Obviously a regulator, or any physical system, to be useful cannot have its output always increasing at an increasing rate. Indeed, if the output increases at an increasing rate, sooner or later one or more components of the system is driven beyond its region of linear operation and saturation occurs.

Equation (20.2) is a first-order differential equation with three dependent variables, e_7, i_6, and E_1. In general, the differential equation of any feedback system, or any physical system with only one input quantity and one output quantity, can be expressed in the form

$$\frac{d^n x_3}{dt^n} + a_{n-1} \frac{d^{n-1} x_3}{dt^{n-1}} + \cdots + a_1 \frac{dx_3}{dt} + a_0 x_3$$

$$= b_m \frac{d^m x_1}{dt^m} + b_{m-1} \frac{d^{m-1} x_1}{dt^{m-1}} + \cdots + b_1 \frac{dx_1}{dt} + b_0 x_1 \quad (20.12)$$

where x_1 and x_3 are the input and the output variables, respectively, of Fig. 20.1. Equation (20.12) can be verified by writing the system of differential equations for the physical system and then combining the equations in such a way as to eliminate all but the output and input variables. Of course, some of the coefficients of Eq. (20.12) are zero. The solution of Eq. (20.12) can be obtained by ascertaining the form of the input variable x_1, substituting x_1 into Eq. (20.12), and solving for the output variable

x_3. Since Eq. (20.12) may be very complex, with many terms and high-order derivatives, the solution is seldom simple.

While the response of a physical system to an arbitrary exciting function may be difficult to obtain, the response to a particular exciting function such as a step function may be relatively easy to find. Fortunately, system response to a step input can be extremely informative, giving information about system stability, speed of response, and d-c steady-state response. This is the general procedure we now pursue.

To find the natural response of the equation of the form of Eq. (20.12), we write the homogeneous equation

$$\frac{d^n x_3}{dt^n} + a_{n-1} \frac{d^{n-1} x_3}{dt^{n-1}} + \cdots + a_1 \frac{dx_3}{dt} + a_0 x_3 = 0 \tag{20.13}$$

Recognizing that the solution of Eq. (20.13) must be of the form

$$x_3 = X_3 \epsilon^{pt} \tag{20.14}$$

we substitute Eq. (20.14) into (20.13) and divide out the exponential term, leaving

$$(p^n + a_{n-1} p^{n-1} + \cdots + a_1 p + a_0) X_3 = 0 \tag{20.15}$$

The roots of the nth-order algebraic equation [Eq. (20.15)] must now be found. If $n = 1$ or $n = 2$, the matter is simple, but for $n = 3$ or greater, finding the root becomes more complicated.

20.3 FINDING THE ROOTS OF A POLYNOMIAL

Consider the special case when $n = 3$ in Eq. (20.15). Since X is not 0, the polynomial in the parentheses of Eq. (20.15) must equal zero, or

$$p^3 + a_2 p^2 + a_1 p + a_0 = 0 \tag{20.16}$$

which can be factored into the form

$$(p + z_1)(p + z_2)(p + z_3) = 0 \tag{20.17}$$

where $-z_1$, $-z_2$, and $-z_3$ are the roots or zeros of Eq. (20.16). Now z_1, z_2, and z_3 can be either real or complex; but since complex roots occur only in conjugate pairs, all three roots cannot be complex together. Either the roots of Eq. (20.16) can be all real or one can be real and two can be complex conjugates. If one real root can be found and factored out, the remaining quadratic can be solved by the quadratic equation and all three roots are then known.

Successive long division can be used to find one real root in the cubic equation. Suppose that Eq. (20.13) can be written

$$\frac{d^3x_3}{dt^3} + 8\frac{d^2x_3}{dt^2} + 17\frac{dx_3}{dt} + 10x_3 = 0 \qquad (20.18)$$

The characteristic equation of Eq. (20.12) is

$$p^3 + 8p^2 + 17p + 10 = 0 \qquad (20.19)$$

By successive long division, we can try to find a factor which, when divided out, leaves no remainder. First we try the factor $p + 4$.

$$
\begin{array}{r}
p^2 + 4p + 1 \\
p + 4\,\overline{\smash{\big)}\,p^3 + 8p^2 + 17p + 10} \\
\underline{p^3 + 4p^2} \\
4p^2 + 17p \\
\underline{4p^2 + 16p} \\
p + 10 \\
\underline{p + 4} \\
+ 6 \text{ remainder}
\end{array}
$$

Since there is the remainder of 6, we know that $p + 4$ is not a factor of Eq. (20.13). Next we try $p + 3$.

$$
\begin{array}{r}
p^2 + 5p + 2 \\
p + 3\,\overline{\smash{\big)}\,p^3 + 8p^2 + 17p + 10} \\
\underline{p^3 + 3p^2} \\
5p^2 + 17p \\
\underline{5p^2 + 15p} \\
2p + 10 \\
\underline{2p + 6} \\
+ 4 \text{ remainder}
\end{array}
$$

The remainder of $+4$ is less than the remainder of $+6$; so next we try $p + 2$ as a factor.

$$
\begin{array}{r}
p^2 + 6p + 5 \\
p + 2\,\overline{\smash{\big)}\,p^3 + 8p^2 + 17p + 10} \\
\underline{p^3 + 2p^2} \\
6p^2 + 17p \\
\underline{6p^2 + 12p} \\
5p + 10 \\
\underline{5p + 10} \\
0 \text{ remainder}
\end{array}
$$

There is no remainder; so $p + 2$ is a factor and $p = -2$ is a root or zero of Eq. (20.19). The other two roots are obtained from the quadratic equation

$$p^2 + 6p + 5 = 0 \tag{20.20}$$

They are

$$p = -3 \pm \sqrt{9 - 5} = -1, -5 \tag{20.21}$$

and Eq. (20.13) can be written in factored form

$$(p + 2)(p + 1)(p + 5) = 0 \tag{20.22}$$

Since the natural response is of the form given by Eq. (20.14) and the three roots of the characteristic equation are now known, the natural response of the system is

$$x_{3n} = A_1 \epsilon^{-2t} + A_2 \epsilon^{-t} + A_3 \epsilon^{-5t} \tag{20.23}$$

where A_1, A_2, and A_3 are arbitrary constants. The system whose homogeneous equation is given by Eq. (20.18) is a stable one, since the natural response approaches 0 as time becomes large. If either of the exponential terms in Eq. (20.17) has a positive exponent, the system would be considered unstable.

Synthetic division can be used to good advantage to locate the real roots of third-order equations. Synthetic division is a shorthand way of accomplishing what long division accomplishes. To find the real roots of Eq. (20.13) by synthetic division, we write the coefficients only, and as a trial divisor we first use the trial factor $x + 4$.

$$
\begin{array}{rrrr|r}
1 & 8 & 17 & 10 & \underline{4} \\
 & 4 & 16 & 4 & \\
\hline
1 & 4 & 1 & 6 & \text{remainder}
\end{array}
$$

With the remainder of $+6$, we next try the trial factor $x + 3$.

$$
\begin{array}{rrrr|r}
1 & 8 & 17 & 10 & \underline{3} \\
 & 3 & 15 & 6 & \\
\hline
1 & 5 & 2 & 4 & \text{remainder}
\end{array}
$$

The remainder of 4 shows that we are probably approaching a real root; so we try the factor $x + 2$.

$$
\begin{array}{rrrr|r}
1 & 8 & 17 & 10 & \underline{2} \\
 & 2 & 12 & 10 & \\
\hline
1 & 6 & 5 & 0 & \text{remainder}
\end{array}
$$

With zero remainder we know that $x + 2$ is a true factor, and thus Eq. (20.19) can be written

$$(x + 2)(x^2 + 6x + 5) = 0 \qquad (20.24)$$

The quadratic equation is used to find the roots of the quadratic factor in Eq. (20.24).

It is usually necessary to try several trial factors before the true factor of the third-order equation is found, especially since, in practice, the factors invariably are not integers as they are in the above example. Fourth-order equations have two pairs of complex conjugate roots, two real roots and two complex conjugate roots, or four real roots. Ordinary synthetic division is useful to find the real roots or factors; quadratic factors can be found by Lin's method (see Further Reading).

Example 20.1

Given the following fourth-order polynomial; find the factors.

$$p^4 + 5.7p^3 + 15.4p^2 + 24.5p + 15 = 0 \qquad (20.25)$$

If a real root exists, it is less than -5.7. We try -4.

1	5.7	15.4	24.5	15	$\underline{\lfloor 4}$
	4	6.8	34.4	-39.6	
1	1.7	8.6	-9.9	54.6 remainder	

The remainder is $+54.6$; next try the root -3.

1	5.7	15.4	24.5	15	$\underline{\lfloor 3}$
	3	8.1	21.9	7.8	
1	2.7	7.3	2.6	7.2 remainder	

The remainder is now $+7.2$; try -2.5 as a root.

1	5.7	15.4	24.5	15	$\underline{\lfloor 2.5}$
	2.5	8.0	18.5	15	
1	3.2	7.4	6.0	0 remainder	

The remainder is zero; then -2.5 is a root, and $p + 2.5$ is a factor. The polynomial can now be written,

$$(p + 2.5)(p^3 + 3.2p^2 + 7.4p + 6) \qquad (20.26)$$

Now we look for another real root in the third-order polynomial in Eq. (20.26).

$$
\begin{array}{llll}
1 & 3.2 & 7.4 & 6 \quad \underline{|2}\\
 & 2.0 & 2.4 & 10 \\
\hline
1 & 1.2 & 5.0 & -4 \text{ remainder}
\end{array}
$$

$$
\begin{array}{llll}
1 & 3.2 & 7.4 & 6 \quad \underline{|1}\\
 & 1 & 2.2 & 5.2 \\
\hline
1 & 2.2 & 5.2 & 0.8 \text{ remainder}
\end{array}
$$

In the last two trials the remainder has changed sign, indicating that the root has been bracketed; it is between -2 and -1 and is probably closer to -1 than to -2.

$$
\begin{array}{llll}
1 & 3.2 & 7.4 & 6 \quad \underline{|1.2}\\
 & 1.2 & 2.4 & 6 \\
\hline
1 & 2.0 & 5.0 & 0 \text{ remainder}
\end{array}
$$

Then -1.2 is a root, and $p + 1.2$ is a factor. The polynomial of Eq. (20.25) can now be written

$$(p + 2.5)(p + 1.2)(p^2 + 2p + 5) = 0 \tag{20.27}$$

Using the quadratic equation on the quadratic factor in Eq. (20.27) gives

$$p = -1 + \sqrt{1 - 5} = -1 \pm j2$$

and Eq. (20.25) can be written in factored form

$$(p + 2.5)(p + 1.2)(p + 1 + j2)(p + 1 - j2) = 0 \tag{20.28}$$

The natural response of a third-order differential equation takes two different forms, depending upon the nature of the root of the characteristic equation. If all three roots are real, then

$$x_{3n} = A_1 \epsilon^{p_1 t} + A_2 \epsilon^{p_2 t} + A_3 \epsilon^{p_3 t} \tag{20.29}$$

where A_1, A_2, and A_3 are the arbitrary constants depending upon the initial conditions and p_1, p_2, and p_3 are the real roots of the characteristic equation. If two of the roots are complex, then the time response can be expressed in the same form as Eq. (20.29) with complex exponents and then resolved into

$$x_{3n} = A_1 \epsilon^{p_1 t} + B_1 \epsilon^{-\omega_n \zeta t} \sin (\omega_n \sqrt{1 - \zeta^2} + \theta) \tag{20.30}$$

where A_1, B_1, and θ are the arbitrary constants which depend upon the initial conditions and p_1 is the one real root of the characteristic conceivable input variable x_1. A transfer-function concept is convenient to use, and it will now be developed for use when the input or exciting function x_1 is an exponential function of time.

The natural response of a linear system can always be expressed as the sum of exponential functions of the form of Eq. (20.14). Then [Eq. (20.14)]

$$x_3 = X_3 \epsilon^{pt}$$

is a solution of the homogeneous equation (20.13)

$$\frac{d^n x_3}{dt^n} + a_{n-1} \frac{d^{n-1} x_3}{dt^{n-1}} + \cdots + a_1 \frac{dx_3}{dt} + a_0 x_3 = 0$$

where p can be real, imaginary, or complex. The natural response is found by substituting Eq. (20.14) into Eq. (20.13) and finding the values of p which satisfy the homogeneous equation (20.13).

But now we seek to determine the response of the system when excited by the input variable x_1. The steady-state response [Eq. (20.12)] of

$$\frac{d^n x_3}{dt^n} + a_{n-1} \frac{d^{n-1} x_3}{dt^{n-1}} + \cdots + a_1 \frac{dx_3}{dt} + a_0 x_3$$

$$= b_m \frac{d^m x_1}{dt^m} + b_{m-1} \frac{d^{m-1} x_1}{dt^{m-1}} + \cdots + b_1 \frac{dx_1}{dt} + b_0 x_1$$

is not easy to determine for any arbitrary input quantity x_1. But if the exciting function x_1 is constrained to be the exponential function

$$x_1 = X_1 \epsilon^{pt} \tag{20.32}$$

then the system steady-state response x_3 must be [Eq. (20.14)]

$$x_3 = X_3 \epsilon^{pt}$$

in order to satisfy Eq. (20.12). Substituting Eqs. (20.14) and (20.32) into Eq. (20.12) and dividing out ϵ^{pt} results in

$$p^n X_3 + a_{n-1} p^{n-1} X_3 + \cdots + a_1 p X_3 + a_0 X_3$$

$$= b_m p^m X_1 + b_{m-1} p^{m-1} X_1 + \cdots + b_1 p X_1 + b_0 X_1 \tag{20.33}$$

Equation (20.33) is an *algebraic* equation, obtained by substituting exponential functions [Eqs. (20.14) and (20.32)] into the differential equation [Eq. (20.12)]. Thus, by assuming an exponential exciting function, the differential equation of the system can be converted to an algebraic equation.

equation. Thus the natural response of the third-order system can be expressed either as the sum of the three exponential terms or as the sum of one exponential term and a damped sinusoid.

The natural response of the fourth-order equation can also be found from the roots of the characteristic equation. If the roots are all real, the natural response is the sum of four exponential terms. If two roots are real and two are complex, the response is the sum of two exponential terms and a damped sinusoid. If the roots consist of two pairs of complex conjugates, the natural response is the sum of two damped sinusoids. Since complex roots always occur in conjugate pairs, equations of odd order (third, fifth, etc.) always contain at least one real root.

The steady-state response of a system to a step input can be found from the general equations given in Eq. (20.12) by letting t become large when the derivative terms approach zero. Thus, solving Eq. (20.12) for x_3 when all derivative terms are 0 gives the steady-state response

$$x_{3s} = \frac{b_0}{a_0} X_1 \tag{20.31}$$

where X_1 is the magnitude of the step exciting function. When X_1 is a step function, all derivative terms on the right-hand side of Eq. (20.12) go to 0 for all finite values of time. The steady-state solution, combined with the natural response, contains considerable information about the behavior of the system. The synthesis of control systems involves adjustment of the system natural response and of the system steady-state response to the step input, in order to obtain the over-all desired response.

20.4 TRANSFER FUNCTIONS

The transfer-function concept for the sinusoidal steady state has been used in Chap. 13 to find the steady-state response when the exciting function is a sinusoid. There are some weaknesses to the frequency-response analysis used in Chap. 13, however. Though it is true that a nonsinusoidal periodic function can be represented by Fourier series of sinusoidal terms, and therefore system response to nonsinusoidal periodic excitation can be found by the frequency-response technique, there is an advantage in breaking away from the sinusoidal analysis altogether. The differential equation of th form of Eq. (20.12) is a general equation which is valid for a

X_3 and X_1 can be factored out from Eq. (20.33), which can be written

$$\frac{X_3}{X_1} = \frac{b_m p^m + b_m p^{m-1} + \cdots + b_1 p + b_0}{p^n + a_{n-1} p^{n-1} + \cdots + a_1 p + a_0} \qquad (20.34)$$

Equation (20.34) is the transfer function G_{13} and as such has significance when written

$$X_3 = \frac{b_m p^m + b_{m-1} p^{m-1} + \cdots + b_1 p + b_0}{p^n + a_{n-1} p^{n-1} + \cdots + a_1 p + a_0} X_1 \qquad (20.35)$$

where X_1, operated on by the transfer function of Eq. (20.35), gives the output X_3.

The transfer function was obtained by assuming that the output variable X_3 is the same form as the input variable X_1, namely, an exponential function. It remains now to show how the output variable can be obtained by means of the transfer function and the input variable in Eq. (20.35).

We have seen how a characteristic equation such as Eq. (20.16) can be factored, each root being the exponent of an exponential function in the natural response. The denominator of Eq. (20.35) is the characteristic equation of the system; its roots determine the exponents or time constants of the exponential terms in the natural response. Furthermore, the numerator of Eq. (20.35) is also a polynomial of the same form as the denominator, which can also be factored. Then Eq. (20.35) can be written in the form

$$X_3 = \frac{K(p + z_1)(p + z_2) \cdots (p + z_m)}{(p + p_1)(p + p_2) \cdots (p + p_n)} X_1 \qquad (20.36)$$

where $K = b_m$, the roots of the numerator of Eq. (20.35) are represented by $-z_1$, $-z_2$, etc., and the roots of the denominator of Eq. (20.36) are represented by $-p_1, -p_2$, etc. The roots of the numerator of Eq. (20.35), $-z_1, -z_2$, etc., are called "zeros," since, when they are substituted for p into Eq. (20.36), X_3 becomes zero. The roots of the denominator of Eq. (20.35), $-p_1, -p_2$, etc., are known as "poles," and when one of the denominator roots is substituted for p into Eq. (20.36), X_3 becomes infinite. These poles and zeros are the critical values of the transfer function, and the pole-zero locations in the complex plane are important graphical aids to system analysis and synthesis. From the location of the poles of the transfer function, the natural response can be determined, since the poles of the transfer function are the roots of the characteristic equation. When the exciting function X_1 is known and the zeros of the transfer function are also known, the magnitude of the natural response and the steady-state response can be determined.

The natural response of the system described by the transfer function [Eq. (20.34)] can be written

$$x_{3n} = A_1 \epsilon^{p_1 t} + A_2 \epsilon^{p_2 t} + \cdots + A_n \epsilon^{p_n t} \qquad (20.37)$$

where A_1, A_2, etc., are arbitrary constants and p_1, p_2, etc., are the poles of the transfer function [Eq. (20.35)]. The transfer function is an expression of the relationship between the output variable and the input variable when the output variable and the input variable are both of the same form, namely, $X \epsilon^{pt}$. The steady-state response to a step input is easily found from Eq. (20.36) when it has been recognized that the step input can be represented by

$$x_1 = X_1 \epsilon^{pt} \qquad (20.38)$$

where $p = 0$ and X_1 is the magnitude of the step input. The steady-state response is then found by substituting $p = 0$ and Eq. (20.38) into Eq. (20.36), giving

$$X_{3s} = \frac{K z_1 z_2 \cdots z_m}{p_1 p_2 \cdots p_n} X_1 \qquad (20.39)$$

where X_{3s} is the steady-state response, or output, of the system. Thus the complete solution of the differential equation (20.12), or the transfer-function form of the equation, Eq. (20.35), when excited by a step function, is

$$x_3 = x_{3n} + x_{3s}$$

$$= A_1 \epsilon^{p_1 t} + A_2 \epsilon^{p_2 t} + \cdots + \frac{K z_1 z_2 \cdots z_m}{p_1 p_2 \cdots p_n} X_1 \qquad (20.40)$$

where p_1, p_2, etc., are the roots of the characteristic equation (and the poles of the transfer function) and z_1, z_2, etc., are the zeros of the transfer function. The arbitrary constants A_1, A_2, etc., can be evaluated from a knowledge of the initial conditions.

Example 20.2

The differential equation of a control system is given by

$$\frac{d^3 x_3}{dt^3} + 15 \frac{d^2 x_3}{dt^2} + 54 \frac{dx_3}{dt} + 40 x_3 = 5 \frac{dx_1}{dt} + 15 x_1 \qquad (20.41)$$

Writing the differential equation in operator form, where $p = d/dt$, $p^2 = d^2/dt^2$, etc., results in

$$p^3 X_3 + 15 p^2 X_3 + 54 p X_3 + 40 X_3 = 5 p X_1 + 15 X_1$$

or

$$X_3 = \frac{5(p + 3)}{p^3 + 15 p^2 + 54 p + 40} X_1$$

The denominator of the transfer function can now be factored, giving

$$X_3 = \frac{5(p + 3)}{(p + 1)(p + 4)(p + 10)} X_1 \qquad (20.42)$$

The natural response, the sum of three exponential terms, is

$$x_{3n} = A_1 \epsilon^{-t} + A_2 \epsilon^{-4t} + A_3 \epsilon^{-10t}$$

where A_1, A_2, and A_3 are arbitrary constants. The steady-state response to a step of voltage of 20 units magnitude is obtained from Eq. (20.39) when $p = 0$, or

$$x_{3s} = \frac{5(3)}{1(4)(10)} 20 \epsilon^{0t} = 7.5$$

Then the complete solution is

$$x_3 = A_1 \epsilon^{-t} + A_2 \epsilon^{-4t} + A_3 \epsilon^{-10t} + 7.5$$

The arbitrary constants must be evaluated from the initial conditions.

20.5 SYNTHESIS OR DESIGN OF CONTROL SYSTEMS

A system is designed to achieve the desired output or response to a given exciting function; this is known as system "synthesis." The ideal response of a positional servo system would be when the output variable follows exactly and instantaneously the input variable. System synthesis is a process whereby the system response is adjusted until it corresponds as nearly as possible to the input variable. A positional servo cannot follow exactly the input variable because of the inertia, inductance, etc., and therefore a compromise must be reached concerning the speed of response, the overshoot, and the oscillation allowable. System synthesis is always a compromise, and it always involves considerable analysis.

Whenever synthesis is attempted, the system components are well in mind and one parameter is made adjustable to attain the most desirable response. For instance, in the voltage regulator discussed in Sec. 20.2, the response variable e_7 to the step of voltage

E_1 is given approximately by Eq. (20.5). The constant K_3 is a function of the setting of potentiometer R_1, and the constant K_1 is the amplifier gain, easily adjusted by a gain control. The design or synthesis of this regulator requires that a choice of K_1 and K_3 be made; K_3 affects both the steady-state response and the time constant, while K_1 affects only the time constant. Thus, K_3 can be used to set the steady-state output voltage e_7 to its desired value, and K_1 can be made very large to keep the time constant short.

In order to visualize the synthesis problem for a simple dynamic system, consider a system describable by the second-order differential equation

$$\frac{d^2x_3}{dt^2} + 2\zeta\omega_n \frac{dx_3}{dt} + \omega_n{}^2x_3 = x_1 \tag{20.43}$$

where x_1 is a step exciting function of magnitude X_1. The steady-state solution of Eq. (20.43) is given by

$$x_{3s} = \frac{X_1}{\omega_n{}^2} \tag{20.44}$$

and a natural response is given by

$$x_{3n} = A_1\epsilon^{p_1 t} + A_2\epsilon^{p_2 t} \tag{20.45}$$

The roots of the characteristic equation are

$$p_1 = -\zeta\omega_n + \omega_n\sqrt{\zeta^2 - 1} \qquad p_2 = -\zeta\omega_n - \omega_n\sqrt{\zeta^2 - 1} \tag{20.46}$$

If ζ is greater than 1, Eq. (20.45) has real exponents. If ζ is less than unity, then

$$p_1 = -\zeta\omega_n + j\omega_n\sqrt{1 - \zeta^2} \qquad p_2 = -\zeta\omega_n - j\omega_n\sqrt{1 - \zeta^2} \tag{20.47}$$

and the natural response can be written in the form

$$x_{3n} = A\epsilon^{-\zeta\omega_n t} \sin(\omega_n\sqrt{1 - \zeta^2}\, t + \theta) \tag{20.48}$$

where A and θ are the arbitrary constants. The complete solution can be written

$$x_3 = x_{3n} + x_{3s}$$
$$= A\epsilon^{-\zeta\omega_n t} \sin(\omega_n\sqrt{1 - \zeta^2}\, t + \theta) + \frac{X_1}{\omega_n{}^2} \tag{20.49}$$

where A and θ are dependent upon the initial conditions of the problem. Under the conditions that $x_3 = 0$ at $t = 0$, the arbitrary constants of Eq. (20.49) can be evaluated, and the complete solution is now written

$$x_3 = \frac{X_1}{\omega_n{}^2} - \frac{X_1}{\omega_n{}^2} \epsilon^{-\zeta \omega_n t} \cos \left(\omega_n \sqrt{1 - \zeta^2}\, t \right) \qquad (20.50)$$

Thus the complete solution of Eq. (20.43) is a function of the coefficients of the equation containing ζ and ω_n. If the complete solution [Eq. (20.50)] is plotted as a function of $\omega_n t$ with ζ as a parameter, the response or output variable is shown in Fig. 20.5. The designer must decide which response most nearly suits his needs. He must compromise between a fast rise time as shown for $\zeta = 0.4$, with its inherent overshoot and oscillations, and the slow rise time for $\zeta = 1.5$, when there is no overshoot. As a rule of thumb, the designer often chooses a value of ζ at about 0.7. This gives relatively fast rise time, only a small amount of overshoot, and oscillations which damp out rapidly.

Example 20.3

The feedback control system shown in Fig. 20.6 is required to have a damping ratio of 0.707.

1. Find the value of K that makes $\zeta = 0.707$.

The closed-loop transfer function is

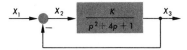

FIG. 20.6 *Feedback control system for Example 20.3.*

$$G_{13} = \frac{G_{23}}{1 + G_{23}} = \frac{K}{p^2 + 4p + (1 + K)}$$

The characteristic equation is $p^2 + 4p + (1 + K) = 0$. Equating the coefficients of the characteristic equation of G_{13} to the coefficients of the general second-order equation $p^2 + 2\zeta\omega_n p + \omega_n{}^2 = 0$, we observe that

$$2\zeta\omega_n = 4 \qquad \omega_n{}^2 = 1 + K$$

Substituting in $\zeta = 0.707$ and solving for K gives

$$\omega_n = \frac{4}{2(0.707)} = 2\sqrt{2}$$

$$K = \omega_n{}^2 - 1 = 7$$

2. Find the frequency of the damped oscillations in the natural response for $K = 7$, $\zeta = 0.707$.

$$\omega = \omega_n\sqrt{1 - \zeta^2} = 2\sqrt{2}\,\sqrt{1 - 0.5} = 2 \text{ radians/sec}$$

The natural response of the feedback control system discussed in Example 20.3 is a damped sinusoid whose damping ratio and frequency of oscillation have been found. A system of higher order would have had additional terms in the natural response, and we would not have been able to find the value of K by comparing the characteristic equation of G_{13} with the standard second-order characteristic equation as we did in the above example. The root-locus technique is an assistance in synthesizing feedback systems of second or higher order.

20.6 ROOT LOCUS

The synthesis of a feedback control system can usually be greatly simplified by using a technique known as "root locus." As the name applies to feedback control problems, the root locus is the locus of the poles of the closed-loop transfer function when a gain constant K is allowed to vary over all positive values. The gain constant is defined in Fig. 20.7, where a closed-loop system is shown with the open-loop transfer function

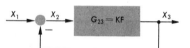

$$G_{23} = KF \tag{20.51}$$

FIG. 20.7 *Equivalent closed-loop system with unity feedback defining gain constant K.*

K is a positive constant, and F is a function of p which can be written in the form

$$F = \frac{(p + z_1)(p + z_2) \cdots}{(p + p_1)(p + p_2) \cdots} \tag{20.52}$$

where $-z_1$, $-z_2$, etc., are the zeros of G_{23} and $-p_1$, $-p_2$, etc., are the poles of G_{23}. Then the closed-loop transfer function can be written

$$G_{13} = \frac{KF}{1 + KF}$$

$$= \frac{K(p + z_1)(p + z_2) \cdots}{(p + p_1)(p + p_2) \cdots + K(p + z_1)(p + z_2) \cdots} \tag{20.53}$$

The denominator of Eq. (20.53) is a characteristic equation of the closed-loop differential equation, and thus the roots of

$$(p + p_1)(p + p_2) \cdots + K(p + z_1)(p + z_2) \cdots = 0 \tag{20.54}$$

must be found before the natural response of the over-all system can be described. The roots of Eq. (20.54) are functions of K. Notice that, as K approaches 0, the roots of Eq. (20.54) approach $-p_1$, $-p_2$, etc.; as K becomes very large, approaching infinity, the roots of Eq. (20.44) approach $-z_1$, $-z_2$, etc. The locus of the roots of Eq. (20.54) as K varies from 0 to infinity is known as the root locus. If the root locus is plotted on the complex plane, the roots of the over-all characteristic equation can be found for any given value of K and, from the roots, the natural response can be determined.

An example of a simple synthesis problem in root locus is based on the feedback system shown in Fig. 20.8, where $x_2 = x_1 - x_3$.

The open-loop transfer function is

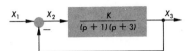

$$G_{23} = \frac{K}{(p+1)(p+3)} \qquad (20.55)$$

FIG. 20.8 *An example of a feedback system with unity feedback.*

and the closed-loop transfer function is given by

$$G_{13} = \frac{G_{23}}{1 + G_{23}} = \frac{K}{(p+1)(p+3) + K} \qquad (20.56)$$

The natural response of the over-all transfer function G_{13} is obtained from the poles of Eq. (20.56), which are the roots or zeros of

$$(p+1)(p+3) + K = 0 \qquad (20.57)$$

The zeros of Eq. (20.57) are functions of K. One way to find the root locus is to substitute several different values of K into Eq. (20.57) and plot the roots of the equation for the various values of K. The roots in question are the roots of the quadratic

$$p^2 + 4p + (1 + K) = 0 \qquad (20.58)$$

which can be found from the quadratic equation. For various values of K, the root or zeros of Eq. (20.58) are shown in Table 20.1 and plotted in Fig. 20.9. The root locus, once plotted, tells the system designer at a glance what the system natural response will be for a given value of K.

Some general characteristics of root-locus plots are illustrated in the above example. First, when $K = 0$, the roots of Eq. (20.54) coincide with the poles of G_{23}, the open-loop transfer function. There are two branches to the locus, each branch terminating on a pole of G_{23} for $K = 0$. Each of the two branches terminates on

TABLE 20.1 *Roots of Eq. (20.58) for Various Values of K*

K	0	0.5	1	2	5	10	17	26
p_1	-1	-1.293	-2	$-2+j2$	$-2+j2$	$-2+j3$	$-2+j4$	$-2+j5$
p_2	-3	-2.707	-2	$-2-j1$	$-2-j2$	$-2-j3$	$-2-j4$	$-2-j5$

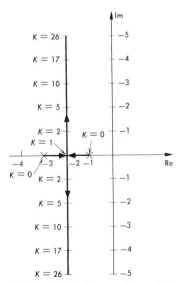

FIG. 20.9 *The root locus of Eq. (20.58) as K varies from zero to infinity.*

zeros of G_{23} for K approaching infinity, and since G_{23} has no finite zeros, the two branches approach zeros of G_{23} at infinity. Thus we see that the damping ratio of the natural response for this example is unity at $K = 1$ and approaches zero for K approaching infinity.

The above example is a simple one, requiring only the solution of a quadratic equation to find the poles of G_{13}. If G_{13} had had more poles and zeros, the root locus would be more complicated and much effort would be expended in finding the roots of the denominator of G_{13} for various values of K. Fortunately, the root locus can be plotted without finding the roots of the denominator of G_{13} for each value of K. The rules for making the root-locus plots of G_{13} are explained in the literature (see Further Reading) and will not be discussed here.

SUMMARY

The analysis and synthesis of automatic control systems and regulators rely upon the system of differential equations which describe the physical system. Feedback is necessary in the physical system to achieve the degree of control necessary. The differential equation of the system can be reduced to the form of Eq. (20.12),

$$\frac{d^n x_3}{dt^n} + a_{n-1} \frac{d^{n-1} x_3}{dt^{n-1}} + \cdots + a_1 \frac{dx_3}{dt} + a_0 x_3$$

$$= b_m \frac{d^m x_1}{dt^m} + b_{m-1} \frac{d^{m-1} x_1}{dt^{m-1}} + \cdots + b_1 \frac{dx_1}{dt} + b_0 x_1$$

where x_3 is the output variable, x_1 is the input variable, and all other system variables have been eliminated from the equation. Equation (20.12) can be converted to an algebraic equation by constraining x_1 and x_3 to be the exponential functions [Eqs. (20.32) and (20.14), respectively]

$$x_1 = X_1 \epsilon^{pt}$$

$$x_3 = X_3 \epsilon^{pt}$$

Substituting Eqs. (20.14) and (20.32) into Eq. (20.12) and solving for X_3 gives Eq. (20.35),

$$X_3 = \frac{b_m p^m + b_{m-1} p^{m-1} + \cdots + b_1 p + b_0}{p^n + a_{n-1} p^{n-1} + \cdots + a_1 p + a_0} X_1$$

where the fraction of two polynomials is known as the transfer function G_{13}. Then

$$X_3 = G_{13}X_1$$

The denominator of the transfer function G_{13} is the characteristic equation of the system, and the roots of the denominator determine the system natural response. Both numerator and denominator of the transfer function can be factored so that Eq. (20.34) can be written as Eq. (20.36),

$$X_3 = \frac{K(p + z_1)(p + z_2) \cdots (p + z_m)}{(p + p_1)(p + p_2) \cdots (p + p_n)} X_1$$

where $z_1, z_2, \ldots, z_m$ are the zeros of the transfer function and $p_1, p_2, \ldots, p_n$ are the poles of the transfer function. Since a step input is represented by Eq. (20.32) when $p = 0$, the response of the system to a step input is obtained by substituting $p = 0$ into Eq. (20.36); then [Eq. (20.39)]

$$X_{3s} = \frac{K z_1 z_2 \cdots z_m}{p_1 p_2 \cdots p_n} X_1$$

is the response of the system to the step input of magnitude X_1. The complete response of the system excited by a step input is [Eq. (20.40)]

$$x_3 = x_{3n} + x_{3s}$$
$$= A_1 \epsilon^{p_1 t} + A_2 \epsilon^{p_2 t} + \cdots + \frac{K z_1 z_2 \cdots z_m}{p_1 p_2 \cdots p_n}$$

where the coefficients of the exponential terms are the arbitrary constants which can be evaluated from a knowledge of the initial conditions.

FURTHER READING

Roots of polynomials can be found by methods outlined in the early and classic textbook by H. Chestnut and R. W. Mayer, *Servomechanisms and Regulating System Design* (John Wiley & Sons, Inc., New York, 1951), vol. 1, chap. 6. Many classical methods of synthesis are discussed in this text. Lin's method for finding quadratic factors is discussed in another classic, G. S. Brown and D. P. Campbell, *Principles of Servomechanisms* (John Wiley & Sons, Inc., New York, 1948), p. 89.

The algebraic properties of the operator p (sometimes the symbol D is used instead) is discussed in David K. Cheng, *Analysis of Linear Sys-*

tems (Addison-Wesley Publishing Company, Reading, Mass., 1959), p. 18. This text is an excellent introduction to linear-system analysis.

The literature of automatic controls and servo mechanisms is very extensive. Two recent texts are L. Dale Harris, *Feedback Systems* (John Wiley & Sons, Inc., New York, 1961), which explores the root-locus method, and John J. D'Azzo and Constantine H. Houpis, *Theory of Feedback Control Systems* (McGraw-Hill Book Company, Inc., New York, 1960).

PROBLEMS

20.1 Find the roots or zeros of the following polynomials, and write the polynomials in factored form: (*a*) $p^2 + 27.5p + 62.5 = 0$. (*b*) $p^3 + 24p^2 + 192p + 576 = 0$. (*c*) $p^3 + 10p^2 + 16p + 160 = 0$.

20.2 The homogeneous equation of a feedback system is

$$\frac{d^3x_3}{dt^3} + 26\frac{d^2x_3}{dt^2} + 125\frac{dx_3}{dt} + 100x_3 = 0.$$

Find the natural response of the system without evaluating the three arbitrary constants.

20.3 The feedback control system shown by the block diagram of Fig. 20.1 can be represented by the following system of equations:

$$x_1 - x_4 = x_2$$

$$x_2 = \frac{d^2x_3}{dt^2} + 4\frac{dx_3}{dt} + 4x_3$$

$$x_4 = x_3$$

(*a*) Find the open-loop natural response of the system.
(*b*) Find the closed-loop natural response of the system.
(*c*) Assuming that x_1 is a unit step input, find the open-loop steady-state response.
(*d*) Assuming that x_1 is a unit step input, find the complete solution $x_3 = x_{3n} + x_{3s}$ for x_1 a unit step input.
(*e*) Is the closed-loop system stable? Is the open-loop system stable? Explain your answer.
(*f*) Find the damping ratio ζ for the closed-loop system.

20.4 Assume for each of the circuits shown in the figure that i_1 is the input variable and e_o is the output variable. If $i_1 = I_1\epsilon^{pt}$, find the transfer function of the circuit as a function of p.

20.5 Assume that the shunt field of a separately excited shunt generator is excited by the input variable e_1 and that the output variable e_o is the terminal voltage of the generator. The generator speed is constant and

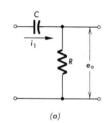

(a)

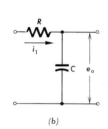

(b)

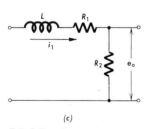

(c)

PROB. 20.4

its armature resistance is negligible. If the input variable e_1 is the exponential function $e_1 = E_1\epsilon^{pt}$, find the transfer function of the generator.

20.6 A shunt motor has a constant voltage impressed across its armature. The input variable is the field voltage, and the output variable is the speed of the shaft. Assume that J is the moment of inertia of both load and rotor and that B_f is the friction constant of both load and rotor. Find the transfer function.

20.7 Find the roots of the following quartic equation: $p^4 + 12.1p^3 + 50.3p^2 + 141.0p + 199.8 = 0$. *Hint:* There is at least one real root.

20.8 Find the roots of the following quartic equation: $p^4 + 10p^3 + 40p^2 + 80p + 64 = 0$.

20.9 Prove that for the cubic equation $p^3 + a_2 p^2 + a_1 p + a_0 = 0$, where all roots are real, the largest root cannot exceed a_2 and must be greater than $a_2/3$.

20.10 A feedback control system, represented by Fig. 20.1, has

$$G_{23} = \frac{K}{p + 2} \text{ and } G_{34} = \frac{1}{p}.$$

(a) Find the over-all transfer function G_{13}. (b) Find the value of K for which the damping ratio ζ of the over-all system is 0.7. (c) What is the natural frequency ω_n when $\zeta = 0.7$? (d) For what value of K is $\zeta = 0$? (e) For what value of K is $\zeta = -1$? What is the natural response of the over-all system when $\zeta = -1$?

20.11 A feedback system has an open-loop gain of

$$G_{23} = \frac{K}{(p + 2)(p + 10)} \text{ and } G_{34} = 1.$$

Plot the locus of the roots of G_{13} as K increases from 0 to infinity.

CHARACTERISTICS OF VACUUM TUBES AND TRANSISTORS

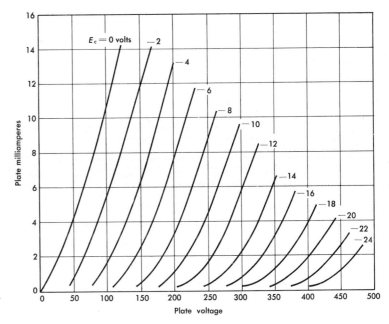

$E_c = 0$ volts   —2   —4   —6   —8   —10   —12   —14   —16   —18   —20   —22   —24

Plate milliamperes

Plate voltage

FIG. A1.1 *Average plate characteristics of the 6J5 triode.*

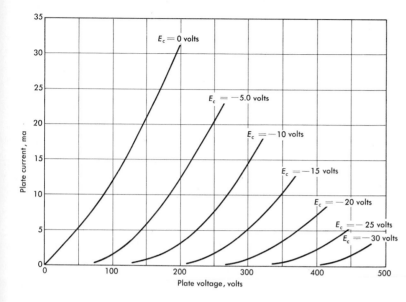

FIG. A1.2 *Average plate characteristics of the 6C4 triode.*

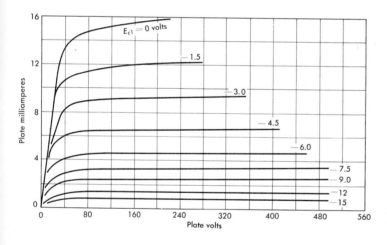

FIG. A1.3 *Average plate characteristics of the 6SK7 variable-μ pentode.*

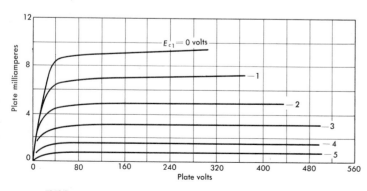

FIG. A1.4 *Average plate characteristics of the 6SJ7 pentode.*

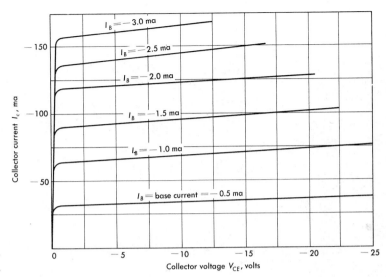

FIG. A1.5 *Grounded-emitter collector characteristic for the 2N226 transistor.*

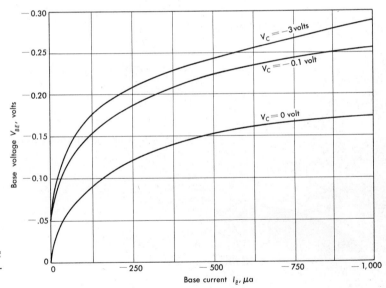

FIG. A1.6 *Grounded-emitter input (base) characteristic of the 2N226 transistor.*

2

ELECTRIC INDICATING INSTRUMENTS

A2.1 D-C INSTRUMENTS

The permanent-magnet moving-coil d-c ammeter described in Sec. 18.11 is the basic instrument for measuring either direct current or direct voltage. This instrument, sometimes called the D'Arsonval instrument, is shown in Fig. A2.1.

It was shown by Eq. (18.92) that the steady-state angle of deflection of the permanent-magnet moving-coil movement excited

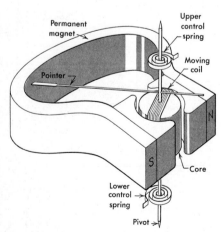

FIG. A2.1 *The permanent-magnet moving-coil d-c indicating instrument.*

by a constant current I is proportional to I, or [Eq. (18.92)]

$$\theta_s = \frac{K_m B}{K} I$$

where K_m, B, and K are constants. The magnetic torque is also proportional to the current I [Eq. (18.86)],

$$T_m = K_m B I$$

where K_m and B are constants. This instrument is an average-reading instrument; if the current I is not constant, the magnetic torque is at any instant proportional to I but because of the inertia of the movement θ_s is an angle proportional to the average value of current I. Thus a sinusoidal current reads zero on the D'Arsonval instrument.

Sensitivity of an indicating instrument is the amount of power required to cause the instrument to read full scale. The permanent-magnet moving-coil instrument is extremely sensitive; in some instruments less than 10^{-6} watt is needed for full-scale deflection. An accuracy of one-fourth of 1 per cent of full-scale reading is common in laboratory instruments.

An electric instrument is a precision device. The movement is mounted on jeweled bearings to minimize friction, and the precision springs which provide the restoring torque must follow Hooke's law exactly and consistently. Constant air-gap flux must be maintained by the permanent magnet throughout the lifetime of the instrument.

The restoring springs serve not only to provide the restoring torque to the movement but also to provide connection between the movement and the stationary circuit. These springs, made of phosphor bronze with a very small cross-sectional area, can carry only very small currents without overheating. Ordinarily 1 ma or less provides full-scale deflection. Consequently, in order to measure high currents, a shunt resistor which carries a large fraction of the total current must be connected in parallel with the indicating instrument. Figure A2.2 shows the shunt R_s in parallel with the instrument movement of resistance R_i. Let I_i be the current which causes the instrument to read full scale. The value of R_s is sought for which I is the total current in the circuit. Equating the voltages across R_s and R_i gives

$$I_i R_i = (I - I_i) R_s \qquad (A2.1)$$

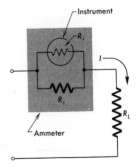

FIG. A2.2 *An ammeter with shunt resistor R_s.*

from which

$$R_s = \frac{I_i R_i}{I - I_i} \tag{A2.2}$$

Example A2.1

A d-c ammeter has an internal resistance of $R_i = 0.975$ ohm, and its full-scale current is $I_1 = 0.001$ amp. The instrument is to be used with a shunt to measure $I = 100$ amp. The required shunt is given by Eq. (A2.2),

$$R_s = \frac{0.001 \times 0.975}{100 - 0.001} = 0.975 \times 10^{-5} \text{ ohm}$$

When $R_s = 0.975 \times 10^{-5}$ ohm is used in parallel with the d-c ammeter, the full-scale reading on the ammeter corresponds to a total current $I = 100$ amp. Thus the basic movement which reads full scale at 1 ma can be used with a shunt to read full scale when the total current is 100 amp.

The permanent-magnet moving-coil instrument can be calibrated as a voltmeter. Figure A2.3 shows the instrument in series with a large resistor R_m, known as the "multiplier." Again, I_i is the full-scale current of the instrument, and R_i is the resistance of the instrument. Then the total full-scale voltage V, as shown in Fig. A2.3, is

$$V = I_i(R_m + R_i) \tag{A2.3}$$

and

$$R_m = \frac{V - I_i R_i}{I_i} \tag{A2.4}$$

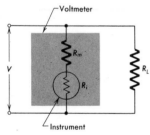

FIG. A2.3 *A voltmeter with multiplier* R_m.

The value of the multiplier is given by Eq. (A2.4), where V is the desired full-scale voltage, I_i is the instrument current at full scale, and R_i is the instrument resistance.

Example A2.2

A d-c ammeter has an internal resistance $R_i = 0.975$ ohm, and its full-scale current $I_i = 0.001$ amp. The instrument is to be used with a multiplier to measure $V = 150$ volts full scale. The required multiplier is given by Eq. (A2.4).

$$R_m = \frac{150 - 0.001(0.975)}{0.001} = 150,000 \text{ ohms}$$

With a multiplier of 150,000 ohms, the instrument reads full scale when $V = 150$ volts is applied.

In order to measure the current in an electric circuit, the ammeter must be connected in series with the circuit, as shown in Fig. A2.2. Because of the low impedance of the movement and its shunt, an ammeter can easily be burned out by connecting it in parallel across a load impedance. A voltmeter must be connected in parallel with the load impedance in order to measure the voltage across the impedance. The voltmeter, with its high-resistance multiplier in series with the instrument, is less subject to instrument burnout than the ammeter.

A2.2 A-C INSTRUMENTS

The average magnetic torque developed in the movement of a D'Arsonval instrument is proportional to the average current; the D'Arsonval instrument reads zero when used to measure alternating current. The average magnetic torque on the movement of the electrodynamometer instrument shown in Fig. A2.4 can be made

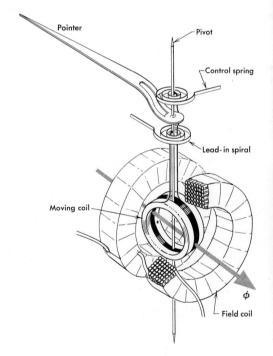

FIG. A2.4 *The electrodynamometer indicating instrument.*

to be approximately proportional to the *square* of the current. The electrodynamometer instrument is the basic a-c instrument, since the magnetic torque can be made to be approximately proportional to the mean-square value of the current.

The basic electrodynamometer movement shown in Fig. A2.4 differs from the D'Arsonval instrument in several respects. The magnetic field is established by a pair of stationary coils called "field" coils through which the current i being measured must flow. The moving coil also carries the current i, the field coil and the moving coil being connected in series. There is no iron in the magnetic circuit of the electrodynamometer instrument as there is in the d-c instrument. Otherwise the electrodynamometer instrument operates with springs and bearings in much the same manner as the D'Arsonval instrument.

The field coil establishes the magnetic flux ϕ proportional in magnitude to the current i. The force on the conductors in the moving coil is proportional to the current in the moving coil and also to the flux density produced by the field coil. If the moving coil is mounted in such a position that the torque is proportional to force, then

$$T_m = Ki^2 \tag{A2.5}$$

where T_m is the magnetic torque, K is a constant of proportionality, and i is the current being measured. In the steady state the moving coil comes to rest at an angle of deflection at which the spring torque is equal to the average magnetic torque, which is always in the same direction. Then the angle of deflection is approximately proportional to the square of the current. Since the torque on the moving coil is not proportional to electromagnetic force for all coil positions, the instrument scale is not exactly a squared scale.

The electrodynamometer instrument can be used as an ammeter or as a voltmeter by incorporating suitable shunts or multipliers with the instrument. Although the average torque is approximately proportional to the mean-square current, the instrument scale is calibrated in amperes or volts. Since the average value of direct current is the same as the rms value of direct current, the instrument can also be used to measure direct current and voltage.

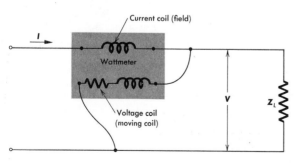

FIG. A2.5 *An electrodynamometer instrument as a wattmeter.*

A wattmeter consists of an electrodynamometer instrument in which the field coil senses the current and the moving coil senses the voltage. In a wattmeter these two coils are not connected in series. The field coil, connected in series with the load impedance, carries the load current. The moving coil, connected with its multiplier R_m in parallel with the load impedance, carries a current in phase with the voltage across Z_L. The average magnetic torque is equal to

$$T_m = K'VI \cos \theta \tag{A2.6}$$

where K' is a constant, a function of the position of the movement, V and I are the rms values of voltage and current, and $\cos \theta$ is the power factor. The wattmeter scale is calibrated in real watts.

An ammeter or the current coil or field coil of a wattmeter must be connected in series with the load impedance in order to sense the load current. A voltmeter or the voltage coil or moving coil of a wattmeter must be connected in parallel with the load impedance in order to sense the load voltage.

LETTER SYMBOLS USED IN THE TEXT

A	area, amplifier gain (same as G)
A_0	midband gain
A_1, A_2	arbitrary constants
$\mathbf{A}$	amplifier gain (complex)
A_v	voltage gain
a	acceleration
B	friction constant (same as B_f), magnetic-flux density
B_1, B_2	arbitrary constants
C	capacitance
D	electric-flux density
d	distance (same as s, L, and l)
E	root-mean-square voltage (same as V)
E_a	average voltage (same as V_a)
$\mathbf{E}$	complex, or phasor, voltage
E_m	maximum value of an alternating voltage
E_b	average anode-cathode voltage
E_h	potential hump
$\mathcal{E}$	electric-field intensity
e	instantaneous voltage (same as v), charge on the electron
F	force, a function of time

F_a average force

f frequency in cycles per second, instantaneous force

f_0 resonant frequency

f_1, f_2 lower and upper cutoff frequencies

G gain, or amplification; transfer function

$\mathbf{G}$ complex transfer function

g acceleration due to gravity

g_m transconductance

H magnetic-field intensity

I root-mean-square current

I_a average current (same as I_{dc})

I_m maximum value of an alternating current

$\mathbf{I}$ complex, or phasor, current

I_b average anode current

I_C average collector current

I_E average emitter current

I_B average base current

i instantaneous current

i_n natural-response current

i_s steady-state current

J current density

j $\sqrt{-1}$

K spring constant (same as K_f), also constant of proportionality

K_1, K_2 constants of proportionality

L length, distance, self-inductance

l length

M mass, mutual inductance

m mass of the electron

N number of turns

n an arbitrary integer

P average power (same as P_a)

p instantaneous power, root of the characteristic equation, number of poles

Q quality factor, electric charge

Q_0 quality factor at resonant frequency

q instantaneous electric charge

R resistance

$\mathcal{R}$ reluctance

r_p dynamic plate resistance

s distance, speed in rpm

T temperature, torque

t	time
V	rms voltage or potential difference (same as E)
V_a	average voltage (same as E_a)
$\mathbf{V}$	complex, or phasor, voltage (same as $\mathbf{E}$)
V_{CB}	average collector-to-base voltage
V_{EC}	average emitter-to-collector voltage
V_{EB}	average emitter-to-base voltage
v	instantaneous voltage, or instantaneous velocity
W, w	energy
x	displacement
Y	admittance magnitude
$\mathbf{Y}$	complex admittance
$Y(p)$	admittance when $v = V\epsilon^{pt}$
$Y(j\omega)$	admittance when $v = V_m \sin \omega t$
Z	impedance magnitude
$\mathbf{Z}$	complex impedance
$Z(p)$	impedance when $i = I\epsilon^{pt}$
$Z(j\omega)$	impedance when $i = I_m \sin \omega t$
α	angular acceleration, temperature coefficient of resistance
ϵ	permittivity or dielectric constant, base of natural logarithms
ζ	damping ratio
θ	a phase angle
μ	permeability, mobility of charges, amplification factor
ρ	resistivity, charge density
τ	time constant
ϕ	a phase angle
ω	radian frequency
$\omega_0, \omega_1, \omega_2$	resonant radian frequency, lower and upper cutoff frequencies
ω_n	undamped natural radian frequency

ANSWERS TO SOME PROBLEMS

CHAPTER 1

1.1 5.47×10^{-9} amp.　*1.3* 333.3 joules or watt-sec.　*1.5* 2.81×10^{23} electrons/day.

CHAPTER 2

2.1 (a) 333.3 watts; (b) 636 watts; (c) 500 watts.
2.4 (a) 6.32 volts; (b) 5.40 volts; (c) 34.8 volts; (d) 50 volts.　*2.6* 1.58 volts.　*2.9* (a) $8 + j2$; (c) $-6 + j8$;

CHAPTER 3

3.1 $q = CV_0\epsilon^{-t/RC}$.　*3.3* $\omega = \omega_0\epsilon^{-(B/J)t}$, $\theta = \dfrac{\omega_0 J}{B}$

$(1 - \epsilon^{-(B/J)t})$.　*3.5* $i = 0$ amp, $\dfrac{di}{dt} = 10^4$ amp/sec,

CHAPTER 4

4.3 (a) 304 volts; (b) 215 volts; (c) $-34.5°$.　*4.4* (a) 628 ohms; (b) $1,000 + j628$; (c) 1,180 ohms; (d) $0.359 - j0.225$ amp; (e) 0.423 amp; (f) 423 volts; (g) 266 volts; (h) 32.1° current lagging.

CHAPTER 5

5.1 16.7 $(1 - \epsilon^{-3000t})$ volts.　*5.2* 0 amp.　*5.4* (a) $0.3\epsilon^{-700t}$ amp; (b) 85.7 $(1 - \epsilon^{-700t})$ volts.

CHAPTER 6

6.3 (a) $\omega_n = \sqrt{1/LC}$ radians/sec; (b) $\omega = \sqrt{1/LC - 1/4R^2C^2}$ radians/sec; (c) $\zeta = 1/2R\sqrt{L/C}$.
6.5 51.8°, current-lagging voltage.

CHAPTER 7

7.1 (a) $0.4 + j4.2$; (b) $3.075 + j4.61$; (c) 1.6 ohms; (d) $j1.6$.　*7.5* (a) $E' = 33.3$ volts, $R = 333.3$ ohms; (b) $E' = 75$ volts, $R = 1,500$ ohms;

1.7 1.053 joules.　*1.8* 0.0203 ohm.　*1.16* (a) 29.0 ohms; (b) 20.55 ohms.　*1.20* 2.81×10^9 farads/m.

(e) $-8 + j38$; (g) $0.138 - j0.655$.　*2.10* (a) $8.66 + j5$; (b) $20\epsilon^{j90°}$; (c) $9.66 + j6.73$; (d) $5\epsilon^{-j30°}$

$\dfrac{d^2i}{dt^2} = -10^8$ amp/sec^2.　*3.6* 12.4 hr.　*3.11* (a) 7,040 volts; (b) 6,638 volts.

4.6 (a) 2,520 watts; (b) 0.848; (c) 94.1 per cent.
4.12 (a) $Q = 44.7$ at resonance; (b) 4,520 radians/sec, 4,420 radians/sec. *4.14* $R = 2,000/\omega$ ohms.

5.5 $i = 0.204 (\epsilon^{-100t} - \epsilon^{-9900t})$ amp.　*5.11* (a) 14.28 amp; (b) 50 amp; (c) $50 - 35.72\epsilon^{-2t}$ amp.

6.8 $-6.05 - j5.06$ amp.　*6.12* 4,840 watts.　*6.14* (a) 19.68 amp; (b) 220 volts; (c) 34.1 amp; (d) 5,810 watts.

(c) $E' = 70.7 \sin(5,000t - 45°)$, $Z = 12,500 + j2,500$.
7.7 (a) $5 - j50$; (b) 1,936 watts; (c) 387 watts.
7.9 $25.92 + j2,410$.　*7.10* 5.87 watts.

CHAPTER 8

8.4 $i = 1 - 0.0333v$.   **8.5** 0.1428 amp, 28.5 volts.
8.7 (a) 1.75 μa; (b) 0.046 lumen; (c) 0.023 lumen,
150 volts.   **8.11** 0.42 m.   **8.13** 0.148 m.

CHAPTER 9

9.2 (a) 100 m/sec²; (b) 200 m/sec; (c) 200 m.
9.4 10^3 volts/m, $v = 1.875 \times 10^7 - 1.76 \times 10^{14}t$,
$0 < t < 1.067 \times 10^{-7}$ sec.   **9.5** 0.246 m.
9.6 2.295×10^7 m/sec at 35.25° from the x direction.

CHAPTER 10

10.1 (a) 66.7 volts, $0 < t < 0.01$ sec; 0 volts,
$0.01 < t < 0.02$ sec; (b) 33.3 volts; (c) 47.1 volts.
10.3 (a) 0.0316 amp; (b) 0.00967 amp;
(c) $0.0572 \sin 1,000t$ amp, $0 < \omega t < \pi$;
$0.0267 \sin 1,000t$ amp, $\pi < \omega t < 2\pi$.   **10.6** 9.7-volt step.
10.13 (a) A current generator of 1.45 ma/lumen;
(b) from 70 to 183 volts.

CHAPTER 11

11.3 12.25.   **11.4** $R_k = 527$ ohms, $C_k = 15.1$ μf.
11.5 $A = 10.67$ at $\omega = 10^4$; $A = 8.14$ at $\omega = 0$;
$A = 19.7$ at $\omega = 10^5$.   **11.9** Assume $E_{bb} = 250$ volts.
Then $C_{sh} = 1,132$ μμf.   **11.12** $R_L = 88,300$ ohms,
$C_c = 0.0059$ μf.

CHAPTER 12

12.3 (a) 0.02 amp clockwise; (b) 0.0446 amp; (c) $i =$
0.1 amp for $e = 100$ volts; $i = 0$ for $e = -50$ volts.
12.5 20 ma.
12.9 $i = 0.5 + 0.5 \cos (2 \times 10^6 + 4 \times 10^3)t$.
12.11 $i = \cos (10^6 + 2 \times 10^3)t + \cos (10^6 - 2 \times 10^3)t$
$+ \cos 2 \times 10^6 t + \cos 4 \times 10^3 t$.   **12.13** 0.00347 watt.

CHAPTER 13

13.1 $G_{34} = 9 \times 10^{-4}$.   **13.3** (b) $G_{16} = \dfrac{ABD}{1 + ABC}$.
13.5 One solution is $G_{23} = \dfrac{G_1 G_2 G_3}{1 + G_1 G_2}$, $G_{34} = \dfrac{1}{G_4}$.
13.10 (a) $\dfrac{R}{R + j\omega L}$; (b) $\dfrac{1}{1 - jR/\omega L}$; (c)
$\dfrac{R_2}{R_1 + R_2 - j/\omega C}$.

CHAPTER 14

14.4 (a) $\tau_1 = 0.0732$ sec, $\tau_2 = 0.426$ sec; (b) $\tau = 0.1$
sec.   **14.5** $V_0 = 0.487 V_{in}$.   **14.6** (a) $\dfrac{dv}{dt} + 25v = 0$,
$v = 10$ at $t = 0$.

CHAPTER 15

15.7 (a) 27; (b) 600; (c) 21,047; (d) 112,008.   **15.9** (a)
25; (b) 44; (c) 113; (d) 753.   **15.10** (a) 10,010; (b)
110,111; (c) 10,000,011; (d) 1,010,100.   **15.12** (a)
1,000,010; (b) 100,011,010,101.

CHAPTER 16

16.2 6.81 amp.   **16.3** 11.6×10^{-3} weber.   **16.4** 4,700
amp-turns.   **16.7** 58.5 amp-turns approximately.
16.9 1.07×10^{-3} weber.

CHAPTER 17

17.4 $1,086 \cos 100t$.   **17.5** 75, 150.   **17.6** 22.3 per cent.
17.9 (a) 217.7 volts; (b) 24.3 amp; (c) 188.7 volts;
(d) 1.55 amp.   **17.13** (a) 40 cps, 192 volts; (b) 1.302.

CHAPTER 18

18.1 (a) 0.278 m; (b) 0.139 m.   **18.5** 1.336×10^{-2}
newton/meter attraction.   **18.9** (a) 312.5 amp; (b)
0.6 ohm.   **18.11** 32.0 amp.   **18.12** (a) 20-hp motor;
(b) 27 amp.

CHAPTER 19

19.2 (a) 107.5 volts; (b) 82 volts.   **19.3** 4,390 watts,
5.89 hp.   **19.5** 1,087 rpm.   **19.7** (a) 1,130 rpm; (b)
12,720 watts, 17.1 hp.   **19.10** 0.035 m.

CHAPTER 20

20.1 (a) $(p + 2.47)(p + 25.03) = 0$; (b) $(p + 12)$
$(p + 6 + j3.46)(p + 6 - j3.46) = 0$; (c) $(p + 10)$
$(p + j4)(p - j4) = 0$.   **20.2** $x_n = A_1\epsilon^{-t} + A_2\epsilon^{-5t} +$
$A_3\epsilon^{-20t}$ **20.5** $G = \dfrac{K}{Lp + R}$.   **20.7** $(p + 2.7)$
$(p + 7.4)(p + 1 + j3)(p + 1 - j3) = 0$.

A-c indicating instruments, 555
    electrodynamometer ammeter, 556
    wattmeter, 557
Acceptors, 233
Access time, 384
Accumulator, 384
Adder, electronic, 363
Addition, binary, 399
    phasor, 54
Address, 386
Admittance, 88
    complex, 142
    transistor, 265
Alternator, 154, 441
    efficiency, 444
    speed and frequency, 442
    synchronous impedance, 444
    voltage regulation, 444
Ampere, 8
Ampère's law, 413
Amplification factor, 252
Amplifier, class A and class B, 326
    direct-coupled, 300
    elementary transistor, 294
    elementary triode, 284
    operational (*see* Operational amplifier)
    power, 329
    push-pull, 328
    RC-coupled, 288
Amplitude modulation, 316
    demodulation, 320
    scale factor, 375
Analogies, 33, 358

Analysis, electric circuit, 2
Anode, 223
Apparent power, 117
Arithmetic unit, 384
Automatic control, 522
Average value, 40
    periodic function, 42

Band limits, 109
Bandwidth, 114
Base, transistor, 264
Bias, cathode, 286
    transistor, 299
    vacuum-tube, 255
Binary arithmetic, 398
Binary numbers, 394
Block-diagram algebra, 335
Branch, circuit, 10

Capacitance, 25, 31
    interelectrode, 259
Capacitor, 31
Carrier, 316
Cathode, 222
Cathode bias, 286
Cathode follower, 348
Cathode-ray tube, 272
Characteristic curves, 18, 191
    transistor, 265, 549
    triode, 249, 256, 549
Characteristic equation, 79
Charge, electric, 3
    electron, 5

Child's law, 224
Circuit elements, 9
Circuits, electric, 8
    magnetic, 415
Class A amplifiers, 326
Class B amplifiers, 326
Clipping circuit, 313
Closed-loop system, 334
    gain, 335
Codes, computer, 386
Commutation, 440
Complete solution, 124
    RC series circuit, 126, 132
    RL series circuit, 125, 132
    RLC series circuit, 129, 134
Complex numbers, 52
Conductors, electric, 5
Conservation of energy, 72, 469
Coulomb, 3
Coulomb's law, 214
Coupled circuits, 182
Critically damped response, 84
Current, electric, 7
Cutoff frequencies, 109, 290, 292

D-c indicating instruments, 552
D'Alembert's principle, 30, 40
Damping ratio, 85
Decimal numbers, 394
Deflection, 275
Delta connection, 155
Demodulation, 316, 320
Detection, 316, 320
Dielectric constant, 26, 214
Differential equations, 69
    first-order, 70
    second-order, 71
Differentiating circuit, RC, 360
Differentiator, operational amplifier, 363
Diffusion, 234
Digital computer, 382
Dimensions, 15
Diodes, 241
Direct-coupled amplifiers, 300
Direct current, 58, 100
    value, 43
    voltage, 58, 100
Distortion, 283, 347
Donors, 232
Dushman's equation, 222
Dynamic plate resistance, 245, 251

Easy current direction, 235
Effective values, 43
    sinusoid, 46
Efficiency, 444
Electric current, 7
Electric field, 9, 213
Electric flux and flux density, 214
Electromagnetic-energy conversion, 404
Electromagnetic torque, 480

Electromotive force, 13
Electron charge, 217
Electron gun, 273
Electron mass, 217
Electron motion, 217
Electron volt, 218
Electronic emission, 220
Electronics, 212
Emitter, transistor, 264
    characteristic, 265
Energy, electric, 14
    potential, 10
Energy conversion, 473
Energy converters, 405
Equations, differential, 69
    loop, 148
    node, 151
Equivalent circuits, 32, 168
    transistor, 269
    triode, 254
Exponential function, 48

Farad, 26
Faraday's law, 429
Feedback, 333
    amplifiers, 342
    block diagram, 334
    effects of, 345
Field, electric, 6, 213
    magnetic, 405
Field intensity, magnetic, 410
Field rheostat, 448
Field strength, electric, 410
Flux linkages, 431
Force, electric, 214
    magnetic, 462, 466
Forced response, 96
Fourier series, 59
Free electrons, 228
Frequency, 46
    RC amplifier, 289
Frequency response, 350

Gain, 283
    closed-loop, 335
    open-loop, 334
Gate, 315
Generator, 441
    d-c, compound, 444
    elementary, 439
    generated voltage, 446
    self-excited, 449, 506
    series, 516
Generators in parallel, 212, 513
Graphical solutions, linear, 195
    nonlinear, 201
Grid, 246

Half-power frequencies, 109, 114
Hole, 228
Homogeneous equation, 73, 123

Impedance, 87, 97
  complex, magnitude, 101
  phase, 102
Impulse function, 136
Impulse response, 137
Induced voltage, 433
Inductance, 22, 31
  mutual, 23, 437
  self-, 23, 436
Induction motor, 489
Inductive coupling, 185
Instruments, D'Arsonval, 494, 552
  electrodynamometer, 556
Insulators, 5
Integrating circuit, 360
Integrator, operational amplifier, 362

Joule's law, 18
Junction, *p-n*, 234

Kirchhoff's laws, 28, 40

Lenz's law, 430
Line voltages, 155
Loop currents, 149
Loop equations, 148

Magnetic circuit, 415
Magnetic energy, 476
Magnetic-field intensity, 410
Magnetic fields, 405
Magnetic flux and flux density, 410
Magnetic force, 406, 477
Magnetic quantities, 409
Magnetic torque, 480
Magnetic units, 409
Magnetization curve, 417
Magnetomotive force, 416
Majority carriers, 232
Maximum power transfer, 180, 181
Mean value, 40
Memory, 383
MKS units, 3
Minority carriers, 232
Mobility, 229
Models, 31
Modulation, 316
  square law, 319
Motors, d-c shunt, 482, 508
  compound, 485
  speed characteristic, 484, 513
  induction, 489
  speed, 490
  synchronous, 492
Multiplication and division, phasor, 57
Multiplier, operational amplifier, 363
  servo, 371
Multivibrator, 323
Mutual inductance, 23, 437
Mutual reactance, 185

Natural response, 68, 123
  first-order system, 73
  second-order system, 78
Network, 10
  analyzers, 357
Node, 10
Node equations, 151
Nonlinear algebraic solutions, 204
Nonlinear graphical solutions, 200
Nonlinear resistances, 193
Norton's theorem, 178

Octal numbers, 394
Ohm's law, 17, 190
Operational amplifier, 361
  differentiator, 363
  integrator, 362
  multiplier, 363
Oscillation, criterion for, 340
Oscillators, 340
Overdamped response, 85

Parameters, transistor, 270
  triode, 251
Pentode characteristics, 258
Period, 42
Periodic functions, 13, 42, 59
Permeability, 409
Permittivity, 213
Phase difference, 46
Phase voltages, 154
Phasors, 52
  addition and subtraction, 54
  diagram, 101, 104
  exponential form, 53
  multiplication and division, **57**
  rectangular form, 53
Phototubes, 193, 242
Pickoff point, 337
Piecewise linear analysis, 503
Plate characteristic, 249
Poles, 537
Polyphase voltages, 153
Potential, 11
Potential difference, 12, 215
Power, average, 116
  electric, 15
Power amplifier, 329
Power factor, 116
Program, 385
Push-pull amplifier, 328

Q, 113

Radian frequency, 46
RC coupling, 288
Reactance, capacitive, 99
  inductive, 99
Rectification, 440
Rectifiers, 306
  filters, 309

Rectifiers, full-wave, 308
  half-wave, 307
Regulators, 524
Reluctance, 416
Resistance, 17, 20, 31
  dynamic, 245, 251
  nonlinear, 193
  static, 245
Resistivity, 20
Resonance, 111, 112
  parallel, 146
  series, 106
Resonant frequency, 106
Right-hand rule, 412
Root locus, 542
Root-mean-square value, 44
Roots, polynomial, 530
Rotating synchronous flux, 487

Saturation current, 236
Scale factors, amplitude, 375
  time, 372
Screen grid, 260
Semiconductors, 226
  intrinsic, 226
  N-type, 232
  P-type, 233
Servomechanisms, 523
Shunt motor, 482
Sidebands, 317
Sink, electric energy, 14
Sinusoid, 46
  exponential representation, 50
Solution, by differentiation, 370
  by integration, 364
Space charge, 224
Steady-state response, 69, 96, 123
Step input, 124
Subtraction, phasor, 54
Successive approximation, 207
Summing point, 334
Superposition principle, 171
Suppressor grid, 262
Switching, vacuum-tube, 312
Symbols, 16, 558–560
Synchronous flux, 487
Synchronous impedance, 444
Synthesis, control system, 539
Synthetic division, 532

T networks, 173
Temperature saturation, 225
Tetrode characteristics, 258
Thermionic emission, 222
Thevenin's theorem, 175
Three-phase circuits, 157
  power, 161
  power measurements, 162
Time constant, 76
Time scale factors, 372
Torque, 480
Transconductance, 253
Transfer functions, 535
Transformers, 432, 451
  equivalent circuit, 453
  exciting current, 453
  open-circuit test, 454
  short-circuit test, 454
Transient response, 69
Transistors, 263
  amplifier, 294
  biasing, 299
  gain, 295
  load-line analysis, 297
  parameters, 270
Triodes, 246
  amplifiers, 284
  biasing, 286
  gain, 285
  load-line analysis, 256
  parameters, 251

Underdamped response, 84
Unit impulse, 136
Units, MKS, 3
  conversion factors, 4

Variables, electric circuit, 1
Volt, 15
Voltage, 14
  regulation, 444
  regulators, 526

Watt, 15
Wattmeter, 557
Work function, 221
Wye connection, 155

Zeros, 537